STATISTICAL MECHANICS
AND DYNAMICS

STATISTICAL
MECHANICS
AND DYNAMICS

HENRY EYRING · *Departments of Chemistry and Metallurgy, University of Utah, Salt Lake City, Utah*

DOUGLAS HENDERSON · *Department of Physics, Arizona State University, Tempe, Arizona*

BETSY JONES STOVER · *Department of Chemistry and Radiobiology Division of the Department of Anatomy, University of Utah, Salt Lake City, Utah*

EDWARD M. EYRING · *Department of Chemistry, University of Utah, Salt Lake City, Utah*

1964

JOHN WILEY & SONS INC.

New York · London · Sydney

PRINTED IN THE UNITED STATES OF AMERICA

PREFACE

WE HAVE called this book *Statistical Mechanics and Dynamics*. One naturally asks how this treatment differs from the usual statistical mechanical presentations? There is much in common. One might almost as well call it statistical mechanics. The distinction, however, lies in the greater emphasis on the time factor. People generally consider statistical mechanics to be an equilibrium theory with just a small amount of kinetic or rate theory included. In contrast we incorporate more of the kinetic aspects thus emphasizing the dynamic nature of all processes, including equilibrium.

Statistical mechanics is, of course, a gambling game. Let us consider what constitutes a physical theory. The mathematical theory of a natural phenomenon is simply a game, a mathematical game, with the rules invented as we go along. It will be of interest if there turns out to be a one-to-one correspondence with experiment. In other words, calculations are made based on a theory, and the numbers obtained are then compared with measurements. If there is correspondence between the two sets of values, one has a physical theory of the experimental phenomenon. It is in this sense that we invent our physics.

The material presented here is intended to form the basis of a year course for graduate students in the physical sciences. A student who has studied chemistry through the usual course in physical chemistry including thermodynamics and who has studied elementary physics and the calculus should encounter no serious difficulties with the material presented here.

In the introduction we survey the theories of statistical mechanics with the intention of developing a working knowledge which should enable the reader to attack many kinetic and thermodynamic problems. In later chapters the theory is developed in more detail. Three methods of developing statistical mechanics are presented and the theory is applied to a wide variety of models of physical phenomena. The methods are (1) the classical approach of Gibbs, (2) the Darwin–Fowler method of steepest descents, and (3) the method of compounding an unknown with a known system. In the appendices the reader will find some of the necessary mathematical tools.

Each chapter is divided into sections and each section usually deals with a single topic. Inside a section equations are numbered sequentially.

Reference to an equation in a different section has an additional number designating the section with a second number added if the reference lies outside the chapter. Thus Eq. (4.12.17) refers to the fourth chapter, the twelfth section, and the seventeenth equation in the section. Frequent reference is made to the book, *Quantum Chemistry*, by H. Eyring, J. Walters, and G. E. Kimball, John Wiley and Sons, Inc., 1944, which we denote by *Q. C.*

With reference to thermodynamic symbols the reader will note that we follow the notation of Lewis and Randall except that G is used instead of F to represent the Gibbs free energy and μ rather than $\bar{F}$ is used for the chemical potential. This convention differs from that of Fowler and Guggenheim only in retaining A in place of F for the Helmholtz free energy. This choice seems to minimize the confusion arising from the concurrent use of the two notations mentioned above.

We have drawn on material from many sources and wish to express our appreciation for permission to use these results. Reference is made to published material, but we are unable to acknowledge specifically the generous contributions of our many colleagues and students. Particularly, we are grateful to Dr. Marilyn Alder Marquis who prepared a set of notes based on lectures given by Henry Eyring during the Winter of 1947–48 which we have used extensively. Thanks are also due to Dr. Gale B. Dick, Dr. Ransom B. Parlin, and Dr. Merrill B. Wallenstein whose critical comments have greatly added to the quality of this work. We also wish to thank the Magnolia Petroleum Company for permission to reproduce material from *Statistical Dynamics*, six lectures given by Henry Eyring, June, 1957. Finally, the authors wish to thank Miss Belva Barlow, Miss Libbie Lyman, and Miss Mehl Ree Draper for their generous assistance in preparing the manuscript, and F. W. and E. Bruenger for their assistance in preparing the subject index.

CONTENTS

1

AN INTRODUCTION TO STATISTICAL MECHANICS

1. Statistical Compounding of Systems

Let us consider how we can set up statistical mechanics in a systematic fashion. First consider a system A characterized by a number of degrees of freedom. As a concrete example, consider a benzene molecule, but let it be emphasized that our mechanical system might be almost anything else; however, the benzene molecule is complicated enough to give the right point of view. It has twelve atoms and to specify each one of these atoms in space requires three positional coordinates, that is, an x-distance, a y-distance, and a z-distance. Each atom is said to have three degrees of freedom so that for all twelve atoms we have thirty-six degrees of freedom. The velocity in each degree of freedom is, in first approximation, independent of the velocity in any other degree of freedom, and, therefore, the energies are also independent, so that the position, momenta, and energy can have values in one degree of freedom without prejudice as to what the values are for another independent degree. It is obvious that the energy of the benzene molecule will be specified only when all thirty-six component energies are specified. As is well known from spectroscopy, the energy levels are quantized. If the benzene molecule is confined to the volume inside a box, then the translational degrees of freedom are quantized. In any case, it is convenient to think of the translational motion as quantized. To specify the exact state of the benzene molecule, the energy level in each of the three translational degrees of freedom must be fixed. The molecule also rotates about each of the three axes (A, B, and C) as illustrated in Figure 1 and has a certain amount of energy associated with each of these rotations. The remaining thirty degrees of freedom are vibrational. To specify completely the energy of the benzene molecule will require a knowledge of the particular quantum state it is in for each of these thirty-six degrees of freedom. We designate the quantum states by quantum numbers which indicate which energy level the molecule is in in each degree of freedom.

Again we emphasize that an equally good system A would be two benzene molecules, or a benzene molecule and three hydrogen molecules. In fact, any system composed of molecules would be equally satisfactory. If the system is highly complex, it will require writing down a lot of quan-

1

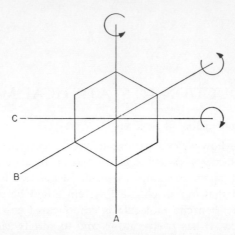

Figure 1. Rotational axes of a benzene molecule.

tum numbers and energies, but it will still exist in certain completely definable energy states. The question now arises: What is the chance that the benzene molecule, or whatever else is taken for system *A*, is in a particular state which is uniquely determined by knowing the individual states for the degrees of freedom? This is a good statistical mechanical question and one for which we require an answer. Degeneracy is said to occur when two or more eigenfunctions correspond to the same energy, that is, one of the degrees of freedom has more than one state corresponding to the same energy. Most of us are probably familiar with the general notion of eigenfunctions. The probability that a molecule is in a certain volume of space, dV, is just the normalized eigenfunction squared, multiplied by dV. We shall take quantum mechanics for granted; that is, either we know the energy levels, or can obtain them from spectroscopy, or can calculate them from quantum mechanics.

Compounding two systems

Now to study this system *A*, we think of it as enclosed in another system *B*. This system *B* can be anything we like because we shall use a principle most of us know from thermodynamics. If the temperature is fixed the chance that a molecule is in a certain energy state does not depend upon the kind of system with which it is in thermal equilibrium. *B* can be any kind of system. This idea that if system *A* is in thermal equilibrium with *B* and *B* is in equilibrium with *C*, then *A* is in equilibrium with *C* can be called the 'Zeroth Law of Thermodynamics'.[1] It will be convenient

[1] R. H. Fowler and E. A. Guggenheim, *Statistical Thermodynamics*, Cambridge University Press, 1939, p. 56.

to choose system B so as to make our calculations simplest, and this will be by choosing a collection of identical harmonic oscillators. Let us think of B as a metal box composed of many, say $s/3$ atoms, and hence s oscillators enclosing system A. Actually we shall end up by wanting the metal very soft so that the forces holding atoms in place, with respect to neighbors, will be very weak and the atom will vibrate with very low frequencies. Under these conditions, the energy levels will be close together. Each of these s oscillators takes up energy in multiples of hv. This principle, of course, goes back to the work of Planck.

Assuming the combined system $A + B$ has a fixed total energy E, we now ask the question: What is the chance that system A has any energy E distributed among its degrees of freedom in some unique allowed way? To answer this, we require a quantum mechanical postulate which is equivalent to the classical ergodic hypothesis. The postulate is that *any unique allowed way of distributing the energy* E *in the combined system* A + B *is equally probable*. The 'allowed' is required since some energy distributions are not compatible with the quantization of the energy levels. The expression we shall finally derive will reflect the fact that there are many ways in which the energy can be distributed among the competing degrees of freedom.

The total energy of the combined system $A + B$ is E; therefore, if the system A has an energy ε, the total number of quanta, n, to be distributed among the s oscillators is just $(E - \varepsilon)/hv$. The probability that system A has the energy ε is proportional to the number of ways n quanta can be distributed among s oscillators of system B. How many ways are there to distribute n quanta to s oscillators? This is a problem of elementary algebra. A picture will help show how to count the number of ways. Let an oscillator be represented by an 'X' and a quantum by an 'O'. The quanta between two oscillators are defined as belonging to the oscillator on the right. This requires that the object on the extreme right always be an oscillator. A particular example for six quanta and four oscillators is thus:

$$(OOOX)(X)(OX)(OOX)$$

Since we must always keep an X on the extreme right, we have $(n + s - 1)$ choices for the extreme left position, $(n + s - 2)$ for the next position and so on. Thus, the total number of such choices is $(n + s - 1)!$ However, our procedure has led us to overcount. If the first and second parentheses are interchanged, this will not change the distribution, for the same quanta still belong to the same oscillator, and thus there are $(s - 1)!$ permutations that we have counted as different that are not different. So $(n + s - 1)!$ is too big by a factor $(s - 1)!$ It is too big in another way also. This calculation assumes that it is possible to distinguish between the quanta. This might or might not be true. Here, experiment must be the final arbiter. In order to get results that will agree with experiment, it must be assumed that the quanta are indistinguishable. It is not that somewhere in the scriptures we read that quanta are indistinguishable. The fact is that if we make such an assumption we get a game that agrees with experiment. This cannot be emphasized too much. Hence, we divide by $n!$ to compensate for the permutation of the quanta. Consequently the expression for the number of ways of distributing n quanta among s oscillators is

$$N = \frac{(n+s-1)!}{(s-1)!\,n!} \tag{1}$$

Equation (1) is an exact expression which can be simplified for large values of n and s to give the very useful form due to Boltzmann. Let us first rewrite Eq. (1) as

$$N = \frac{(n+s-1)(n+s-2)\dots(n+1)}{(s-1)!}$$

$$= \frac{1}{(s-1)!} \prod_{i=1}^{s-1} (n+s-i) \tag{2}$$

From our definition of n we have

$$n+s-i = \left(\frac{E-\varepsilon}{h\nu} + s - i\right)$$

$$= \left(\frac{E+(s-i)h\nu}{h\nu}\right)\left(1 - \frac{\varepsilon}{E+(s-i)h\nu}\right) \tag{3}$$

hence we may rewrite Eq. (2) as

$$N = \frac{1}{(s-1)!} \prod_{i=1}^{s-1} \left(\frac{E+(s-i)h\nu}{h\nu}\right) \prod_{i=1}^{s-1} \left(1 - \frac{\varepsilon}{E+(s-i)h\nu}\right) \tag{4}$$

We shall let $\gamma = (E-\varepsilon)/s$, the average energy per low frequency oscillator. We shall also require that $E \gg \varepsilon$ and $n \gg s$. It therefore follows that $\gamma \gg h\nu$ and

$$E+(s-i)h\nu \approx s\gamma+(s-i)h\nu \approx s\gamma \tag{5}$$

to a good approximation for all i. Equation (4) now becomes

$$N = C\left(1 - \frac{\varepsilon}{s\gamma}\right)^{s-1} \tag{6}$$

where the constant C is independent of ε. A descending exponential can be evaluated from the relation

$$e^{-x} = \lim_{s\to\infty} \left(1 - \frac{x}{s}\right)^s \tag{7}$$

and since s is large in Eq. (6), we have the excellent approximation

$$N = C\, e^{-\varepsilon/\gamma} \tag{8}$$

We have defined γ as the average energy of a low frequency oscillator. Dulong and Petit found that the heat capacity of a mole of metal was 6.2 calories per degree. This same heat capacity is found for all metals if the temperature is sufficiently high so that the metal is acting classically, that is, if $h\nu \ll kT$. We take as our hypothetical metal a very soft one so that it behaves classically as near as we please down to absolute zero. This would be an unusual metal, but one has the general principle that the result cannot depend on the particular properties of the substance we use for system B. Thus, we know the average energy, γ, of such an oscillator is kT, where T is the absolute temperature. We next calculate the value of k. In a mole there are Avogadro's number of atoms and each atom has three degrees of freedom, so we divide the heat capacity by $3 \times 6.023 \times 10^{23}$. To convert from calories to ergs, one must multiply by 4.183×10^7; therefore, we have

$$k = \frac{(6.2)(4.183 \times 10^7)}{(3)(6.023 \times 10^{23})} = 1.4 \times 10^{-16}\ \text{ergs deg}^{-1} \tag{9}$$

If an accurate evaluation is carried out, one finds a value of 1.37×10^{-16} ergs per degree for k. To get the average energy, one must multiply k by the absolute temperature so $\gamma = kT = 1.37 \times 10^{-16}T$. There is a point here which might worry us. We have been developing a theoretical argument and suddenly we bring in an experimental measurement. The absolute value of k is one of the constants of nature and at present no satisfactory theory for calculating it exists. We could have compared some other experimental measurement with theory to evaluate k, such as the pressure of a perfect gas. The result would be the same. There are, in fact, many ways k can be evaluated.

Now the probability p_i that system A is in a particular state i is just the ratio of N for state i divided by N summed for all states. Thus:

$$p_i = \frac{C\, e^{-\varepsilon_i/kT}}{\sum\limits_i C\, e^{-\varepsilon_i/kT}} = \frac{e^{-\varepsilon_i/kT}}{\sum\limits_i e^{-\varepsilon_i/kT}} \tag{10}$$

The constant C being independent of ε_i, it cancels out. Here, for the first time, we see the partition function $\sum_i e^{-\varepsilon_i/kT}$ for system A. The summation is over all possible states which the system A can assume. One can see how this sum arose. We had to consider all possible ways the energy could be distributed in the compound system $(A+B)$. To do this, for each state of A we summed over all possible corresponding states of B. The sum over all possible states of the system $(A+B)$ required finally summing over all the possible states of A. Let us review the general aspects of the whole problem. For system A, we can choose any system, e.g. one molecule, two molecules, three molecules, or in fact anything that has a certain set of degrees of freedom. The whole energy ε for the particular case where A consists of say two benzene molecules is the sum of $2 \times 36 = 72$ terms. Next, we chose an extremely soft metal, B, for A to be in equilibrium with because such a metal has the energy kT per oscillator at all temperatures. System B may be chosen arbitrarily because of the theorem that if A is in thermal equilibrium with B and B is in equilibrium with C, then A is in equilibrium with C. Thus, any change in B cannot affect the result we get for the probability that A is in a given state at a fixed temperature and volume. It is, of course, assumed that A and B do not react chemically. The restriction that the volume, V, must be specified arises because, as we shall find, at least the translational energy states of A change with volume. In the combined system $A + B$, we assume the energy is fixed as well as the volume. In system A, on the contrary, the energy is not fixed. We must consider all possible allowed energies of A. The various allowed ways of distributing energy are equally likely only for those systems where the total energy stays the same.

In the mathematical development, certain assumptions were necessary. s was taken as the order of Avogadro's number, n was considered to be large compared to s, and E was taken large compared to ε. If one is concerned with a problem in which these assumptions do not apply, one should use Eq. (1) directly. Simply count the quanta, count the oscillators, and substitute in Eq. (1). The Boltzmann expression is a limiting value derived by making the assumptions just listed.

2. The Statistical Mechanical Basis of Thermodynamics

The postulate we used in the development of the probability is very important, namely, that *any allowed way of distributing the energy in the system* $A + B$ *is equally likely*. This is a form of the ergodic hypothesis. Since this hypothesis is so basic, a few additional points should be made about it. First, we define phase space. For each degree of freedom there is, in classical mechanics, a position and a momentum to specify so that for each particle we require six coordinates. For $s/3$ particles we shall thus require a $2s$ dimensional space in which the point representing the system moves. This is called *phase space*. A system moves through phase space in obedience to the laws of mechanics. As Liouville showed, such a point spends equal times in the parts of phase space lying along its trajectory. A complete proof of the ergodic hypothesis never quite comes off. We can prove the system does not favor any part of the phase space it visits, but we cannot prove that it visits all parts of space, and indeed it may not in any finite time. A very clear-cut example is found in our solar system where all of the planets are along the ecliptic. They could be off the ecliptic and have the same energy, so there are other regions of phase space accessible to them energetically, but they have not visited these regions in some five billion years. No doubt, in a long time the system will visit all points in phase space having the same energy as a result of slight disturbances; nevertheless, one can only prove that the moving point in phase space does not show favoritism in the regions it does visit. When we give up classical mechanics for quantum mechanics, we have added complications. Thus, in accordance with the uncertainty principle, we can no longer simultaneously specify the positions and the conjugate momenta exactly. In quantum mechanics our system does not have access to all regions of phase space because the levels are quantized. This quick statement of the ergodic hypothesis should be of some help in the remaining discussion. If the system does not visit all regions accessible to it energetically, we say it is *metastable*. The part of space the system does visit during the time of the experiment is visited impartially. Thus, we use statistical mechanics, including the ergodic hypothesis, on a mixture of hydrogen and oxygen which is metastable with respect to the formation of water. A little platinum in this mixture will cause it to react immediately to form water. Nearly everyone is familiar with and has used the restricted ergodic hypothesis.

To write the average value of any property that can be expressed in terms of the coordinates of the system we employ the probability expression, Eq. (1.10). If one knows the probability of being in a state and the value the property has when the system is in that state, then the average value is calculated as this product summed over the various states. Thus, the average value of the property x is given by:

$$\bar{x} = \sum_i p_i x_i \qquad (1)$$

By definition, the probability when summed over all states adds up to unity. When the property of interest is the energy, we have the expression:

$$E = \sum_i \varepsilon_i p_i = \frac{\sum_i \varepsilon_i e^{-\varepsilon_i/kT}}{\sum_i e^{-\varepsilon_i/kT}} \equiv KT^2 \frac{\partial}{\partial T} \left(\ln \sum_i e^{-\varepsilon_i/kT} \right) \qquad (2)$$

This identity is readily justified since a uniformly convergent series can be differentiated term by term. The thermodynamic relations needed here are developed in Chapter 3. Thus we write:

$$T \, dS = dE + dW \qquad (3)$$

In the particular case where the only work done is against the pressure, p, we can write for the work (dW) the term $p \, dV$. If there are other kinds of work, they should be added to the $p \, dV$ term. This equation is a combina-

tion of the first and second laws. We next define the Helmholtz free energy,
A:[1]

$$A = E - TS \tag{4}$$

The Helmholtz free energy, A, being a property of the system has a perfect
differential. This is clearly so since it is defined in terms of quantities
which are themselves properties. Thus we write

$$dA = dE - T\,dS - S\,dT \tag{5}$$

Subtracting the expression for $T\,dS$, Eq. (3) yields

$$dA = -S\,dT - dW \tag{6}$$

Now at constant temperature the $S\,dT$ term vanishes and the change in A
is the work done by the system. Thus, if A decreases, then the system does
positive work on some other system. If A increases, the external system
does work on the system under consideration. A is an interesting function
since one can integrate it over a path at constant temperature and have an
expression for the work done on a system. The Helmholtz free energy is
also called the maximum work function. It is very useful. If we substitute
$p\,dV$ for dW, we obtain

$$dA = -S\,dT - p\,dV \tag{7}$$

From (7) we see that

$$\left(\frac{\partial A}{\partial T}\right)_V = -S \tag{8}$$

Combining Eqs. (4) and (8), we have

$$A = E + T\left(\frac{\partial A}{\partial T}\right)_V \tag{9}$$

or

$$A - T\left(\frac{\partial A}{\partial T}\right)_V = E \tag{10}$$

Consider the expression

$$\frac{\partial (A/T)}{\partial T} = -\frac{A}{T^2} + \frac{1}{T}\frac{\partial A}{\partial T} \tag{11}$$

Multiplying Eq. (11) by $-T^2$ yields

$$-T^2\frac{\partial (A/T)}{\partial T} = A - T\frac{\partial A}{\partial T} \tag{12}$$

or

$$-T^2\frac{\partial (A/T)}{\partial T} = E \tag{13}$$

---

[1] As mentioned earlier, notation is a problem. In this book we shall follow the notation of G. N. Lewis, with the exceptions that G will be used for the Gibbs' free energy
and μ (instead of $\overline{F}$) for the chemical potential.

We next identify this thermodynamic expression for the energy with the statistical mechanical expression

$$-T^2 \frac{\partial(A/T)}{\partial T} = kT^2 \frac{\partial}{\partial T} \ln \sum_i e^{-\varepsilon_i/kT} \qquad (14)$$

Integrating at constant volume with respect to the temperature gives:

$$\frac{A}{T} = -k \ln \sum_i e^{-\varepsilon_i/kT} - C \qquad (15)$$

In the above expression, we have taken the integration constant as $-C$ for convenience later. C is necessarily independent of the temperature and is a function of the volume. We write

$$A = -kT \ln \sum_i e^{-\varepsilon_i/kT} - CT \qquad (16)$$

Let us see what Eq. (16) tells us about the third law or rather what the third law and this equation together imply. We write out the summation in Eq. (16) using ω_i to indicate the degeneracy, i.e. the number of states with the same energy, ε_i. Thus, Eq. (16) becomes:

$$A = -kT \ln (\omega_1 e^{-\varepsilon_1/kT} + \omega_2 e^{-\varepsilon_2/kT} + \ldots) - CT \qquad (17)$$

Since $\varepsilon_2, \varepsilon_3, \ldots$, are larger than ε_1, all terms except the term with ε_1 will become vanishingly small as T goes to zero, so that for very low temperatures we have

$$A = -kT \ln \omega_1 + \varepsilon_1 - CT \qquad (18)$$

What does the third law of thermodynamics mean? Consider the following reaction:

$$H_2 + Br_2 \longrightarrow 2\,HBr \qquad (19)$$

From the second law of thermodynamics, we know that the entropy change in a reaction is independent of the path followed between the initial and the final state. Thus, if a mole of hydrogen and a mole of bromine, having been heated from absolute zero up to some temperature T_1, are allowed to react to form two moles of hydrogen bromide and the system is then cooled down again to $T = 0$, the entropy change around this cycle (Figure 1, path 2, 3, 4) must be the same as by the direct reaction at absolute zero indicated by path 1 (see Figure 1). To obtain the entropy change with temperature, we simply plot the specific heat divided by the temperature versus the temperature. The area under the curve obtained is equal to the entropy change. For any system of this kind in which the initial and final products are both crystalline, the third law of thermodynamics states that there is no entropy change in going from one state to another at the absolute zero. Since there is zero entropy change along path 1, this is equally true for path 2 according to the second law. If for all

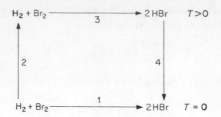

Figure 1. Entropy change for reaction $H_2 + Br_2 \rightarrow 2\,HBr$.
$$\Delta S_1 = \Delta S_2 + \Delta S_3 + \Delta S_4.$$

chemical reactions occurring at absolute zero there is zero entropy change, we may as well say any crystalline substance has zero entropy at the absolute zero. This will be true for all substances because, if it is true for one substance, and, if by any reaction this substance is transformed into another, there being no entropy change, then the new substances must likewise have zero entropy. Now let us see what statistical mechanics tells us about this situation. We can express the equilibrium constant as the product of two factors,

$$K = e^{-\Delta H/RT} \cdot e^{\Delta S/R} \qquad (20)$$

This can be accomplished by using experimental data for K at different temperatures. We can put hydrogen and bromine in a container and measure the entropy change from $T = 0$ to $T = T$, and to this add ΔS from Eq. (19). Then put hydrogen bromide in a container and measure the entropy change from $T = T$ to $T = 0$ and add this to the other two entropies. If the third law is true, the sum is zero. In this way the third law is established.

Returning to Eq. (18), as T approaches zero we have:

$$A = -kT \ln \omega_1 + \varepsilon_1 - CT = E - TS \qquad (21)$$

We must necessarily identify the energy of the lowest state ε_1 with the energy E and it is apparent that the entropy at absolute zero is

$$S = k \ln \omega_1 + C \qquad (22)$$

In statistical mechanics the quantity $k \ln \omega_1 + C$ must vanish if the third law is to hold. Suppose state 1 is non-degenerate ($\omega_1 = 1$). Further, suppose C is k times the logarithm of some other degeneracy, ω_1'. That is, let ω_1 be the degeneracy for the energy levels outside the nucleus and suppose $C = k \ln \omega_1'$ is the entropy of the nucleus. Since the third law shows ω_1 and ω_1' are unchanged in chemical reactions, it is convenient to suppose that ω_1 and ω_1' are each equal to unity for all systems. Thus, in view of the experimental evidence supporting the third law, we write

$$A = -kT \ln \sum_i e^{-\varepsilon_i/kT} \tag{23}$$

Although the third law is readily understood if the ground state is non-degenerate, there is no general quantum mechanical proof of non-degeneracy of the lowest state. The evidence for non-degeneracy is rather the experimental evidence supporting the third law. All of thermodynamics is calculable from the partition function if the energy levels are available as functions of volume and temperature. The expression for energy in terms of the partition function has already been obtained [Eq. (2)], as has the expression for the Helmholtz free energy [Eq. (23)]. There are eight more thermodynamic functions that can be written down immediately in terms of the partition functions. To simplify the writing of these equations, let us write the partition function as

$$\equiv \sum_i e^{-\varepsilon_i/kT} \tag{24}$$

Then, the ten thermodynamic functions are

(i)
$$E = kT^2 \left(\frac{\partial \ln f}{\partial T} \right)_V \tag{25}$$

(ii)
$$A = -kT \ln f \tag{26}$$

Treating A as a function of T and V gives

$$dA = \left(\frac{\partial A}{\partial T} \right)_V dT + \left(\frac{\partial A}{\partial V} \right)_T dV \tag{27}$$

Comparison of Eqs. (7) and (27) leads to

(iii)
$$-\left(\frac{\partial A}{\partial V} \right)_T = p = kT \left(\frac{\partial \ln f}{\partial V} \right)_T \tag{28}$$

From Eq. (8) we have

(iv)
$$-\left(\frac{\partial A}{\partial T} \right)_V = S = k \left(\frac{\partial (T \ln f)}{\partial T} \right)_V \tag{29}$$

Gibbs' free energy is defined as

(v)
$$G = A + pV = -kT \ln f + VkT \left(\frac{\partial \ln f}{\partial V} \right)_T \tag{30}$$

The enthalpy is

(vi)
$$H = E + pV = kT^2 \left(\frac{\partial \ln f}{\partial T} \right)_V + VkT \left(\frac{\partial \ln f}{\partial V} \right)_T \tag{31}$$

The heat capacity of a substance at constant volume is

$$(vii) \qquad C_V = \left(\frac{\partial E}{\partial T}\right)_V = k\left(\frac{\partial}{\partial T}\frac{T^2 \partial \ln f}{\partial T}\right)_V \tag{32}$$

The coefficient of thermal expansion is given by

$$\alpha = \frac{1}{V}\left(\frac{\partial V}{\partial T}\right)_p \tag{33}$$

Pressure is a function of temperature and volume; thus:

$$dp = \left(\frac{\partial p}{\partial T}\right)_V dT + \left(\frac{\partial p}{\partial V}\right)_T dV \tag{34}$$

At constant pressure $dp = 0$ and we have

$$\left(\frac{\partial V}{\partial T}\right)_p = -\frac{\left(\frac{\partial p}{\partial T}\right)_V}{\left(\frac{\partial p}{\partial V}\right)_T} \tag{35}$$

Whence we can write

$$(viii) \qquad \alpha = -\frac{1}{V}\frac{\left[\frac{\partial}{\partial T}(kT)\left(\frac{\partial \ln f}{\partial V}\right)_T\right]_V}{kT\left(\frac{\partial^2 \ln f}{\partial V^2}\right)_T} \tag{36}$$

The coefficient of volume expansion is

$$(ix) \qquad \beta = -\frac{1}{V}\left(\frac{\partial V}{\partial p}\right)_T = -\frac{1}{V}\frac{1}{kT\left(\frac{\partial^2 \ln f}{\partial V^2}\right)_T} \tag{37}$$

The last expression we shall derive is the heat capacity at constant pressure

$$(x) \quad C_p = C_V + \frac{\alpha^2 VT}{\beta} = \frac{\partial}{\partial T}\left(kT^2\frac{\partial \ln f}{\partial T}\right)_V - \frac{k\left[\frac{\partial}{\partial T}\left\{T\left(\frac{\partial \ln f}{\partial V}\right)_T\right\}\right]_V^2}{\left(\frac{\partial^2 \ln f}{\partial V^2}\right)_T} \tag{38}$$

Clearly, if we know the energy levels as functions of volume and temperature, we can calculate all of thermodynamics. This is very satisfying. At the present time we need not measure thermodynamic properties experimentally if we have the necessary absorption spectra.

3. The Explicit Expressions for Partition Functions

Consider the partition function itself for some molecule like benzene. Equations (2.24) and (2.26) relate the Helmholtz free energy and the partition functions. If we look at benzene in the ith state, then the energy, ε_i, is the sum of the energy in each degree of freedom—a sum of thirty-six terms:

$$\varepsilon_i = \varepsilon_A^{I} + \varepsilon_B^{II} \ldots + \varepsilon_\lambda^{XXXVI} \tag{1}$$

Insofar as the energy in one degree of freedom does not depend upon the state of the molecule in another degree of freedom, we can do something very interesting. We write the expression for A as:

$$A = -kT \ln \left[\sum_A e^{-\varepsilon_A^{I}/kT} \sum_B e^{-\varepsilon_B^{II}/kT} \ldots \sum_\lambda e^{-\varepsilon_\lambda^{XXXVI}/kT} \right] \tag{2}$$

This is obviously true, because if we take the Boltzmann factor for any one of the levels ε_A^{I} and multiply it by the factor for the levels of ε_B^{II}, exponents are simply added. In this fashion, we can obtain the required sum over all possible energy levels. This procedure is correct to the approximation that the energy levels in one degree of freedom are independent of the state occupied in other degrees of freedom. When the molecule is rotating, centrifugal force changes the force constant between atoms so that the vibrational degree of freedom is slightly modified. If it is necessary to account for this difference, additional terms must be added to the energies to make the necessary correction. For most considerations, this is unnecessary. It is therefore useful to develop this product of terms for the partition function. Accordingly, we write the energy of the ith level as:

$$\varepsilon_i = \varepsilon_i(t) + \varepsilon_i(r) + \varepsilon_i(v) + \varepsilon_i(e) + \varepsilon_i(n) \tag{3}$$

where we have the energy of the molecule expressed as the sum of the energy levels associated with the translational, the rotational, the vibrational, the electronic, and the nuclear degrees of freedom respectively. According to this procedure, the partition function for the molecule is written

$$f_i = f_t f_r f_v f_e f_n \tag{4}$$

Because in most chemical reactions and phase transformations the electronic and nuclear states do not change, they are without effect on such equilibria and may be omitted.

4. Translational Partition Functions

First, consider the translational partition function. Suppose we have a benzene molecule in a rectangular box moving with a certain velocity in the x-direction. In the perfect gas approximation we can neglect the effect of other molecules. The molecule travels until it hits a wall at $x = a$ where it is reflected with negative momentum only to be again reflected at $x = 0$. The energy levels may be calculated equally well from quantum mechanics or from old quantum theory. Using the latter procedure we have the well known Wilson–Sommerfeld quantization rule

$$nh = \oint p_i dq_i \tag{1}$$

where q_i is the coordinate representing a degree of freedom of the system and p_i is the corresponding momentum. The integral is taken over a complete cycle. For the molecule moving in the box we thus have

$$nh = \oint p_i \, dq_i = m\dot{x}a + (-m\dot{x})(-a) = 2m\dot{x}a \tag{2}$$

The translational energy of the molecule in the x-direction is

$$\varepsilon = \tfrac{1}{2}m\dot{x}^2 \tag{3}$$

Substituting the value of $\dot{x}$, we have

$$\varepsilon_n = \tfrac{1}{2}m \left(\frac{nh}{2ma} \right)^2 = \frac{n^2h^2}{8a^2m} \tag{4}$$

Thus the partition function for translation in the x-direction is

$$f_{t(x)} = \sum_{n=1}^{\infty} e^{-\varepsilon_n/kT} = \sum_{n=1}^{\infty} e^{-n^2h^2/8a^2mkT} \tag{5}$$

The summation in Eq. (5) is the sum of the rectangular areas in Figure 1. To an excellent approximation this summation can be replaced by the integral corresponding to the area under the curve.

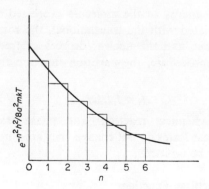

Figure 1. Illustration of the approximation of the summation of Eq. (5) by integration.

Thus we have

$$f_{t(x)} = \int_0^{\infty} e^{-n^2h^2/8a^2mkT} \, dn = \frac{(2\pi mkT)^{\frac{1}{2}}a}{h} \tag{6}$$

where we have used Integral (2) in Appendix 2. If this is now repeated for the y- and z-directions, the same expression is obtained except that the other box dimensions b and c replace a. Whence we have

$$f_t = \frac{(2\pi mkT)^{\frac{3}{2}}abc}{h^3} = \frac{(2\pi mkT)^{\frac{3}{2}}V}{h^3} \tag{7}$$

5. Rotational Partition Functions

A discussion of the energy levels of the restricted rotator can be found elsewhere.[1] For the one-dimensional rotator such as CH_3—CI_3 the angular momentum is

$$p = I\dot{\phi} \tag{1}$$

where $I = I_1 I_2/(I_1 + I_2)$. Here $\dot{\phi}$ is the angular velocity about the axis of rotation, I_1 is the moment of inertia of CH_3 about the C—C axis and I_2 is the CI_3 moment of inertia. As usual we have

$$nh = \oint p\,dq = \int_{\phi=0}^{2\pi} I\dot{\phi}\,d\phi = I\dot{\phi}2\pi \tag{2}$$

We can also write for the energy

$$\varepsilon = \tfrac{1}{2}I\dot{\phi}^2 = \tfrac{1}{2}I\left(\frac{nh}{2\pi I}\right)^2 = \frac{n^2 h^2}{8\pi^2 I} \tag{3}$$

Here all positive and negative integral values of the quantum number n are allowed including zero so that

$$f_{1r} = \frac{1}{\sigma}\left(1 + 2\sum_{n=1}^{\infty} e^{-n^2 h^2/8\pi^2 IkT}\right) = \frac{1}{\sigma}\int_{-\infty}^{\infty} e^{-n^2 h^2/8\pi^2 IkT}\,dn$$

$$= \frac{1}{\sigma}\sqrt{\frac{\pi 8\pi^2 IkT}{h^2}} = \frac{(2\pi IkT)^{\frac{1}{2}}2\pi}{\sigma h} \tag{4}$$

where σ, the symmetry number, will be discussed below.

Next, we consider the partition function for rotational degrees of freedom, as in the hydrogen or hydrogen iodide molecule. Let us take for the energy the result we get from spectroscopy or from quantum theory,[2] which is

$$\varepsilon_r = \frac{J(J+1)h^2}{8\pi^2 I} \tag{5}$$

where J is the rotational quantum number and I is the moment of inertia of the molecule. The two-dimensional rotator is $(2J+1)$-fold degenerate.

---

[1] Q.C., p. 358. See also Sect. 11.2.
[2] Q.C., Eq. (5.35), p. 74.

Figure 1 illustrates the configuration of the hydrogen molecule as a two-dimensional rotator. Now, if the two atoms of a diatomic molecule, e.g. HI, are different, J can have values 0, 1, 2, 3, . . . However, if both atoms

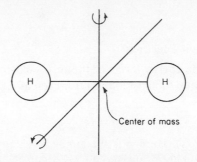

Figure 1. The hydrogen molecule as a two-dimensional rotator.

are the same, as in H_2, the J's will be either even (0, 2, 4, . . .) or odd (1, 3, 5, . . .), but not both.[3] Consequently, when the atoms are alike, the allowed energy levels will result in a summation term just half as big as if the atoms were different. In fact, there are really two kinds of hydrogen molecule—one with even and one with odd rotational levels. We write the partition function for the two-dimensional rotator as

$$f_{2r} = \sum (2J+1) \, e^{-J(J+1)h^2/8\pi^2 IkT} \tag{6}$$

Thus, for a molecule with identical atoms the summation over all states must be divided by the symmetry number $\sigma = 2$. In the same manner as before, we plot the term values of the summation for different J's.

We again replace the sum by the appropriate integral (see Figure 2) and obtain

$$f_{2r} = \frac{1}{\sigma} \int_0^\infty (2J+1) \, e^{-J(J+1)h^2/8\pi^2 IkT} \, dJ$$

$$= \frac{8\pi^2 IkT}{\sigma h^2} \int_0^\infty e^{-x} \, dx$$

$$= \frac{8\pi^2 IkT}{\sigma h^2} \tag{7}$$

When the summation differs significantly from the integral the summation must be used, but most of the time the integral is a sufficiently good approximation.

[3] See Sect. 11.1.

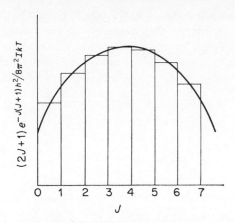

Figure 2. Illustration of the approximation of the summation of Eq. (6) by integration.

The expression for the three-dimensional rotator

$$f_{3r} = \frac{8\pi^2(8\pi^3 ABC)^{\frac{1}{2}}(kT)^{\frac{3}{2}}}{\sigma h^3} \tag{8}$$

is derived in Sect. 2.6.

Returning to benzene, we ask what is the symmetry number, σ, of a benzene molecule? The symmetry number is just the number of indistinguishable orientations of the molecule. We see that any one of the six carbon atoms can be at the top in Figure 1.1 and if the ring is turned over, any one of the six carbon atoms again can be at the top. Thus, in the case of benzene, there are twelve indistinguishable positions of the rigid molecule so that $\sigma = 12$. Thus $\sigma = 2$ for H_2O, 3 for NH_3 and 12 for methane. The quantum mechanical explanation of the symmetry number is that any particular molecule can only exist in $1/\sigma$ of the rotational energy levels.

6. The Partition Function for a Harmonic Oscillator

Another partition function we need to know is the one for the harmonic oscillator. For a harmonic oscillator, the partition function is just

$$f_r = e^{-0/kT} + e^{-h\nu/kT} + e^{-2h\nu/kT} + \ldots \tag{1}$$

since the oscillator is restricted to energy levels which are integral multiples of $h\nu$. For such an oscillator (see Figure 1) we chose as our zero of energy the lowest energy level. Actually in this state the oscillator has one-half quantum ($\frac{1}{2} h\nu$) of energy. We might equally well have chosen the minimum in Figure 1 in which case $\frac{1}{2} h\nu/kT$ would be added to each exponent in Eq. (1), or more simply, the series on the right-hand side of Eq. (1) would just be multiplied by $\exp(-\frac{1}{2} h\nu/kT)$. Actually any other arbitrary choice of a standard energy level would serve equally well providing the same reference level was adopted for initial, activated, and final states.

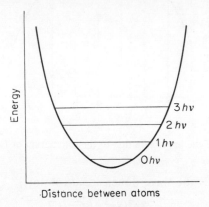

Figure 1. Energy levels of the harmonic oscillator.

If we write

$$x = e^{-h\nu/kT} \tag{2}$$

then

$$f_r = 1 + x + x^2 + x^3 + \ldots = \frac{1}{1-x} \tag{3}$$

Hence we have

$$f_r = \frac{1}{1 - e^{-h\nu/kT}} \tag{4}$$

This completes the partition functions required for the usual degrees of freedom. We are now in a position to calculate all the thermodynamic properties of benzene. For one mole, the Helmholtz free energy is given by

$$A = -kT \ln \left[\left\{ \frac{\int (2\pi m kT)^{\frac{3}{2}}}{h^3} V \frac{8\pi^2 (8\pi^3 ABC)^{\frac{1}{2}} (kT)^{\frac{3}{2}}}{12h^3} \cdot \right. \right.$$
$$\left. \left. \prod_{i=1}^{30} \frac{1}{1 - e^{-h\nu_i/kT}} \right\}^N (N!)^{-1} \right] \tag{5}$$

The factor $(N!)^{-1}$ is a symmetry number and is the number of indistinguishable arrangements obtained by interchanging N identical gas molecules over any set of N spatial positions. If the various thermodynamic properties of benzene are calculated using the equations of Sect. 2, they will be found to be in satisfactory agreement with the experimental values.

7. Equilibrium Constants

Now that we have the partition functions for the various degrees of freedom we are prepared to calculate equilibrium constants. Consider the reaction

$$H_2 + I_2 \rightleftharpoons 2\,HI \tag{1}$$

which we indicate schematically by Figure 1. To depict the potential energy surface completely in configuration space for four atoms at the corners of a quadrilateral we must specify the lengths of the four sides and of the

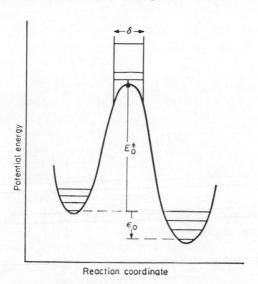

Figure 1. Schematic illustration of the potential energy surface for the reaction $H_2 + I_2 \rightleftharpoons 2\,HI$. (Adapted from H. Eyring, *Statistical Dynamics*, Magnolia Petroleum Company, Colloquium Lectures in Pure and Applied Science, No. 3. Copyright 1958 by Magnolia Petroleum Company, Dallas, Texas.)

two diagonals to fix the relative positions of the atoms. A seventh dimension is then required for the energy. Actually a table of energy values for various configurations to which a potential surface can be fitted for use in the theory of small vibrations is all that is required for statistical mechanics. From the point of view of statistical mechanics the four atoms constitute a single system whether they exist in the initial state $H_2 + I_2$ or in the final state 2 HI. Any HI molecule with any other HI is a representative of the four-atom system in the state corresponding to hydrogen iodide. We represent the total number of H_2, I_2 and HI molecules in the system by n_1, n_2 and n_3 respectively. The number of representations of the final state is thus $n_3(n_3 - 1)/2$. The number of examples of the initial state is

$n_1 n_2$ and the ratio of the numbers of examples of the two states must be in the same ratio as the respective partition functions for the two states, leading to the equation

$$n_3(n_3-1)/2n_1 n_2 = \sum_f e^{-\varepsilon_f/kT}/2 \sum_i e^{-\varepsilon_i/kT} \tag{2}$$

If we are dealing with a large number of molecules, then $n_3(n_3-1)$ will be equal to n_3^2 for all practical purposes and the half cancels from each side of the equation leaving

$$n_3^2/n_1 n_2 = \sum_f e^{-\varepsilon_f/kT}/\sum_i e^{-\varepsilon_i/kT} \tag{3}$$

Substituting expressions for the partition function yields the equation

$$\frac{n_3^2}{n_1 n_2} = \frac{\left[\dfrac{(2\pi m_3 kT)^{\frac{3}{2}}V}{h^3} \dfrac{8\pi^2 I_3 kT}{h^2} \dfrac{1}{1-e^{-hv_3/kT}}\right]^2}{\dfrac{(2\pi m_1 kT)^{\frac{3}{2}}V}{h^3} \dfrac{8\pi^2 I_1 kT}{2h^2} \dfrac{1}{1-e^{-hv_1/kT}}}$$

$$\frac{e^{-\varepsilon_0/kT}}{\dfrac{(2\pi m_2 kT)^{\frac{3}{2}}V}{h^3} \dfrac{8\pi^2 I_2 kT}{2h^2} \dfrac{1}{1-e^{-hv_2/kT}}} = \frac{f_3^2 e^{-\varepsilon_0/kT}}{f_1 f_2} \tag{4}$$

The factor $e^{-\varepsilon_0/kT}$ (ε_0 is the energy of reaction at absolute zero as indicated in Figure 1) refers the partition function for the final state to the lowest level of the initial state. Dividing the number of molecules by the volume yields concentrations and we have

$$K = (n_3/V)^2/(n_1/V)(n_2/V) \tag{5}$$

Thus, we have for the equilibrium constant

$$K = \frac{\left[\dfrac{(2\pi m_3 kT)^{\frac{3}{2}}}{h^3} \dfrac{8\pi^2 I_3 kT}{h^2} \dfrac{1}{1-e^{-hv_3/kT}}\right]^2 e^{-\varepsilon_0/kT}}{\left[\dfrac{(2\pi m_1 kT)^{\frac{3}{2}}}{h^3} \dfrac{8\pi^2 I_1 kT}{2h^2} \dfrac{1}{1-e^{-hv_1/kT}}\right]}$$

$$\frac{1}{\left[\dfrac{(2\pi m_2 kT)^{\frac{3}{2}}}{h^3} \dfrac{8\pi^2 I_2 kT}{2h^2} \dfrac{1}{1-e^{-hv_2/kT}}\right]} \tag{6}$$

From thermodynamics we have

$$\Delta E = kT^2 \frac{\partial \ln K}{\partial T} \tag{7}$$

where ΔE is the difference in the energy between the two states. If we carry out this differentiation on our expression, we obtain

$$\Delta E = \frac{2hv_3}{e^{hv_3/kT}-1} - \frac{hv_1}{e^{hv_1/kT}-1} - \frac{hv_2}{e^{hv_2/kT}-1} + \varepsilon_0 \tag{8}$$

In order to obtain ε_0, we usually require a calorimetric measurement or heats of dissociation from spectroscopy. To obtain the heat of combustion, H_2 and I_2 are put in a combustion chamber with oxygen, burned and the heat measured. This procedure is then repeated with two moles of HI and oxygen. The heat of combustion of the two moles of HI minus the heat for $H_2 + I_2$ is ΔH. In the case of gases, we have

$$\Delta H = \Delta E + \Delta nRT \tag{9}$$

According to Eq. (1) the number of molecules after reaction equals the number before so that Δn is equal to zero. Using Eqs. (8) and (9) we can obtain the numerical value of ε_0.

8. Nature of Chemical Bonding

A hydrogen atom, being composed of a positive nucleus and an electron, should, according to classical mechanics, radiate energy and reach a negatively infinite potential as the two charges come together. The fact that they do not do this can be understood on the basis that quantum mechanically such particles are 'claustrophobic' and resist confinement in a restricted space. In terms of the Bohr theory this fact is expressed by the Wilson–Sommerfeld quantization rule discussed earlier in connection with Eq. (4.1). The Heisenberg uncertainty principle

$$\Delta p \cdot \Delta q \approx \hbar$$

indicates that, if we restrict position to a length Δq, the uncertainty in momentum increases in a reciprocal fashion. This means that the uncertainty in the kinetic energy increases correspondingly. The Schrödinger equation for a particle[1]

$$\left[-\frac{h^2}{8\pi^2 m}\left(\frac{\partial^2}{\partial x^2} + \frac{\partial^2}{\partial y^2} + \frac{\partial^2}{\partial z^2} \right) + V \right] \psi = E\psi \tag{1}$$

embodies the fact that the allowable energy, E, is the best compromise between the positive kinetic and the negative potential energy. The kinetic energy arising from the operator

$$T = -\frac{h^2}{8\pi^2 m}\left(\frac{\partial^2}{\partial x^2} + \frac{\partial^2}{\partial y^2} + \frac{\partial^2}{\partial z^2} \right) \tag{2}$$

increases as the eigenfunction ψ and restricts the electron to the neighborhood of the nucleus. In Figure 1 the area under $|\psi|^2$ integrated over space is normalized to unity since $|\psi|^2$ is interpreted as the probability of occupying a given position. Clearly, a curve such as Figure 1B which restricts the electron to being near the nucleus will involve larger values for

[1] *Q.C.*, p. 24.

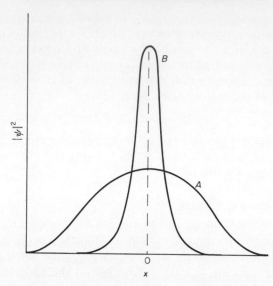

Figure 1. The probability of an electron's being near a nucleus in the x-direction. Similar curves apply in the y- and z-directions.

the second derivatives of ψ, and therefore the associated kinetic energy as given by the wave equation, Eq. (1), will be larger than for the less restrictive curve A. Restriction of the electron to the immediate vicinity of the nucleus as in curve B gives rise to a favorable decrease in the potential energy V. The bonding of two atoms is simply a method of overcoming this quantum mechanical claustrophobia without at the same time unduly increasing the potential energy. Thus, as the two atoms come together the bonding electrons escape from confinement in the space about a single nucleus by changing to paths which encircle both nuclei. The final bonded configuration is again the best compromise between kinetic and potential energy. Experimentally it was discovered by Pauli[2] that a social regulation exists to prevent overcrowding among the electrons (also among other identical particles). The Pauli exclusion principle requires that electrons have unlike spins if they are to occupy simultaneously the space described by a single eigenfunction ψ, i.e. occupy the same orbital. As Stern and Gerlach[3] showed, there are only two possible spins for an electron, corresponding to the two components of the angular momentum $+h/4\pi$ and $-h/4\pi$. Thus no more than two electrons can occupy a given orbital, such as a single chemical bond.

[2] W. Pauli, *Z. Physik*, **31,** 765 (1925).
[3] O. Stern and W. Gerlach, *Z. Physik*, **8,** 110; **9,** 349 (1922).

The exclusion principle is of the utmost importance for chemical stability. Thus, if two molecules carrying their full complement of electrons, filling the low lying orbitals, collide with each other, the exclusion principle ensures that the electrons on one molecule are unable to share their orbitals with the electrons on the approaching molecule.

Each filled orbital acts like an inflated gas bag, fastened by an elastic band to its nucleus. As the molecules approach each other great pressures develop which can only be relieved by stretching the elastic bands holding the gas bags in place. This stretching, which shifts the orbital into a higher state, is called energy of promotion. The promotional energy together with other repulsion energies, notably nuclear repulsions, constitutes the activation energy of chemical reaction. The activation energy is the energy required to push two or more molecules together to the point of no return, i.e. to the point where the electrons find it as profitable energetically to circulate between approaching atoms as to continue to circulate between those which were originally bonded together. Beyond the activated state the atoms continue to rearrange in such a way that the new bonds increase in strength as old bonds weaken.

If we think of the coordinate z as lying along the bond direction, then the initiation of a new bond has its principal effect in lessening the kinetic energy associated with the term $\partial^2/\partial z^2$ in Eq. (1). The other second derivatives are made small by keeping bonding orbitals smooth and unbent. This latter method of lowering bond energies has been called the 'Principle of Minimum Bending of Orbitals' and is widely applicable in explaining molecular structure and rates of chemical reaction.[4] The planar structure of chlorine trifluoride, ClF_3, is an interesting example.[5] The central

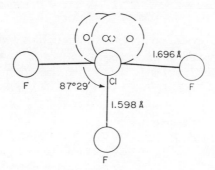

Figure 2. Chlorine trifluoride. [From G. H. Stewart and H. Eyring, *J. Chem. Educ.*, **35**, 550 (1958).]

4 G. H. Stewart and H. Eyring, *J. Chem. Educ.*, **35**, 550 (1958).
5 D. F. Smith, *J. Chem. Phys.*, **21**, 609 (1953).

fluorine atom (see Figure 2) makes an angle of 87° 29' with the chlorine and with either of the fluorine atoms while the central Cl—F distance is 1.598 Å compared with a more extended 1.696 Å for the two outer Cl—F bonds. The two non-bonding orbital gas bags each containing two electrons preempt as much of the chlorine surface as they can while the electronegative fluorine atoms each obligingly draws off the electron pair joining it to the chlorine. Thus, whereas we might expect four bags to fill the space around a chlorine, five are here accommodated with three of them being markedly distorted in the direction of the fluorine atoms.

Typical of the many reactions illustrating the Principle of Minimum Bending of Orbitals is the displacement by a chloride ion of an ammonia molecule in $Pt(NH_3)_3Cl$, the Peyrone reaction. In Figure 3 the preferred

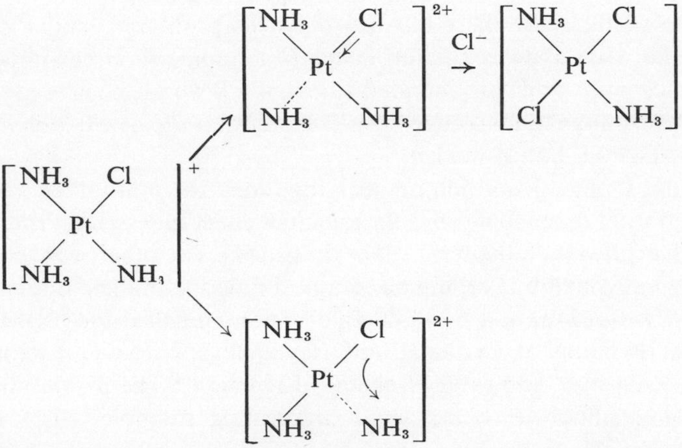

Figure 3. Peyrone reaction. [From G. H. Stewart and H. Eyring, *J. Chem. Educ.*, **35**, 550 (1958).]

reaction path is the upper one in which an ammonia *trans* to the resident chloride ion is displaced in preference to an adjacent ammonia. This is preferred because the empty space left by the departing NH_3 can be temporarily occupied by the electrons of the resident chloride ion without having to turn a corner as would be necessary if the ammonia were in the adjacent position. This preference for *trans* over *cis* substitution was first postulated by Werner[6] to account for the Peyrone[7] and Jorgensen[8] reactions of the isomers of dichlorodiammineplatinum, and it was formulated by Chernyaev as a regularity of the effect of acidic ligands exercising a much greater stabilizing effect on bonds *trans* to the ligand than do

6 A. Werner, *Z. Anorg. Allgem. Chem.*, **3**, 267 (1893).
7 M. Peyrone, *Ann. Chem.*, **51**, 1 (1845).
8 S. M. Jorgensen, *J. Prakt. Chem.*, **33**, 489 (1886).

neutral coordinating groups.[9] Syrkin[10] has recently developed a reasonable explanation of this effect in terms of hybridization and resonance, but the principles discussed here provide added clarification of the factors involved. Various examples can be cited of facilitation of reactions by the efficient utilization by resident electrons of the space left by a departing group.[11]

Coordination compounds, such as those just noted in which NH_3 and Cl^- add to Pt, arise because the Pt provides a low lying empty orbital which can accommodate an electron pair of the addend. The activated complex with its surfeit of electrons in low lying levels is catalyzed by molecules which coordinate the promoted electrons during the difficult period of the transition. It is thus to be expected that the transition metals with their low lying vacant d shells, as indicated by a variable valence, are frequently strongly catalytic. Boron trifluoride shows this same proclivity for electron 'baby tending' by catalyzing many organic reactions.

9. The Principle of Detailed Balance at Equilibrium[1] and the Ultimate Kinetic Unit

Long ago van't Hoff pointed out the dynamic nature of chemical equilibria.[2] Thus, even at equilibrium, molecules pass from state A to state B and this process is just balanced by an equal number of molecules passing from B to A. The important point is that the various paths proceeding in one direction are dynamically independent of the reverse paths. The principle of detailed balance goes beyond the early considerations of van't Hoff and states that, even if we replace the chemical states A and B by single quantum states, still at equilibrium, as many systems pass from A to B as pass in the reverse direction. Hamilton's equations in classical mechanics and Schrödinger's time-dependent equation are alike in being reversible in the time. That is, if we replace t by $-t$, we simply obtain a new solution which traverses the original path in the reverse direction· Thus, from mechanics we have the result that a moving picture film of all paths from A to B, at equilibrium, when run backward will faithfully picture all the reverse processes from B to A.

A quantum mechanically unique state is one in which there is a unique set of quantum numbers. In quantum mechanics it is assumed that specifying that the system is in the pure state A is a sufficient description for

9 I. I. Chernyaev, *Ann. inst. platine (U.S.S.R.)*, **5**, 109 (1927).

10 Y. K. Syrkin, *Bull. Acad. Sci. U.S.S.R., Classe sci. chim.*, 69 (1948).

11 R. P. Smith and H. Eyring, *J. Am. Chem. Soc.*, **74**, 229 (1952).

1 R. C. Tolman, *The Principles of Statistical Mechanics*, Oxford University Press, 1938, p. 165.

2 J. H. van't Hoff, *Z. Physik. Chem.*, **1**, 481 (1887); *Etudes de Dynamique Chimique*, Frederick Moller and Co., Amsterdam, 1884.

predicting the probability of what the system will do next. This assumption of quantum mechanics conceivably may not always be true. Thus, the population of the pure state A at equilibrium is made up in certain proportions of systems each with its own particular quantum mechanical heredity. By populating A by various non-equilibrium schemes we can greatly modify the distribution of its population with respect to heredity (although not with respect to its quantum mechanical description), i.e. the sequence of states a system descended from. The question is then can we use the rate constant for the transition probability, $k_{A \to B}$, appropriate at equilibrium, for a non-equilibrium case. According to quantum mechanics we can, and we shall proceed on this assumption. Actually experiments should and could now be carried out to test quantum mechanics on this point. We are thus assuming for pure states the 'principle of complete forgetfulness', i.e. that a population in the stable pure state A is, to a sufficient approximation, completely forgetful of its past. In contrast (for the metastable transition states of chemical reactions) the essence of the situation is that a reacting system faithfully remembers its origin as long as it is in transit but then by the time it has settled into a pure stable state it has completely forgotten its past.

The 'principle of complete forgetfulness' negates classical causality since it requires that for a system in state A the chance of proceeding next to state B is unconnected with its prior history.

Experiments which test forgetfulness are easily formulated. Thus, if we have the spectral diagram of Figure 1 in which A, B and C represent pure states the intensity of the line A to B is

$$I_{A \to B} = n_A k_{A \to B} \tag{1}$$

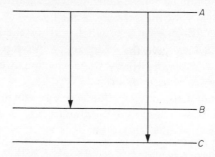

Figure 1. Spectral diagram for transitions A to B and A to C.

and of A to C is

$$I_{A \to C} = n_A k_{A \to C} \tag{2}$$

Here n_A is the population in state A and $k_{A \to B}$ and $k_{A \to C}$ are the corresponding Einstein coefficients for spontaneous emission. Hence,

$$\frac{I_{A \to B}}{I_{A \to C}} = \frac{k_{A \to B}}{k_{A \to C}} \tag{3}$$

Thus, if the relative intensities of these two lines are independent of how the population was kinetically made up, we can assume complete forgetfulness. Complete forgetfulness is presumably achieved only in a state with an infinitely long lifetime.

We thus arrive at the conception of the ultimate kinetic unit as a transition from a pure state A to a pure state B with a transition probability $k_{A \to B}$ completely calculable from quantum mechanics. The usual states of applied statistical mechanics are collections of pure states, which are treated as pools at equilibrium for which it is useful to define overall rate constants in the van't Hoff sense. The equilibrium pools chosen to treat kinetics always represent a workable compromise between the complete exactness of dealing with the pure quantum mechanical states and the rapid methods made possible by dealing with the molecular states of the chemist.

10. Absolute Activities and Rates of Reaction

From thermodynamics we have for the chemical potential

$$\mu_i = \left(\frac{\partial A}{\partial n_i} \right)_{V, T, n_j} = \left(\frac{\partial G}{\partial n_i} \right)_{p, T, n_j} = kT \ln \lambda_i \tag{1}$$

where we call λ_i the absolute activity. The zero of energy is arbitrary in μ_i and therefore in λ_i. We shall ordinarily take the lowest energy level of the initial state of our reacting system as the zero of energy. Departures from this procedure will be explicitly noted. The thermodynamic condition for a reacting system to be in equilibrium at constant temperature and pressure is that $\Delta G = 0$. Consider the chemical reaction

$$a\, A + b\, B + \ldots \rightleftharpoons l\, L + m\, M + \ldots \tag{2}$$

Thus, at equilibrium we have:

$$0 = \Delta G = l\mu_L + m\mu_M + \ldots - a\mu_A - b\mu_B - \ldots \tag{3}$$

or alternatively

$$\lambda_L^l \lambda_M^m \ldots = \lambda_A^a \lambda_B^b \ldots \tag{4}$$

With the definitions $\lambda_i = \lambda_A^a \lambda_B^b \ldots$ and $\lambda_f = \lambda_L^l \lambda_M^m \ldots$, where subscripts i, f mean initial and final respectively, we can rewrite Eq. (4) as

$$\lambda_i = \lambda_f \tag{5}$$

Now by the principle of detailed balance, summing over the ultimate kinetic units, we can write, at equilibrium, the velocity of the forward reaction, v_{if}, for Eq. (2) equal to the velocity of the backward reaction, v_{fi}. That is

$$v_{if} = -v_{fi} \tag{6}$$

The negative sign comes from attributing a direction to the velocity. Now from Eqs. (5) and (6) we have at equilibrium

$$\frac{v_{if}}{\lambda_i} = -\frac{v_{fi}}{\lambda_f} = k_{if} = -k_{fi} \tag{7}$$

In the derivation of Eq. (7) we have not needed to specify the type of statistics used, so the equation applies for all types.[1] The number of molecules of A in the gaseous state or in solution, n_A, contribute the term A_A to the total Helmholtz free energy where:

$$A_A = -kT \ln\left(\frac{f_A^n}{n_A!}\right) = -kT \ln\left(\frac{f_A e}{n_A}\right)^{n_A} \tag{8}$$

Hence

$$\mu_A = -kT \ln\left(\frac{f_A e}{n_A}\right) + kT = -kT \ln\left(\frac{f_A}{n_A}\right) \tag{9}$$

and

$$\lambda_A = e^{\mu_A/kT} = n_A/f_A \tag{10}$$

Substituting Eq. (10) into Eq. (4) gives

$$\left(\frac{n_L}{f_L}\right)^l \left(\frac{n_M}{f_M}\right)^m \cdots = \left(\frac{n_A}{f_A}\right)^a \left(\frac{n_B}{f_B}\right)^b \cdots$$

or

$$K = \frac{(n_L/v)^l (n_M/v)^m \cdots}{(n_A/v)^a (n_B/v)^b \cdots} = \frac{(f_L/V)^l (f_M/V)^m \cdots}{(f_A/V)^a (f_B/V)^b \cdots} \tag{11}$$

Clearly, Eq. (11) for an equilibrium is just Eq. (7.4) which we derived earlier in a slightly different way. Using Eqs. (6), (7), and (11), we see that at equilibrium

$$v_{if} = \left(\frac{n_A}{f_A}\right)^a \left(\frac{n_B}{f_B}\right)^b \cdots k_{if} = -\left(\frac{n_L}{f_L}\right)^l \left(\frac{n_M}{f_M}\right)^m \cdots k_{fi} \tag{12}$$

For reactions taking place under non-equilibrium conditions it is necessary to break up Eq. (12) into a sum over the ultimate kinetic units. We let λ_{ij} and λ_{fk} be the absolute activities of each pure quantum state in the initial and in the final chemical states respectively. At equilibrium all λ_{ij} are equal among themselves and are in turn equal to each absolute activity in the final state, λ_{fk}. Under non-equilibrium conditions we choose λ_{ij}

---

[1] The various types of statistics will be developed later.

and λ_{fk} as our initial and final standard quantum states respectively, and then have

$$\lambda'_{ij} = r_{ij}\lambda_{ij} \tag{13}$$

and

$$\lambda'_{fk} = r_{fk}\lambda_{fk} \tag{14}$$

where λ'_{ij} and λ'_{fk} are the absolute activities of the non-equilibrium populations of the pure quantum states. Here r_{ij} and r_{fk} we call the imbalance factors and they give the ratio of the population of a state to what it would be if it were in equilibrium, or in balance, with the standard state.

Now for the non-equilibrium velocity in the forward direction we have

$$v_{if}(\text{non-eq}) \equiv v'_{if} = \sum_j \sum_k \lambda'_{ij} k'_{ijkf} = \sum_j \sum_k \lambda_{ij} r_{ij} k'_{ijkf}$$

$$= \sum_j \lambda_{ij} r_{ij} k'_{ijf} = \lambda_{ij} k'_{if} \tag{15}$$

since the equilibrium λ_{ij}'s are all equal.

Here k'_{ijkf} is the specific velocity constant for the particular ultimate kinetic unit corresponding to passing from the initial state ij to the final state kf, and $k'_{ijkf} = \sum_k k'_{ijkf}$ is the specific velocity from the state ij to all possible final states. Finally k'_{if} is the non-equilibrium specific velocity constant and frequently closely approximates the equilibrium specific velocity constant k_{if}.

If we represent I_{if} as the current from the initial state i to the final state f we can write

$$I_{if} = v'_{if} + v'_{fi} \approx (\lambda_i - \lambda_f) k_{if} \tag{16}$$

11. Ultimate Reaction Kinetics

If for some collection of atoms or molecules the absolute activity λ_i of each ultimate (pure) quantum state i is related to some initial chosen standard state by the imbalance factor, r_i, and if k_{ij} represents the specific velocity constant for the ultimate reaction i to j then the state of the system is described by the following set of equations, one for each state i:

$$-\frac{dr_i}{dt} = \sum_j (k_{ij} r_i + k_{ji} r_j) \tag{1}$$

While for simple closed systems this set of equations is uniquely defined, the addition of such things as solvents and catalysts modifies the values of the k_i velocity constants. Because each $k_{ij} = -k_{ji}$ it follows from Eq. (1) that all changes in r_i vanish when the r_i's become equal. This is the equilibrium condition, and is of course in accord with our definition of the imbalance ratios, r_i.

We now turn to practical methods of arriving at rate constants.

12. Theory of Absolute Reaction Rates

The results we shall now obtain for the hydrogen plus iodine reaction can be readily generalized.

How does a chemical reaction take place? Gaseous H_2 and I_2 molecules collide with each other. Nearly always the result of the collision is only a redistribution of energy but for certain violent collisions the atomic arrangement gets scrambled and the atoms depart with new partners. The activated complex is the point of no return on the potential surface in configuration space. For each different way of rotating and vibrating the colliding molecules will have a slightly different position of no return along the reaction coordinate. However, we can assign a mean effective configuration of the activated complex. The same problem occurs for a stable molecule in different vibrational and rotational states. Changes in the vibrational and rotational states of an anharmonic molecule will

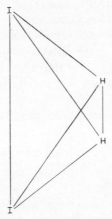

Figure 1. The six lengths which determine the configuration for the reaction $H_2 + I_2 \rightarrow 2\,HI$. (From H. Eyring, *op. cit.*)

slightly alter the dimensions and therefore the moments of inertia of the molecule. To fix the configuration, Figure 1, of the activated complex, we must fix the six lengths between the four atoms since the system may be non-planar. Thus to describe the activated complex, it takes a seven-dimensional space with the six distances all plotted at right angles to each other in a 'horizontal' hyper-plane with energy plotted 'vertically'. If we consider this map in seven-dimensional space, it will consist of valleys or plateaus where the atoms are far apart. The surface will rise to high elevations as atoms approach each other closely, with passes connecting the valleys. A reaction coordinate leads from one valley to another by way of a pass and is always normal to the contour lines. Each valley corresponds to a chemical compound. Several passes may connect one valley with another. Each such path is a mechanism of passing from reactants to products. The problem of reaction rate theory, for elementary reactions, is to use statistical mechanics to calculate how fast systems pass through a saddle point. To do this we first calculate the concentration of activated complexes, $C^{\ddagger}$, in molecules per cm^3. These activated complexes lie within a length δ along the reaction coordinate at the top of the pass. We now multiply $C^{\ddagger}$ by the mean rate, $\bar{v}/\delta$, of traversing the length of path δ. Here $\bar{v} = 2(kT/2\pi m^{\ddagger})^{\frac{1}{2}}$, the mean velocity at the top of the barrier. Since only half of the equilibrium number, $C^{\ddagger}$, of activated complexes moves in the forward direction we include the factor $\frac{1}{2}$. Finally, we multiply by the transmission coefficient, κ, which corrects the number passing forward across the barrier at equilibrium to its non-equilibrium value. This gives, for v_{if}, the rate of reaction

$$v_{if} = \tfrac{1}{2}C^{\ddagger}\frac{\bar{v}}{\delta}\kappa \tag{1}$$

In accord with the method of Eq. (7.4) we relate the concentration, $C^{\ddagger}$, of the activated complex to the concentration, C_1, of H_2, and C_2, of iodine by the equation

$$\frac{n^{\ddagger}}{n_1 n_2} = \frac{f^{\ddagger}}{f_1 f_2}$$

where $f^{\ddagger} = \dfrac{(2\pi m^{\ddagger}kT)^{\frac{1}{2}}\delta}{h}\dfrac{8\pi^2(8\pi^3 A^{\ddagger}B^{\ddagger}C^{\ddagger})^{\frac{1}{2}}(kT)^{\frac{3}{2}}}{2h^3}$

$$\times \frac{(2\pi m^{\ddagger}kT)^{\frac{3}{2}}V}{h^3}\prod_{i=1}^{5}(1-e^{-hv_i^{\ddagger}/kT})\,e^{-E_0^{\ddagger}/RT}$$

and $\dfrac{n^{\ddagger}}{n_1 n_2} \equiv \dfrac{\dfrac{(2\pi m^{\ddagger}kT)^{\frac{1}{2}}\delta}{h}F^{\ddagger}Ve^{-E_0^{\ddagger}/RT}}{f_1 f_2}$ (2)

Thus $\qquad C^{\ddagger} = \dfrac{n^{\ddagger}}{V} = \dfrac{(2\pi m^{\ddagger}kT)^{\frac{1}{2}}}{h}\delta F^{\ddagger}e^{-E_0^{\ddagger}/RT}\lambda_1\lambda_2$ (3)

and the velocity of reaction then becomes

$$v_{if} = \kappa\,\frac{kT}{h}\,F^{\ddagger}\,e^{-E_0^{\ddagger}/RT}\,\lambda_1\lambda_2$$

$$\equiv \kappa\,\frac{kT}{h}\,F^{\ddagger}\,e^{-E_0^{\ddagger}/RT}\,\lambda_i \tag{4}$$

Here $\lambda_i = \lambda_1\lambda_2$, the absolute activity of the initial state. It is sometimes convenient to break the transmission coefficient κ into two factors, and write

$$\kappa = \kappa_i\kappa_q \tag{5}$$

Thus κ corrects the classical equilibrium rate by a mean imbalance factor κ_i, which measures the weighted mean departure from equilibrium of the various initial states of the reactants, and by κ_q which is the mean weighted transmission coefficient. κ_q corrects for the mean number of times systems cross the barrier to bring about reaction and should be calculated using quantum mechanics for each elemental transition $i \rightarrow j$. These must then be weighted appropriately. The essential point is that although κ is a complicated quantity it is in principle calculable and is often near unity. When we wish to analyze Eq. (4) or calculate v_{if} in detail it is convenient to use Eq. (10.15).

13. Saturation Statistics,[1] the Langmuir Adsorption Isotherm and Fermi-Dirac Statistics

Consider a system in which n_g gaseous particles in a volume V are in equilibrium with a variety of sites of which ω_r are alike, and each yields the energy ε_r per particle absorbed. Here ε_r is the energy of reaction at absolute zero on the r sites (ε_0 of Figure 7.1). In Figure 1 we have indi-

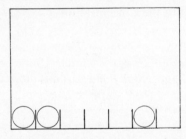

Figure 1. Diagram of $\omega_r = 7$ adsorption sites with $n_r = 3$ molecules adsorbed, one per site.

cated a case where the number of adsorption sites, ω_r, is 7, with $n_r = 3$ filled. At equilibrium adsorption and desorption balance so that

$$n_g k_g (\omega_r - n_r) = n_r k_r \tag{1}$$

Here according to Eq. (12.4) the specific rate of adsorption at equilibrium per surface site is

$$n_g k_g = \lambda \left(\kappa \frac{kT}{h} F^{\ddagger} e^{-E_0^{\ddagger}/kT} \right) \tag{2}$$

and the specific rate for desorption is

$$k_r = \frac{1}{f_r e^{-\varepsilon_r/kT}} \left(\kappa \frac{kT}{h} F^{\ddagger} e^{-E_0^{\ddagger}/kT} \right) \tag{3}$$

In Eqs. (2) and (3) the initial states are the desorbed and adsorbed states,

[1] H. Eyring and M. Wallenstein, *Proc. Natl. Acad. Sci. U.S.*, **39**, 138 (1953). See also P. T. Landsberg, *J. Chem. Phys.*, **21**, 2228 (1953).

respectively, and the activated complex is the final state in both cases. The factor $e^{-\varepsilon_r/kT}$ in the denominator of the right-hand side of Eq. (3) refers the partition function for the adsorbed molecules to the lowest level of the desorbed molecules. A schematic illustration of the potential energy surface is given in Figure 2. Whenever, as in Eqs. (2) and (3), kT is used

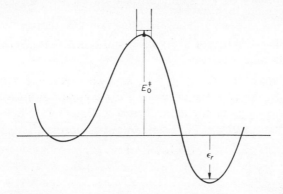

Figure 2. Schematic illustration of the potential energy surface for the adsorption reaction.

in the denominator of the exponential rather than RT the energies in the numerator are necessarily per particle rather than per mole of particles. In Eq. (2) λ is the absolute activity of a gaseous molecule and f_r is the partition function for an adsorbed particle. The quantities in parentheses in Eqs. (2) and (3) refer to the activated complex, and, under equilibrium conditions, are necessarily identically equal. Introducing Eqs. (2) and (3) into (1) we obtain

$$\lambda(\omega_r - n_r) = n_r/f_r \; e^{-\varepsilon_r/kT} \tag{4}$$

Hence

$$n_r = \frac{\omega_r}{(f_r\lambda)^{-1} \, e^{\varepsilon_r/kT} + 1} \tag{5}$$

When the particle is an electron in equilibrium with the rth level of a metal, the partition function for the rth level, f_r, becomes unity and we have the familiar Fermi–Dirac expression[2, 3]

$$n_r = \frac{\omega_r}{\lambda^{-1} \, e^{\varepsilon_r/kT} + 1} \tag{6}$$

The above procedure was used by Langmuir for the adsorption of a gas on a solid surface.[4] If we write $\theta = n_r/\omega_r$ for the fraction of the surface

2 E. Fermi, *Z. Physik*, **36**, 902 (1926).
3 P. A. M. Dirac, *Proc. Roy. Soc. (London)*, **A112**, 661 (1926).
4 I. Langmuir, *J. Am. Chem. Soc.*, **40**, 1361 (1918).

covered, and $\lambda f_r e^{-\varepsilon_r/kT} \equiv pK$, where K is the adsorption coefficient, then Eq. (5) takes the well-known Langmuir form

$$\theta = \frac{Kp}{Kp+1} \tag{7}$$

Familiar examples of Langmuir adsorption are nitrogen on mica[4] and oxygen on tungsten.[5]

14. Condensation Statistics,[13.1] Condensation of a Homogeneous Phase, Bose–Einstein Statistics

We again suppose that we have ω_r sites on which n_r particles are condensed, but in this case the particles are indifferent as to whether or not they pile up on a given site as indicated in Figure 1. When there are n_g particles in the gas phase, we can write at equilibrium

$$n_g k_g(\omega_r + n_r) = k_r n_r \tag{1}$$

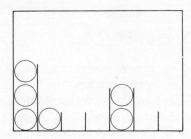

Figure 1. Diagram of $\omega_r = 7$ adsorption sites with $n_r = 6$ molecules adsorbed and no limitation on the number per site.

The factor $\omega_r + n_r$ for the number of sites on which a particle can condense is correct since, by hypothesis, condensation can occur equally well upon the original sites or upon any of the particles which are condensed upon these sites.

If any one of the $\omega_r + n_r$ sites is kinetically less accessible than another, its rate may be supposed to be appropriately catalyzed so that all rates are made the same. This is an interesting and essential point, and is justifiable since at equilibrium the factor describing the activated complexes is common to both sides of Eq. (1) and so modifying the activated complex is without influence on the final equilibrium result. The usual statement of this point is that catalysts do not influence equilibria, although they may greatly shift non-equilibrium states.

5 I. Langmuir and D. S. Villars, *J. Am. Chem. Soc.*, **51**, 486 (1931).

As before we have

$$n_g k_g = \lambda \left(\kappa \frac{kT}{h} F^{\ddagger} e^{-E_0^{\ddagger}/kT} \right) \qquad (2)$$

and

$$k_r = \kappa \frac{kT}{h} \frac{F^{\ddagger}}{f_r e^{-\varepsilon_r/kT}} e^{-E_0^{\ddagger}/kT} \qquad (3)$$

Substituting Eqs. (2) and (3) into Eq. (1) gives

$$n_r = \frac{\omega_r}{(f_r \lambda)^{-1} e^{\varepsilon_r/kT} - 1} \qquad (4)$$

Now f_r for the single states of Bose–Einstein statistics[1, 2] has the value unity and Eq. (4) becomes

$$n_r = \frac{\omega_r}{\lambda^{-1} e^{\varepsilon_r/kT} - 1} \qquad (5)$$

For the condensation of a liquid we have, as in the preceding section, $n_r/\omega_r = \sigma$ as the ratio of adsorbed molecules to the original number of condensation sites and $f_r \lambda e^{-\varepsilon_r/kT} = Kp$, where p is the pressure and K is the adsorption coefficient. Substituting into Eq. (4) gives:

$$\sigma = \frac{Kp}{1 - Kp} \qquad (6)$$

As long as $Kp < 1$ in Eq. (6) one obtains positive finite values for the ratio, σ, of adsorbed molecules to surface sites. This corresponds to adsorption on the surface without condensation of the liquid phase. When $Kp = 1$ the value of σ suddenly becomes infinite, corresponding to the appearance of a new phase. For $Kp > 1$ we have supersaturation, for which no equilibrium is possible as the physically impossible negative values of σ of Eq. (6) indicate.

15. Maxwell–Boltzmann or Classical Statistics (Dilute Statistics)

In the two preceding sections we have considered first, the case where one occupant fills a state, and then, the case where an infinite number of occupants can be accommodated in each site, i.e. all occupants are assigned the same quantum number. Classical or Maxwell–Boltzmann statistics is simply the limiting statistics approached by any dilute system, i.e. the case where $n_r \ll \omega_r$. In that case both Eqs. (13.1) and (14.1) reduce to

$$n_g k_g \omega_r = k_r n_r \qquad (1)$$

[1] S. N. Bose, *Z. Physik*, **26**, 178 (1924).
[2] A. Einstein, *Berliner Ber.*, **1924**, 261; **1925**, 3, 18.

Whence proceeding as before we have

$$n_r = \lambda \omega_r \, e^{-\varepsilon_r/kT} = \frac{n_A}{f_A} \, \omega_r \, e^{-\varepsilon_r/kT} \tag{2}$$

The last equality follows from Eq. (10.10) where n_A is the total number of particles (or systems) at equilibrium distributed over the total number of states included in the partition function f_A. We note again that the absolute activity, λ, of any state, or any collection of states in equilibrium, is the same. We may see this as follows. At equilibrium we have for the ratio of populations in the ith and jth states

$$\frac{n_i}{n_j} = \frac{\omega_i \, e^{-\varepsilon_i/kT}}{\omega_j \, e^{-\varepsilon_j/kT}} \tag{3}$$

where ω_i and ω_j are the degeneracies of the respective states. Hence

$$\frac{n_i}{\omega_i \, e^{-\varepsilon_i/kT}} = \frac{n_j}{\omega_j \, e^{-\varepsilon_j/kT}} = \lambda \tag{4}$$

Further

$$\lambda = \frac{n_i}{\omega_i \, e^{-\varepsilon_i/kT}} = \frac{n_j}{\omega_j \, e^{-\varepsilon_j/kT}}$$

$$= \frac{n_j \left(1 + \dfrac{n_i}{n_j}\right)}{\omega_j \, e^{-\varepsilon_j/kT} \left(1 + \dfrac{n_i}{n_j}\right)} = \frac{n_j + n_i}{\omega_j \, e^{-\varepsilon_j/kT} + \omega_i \, e^{-\varepsilon_i/kT}} \tag{5}$$

The last equality in Eq. (5) follows by replacing n_i/n_j where it occurs in the denominator by making use of Eq. (3). This argument is readily extended. Since

$$\lambda = \frac{n_j + n_i}{\omega_j \, e^{-\varepsilon_j/kT} + \omega_i \, e^{-\varepsilon_i/kT}} = \frac{n_k}{\omega_k \, e^{-\varepsilon_k/kT}} \tag{6}$$

we have

$$\lambda = \frac{n_j + n_i \left(1 + \dfrac{n_k}{n_j + n_i}\right)}{(\omega_j \, e^{-\varepsilon_j/kT} + \omega_i \, e^{-\varepsilon_i/kT}) \left(1 + \dfrac{n_k}{n_j + n_i}\right)}$$

$$= \frac{n_j + n_i + n_k}{\omega_j \, e^{-\varepsilon_j/kT} + \omega_i \, e^{-\varepsilon_i/kT} + \omega_k \, e^{-\varepsilon_k/kT}} \tag{7}$$

As before we have substituted for $n_j + n_i$ from Eq. (6). By an obvious continuation of these arguments we have

$$\lambda = \frac{\sum_i n_i}{\sum_i \omega_i \, e^{-\varepsilon_i/kT}} \tag{8}$$

The only requirement on the summations in Eq. (6) is that they be over the same states.

16. Intermediate Statistics, Condensation in Fissures and Capillaries[1,2]

We consider next the intermediate case where a particles saturate a site. As before we have n_g particles in the gas state equilibrating on the ω sites.[3] The equation for adsorption balancing desorption is then

$$n_g k_g [\omega + n - p\omega(a+1)] = kn \tag{1}$$

Here p is the probability that a particular site has the a particles which would saturate it, in which case each such saturated site eliminates $(a+1)$ prospective condensation loci. In the case where a is infinite, p is necessarily zero and Eq. (1) reduces to Eq. (14.1), while if $a = 1$, Eq. (1) reduces to Eq. (13.1), as it must. If $A(\omega, n, a)$ is the number of ways that n particles can be arranged on ω sites where a particles saturate any site, then

$$p = \frac{A(\omega - 1, n - a, a)}{A(\omega, n, a)} \tag{2}$$

The number $A(\omega, n, a)$ is the coefficient of z^n in the polynomial

$$(1 + z + z^2 + z^3 + \ldots + z^a)^\omega \tag{3}$$

This is because the coefficients of the terms $1, z, z^2, \ldots, z^a$ may be thought of as proportional to the probability of introducing $0, 1, 2$ up to a particles in any particular site and in Eq. (3) there are ω such factors, corresponding to the ω sites. Thus, the coefficient of z^n includes all possible ways of introducing n particles on the sites. The coefficient of z^n is just

$$\left[\frac{1}{n!} \frac{d^n}{dz^n} (1 + z + z^2 + \ldots + z^a)^\omega \right]_{z=0} = \frac{1}{n!} \left[\frac{d^n}{dz^n} \{ (1-z)^{-\omega}(1 - z^{a+1})^\omega \} \right]_{z=0} \tag{4}$$

[1] G. Gentile, *Nuovo Cimento*, **17**, 493 (1940). See also J. R. Partington, *Advanced Treatise of Physical Chemistry*, Vol. I, Longmans, Green, London, 1949, pp. 368–370.

[2] R. B. Parlin, M. B. Wallenstein, B. J. Zwolinski and H. Eyring in *Catalysis* (P. H. Emmett, Ed.), Vol. II, Reinhold, New York, 1955, pp. 298–301.

[3] Because one may have more than one type of statistical system a subscript r has been appended previously to the symbol n, the number of particles absorbed, and to ω, the number of sites. We now drop the subscript remembering our results are readily generalized to a plurality of types of sites.

According to Leibnitz' rule, we have

$$\frac{d^n}{dz^n}(uv) = \left(\frac{d^n u}{dz^n}\right)v + n\frac{d^{n-1}u}{dz^{n-1}}\frac{dv}{dz} + \ldots + \frac{n!}{(n-m)!\,m!}\frac{d^{n-m}u}{dz^{n-m}}\frac{d^m v}{dz^m} + \ldots \tag{5}$$

Carrying out the indicated differentiations we have

$$\left[\frac{d^{n-m}}{dz^{n-m}}(1-z)^{-\omega}\right]_{z=0} = \left[\frac{(\omega+n-m-1)!}{(\omega-1)!}(1-z)^{-\omega-n+m}\right]_{z=0}$$

$$= \frac{(\omega+n-m-1)!}{(\omega-1)!} \tag{6}$$

and

$$\left[\frac{d^m}{dz^m}(1-z^{a+1})^\omega\right] = \frac{d^m}{dz^m}\left\{1 + \omega(-z^{a+1})\right.$$

$$\left. + \frac{\omega(\omega-1)}{2}(-z^{a+1})^2 + \ldots + (-z^{a+1})^\omega\right\} \tag{7}$$

We note that

$$\left[\frac{d^m}{dz^m}(1-z^{a+1})^\omega\right]_{z=0,\,m\neq s(a+1)} = 0 \tag{8}$$

except when m has the values $s(a+1)$ where s goes from 0 to ω. For these cases we obtain

$$\left[\frac{d^{s(a+1)}}{dz^{s(a+1)}}(1-z^{a+1})^\omega\right]_{z=0} = \frac{\omega!(-1)^s}{(\omega-s)!\,s!}[s(a+1)]! \tag{9}$$

whence

$$A(\omega,n,a) = \frac{1}{n!}\left[\frac{d^n}{dz^n}\{(1-z)^{-\omega}(1-z^{a+1})^\omega\}\right]_{z=0}$$

$$= \sum_{s=0}^{l}\frac{(-1)^s\omega[\omega+n-s(a+1)-1]!}{[n-s(a+1)]!\,s!\,(\omega-s)!} \tag{10}$$

where l is equal to the largest integer smaller than $n/(a+1)$. In general,

$$P(\omega,n,a) \equiv \frac{A(\omega-1,n-1,a)}{A(\omega,n,a)} \tag{11}$$

is quite complicated, but it is simple for saturation statistics where one particle saturates a cell.

In this case

$$P(\omega, n, 1) = \frac{\left[\dfrac{1}{(n-1)!} \dfrac{d^{n-1}}{dz^{n-1}}(1+z)^{\omega-1}\right]_{z=0}}{\left[\dfrac{1}{n!} \dfrac{d^{n}}{dz^{n}}(1+z)^{\omega}\right]_{z=0}}$$

$$= \frac{\dfrac{(\omega-1)!}{(\omega-n)!\,(n-1)!}}{\dfrac{\omega!}{(\omega-n)!\,n!}} = \frac{n}{\omega} \tag{12}$$

We of course knew this result *a priori*, since each of the n particles saturates one of the ω cells giving for the chance that any particular cell is saturated the value n/ω. $P(n, \omega, \infty)$ is zero, since we have a finite number of particles to saturate a cell of infinite capacity.

We next consider condensation in fissures formed by two parallel infinite planes. In Figure 1 we see that $\omega/2$ sites lie opposite an equal number of like sites and the cavities can be filled by adding particles from above and below.

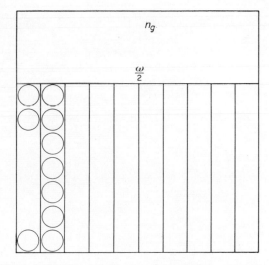

Figure 1. Diagram of a fissure with $\omega/2$ sites on each side.

As before we write

$$n_g k_g \left[\omega + n - p \frac{\omega}{2}(a+2)\right] = nk \tag{13}$$

Here p is the probability a site is saturated, but in this case saturation withdraws two sites on the surface plus an additional number a of condensation sites corresponding to the a particles. The space between two paired sites in Figure 1 can accommodate l particles as long as $l < a$ in $l+1$ ways. This is readily seen as follows. If m particles are placed on the upper site, the remaining $l-m$ particles can be accommodated on the lower site. In this partition of particles m can take all values between zero and l, thus giving us $l+1$ possible partitions for each value of l from 0 to a. Hence, in this case we have for the number of ways, A, of distributing n particles in $\omega/2$ pairs of boxes the equation

$$A(\omega, n, a) = \left[\frac{1}{n!} \frac{d^n}{dz^n} \left(\sum_{l=0}^{a} (l+1)z^l \right)^{\omega/2} \right]_{z=0}$$

$$= \left[\frac{1}{n!} \frac{d^n}{dz^n} \left(\frac{d}{dz} \sum_{l=0}^{a} z^{l+1} \right)^{\omega/2} \right]_{z=0} \tag{14}$$

Proceeding as above, $A(\omega, n, a)$ can be calculated, but the resulting series is even more complicated than that of Eq. (10). Various types of adsorption isotherms are discussed in the interesting book by Brunauer.[4]

[4] Stephen Brunauer, *The Adsorption of Gases and Vapors*, Vol. I. *Physical Adsorption*, Princeton University Press, 1945.

2

CLASSICAL MECHANICS

1. Introduction

Mechanics is the science of motion of material bodies. With the advent of quantum mechanics, the older body of knowledge has come to be called classical mechanics. The development of mechanics began with observations of the macroscopic world, but, when investigations reached the atomic and subatomic level, the old laws failed to explain the experimental results. This failure led to the development of a more general science of motion, quantum mechanics, of which classical mechanics is now recognized as a special case.

Fundamental to classical mechanics is the concept that, if we know the laws governing the motion of a particular particle of mass m and can determine its state (i.e. position and momentum) at a given instant, then the mechanical state of the particle can be calculated exactly at any other time, which is equivalent to saying that the future mechanical behavior of the particle can be predicted completely. This concept applies also to a system of particles if we know the nature of the interactions between the particles. The principle of complete predictability has been abandoned in the new mechanics, which permits calculation of probabilities rather than exact values.

2. Newton's Law of Motion

A great step in mechanics was taken by Galileo Galilei (1564–1642) who studied the motion of falling bodies from the point of view that theory must conform with the results of experiment. Although he lacked the mathematics to express his experimental results, he proved that acceleration of a moving body results from the application of an external force. However, it was not until Isaac Newton (1642–1727) invented his 'method of fluxions' (calculus) with which Galileo's results could be described mathematically, that the law of motion could be expressed in a useful form.

In classical mechanics Newton's law of motion determines the motion of a material body or particle. If the Cartesian coordinates x, y, and z specify the location in space of a particle of mass m, and if the components of the force, F, acting on the particle are X, Y, and Z, then Newton's law states that[1]

$$m\ddot{x} = X$$
$$m\ddot{y} = Y$$
$$m\ddot{z} = Z \tag{1}$$

If the system of interest consists of more than one particle, a set of co-ordinates and a set of Eqs. (1) are needed for each particle. Thus location in space and description of the classical motion of a mole of non-interacting gas molecules requires $3 \times N$ (Avogadro's number) coordinates and $3 \times N$ equations of the form $m\ddot{x}_i = X_i$.

Consider a single particle of mass m which moves from a point (x_1, y_1, z_1) to a second point (x_2, y_2, z_2) in response to the forces X, Y, and Z. The work done is

$$W_{12} = \int_{x_1}^{x_2} X \, dx + \int_{y_1}^{y_2} Y \, dy + \int_{z_1}^{z_2} Z \, dz$$
$$= \int_{x_1}^{x_2} m\ddot{x} \, dx + \int_{y_1}^{y_2} m\ddot{y} \, dy + \int_{z_1}^{z_2} m\ddot{z} \, dz \tag{2}$$

But Eqs. (1) can also be written $m \, (d\dot{x}/dt) = X$, etc., where $\dot{x}$ ($= dx/dt$) is the x component of the velocity; Eq. (2) thus becomes

$$W_{12} = \int_{\dot{x}_1}^{\dot{x}_2} m\dot{x} \, d\dot{x} + \int_{\dot{y}_1}^{\dot{y}_2} m\dot{y} \, d\dot{y} + \int_{\dot{z}_1}^{\dot{z}_2} m\dot{z} \, d\dot{z}$$
$$= \tfrac{1}{2}m[(\dot{x}_2^2 + \dot{y}_2^2 + \dot{z}_2^2) - (\dot{x}_1^2 + \dot{y}_1^2 + \dot{z}_1^2)] = T_2 - T_1 \tag{2a}$$

where T is the kinetic energy of the particle. Thus the work done is equal to the difference in kinetic energy of the particle at the two points. When

$$W = \oint (X \, dx + Y \, dy + Z \, dz) = 0 \tag{3}$$

(where $\oint$ means integration around a complete cycle), the forces (and system) are said to be conservative. When Eq. (3) holds, W_{12} is independent of the path of integration and can also be expressed as the change in some function which depends on the coordinates only. The potential energy V is this kind of function, and

$$W_{12} = V_1 - V_2 \tag{4}$$

Combining Eq. (2a) and Eq. (4) gives

$$T_1 + V_1 = T_2 + V_2 \tag{5}$$

[1] $\dot{x} = dx/dt$, $\ddot{x} = d^2x/dt^2$ from Newton's method of fluxions notation. Newton's notation was ambiguous in that it did not specify with respect to which variable the function was differentiated. In this discussion, the dot notation always means differentiation with respect to time.

Since the choice of points 1 and 2 is arbitrary,

$$E = T + V = \text{constant} \tag{6}$$

for a conservative system. Accordingly, in a non-conservative system the total energy is not constant, but changes as a result of applied external forces, and frictional and other dissipative forces.

3. Generalized Coordinates

Many problems can be solved more expediently when the forces in Eq. (2.1) are formulated using coordinate systems other than rectangular. Spherical coordinates are more appropriate for problems involving motion of the planets; other problems may be best handled if cylindrical or elliptical coordinates are used. Thus, we shall find it advantageous to introduce a set of generalized coordinates to use in subsequent formulations of mechanics. This will permit choice of the most desirable set for a particular problem.

Treatment of another kind of problem will also be facilitated by use of generalized coordinates. Frequently we encounter mechanical systems in which the motion is subject to certain constraints. Some examples of constrained systems are (a) a system of two or more particles which moves so that the distance between any two particles is constant, (b) a particle whose motion is limited to a specified surface, (c) an object rolling on a surface without slipping, and (d) gas molecules moving in a leak-proof box and thus constrained by the walls of the box. The $3n$ coordinates (where n is the number of particles) of a constrained system are not all independent for some of the coordinates are related by the conditions of constraint. When the equation of constraint is an integrated function of one or more coordinates, the constraint is *holonomic*. It is *non-holonomic* if the equation is a non-integrable function of differentials of the coordinates. One method of treating systems with non-holonomic constraints is Lagrange's method of undetermined multipliers, which is used in Sect. 4.4.

When the constraints are holonomic, the system can always be treated by changing to generalized coordinates and using the equations of constraint to eliminate the dependent coordinates. Some examples follow in which the dependent coordinates have been eliminated.

(a) To describe the motion of a harmonic oscillator, a particle moving in one direction subject to a force proportional to its displacement from its equilibrium position, we need only one coordinate, the direction of motion.

(b) Motion of a particle constrained to move on the surface of a sphere is best described using spherical coordinates (r, θ, φ). The condition of constraint, r = constant, eliminates that coordinate and leaves the two independent coordinates, θ and φ.

(c) A rigid body can be considered a system of n particles subject to the constraints that the distance between any two particles be constant. The positions of the n particles are given by $3n$ coordinates which clearly are not all independent. If we choose the nine coordinates for three non-collinear particles, the positions of all other particles can be specified in terms of these coordinates. However, even the chosen nine are not all independent for the distances between each of the three possible pairs of particles are constant. Consequently, only six independent coordinates are needed to give the position of the rigid body. If all n particles lie on a straight line, which is equivalent to introducing another constraint, there are but five independent coordinates.

The number of independent coordinates required to locate a system in space is referred to as the number of degrees of freedom of the system. From the preceding it follows that the number of degrees of freedom for a system of n particles is $3n-k$ where k is the number of holonomic constraints. The constraints, if any, are eliminated by transforming the $3n$ rectangular coordinates to $3n-k$ independent generalized coordinates plus k generalized coordinates which have constant values. If x_1, x_2, x_3 are the coordinates of the first particle, x_4, x_5, x_6 are those of the second, etc., and if $q_1, q_2, \ldots, q_{3n}$ are the generalized coordinates, then each x_i (of which there are $3n$) can be expressed as a function of q_i as follows:

$$x_1 = f_1(q_1, q_2, \ldots, q_{3n})$$
$$x_2 = f_2(q_1, q_2, \ldots, q_{3n})$$
$$\vdots$$
$$x_{3n} = f_{3n}(q_1, q_2, \ldots, q_{3n}) \tag{1}$$

4. Lagrange's Equations

Corresponding to any q_i of the generalized coordinates there is a generalized velocity $\dot{q}_i$ and a generalized force Q_i, which are necessary to express the equations of motion in generalized coordinates. If $x_i = f_i$ $(q_1, q_2, \ldots, q_n)$ is any one of the original rectangular coordinates, then

$$dx_i = \sum_j \frac{\partial x_i}{\partial q_j} dq_j \tag{1}$$

From Eq. (1) we obtain $\dot{x}_i$ as a function of the generalized velocities,

$$\dot{x}_i = \sum_j \frac{\partial x_i}{\partial q_j} \dot{q}_j \tag{2}$$

Differentiation of Eq. (2) with respect to $\dot{q}_j$ results in

$$\frac{\partial \dot{x}_i}{\partial \dot{q}_j} = \frac{\partial x_i}{\partial q_j} \tag{3}$$

Next we differentiate Eq. (2) with respect to q_k to obtain

$$\frac{\partial \dot{x}_i}{\partial q_k} = \sum_j \frac{\partial}{\partial q_k} \left(\frac{\partial x_i}{\partial q_j} \right) \dot{q}_j \tag{4}$$

We can also write

$$d \left(\frac{\partial x_i}{\partial q_k} \right) = \sum_j \frac{\partial}{\partial q_j} \left(\frac{\partial x_i}{\partial q_k} \right) dq_j \tag{5}$$

and

$$\frac{d}{dt} \left(\frac{\partial x_i}{\partial q_k} \right) = \sum_j \frac{\partial}{\partial q_j} \left(\frac{\partial x_i}{\partial q_k} \right) \dot{q}_j \tag{6}$$

Since the order of partial differentiation does not matter, the quantities on the right-hand sides of Eqs. (4) and (6) are equal, and

$$\frac{\partial \dot{x}_i}{\partial q_k} = \frac{d}{dt} \left(\frac{\partial x_i}{\partial q_k} \right) \tag{7}$$

Next we calculate the work done on a conservative system when it is subjected to an infinitesimal displacement dq_k of one coordinate:

$$dW_{q_k} = \sum_i X_i \frac{\partial x_i}{\partial q_k} dq_k = Q_k dq_k \tag{8}$$

where Q_k is the generalized force[1] associated with the generalized coordinate q_k, and

$$Q_k = \sum_i X_i \frac{\partial x_i}{\partial q_k} \tag{9}$$

Using Eq. (1.1), the expression for the work done becomes

$$dW_{q_k} = \sum_i m_i \ddot{x}_i \frac{\partial x_i}{\partial q_k} dq_k \tag{10}$$

Next we write the identity

$$\ddot{x}_i \frac{\partial x_i}{\partial q_k} = \frac{d}{dt} \left(\dot{x}_i \frac{\partial x_i}{\partial q_k} \right) - \dot{x}_i \frac{d}{dt} \left(\frac{\partial x_i}{\partial q_k} \right) \tag{11}$$

which, upon substitution from Eqs. (3) and (7), becomes

$$\ddot{x}_i \frac{\partial x_i}{\partial q_k} = \frac{d}{dt} \left(\dot{x}_i \frac{\partial \dot{x}_i}{\partial \dot{q}_k} \right) - \dot{x}_i \frac{\partial \dot{x}_i}{\partial q_k} \tag{12}$$

[1] Note that q_k may not have the dimension length, i.e. it may be an angle. If so, Q_k must have dimensions such that W has dimensions of work.

Our equation for the work done now assumes the form

$$dW_{q_k} = \sum_i m_i \left[\frac{d}{dt}\left(\dot{x}_i \frac{\partial \dot{x}_i}{\partial \dot{q}_k} \right) - \dot{x}_i \frac{\partial \dot{x}_i}{\partial q_k} \right]$$

$$= \frac{d}{dt}\left[\frac{\partial}{\partial \dot{q}_k}\left(\sum_i \tfrac{1}{2} m_i \dot{x}_i^2 \right) \right] - \frac{\partial}{\partial q_k}\left(\sum_i \tfrac{1}{2} m_i \dot{x}_i^2 \right) \tag{13}$$

Since the kinetic energy of the system is

$$T = \sum_i \tfrac{1}{2} m_i \dot{x}_i^2 \tag{14}$$

Eq. (13) becomes

$$dW_{q_k} = \left(\frac{d}{dt}\frac{\partial T}{\partial \dot{q}_k} - \frac{\partial T}{\partial q_k} \right) dq_k = Q_k \, dq_k \tag{15}$$

The set of Eqs. (15) thus expresses the generalized forces in terms of the kinetic energy. For a conservative system the forces can also be derived from the potential V, which is a function of the coordinates only. If

$$X_i = -\partial V/\partial x_i$$

then

$$Q_k = -\sum_i \frac{\partial V}{\partial x_i}\frac{\partial x_i}{\partial q_k} = -\frac{\partial V}{\partial q_k} \tag{16}$$

Combining Eqs. (15) and (16) gives

$$\frac{d}{dt}\frac{\partial T}{\partial \dot{q}_k} - \frac{\partial(T-V)}{\partial q_k} = 0 \tag{17}$$

We now define a new function, the kinetic potential, $L \equiv T-V$, which is frequently called the *Lagrangian* (Joseph Louis Lagrange, 1736–1813). Since V is not a function of the generalized velocities, we can rewrite Eq. (17) as

$$\frac{d}{dt}\frac{\partial L}{\partial \dot{q}_k} - \frac{\partial L}{\partial q_k} = 0 \tag{18}$$

The set of Eqs. (18) is known as Lagrange's equations of motion for a conservative system, and the number of equations equals the number of degrees of freedom of the system.

For a non-conservative system Lagrange's equations are

$$\frac{d}{dt}\frac{\partial L}{\partial \dot{q}_k} - \frac{\partial L}{\partial q_k} = Q'_k \tag{19}$$

where Q'_k represents those forces which are not derivable from a potential. Further treatment of (19) requires a knowledge of the non-conservative forces involved.

5. Hamilton's Equations

Frequently for theoretical discussions it is more convenient to use generalized momenta rather than generalized velocities. The generalized momenta p_i are defined by the set of equations

$$p_i = \frac{\partial L}{\partial \dot{q}_i} \tag{1}$$

which for conservative systems are equivalent to

$$p_i = \frac{\partial T}{\partial \dot{q}_i} \tag{2}$$

The generalized momentum p_i is said to be conjugate to the generalized coordinate q_i. Now we wish to express the equations of motion in terms of the generalized momenta and coordinates rather than the generalized velocities and coordinates.

Since the Lagrangian is a function of the q and $\dot{q}$, its differential is

$$dL = \sum_i \left(\frac{\partial L}{\partial \dot{q}_i} \, d\dot{q}_i + \frac{\partial L}{\partial q_i} \, dq_i \right) \tag{3}$$

From Lagrange's equations,

$$\frac{\partial L}{\partial q_i} = \frac{d}{dt} \frac{\partial L}{\partial \dot{q}_i} = \dot{p}_i \tag{4}$$

Using the definition of p_i and Eq. (4), Eq. (3) becomes

$$dL = \sum_i (p_i \, d\dot{q}_i + \dot{p}_i \, dq_i) \tag{5}$$

Next we subtract Eq. (5) from the identity

$$d \left(\sum_i p_i \dot{q}_i \right) = \sum_i (p_i \, d\dot{q}_i + \dot{q}_i \, dp_i) \tag{6}$$

and obtain

$$d \left(\sum_i p_i \dot{q}_i - L \right) = \sum_i (\dot{q}_i \, dp_i - \dot{p}_i \, dq_i) \tag{7}$$

The *Hamiltonian* (William Rowan Hamilton, 1805–1865) of the system is by definition

$$H = \sum_i p_i \dot{q}_i - L \tag{8}$$

and

$$dH = \sum_i (\dot{q}_i \, dp_i - \dot{p}_i \, dq_i) \tag{9}$$

From Eq. (9) we readily obtain Hamilton's canonical equations of motion

$$\frac{\partial H}{\partial p_i} = \dot{q}_i \quad \text{and} \quad \frac{\partial H}{\partial q_i} = -\dot{p}_i \tag{10}$$

Note that, in contrast to Lagrange's equations, these are first-order differential equations and there are two equations for each degree of freedom.

Since the kinetic energy T is a homogeneous quadratic function of the $\dot{x}_i$'s which are homogeneous linear functions of the $\dot{q}$'s, T is also a homogeneous quadratic function of the $\dot{q}$'s, and can be written as $T = \sum_i \sum_j a_{ij} \dot{q}_i \dot{q}_j$. Euler's theorem states that if f is a homogeneous function of order n of a set of variables y_i, then

$$\sum_i y_i \frac{\partial f}{\partial y_i} = nf$$

Consequently,

$$\sum_i \dot{q}_i \frac{\partial T}{\partial \dot{q}_i} = 2T \tag{11}$$

For conservative systems then,

$$p_k = \frac{\partial T}{\partial \dot{q}_k} = \sum_j a_{kj} \dot{q}_j + \sum_i a_{ik} \dot{q}_i$$

and, using Eq. (11),

$$\sum_k p_k \dot{q}_k = \sum_k \sum_j a_{kj} \dot{q}_k \dot{q}_j + \sum_i \sum_k a_{ik} \dot{q}_i \dot{q}_k = 2T \tag{12}$$

Combining Eqs. (8) and (12) then gives

$$H = 2T - L = T + V \tag{13}$$

and the Hamiltonian function is equal to the total energy for a conservative system.

The lives of Newton, Lagrange, and Hamilton, whose formulations of the laws of motion we have just seen, span the period from the mid-seventeenth to mid-nineteenth centuries. For mathematics the seventeenth and eighteenth centuries were an era of brilliance, and the successful application of mathematics to solve mechanical problems, especially those of astronomy, profoundly affected many other fields. Poets, for example, attempted to introduce mathematical conciseness into their works, but much more important was the influence on religious and philosophical thinking. The latter arose from the realization that, if the laws of motion and the interaction potentials are known for a given mechanical system, and if the coordinates and momenta (or velocities) of that system are known at some instant t, then all future and all prior mechanical behavior of the system can be calculated and is therefore completely determined. Because many applications of Newton's mechanics to explain natural phenomena proved successful, it was reasoned that the behavior of all nature, including man, must likewise be completely determined.

Since that time, however, the science of mechanics has been radically changed by the introduction of the theory of relativity and the quantum theory, both of which offer new concepts for philosophical thought.

6. Motion of a Rigid Body

If we consider a rigid body to be a system of n particles subject to the set of constraints

$$r_{ij} = c_{ij}$$

where r_{ij} is the distance between the ith and jth particles and the c_{ij}'s are constants, then only six independent generalized coordinates are required to specify the position of the rigid body. The problem thus becomes one of choosing the six coordinates so that we can obtain equations of motion for the system.

First we select a set of Cartesian axes, x', y', z', which has its origin at a fixed point within the rigid body and which we shall call the body axes. The problem is solved when these coordinates are related to an external set of reference coordinates, which are also Cartesian. Three of the six generalized coordinates serve to locate the origin of the body axes with respect to the origin of the external axes. The second set of three generalized coordinates gives the orientation of x', y', z' relative to three fixed axes which have the same origin as the body axes but which are parallel to the external axes as shown in Figure 1. To relate x', y', z' to the fixed axes we employ three angles, ϕ, θ, ψ, which are the Eulerian angles and correspond to a specified succession of three rotations. Furthermore, if we locate the origin of the body axes at the center of mass, then when ϕ, θ, ψ remain

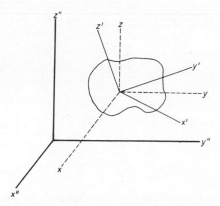

Figure 1. The external reference axes are x'', y'', z'', and they are parallel to x, y, z, the fixed axes within the rigid body. The center of mass is at the common origin of x, y, z and the body axes, x', y', z'.

constant, the motion is just the translation of the center of mass. Likewise, when the origin does not change, the motion is rotation about the center of mass. The total kinetic energy can thus be written as the sum of the kinetic energies for translation of and rotation about the center of mass,

$$T = T(x, y, z) + T(\phi, \theta, \psi) \tag{1}$$

To determine $T(\phi, \theta, \psi)$ we must relate the body axes, x', y', z', to the fixed axes, x, y, z, by means of the three angles, ϕ, θ, ψ.

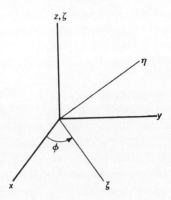

Figure 2. The first rotation through the angle ϕ about the z axis.

The first step in the transformation from x, y, z to x', y', z' is a counterclockwise rotation about z through the angle ϕ to give the intermediate set of axes ξ, η, (in the xy plane) and ζ ($= z$) of Figure 2.

The xy plane of Figure 2 is reproduced in Figure 3. Next we express x, y, ξ and η in the plane polar coordinates r and α:

$$x = r \cos \alpha$$
$$y = r \sin \alpha \tag{2}$$

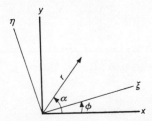

Figure 3. The xy plane of Figure 2 showing the relation between the coordinates x, y and the plane polar coordinates, r, α.

and

$$\xi = r\cos(\alpha - \phi) = r(\cos\alpha\cos\phi + \sin\alpha\sin\phi)$$
$$\eta = r\sin(\alpha - \phi) = r(\sin\alpha\cos\phi - \cos\alpha\sin\phi) \tag{3}$$

Combining Eqs. (2) and (3) and including $z = \zeta$ gives the set of transformation equations

$$\xi = x\cos\phi + y\sin\phi$$
$$\eta = -x\sin\phi + y\cos\phi$$
$$\zeta = z \tag{4}$$

The coefficients of Eqs. (4) can be written in the form of a transformation matrix[1] $\mathbf{D}$ for rotation about the z axis through the angle ϕ, as follows

$$\mathbf{D} = \begin{pmatrix} \cos\phi & \sin\phi & 0 \\ -\sin\phi & \cos\phi & 0 \\ 0 & 0 & 1 \end{pmatrix} \tag{5}$$

If $\mathbf{x}$ and $\boldsymbol{\xi}$ are column matrices with elements x, y, z, and ξ, η, ζ, respectively, this first rotation can be expressed in matrix notation as

$$\begin{pmatrix} \xi \\ \eta \\ \zeta \end{pmatrix} = \begin{pmatrix} \cos\phi & \sin\phi & 0 \\ -\sin\phi & \cos\phi & 0 \\ 0 & 0 & 1 \end{pmatrix} \begin{pmatrix} x \\ y \\ z \end{pmatrix}$$

or, more compactly, as

$$\boldsymbol{\xi} = \mathbf{Dx} \tag{6}$$

Equation (6) expresses the same information that Eqs. (4) do; the difference is in notation only.

The second rotation is counterclockwise about the ξ axis through an angle θ to produce another set of axes, ξ', η', ζ' as illustrated in Figure 4. The ξ' (or ξ) axis is the line of intersection of the xy and $\xi'\eta'$ planes; it is called the line of nodes. Applying the procedure used to obtain Eqs. (4) to the second rotation gives

$$\xi' = \xi$$
$$\eta' = \eta\cos\theta + \zeta\sin\theta$$
$$\zeta' = -\eta\sin\theta + \zeta\cos\theta \tag{7}$$

---

[1] The elements of matrix algebra are presented in part in Chapter 5, in *Q.C.*, Chap. 10, and in H. Goldstein, *Classical Mechanics*, Addison-Wesley, Reading, Mass., 1950, Chap. 4. More complete treatments can be found in modern algebra texts.

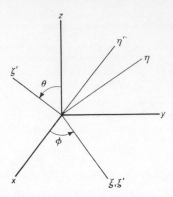

Figure 4. The second rotation through the angle θ about the ξ axis.

For rotation about ξ through θ the transformation matrix $\mathbf{C}$ is thus

$$\mathbf{C} = \begin{pmatrix} 1 & 0 & 0 \\ 0 & \cos\theta & \sin\theta \\ 0 & -\sin\theta & \cos\theta \end{pmatrix} \tag{8}$$

and

$$\xi' = \mathbf{C}\xi \tag{9}$$

The third and last rotation is made about the ζ' axis in a counterclockwise direction through the angle ψ. The resulting axes are the desired x', y', z' shown in Figure 5.

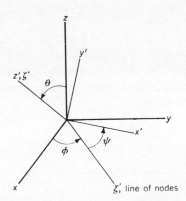

Figure 5. The third rotation through the angle ψ about the ζ' axis. The line of nodes, the intersection of the xy and $\xi'\eta'$ planes, is shown.

Similarly we obtain

$$x' = \xi' \cos\psi + \eta' \sin\psi$$
$$y' = -\xi' \sin\psi + \eta' \cos\psi$$
$$z' = \zeta' \tag{10}$$

$$\mathbf{B} = \begin{pmatrix} \cos\psi & \sin\psi & 0 \\ -\sin\psi & \cos\psi & 0 \\ 0 & 0 & 1 \end{pmatrix} \tag{11}$$

and

$$\mathbf{x}' = \mathbf{B}\xi' \tag{12}$$

Each of the three matrices $\mathbf{B}$, $\mathbf{C}$, $\mathbf{D}$ for the linear transformations of coordinates of Eqs. (4), (7), and (10) is orthogonal. If b_{ij} is the element in the ith row and jth column of the matrix $\mathbf{B}$, then $\mathbf{B}$ is an orthogonal matrix if

$$\sum_i b_{ij}^2 = 1, \qquad j = 1, 2, \ldots$$
$$\sum b_{ij} b_{ik} = 0, \qquad j \neq k, \text{ and } j, k = 1, 2, \ldots \tag{13}$$

Using (13) the orthogonality of $\mathbf{B}$, $\mathbf{C}$, $\mathbf{D}$ can be readily verified.

Substitution of Eqs. (9) and (12) into Eq. (6) gives

$$\mathbf{x}' = \mathbf{BCDx} = \mathbf{Ax} \tag{14}$$

where $\mathbf{A}$ is the matrix for the complete transformation resulting from the three successive transformations made in the order specified above. Matrix multiplication is not commutative; a change in the order of application of the successive transformations produces a different complete transformation. If b_{ik}, c_{kl}, and d_{lj} are elements of the matrices $\mathbf{B}$, $\mathbf{C}$, and $\mathbf{D}$, respectively, then by the rules of matrix multiplication the element a_{ij} of $\mathbf{A}$ is given by

$$a_{ij} = \sum_k \sum_l b_{ik} c_{kl} d_{lj} \tag{15}$$

Using Eqs. (14) and (15) we obtain

$$\mathbf{A} =$$

$$\begin{pmatrix} \cos\psi\cos\phi - \sin\psi\cos\theta\sin\phi & \cos\psi\sin\phi + \sin\psi\cos\theta\cos\phi & \sin\psi\sin\theta \\ -\sin\psi\cos\phi - \cos\psi\cos\theta\sin\phi & -\sin\psi\sin\phi + \cos\psi\cos\theta\cos\phi & \cos\psi\sin\theta \\ \sin\theta\sin\phi & -\sin\theta\cos\phi & \cos\theta \end{pmatrix}$$

$$\tag{16}$$

where ϕ, θ, and ψ are Euler's angles. By the application of Eqs. (13) A is shown to be orthogonal. The inverse transformation is given by the transposed (rows and columns are interchanges) matrix **A**,

$$\mathbf{x} = \mathbf{A}\mathbf{x}' \tag{17}$$

Before the rotating body coordinate system can be used, the time rate of change of a vector **G** in such a coordinate system must be related to the time rate of change of the vector in the non-rotating space coordinate system.

As before, let (x', y', z') be the three coordinate axes of the body system and (x, y, z) be the three axes of the space system. Further, let $\mathbf{i}'$, $\mathbf{j}'$, $\mathbf{k}'$ be unit vectors in the x', y', z' directions and $\mathbf{i}$, $\mathbf{j}$, $\mathbf{k}$ be unit vectors in the x, y, z directions. Hence,

$$\mathbf{G} = G_x\mathbf{i} + G_y\mathbf{j} + G_z\mathbf{k} \tag{18}$$

$$\mathbf{G} = G_{x'}\mathbf{i}' + G_{y'}\mathbf{j}' + G_{z'}\mathbf{k}' \tag{19}$$

where (G_x, G_y, G_z) and $(G_{x'}, G_{y'}, G_{z'})$ are the components of **G** in the x, y, z directions and in the x', y', z' directions, respectively.

Differentiation of Eq. (19) with respect to the time gives

$$\frac{d\mathbf{G}}{dt} = \frac{dG_{x'}}{dt}\mathbf{i}' + \frac{dG_{y'}}{dt}\mathbf{j}' + \frac{dG_{z'}}{dt}\mathbf{k}' + G_{x'}\dot{\mathbf{i}}' + G_{y'}\dot{\mathbf{j}}' + G_{z'}\dot{\mathbf{k}}' \tag{20}$$

If the rate of change of **G** in the body system is denoted by $\partial\mathbf{G}/\partial t$ then

$$\frac{d\mathbf{G}}{dt} = \frac{\partial\mathbf{G}}{\partial t} + G_{x'}\dot{\mathbf{i}}' + G_{y'}\dot{\mathbf{j}}' + G_{z'}\dot{\mathbf{k}}' \tag{21}$$

But $\mathbf{i}' \cdot \mathbf{i}' = 1$ and so

$$\frac{d}{dt}(\mathbf{i}' \cdot \mathbf{i}') = 2\dot{\mathbf{i}}'\mathbf{i}' = 0$$

so that $\mathbf{i}'$ is orthogonal to $\dot{\mathbf{i}}'$ and similarly $\mathbf{j}'$ and $\mathbf{k}'$ are orthogonal to $\dot{\mathbf{j}}'$ and $\dot{\mathbf{k}}'$, respectively. Thus

$$\dot{\mathbf{i}}' = c\mathbf{j}' - b\mathbf{k}'$$
$$\dot{\mathbf{j}}' = a\mathbf{k}' - f\mathbf{i}'$$
$$\dot{\mathbf{k}}' = e\mathbf{i}' - d\mathbf{j}' \tag{22}$$

where a, b, c, d, e, and f are to be determined. We also have the condition

$$\mathbf{i}' = \mathbf{j}' \times \mathbf{k}' \tag{23}$$

Differentiating

$$\dot{\mathbf{i}}' = \dot{\mathbf{j}}' \times \mathbf{k}' + \mathbf{j}' \times \dot{\mathbf{k}}' = (a\mathbf{k}' - f\mathbf{i}') \times \mathbf{k}' + \mathbf{j}' \times (e\mathbf{i}' - d\mathbf{j}')$$
$$= f\mathbf{j}' - e\mathbf{k}' \tag{24}$$

Comparing Eqs. (22) and (24) shows that $f = c$ and $e = b$. By similar reasoning $a = d$. Hence

$$\begin{aligned} G_{x'}\mathbf{i}' + G_{y'}\mathbf{j}' + G_{z'}\dot{\mathbf{k}}' &= (c\mathbf{j}' - b\mathbf{k}')G_{x'} + (a\mathbf{k}' - c\mathbf{i}')G_{y'} + (b\mathbf{i}' - a\mathbf{j}')G_{z'} \\ &= (bG_{z'} - cG_{y'})\mathbf{i}' + (cG_{x'} - aG_{z'})\mathbf{j}' + (aG_{y'} - bG_{x'})\mathbf{k}' \quad (25) \end{aligned}$$

If we introduce the vector $\omega = a\mathbf{i}' + b\mathbf{j}' + c\mathbf{k}'$ then we have

$$G_{x'}\mathbf{i}' + G_{y'}\mathbf{j}' + G_{z'}\dot{\mathbf{k}}' = \omega \times \mathbf{G} \tag{26}$$

Therefore

$$\frac{d\mathbf{G}}{dt} = \frac{\partial \mathbf{G}}{\partial t} + \omega \times \mathbf{G} \tag{27}$$

If the case where $\mathbf{G} = \mathbf{r}$ and z and z' coincide is considered ω can easily be seen to be the angular velocity.

Next we must determine $T(\phi, \theta, \psi)$, the kinetic energy for rotation about the center of mass, of Eq. (1).

$$T = \tfrac{1}{2} \sum_i m_i v_i^2 \tag{28}$$

Substituting (27) into (28) with $\mathbf{G} = \mathbf{v}_i$ we obtain

$$T = \tfrac{1}{2} \sum_i m_i (\omega \times \mathbf{r}_i) \cdot (\omega \times \mathbf{r}_i) = \tfrac{1}{2} \sum_i m_i \{\omega^2 \mathbf{r}_i^2 - (\omega \cdot \mathbf{r}_i)^2\}$$

$$= \tfrac{1}{2} \{I_{xx}\omega_x^2 + I_{yy}\omega_y^2 + I_{zz}\omega_z^2 + 2I_{xy}\omega_x\omega_y + 2I_{xz}\omega_x\omega_z + 2I_{yz}\omega_y\omega_z\} \tag{29}$$

where

$$I_{xx} = \sum_i m_i \{r_i^2 - x_i^2\}$$

$$I_{xy} = I_{yx} = -\sum_i m_i x_i y_i \tag{30}$$

etc. If we make the definitions

$$\mathbf{I} = \begin{pmatrix} I_{xx} & I_{xy} & I_{xz} \\ I_{yx} & I_{yy} & I_{yz} \\ I_{zx} & I_{zy} & I_{zz} \end{pmatrix}$$

$$\omega = \begin{pmatrix} \omega_x \\ \omega_y \\ \omega_z \end{pmatrix} \tag{31}$$

then Eq. (29) can be written in matrix[2] notation:

---

[2] **I** is actually a tensor of the second rank. However, in Cartesian coordinates there is no difference between second rank tensors and matrices and so we shall not dwell on this point.

$$T = \tfrac{1}{2}\omega \mathbf{I} \omega \tag{32}$$

Up to the present the coordinate system used in resolving ω has not been specified. If a body coordinate system, fixed in the rigid body, is used the components of the matrix $\mathbf{I}$ will be constants depending only on the properties of the rigid body and not on its motion.

The matrix $\mathbf{I}$ is symmetric with respect to interchange of indices. As a result it is possible to choose a coordinate system (x', y', z') such that only the three diagonal elements of $\mathbf{I}$ are non-vanishing. These non-vanishing elements are called the principal moments of inertia of the rigid body and are denoted by A, B, and C. If such a coordinate system is used Eq. (29) becomes

$$T = \tfrac{1}{2}\{A\omega_{x'}^2 + B\omega_{y'}^2 + C\omega_{z'}^2\} \tag{33}$$

It is now desirable to express the angular velocities $\omega_{x'}$, $\omega_{y'}$, and $\omega_{z'}$ in terms of ϕ, θ, and ψ, which are the angular velocities corresponding to rotations about the z, ξ', and z' axes respectively. The direction of the velocity vector θ is the z axis of Figure 2. In the x, y, z system the components of ϕ are

$$\phi_x = 0$$
$$\phi_y = 0$$
$$\phi_z = \phi$$

We need the components of ϕ in the x', y', z' coordinate system, which are given by applying the complete transformation $\mathbf{A}$, Eq. (16), to ϕ to obtain

$$\phi_{x'} = \phi \sin \psi \sin \theta$$
$$\phi_{y'} = \phi \cos \psi \sin \theta$$
$$\phi_{z'} = \phi \cos \theta \tag{34}$$

The velocity θ is in the direction of the ξ' axis of Figure 4. To obtain the components of θ in the x', y', z' system, we need only the transformation $\mathbf{B}$. Application of $\mathbf{B}$ to θ gives

$$\theta_{x'} = \theta \cos \psi$$
$$\theta_{y'} = \theta(-\sin \psi)$$
$$\theta_{z'} = 0 \tag{35}$$

Since ψ is parallel to the z' axis, no transformation is needed. From Eqs. (34) and (35) and $\psi = \psi_{z'}$, we write

$$\omega_{x'} = \phi_{x'} + \theta_{x'} + \psi_{x'} = \phi \sin \psi \sin \theta + \theta \cos \psi$$
$$\omega_{y'} = \phi_{y'} + \theta_{y'} + \psi_{y'} = \phi \cos \psi \sin \theta - \theta \sin \psi$$
$$\omega_{z'} = \phi_{z'} + \theta_{z'} + \psi_{z'} = \phi \cos \theta + \psi \tag{36}$$

Substitution of these results in Eq. (33) gives T in the desired form,

$$T = \tfrac{1}{2}[A(\dot{\phi}\sin\psi\sin\theta + \dot{\theta}\cos\psi)^2 + B(\dot{\phi}\cos\psi\sin\theta - \dot{\theta}\sin\psi)^2$$
$$+ C(\dot{\phi}\cos\theta + \dot{\psi})^2] \quad (37)$$

When there is no net applied torque, $V = 0$, $L = T$, and the Lagrangian for rotation about the center of mass in terms of Euler's angles is given by Eq. (37).

Next we calculate the momenta, p_ϕ, p_θ, p_ψ, from Eqs. (36) and (37).

$$p_\phi = \partial T/\partial\dot{\phi} = A\omega_{x'}\sin\psi\sin\theta + B\omega_{y'}\cos\psi\sin\theta + C\omega_{z'}\cos\theta$$

$$p_\theta = \partial T/\partial\dot{\theta} = A\omega_{x'}\cos\psi - B\omega_{y'}\sin\psi$$

$$p_\psi = \partial T/\partial\dot{\psi} = C\omega_{z'} \quad (38)$$

From Eqs. (38) we obtain the angular velocities, $\omega_{x'}$, $\omega_{y'}$, $\omega_{z'}$, as a function of ϕ, θ, ψ, and p_ϕ, p_θ, p_ψ:

$$\omega_{x'} = \frac{\begin{vmatrix} p_\phi & B\cos\psi\sin\theta & C\cos\theta \\ p_\theta & -B\sin\psi & 0 \\ p_\psi & 0 & C \end{vmatrix}}{\begin{vmatrix} A\sin\psi\sin\theta & B\cos\psi\sin\theta & C\cos\theta \\ A\cos\psi & -B\sin\psi & 0 \\ 0 & 0 & C \end{vmatrix}}$$

$$= \frac{1}{A}\left[p_\theta\cos\psi + (p_\phi - p_\psi\cos\theta)\frac{\sin\psi}{\sin\theta}\right]$$

$$\omega_{y'} = -\frac{1}{B}\left[p_\theta\sin\psi - (p_\phi - p_\psi\cos\theta)\frac{\cos\psi}{\sin\theta}\right]$$

$$\omega_{z'} = \frac{1}{C}\,p_\psi \quad (39)$$

Use of Eqs. (33) and (39) gives T in terms of the momenta,

$$T = \frac{1}{2A}\left(p_\theta\cos\psi + (p_\phi - p_\psi\cos\theta)\frac{\sin\psi}{\sin\theta}\right)^2$$

$$+ \frac{1}{2B}\left(p_\theta\sin\psi - (p_\phi - p_\psi\cos\theta)\frac{\cos\psi}{\sin\theta}\right)^2 + \frac{1}{2C}\,p_\psi^2$$

$$= \frac{u^2}{2A} + \frac{v^2}{2B} + \frac{w^2}{2C} \quad (40)$$

where

$$u = \left(p_\theta \cos \psi + (p_\phi - p_\psi \cos \theta) \frac{\sin \psi}{\sin \theta} \right)$$

$$v = - \left(p_\theta \sin \psi - (p_\phi - p_\psi \cos \theta) \frac{\cos \psi}{\sin \theta} \right)$$

$$w = p_\psi \tag{41}$$

For $V = 0$, $H = T$, and the Hamiltonian for rotation of a rigid body about its center of mass is thus given by Eq. (40) in terms of Euler's angles, which relate the body axes to a set of fixed axes. This is the form of H required in the classical statistical mechanical treatment of the three-dimensional rotator.

In classical statistical mechanics (see Chapter 4), the expression for the partition function for three rotational degrees of freedom is

$$f = \frac{1}{h^3} \int_0^\pi \int_0^{2\pi} \int_0^{2\pi} \int_{-\infty}^{+\infty} \int_{-\infty}^{+\infty} \int_{-\infty}^{+\infty} e^{-H/kT} \, dp_\theta \, dp_\phi \, dp_\psi \, d\theta \, d\phi \, d\psi \tag{42}$$

where $H(= T)$ is given by Eq. (40). This multiple integral is more readily evaluated if it is transformed to an iterated (or repeated) integral in the variables u, v, w, which are functions of p_θ, p_ϕ, p_ψ as shown above. The general formula[3] for transformation of a multiple integral is

$$\int \cdots \int f(x_1 x_2 \ldots x_n) \, dx_1 \, dx_2 \ldots dx_n$$

$$= \int \cdots \int g(y_1 y_2 \ldots y_n) \frac{\partial(x_1 x_2 \ldots x_n)}{\partial(y_1 y_2 \ldots y_n)} \, dy_1 \, dy_2 \ldots dy_n \tag{43}$$

where $\dfrac{\partial(x_1 x_2 \ldots x_n)}{\partial(y_1 y_2 \ldots y_n)}$ is the Jacobian determinant of the transformation.

Accordingly we rewrite Eq. (42) as

$$f = \frac{1}{h^3} \int \cdots \int e^{-H(u, v, w)/kT} \frac{\partial(p_\theta p_\phi p_\psi)}{\partial(uvw)} \, du \, dv \, dw \, d\theta \, d\phi \, d\psi \tag{44}$$

Next we calculate the Jacobian of the transformation from p_θ, p_ϕ, p_ψ to u, v, w. Since we have explicit expressions for the latter, we make use of the relationship

$$\frac{\partial(p_\theta p_\phi p_\psi)}{\partial(uvw)} = 1 \bigg/ \frac{\partial(uvw)}{\partial(p_\theta p_\phi p_\psi)} \tag{45}$$

[3] E. U. Condon and H. Odishaw (Eds.), *Handbook of Physics*, McGraw-Hill, New York, 1958, pp. 1–35.

and calculate

$$\frac{\partial(uvw)}{\partial(p_\theta p_\phi p_\psi)} = \begin{vmatrix} \dfrac{\partial u}{\partial p_\theta} & \dfrac{\partial v}{\partial p_\theta} & \dfrac{\partial w}{\partial p_\theta} \\[2mm] \dfrac{\partial u}{\partial p_\phi} & \dfrac{\partial v}{\partial p_\phi} & \dfrac{\partial w}{\partial p_\phi} \\[2mm] \dfrac{\partial u}{\partial p_\psi} & \dfrac{\partial v}{\partial p_\psi} & \dfrac{\partial w}{\partial p_\psi} \end{vmatrix}$$

$$= \begin{vmatrix} \cos\psi & -\sin\psi & 0 \\[2mm] \dfrac{\sin\psi}{\sin\theta} & \dfrac{\cos\psi}{\sin\theta} & 0 \\[2mm] -\dfrac{\cos\theta\sin\psi}{\sin\theta} & -\dfrac{\cos\theta\cos\psi}{\sin\theta} & 1 \end{vmatrix} = \frac{1}{\sin\theta} \qquad (46)$$

Substitution of Eqs. (45) and (46) in Eq. (44) then gives

$$f = \frac{1}{h^3} \int_0^\pi d\theta \int_0^{2\pi} d\phi \int_0^{2\pi} d\psi \int_{-\infty}^{+\infty} du \int_{-\infty}^{+\infty} dv \int_{-\infty}^{+\infty} e^{-(u^2/2AkT + v^2/2BkT + w^2/2CkT)} \sin\theta \, dw$$

$$(47)$$

which is easily evaluated since the exponential in the integrand is of the form e^{-ax^2} (see Appendix 2). The six successive integrations give

$$f = \frac{8\pi^2 (8\pi^3 ABC)^{\frac{1}{2}} (kT)^{\frac{3}{2}}}{h^3} \qquad (48)$$

the partition function for the three-dimensional rigid rotator.

7. Theory of Small Vibrations

The theory of small vibrations concerns small oscillatory motion about a point of equilibrium. Of the many physical applications of this theory, perhaps the one most pertinent to us is its use in the problem of molecular vibrations. Let us consider a conservative system slightly displaced from a position of stable equilibrium. Its coordinates will differ but slightly from the equilibrium values, and, if we choose a set of generalized coordinates which vanish at the point of equilibrium, these coordinates will measure the displacement. The kinetic energy of the system is

$$T = \tfrac{1}{2} \sum_i \sum_j a_{ij} \dot{q}_i \dot{q}_j \qquad (1)$$

Although the a_{ii}'s are in general functions of the q_j's, a valid approximation, for small vibrations, is to assume that the a_{ij}'s are constant and equal to their value at the point of equilibrium.

Next we expand the potential energy function in a Taylor's series about the equilibrium position to obtain

$$V(q_1 q_2 \ldots q_n) = V_0 + \sum_i \left(\frac{\partial V}{\partial q_i}\right)_0 q_i + \tfrac{1}{2} \sum_i \sum_j \left(\frac{\partial^2 V}{\partial q_i \partial q_j}\right)_0 q_i q_j + \ldots \quad (2)$$

where the subscript 0 is used to designate values at equilibrium. The zero of potential energy is arbitrary and we may choose $V_0 = 0$. For a conservative system the condition for equilibrium is that the forces acting on the system vanish, i.e.

$$\left(\frac{\partial V}{\partial q_i}\right)_0 = 0 \quad (3)$$

Consequently, if we neglect higher terms, Eq. (2) becomes

$$V = \tfrac{1}{2} \sum_i \sum_j \left(\frac{\partial^2 V}{\partial q_i \partial q_j}\right)_0 q_i q_j = \tfrac{1}{2} \sum_i \sum_j b_{ij} q_i q_j \quad (4)$$

where the constant $b_{ij} = \left(\dfrac{\partial^2 V}{\partial q_i \partial q_j}\right)_0$.

The Lagrangian of the system is

$$L = T - V = \tfrac{1}{2} \sum_i \sum_j a_{ij} \dot{q}_i \dot{q}_j - \tfrac{1}{2} \sum_i \sum_j b_{ij} q_i q_j \quad (5)$$

and Lagrange's equations of motion, equal in number to the number of degrees of freedom of the system, are

$$\sum_j a_{ij} \ddot{q}_j + \sum_j b_{ij} q_j = 0 \quad (6)$$

Next we want to find a set of constants c_i which, if we multiply the first of Eqs. (6) by c_1, the second by c_2, and so on, and then add the resulting equations, will give a new set of equations of the form

$$\ddot{Q}_k + \lambda^2 Q_k = 0 \quad (7)$$

The Q_k's are linear combinations of the q_j's,

$$Q_k = \sum_j h_{kj} q_j \quad (8)$$

and the various constants are related by the sets of equations

$$\sum_i c_i a_{ik} = \frac{1}{\lambda^2} \sum_i c_i b_{ij} = h_{kj} \quad (9)$$

From Eq. (9) we write

$$\sum_i (\lambda^2 a_{ij} - b_{ij}) c_i = 0 \quad (10)$$

which we want to solve for the c_i's. Solutions other than the trivial solution, $c_i = 0$, exist only if the determinant of the coefficients of the c_i's vanishes,[1] i.e.

$$|\lambda^2 a_{ij} - b_{ij}| = 0 \qquad (11)$$

This determinant is an nth degree equation in λ^2 which can be solved for the n roots, $\lambda_1^2, \lambda_2^2, .., \lambda_n^2$. Each value of λ^2 can then be used in turn in Eqs. (10) to calculate a set of c_i's. For a given value of λ^2, $n-1$ of the c_i's can be determined in terms of the nth one from Eqs. (10). The value for c_n must then be determined arbitrarily. Once we know the c_i's the h_{kj}'s are readily obtained from Eqs. (9).

The Q_k's which we have now calculated are the normal coordinates of the system. In normal coordinates the kinetic and potential energies assume the simple forms,

$$T = \tfrac{1}{2} \sum_i \dot{Q}_i^2 \qquad V = \tfrac{1}{2} \sum_i \lambda_i^2 Q_i^2 \qquad (12)$$

Accordingly, $\lambda_i^2 = \left(\dfrac{\partial^2 V}{\partial Q_i^2}\right)_0$ and is real and positive for stable equilibrium. Therefore the solution of Eq. (7) is

$$Q_k = A_k \cos(\lambda_k t + \varepsilon_k) = A_k \cos(2\pi \nu_k t + \varepsilon_k) \qquad (13)$$

where A_k and ε_k are arbitrary constants and $\nu_k = \lambda_k/2\pi$. The n ν_k's are the frequencies of the n normal modes of vibration. By transforming to normal coordinates we have seen that the small vibrations of the system can be described by a set of harmonic oscillators of frequencies ν_k. If we wish to express the solution in terms of the q_j's, we use the inverse transformation

$$q_j = \sum_k g_{jk} Q_k \qquad (14)$$

to obtain

$$q_j = \sum_k g_{jk} A_k \cos(2\pi \nu_k t + \varepsilon_k) \qquad (15)$$

As an example, we obtain the longitudinal normal modes of a linear symmetrical triatomic molecule. Let M be the mass of the central atom, m the mass of each of the end atoms, and l the equilibrium distance between the central atom and each end atom, as shown in Figure 1. First we change to coordinates which measure the displacement from the equilibrium position and which are

$$X_i = x_i - x_{ei} \qquad (16)$$

where the subscript e indicates the equilibrium value. If we assume the atoms are held together in a straight line with springs of force constant k

---

[1] Q.C., Appendix IV.

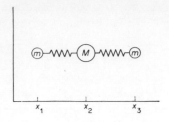

Figure 1. Model of a linear symmetrical triatomic molecule, which is at the equilibrium position when $x_2 - x_1 = x_3 - x_2 = l$.

(i.e. a linear restoring force), the potential energy is given by the expression

$$V = \tfrac{1}{2}k(x_2 - x_1 - l)^2 + \tfrac{1}{2}k(x_3 - x_2 - l)^2$$
$$= \tfrac{1}{2}k[(X_2 - X_1)^2 + (X_3 - X_2)^2]$$
$$= \tfrac{1}{2}k[X_1^2 + 2X_2^2 + X_3^2 - X_1X_2 - X_2X_1 - X_2X_3 - X_3X_2] \quad (17)$$

The kinetic energy is

$$T = \tfrac{1}{2}m\,(\dot{X}_1^2 + \dot{X}_3^2) + \tfrac{1}{2}M\,(\dot{X}_2^2) \quad (18)$$

Thus Lagrange's equations of motion are

$$m\ddot{X}_1 + k(X_1 - X_2) = 0 \quad (19)$$
$$M\ddot{X}_2 + k(2X_2 - X_1 - X_3) = 0 \quad (20)$$
$$m\ddot{X}_3 + k(X_3 - X_2) = 0 \quad (21)$$

Multiplying Eqs. (19), (20) and (21) by c_1, c_2, c_3, respectively, and adding gives

$$c_1 m\ddot{X}_1 + c_2 M\ddot{X}_2 + c_3 m\ddot{X}_3 + k(c_1 - c_2)X_1$$
$$+ k(-c_1 + 2c_2 - c_3)X_2 + k(-c_2 + c_3)X_3 = 0 \quad (22)$$

Putting these results in the form of Eq. (9) we have

$$c_1 m = (k/\lambda^2)(c_1 - c_2) = h_1 \quad (23)$$
$$c_2 M = (k/\lambda^2)(-c_1 + 2c_2 - c_3) = h_2 \quad (24)$$
$$c_3 m = (k/\lambda^2)(-c_2 + c_3) = h_3 \quad (25)$$

To obtain a non-trivial solution for the c_i's we must have

$$\begin{vmatrix} \lambda^2 m - k & k & 0 \\ k & \lambda^2 M - 2k & k \\ 0 & k & \lambda^2 m - k \end{vmatrix} = 0 \quad (26)$$

The roots of Eq. (26) are $\lambda^2 = 0$, k/m, $k[(2m+M)/mM]$, so that the new equations of motion are

$$\ddot{Q}_1 = 0 \tag{27}$$

$$\ddot{Q}_2 + (k/m)Q_2 = 0 \tag{28}$$

$$\ddot{Q}_3 + k[(2m+M)/mM]Q_3 = 0 \tag{29}$$

Equation (27), for $\lambda^2 = 0$, is actually a translational motion rather than a vibration, for there is no relative displacement of the atoms. By Eqs. (8) and (9) we obtain for Q_1, if $c_1 = 1$,

$$Q_1 = mX_1 + MX_2 + mX_3 \tag{30}$$

For $\lambda^2 = k/m$, we obtain

$$Q_2 = mX_1 - mX_2 \tag{31}$$

In this normal mode there is no displacement of the central atom and the end atoms move in opposite directions with a frequency $v_2 = (k/m)^{\frac{1}{2}}/2\pi$. For $\lambda^2 = k[(2m+M)/mM]$ we have

$$Q_3 = mX_1 - (2m+M)X_2 + mX_3 \tag{32}$$

In this normal mode the relative displacement of the central atom is opposite in direction and differs in amplitude from that of the end atoms. The frequency is $v_3 = \{k[(2m+M)/mM]\}^{\frac{1}{2}}/2\pi$. Any other longitudinal vibration of this molecule can be expressed as a linear combination of these two normal modes.

In the foregoing discussion, we have considered motion in one direction only. Were we to give full consideration to the nine degrees of freedom we should find three translational motions, two rotational, and four vibrational. The other two normal modes are bending motions perpendicular to the x-axis. From the symmetry of the molecule a bending in the y direction is seen to be equivalent to one in the z direction. Thus the two normal modes for bending are degenerate and have the same frequency.

8. The Virial Theorem

The mechanics which we have developed so far enables us to calculate the mechanical state of a system at any given time. When the system comprises a very large number of particles, as in the case of a mole of gas molecules, the time averages of the various mechanical properties prove very useful.

The mechanical state of a system of n particles is specified by $3n$ generalized coordinates $(q_1, q_2, \ldots, q_{3n})$ and $3n$ generalized momenta $(p_1, p_2, \ldots, p_{3n})$. Consider the function

$$G = \sum_i p_i q_i \tag{1}$$

The total time derivative is

$$\frac{dG}{dt} = \sum_i \dot{p}_i q_i + \sum_i p_i \dot{q}_i \tag{2}$$

and the time average of Eq. (2) over the period from $t = 0$ to $t = \tau$ is

$$\frac{1}{\tau} \int_0^\tau \frac{dG}{dt} \, dt \equiv \overline{\frac{dG}{dt}} = \overline{\sum_i \dot{p}_i q_i} + \overline{\sum_i p_i \dot{q}_i} \tag{3}$$

where the bars are used to denote time averages. The leftmost member of Eq. (3) can also be written

$$\frac{1}{\tau} \int_0^\tau \frac{dG}{dt} \, dt = \frac{1}{\tau} [G(\tau) - G(0)] \tag{4}$$

If G has an upper bound, and it will if all the coordinates and momenta remain finite, then τ can be chosen to be sufficiently long to make the right hand side as small as desired. Consequently, remembering that (Eq. 5.12),

$$\sum_i p_i \dot{q}_i = 2T$$

Eq. (3) becomes

$$\overline{T} = -\tfrac{1}{2} \overline{\sum \dot{p}_i q_i} \tag{5}$$

The right member of Eq. (5) is known as the virial of Clausius, and the virial theorem states that the average total kinetic energy of the system is equal to its virial.

If we change to rectangular coordinates, the more familiar form of Eq. (5) is obtained.

$$\overline{T} = \overline{\sum_i \tfrac{1}{2} m_i (\dot{x}_i^2 + \dot{y}_i^2 + \dot{z}_i^2)}$$

$$= -\tfrac{1}{2} \overline{\sum_i (X_i x_i + Y_i y_i + Z_i z_i)} \tag{6}$$

where the summation is over all the particles of the system, and X_i is the component of force in the x_i direction acting on the ith particle, etc.

3

THERMODYNAMICS

1. Introduction

The basic laws of thermodynamics concern the conversion of energy from one form to another and the transfer of energy from one body to another. The origins of these laws were empirical, even though classical mechanics, which was thoroughly developed at that time, recognized energy as a property of the system. In the conservative system of classical mechanics energy is constant, Eq. (2.2.6.); in the non-conservative system subject to frictional losses energy decreases. The appearance of the lost energy as heat was not recognized for some time, and heat, as the weightless fluid 'caloric', was still included in Lavoisier's listing of chemical elements in 1789.

Observations of the heat produced in the boring of cannon led Thompson (Count Rumford) in 1798 to suggest the conversion of mechanical work to heat, and to measure roughly the amount of heat produced by the expenditure of a given amount of mechanical energy. More than forty years later James Joule demonstrated that a given amount of work, mechanical or electrical, always produced the same amount of heat. Joule's work led to the widespread recognition of heat as energy and to the first law of thermodynamics. Somewhat earlier the foundations of the second law were laid by Sadi Carnot (1824). Using the caloric concept of heat, Carnot derived the maximum efficiency of an ideal heat engine. Following recognition of the two basic laws, the science of thermodynamics grew rapidly both in theoretical development and in application to problems of chemical equilibrium.

2. The First Law of Thermodynamics

The first law of thermodynamics is the law of conservation of energy, i.e. that energy is neither created nor destroyed. Its initial formulation resulted from the demonstration that the expenditure of a given amount of mechanical work resulted not in the loss of that energy but in the production of an equivalent amount of heat energy. The modern statement includes all forms of energy, electrical, gravitational, and electromagnetic energies, and matter itself, for which the equivalence relation is $E = mc^2$. If additional forms of energy are discovered, they will also be included. In general, thermodynamics is concerned with macroscopic amounts of matter, but the first law is more fundamental in that it applies to individual atoms and molecules. The phenomenon of radioactive decay illustrates this fact.

In the following discussion, we shall usually consider only heat and mechanical work. The study of heat requires the concept of temperature. When two systems are brought into contact, either there is no net flow of heat between them, in which case they are in thermal equilibrium, or there is a flow of heat from one system to the other which continues until thermal equilibrium is established. In thermal equilibrium the temperatures of the systems are the same; if heat flows from system A to system B, then the temperature of A decreases as that of B increases until the temperatures become equal. This leads to the concept—for which the name 'zeroth law of thermodynamics' has been suggested[1]—that if systems A and B are each in thermal equilibrium with system C, then A and B are also in thermal equilibrium. In more familiar words, A, B, and C have the same temperature.

Next let E equal the internal energy of the system. Then the mathematical statement of the first law is

$$dE = dq - dw \tag{1}$$

where dE, the change in internal energy of the system, is equal to the heat, dq, *absorbed by the system* less dw, the work *done by the system*. If the system goes from state 1 by any path to state 2, then to other states, eventually returning to state 1, the first law requires that

$$dE = 0 \tag{2}$$

If the right-hand side of Eq. (2) is not zero then energy is not conserved and perpetual motion machines become possible.

Mathematically Eq. (2) shows that dE is an exact differential; the value of the integral of an exact differential, du, between two points depends only on the two points and not on the path between them, and u is called a point function.[2] In thermodynamics we usually call a function of this kind a state function. The internal energy, E, is thus a state function, and the change in internal energy of a system in going from state 1 to state 2 depends only on these states and not on the path between them. In contrast, dq and dw are not exact, and the changes in these quantities do depend on the path followed in going from state 1 to state 2.

[1] R. H. Fowler and E. A. Guggenheim, *Statistical Thermodynamics*, Cambridge University Press, 1939, p. 56. See also Sect. 1.1.

[2] H. Margenau and G. M. Murphy, *The Mathematics of Physics and Chemistry*, 2nd Ed., van Nostrand, Princeton, N.J., 1956, p. 8.

3. The Second Law of Thermodynamics

The second law is known variously as the law of degradation of energy and the law of increase of entropy. It extends the concepts of the first law, in that, when energy is converted from one form to another, the second law tells us the direction of the change. Early statements of the law, relating mainly to macroscopic observations, tend to describe prohibitions resulting from the second law: 'Heat cannot of itself pass from a colder to a hotter body' (Clausius, 1850), and 'It is impossible by means of inanimate material agency to derive mechanical effect from any portion of matter by cooling it below the temperature of the coldest of the surrounding objects' (Lord Kelvin, 1853). More modern statements take cognizance of the microscopic states of matter and the consequent statistical concepts. For example, see Lewis and Randall's discussion.[1]

We follow the historical development by considering, in the manner of Carnot, the efficiency of an ideal heat engine. Our system is the engine and its working fluid. There are two heat reservoirs at different temperatures which exchange heat with the engine, which consists of a cylinder and a frictionless piston. The working fluid is an ideal gas which obeys the following relationships,

$$pV = RT \tag{1}$$

$$\left(\frac{\partial E}{\partial V}\right)_T = 0 \tag{2}$$

To determine the efficiency, we calculate the heat and work for four successive reversible processes shown in Figure 1. They are (a) an iso-

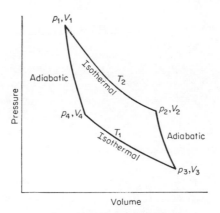

Figure 1. The Carnot cycle.

[1] G. N. Lewis and M. Randall, *Thermodynamics*, 2nd Ed., McGraw-Hill, New York, 1961, p. 92.

thermal expansion at the higher temperature T_2, (b) an adiabatic expansion from T_2 to T_1, (c) isothermal compression at T_1, followed by (d) an adiabatic compression to complete the cycle. From Eq. (2.2), $\Delta E = 0$ for the complete cycle. In the reversible isothermal expansion there is no change in E, and the heat added to the system is thus equal to the work done. Since $dw = p\,dV$ is a perfect differential in the case of a reversible isothermal expansion, we can write for q_1, using Eq. (1),

$$q_1 = w_1 = \int_{V_1}^{V_2} p\,dV = \int_{V_1}^{V_2} \frac{RT_2}{V}\,dV = RT_2 \ln \frac{V_2}{V_1} \tag{3}$$

In the adiabatic expansion which follows, no heat is added to the system ($q_2 = 0$), hence the work done is equal to the negative of the change in internal energy. To calculate w_2 we must first define the heat capacity at constant volume, which is

$$\left(\frac{\partial E}{\partial T}\right)_V = C_V \tag{4}$$

For an ideal gas we require

$$\left(\frac{\partial C_V}{\partial V}\right)_T = 0 \tag{5}$$

By virtue of Eqs. (4) and (5) we now write

$$w_2 = \int_{V_2}^{V_3} p\,dV = -\int_{T_2}^{T_1} dE = -C_V(T_1 - T_2) \tag{6}$$

Similarly, we write for the two compressions,

$$q_3 = w_3 = \int_{V_3}^{V_4} p\,dV = RT_1 \ln \frac{V_4}{V_3} \tag{7}$$

$$w_4 = \int_{V_4}^{V_1} p\,dV = -C_V(T_2 - T_1) \tag{8}$$

and note that $q_4 = 0$ and

$$w_2 + w_4 = 0 \tag{9}$$

In one complete cycle our engine thus does work,

$$w = w_1 + w_3 \tag{10}$$

and, in doing so, it absorbs the heat q_1 from the reservoir at T_2 and gives off the heat q_3 to the reservoir at T_1. From the above, it is readily verified that

$$\Delta E = q - w = q_1 + q_3 - w_1 - w_3 = 0 \tag{11}$$

The efficiency, η, of the engine is defined as the ratio of the total work to the heat absorbed, and, thus,

$$\eta = \frac{w_1 + w_3}{q_1} = \frac{q_1 + q_3}{q_1} \tag{12}$$

Next we must find a relationship between the four volumes. In the adiabatic processes,

$$dq = dE + dw = C_V dT + p\, dV = 0 \tag{13}$$

Substituting for p from Eq. (1), rearranging, and integrating over the adiabatic expansion from V_2 to V_3, Eq. (13) becomes

$$-C_V \int_{T_2}^{T_1} \frac{dT}{T} = \int_{V_2}^{V_3} \frac{R\, dV}{V} = -C_V \ln \frac{T_1}{T_2} = R \ln \frac{V_3}{V_2} \tag{14}$$

For the adiabatic compression the similar result is

$$-C_V \ln \frac{T_2}{T_1} = R \ln \frac{V_1}{V_4} \tag{15}$$

and, therefore,

$$\frac{V_1}{V_4} = \frac{V_2}{V_3} \tag{16}$$

Substitution from Eqs. (3) and (16) enables us to rewrite the efficiency, Eq. (12), as

$$\eta = \frac{T_2 - T_1}{T_2} \tag{17}$$

Suppose now that we have a second reversible engine which employs a different substance as a working fluid. Assume that the efficiency of this engine is less than that of the ideal gas engine. If both engines absorb the same amount of heat from the hot reservoir (at T_2) the more efficient one delivers more work. This does not violate the first law, for less heat can be discarded to the cold reservoir (at T_1) to compensate for the extra work. Next we operate the more efficient engine as a heat engine, and use it to run the other in reverse as a heat pump or refrigerator. We adjust the pair so that during each cycle of operation the refrigerator gives up an amount of heat to the hot reservoir equal to that absorbed by the heat engine. At the end of one cycle, equal amounts of heat have been absorbed from and discarded to the hot reservoir, but the heat engine discarded less heat to the cold reservoir than was absorbed by the refrigerator and the heat engine also delivered more work than was required to operate the refrigerator. Thus, we are led to the conclusion, which is contrary to all our experience, that heat can be extracted from the cold reservoir and converted into work while no other changes of any kind have taken place.

If we adjust the engines so that the work delivered by the heat engine in one cycle is just sufficient to operate the refrigerator through one cycle, then, as a consequence of the first law, we are led to the conclusion that heat has been transferred from the cold to the hot reservoir with no other change taking place. Furthermore, if we assume that the ideal gas engine is less efficient, we need only to interchange the two engines in the previous arguments to reach the same conclusions. The only conclusion compatible with experience is that the efficiencies of the two heat engines are the same. Since there are no restrictions on our choice for the working fluid of the second one, it follows that the efficiency of any reversible heat engine working in a Carnot cycle is independent of the working fluid and depends only on the temperatures of the hot and cold heat reservoirs.

From Eqs. (12) and (17), the equations for the efficiency of the reversible heat engine, we obtain

$$\frac{q_3}{T_1} + \frac{q_1}{T_2} = 0 \tag{18}$$

Remembering that $q_2 = q_4 = 0$, we can rewrite Eq. (18) as

$$\oint \frac{dq}{T} = 0 \tag{19}$$

Thus, while dq is not an exact differential, dq/T is exact for a reversible heat engine operating through a Carnot cycle. Furthermore, any reversible cyclic process can be represented by a number of Carnot cycles, which leads to the very important result that Eq. (19) applies to all reversible cyclic processes. Hence, dq/T is the differential of a property of the system which, analogous to the internal energy, depends only on initial and final states and thus is a state function. This property is the entropy, and substitution of $dS = dq/T$ into Eq. (2.1) gives

$$dE = T\,dS - dw \tag{20}$$

Equation (20) is a combined statement of the first and second laws of thermodynamics. For a reversible process, $\Delta S = q/T$; for a cyclic reversible process, $\Delta S = 0$; and for irreversible processes, $\Delta S > 0$. The above considerations apply to macroscopic systems. The recognition of the relationship between entropy and probability by Gibbs, Boltzmann, and others permits calculation of the chance of deviations on a microscopic scale. We, however, defer the topic of fluctuations to the next chapter.

4. The Third Law of Thermodynamics

The third law of thermodynamics is frequently stated 'every substance has a finite positive entropy, but at the absolute zero of temperature the entropy may become zero, and does so become in the case of perfect crystalline substance'.[1] Historically the law arose from Nernst's heat theorem (1906) and other related work. The heat theorem was based on thermal data then available and stated that, in an isothermal reaction involving condensed phases only, the entropy change approaches zero as the absolute temperature approaches zero, i.e.

$$\lim_{T \to 0} \Delta S = 0 \tag{1}$$

As a consequence of Eq. (1), all condensed substances would have the same entropy at the absolute zero. Planck reasoned that this common entropy must be equal to zero on the basis that translational motion ceases at the absolute zero. Later work, a large part of which was done by G. N. Lewis and colleagues, showed that only perfect crystalline solids have zero entropy at $0°K$. The statistical role of the third law in which the entropy at absolute zero is determined by the degeneracy of the lowest state has been presented in Sect. 1.2.

5. Thermodynamic Functions and Criteria of Equilibrium

In the preceding sections, the laws of thermodynamics have been expressed in terms of the extensive properties, internal energy, entropy, and volume, and the intensive properties, temperature and pressure. Next we examine some mathematical relations between these and other useful thermodynamic functions, and consider several criteria of equilibrium. Unless otherwise specified, only expansion–compression work will be considered throughout this section. Then Eq. (3.20), the combined statement of the first and second laws for a closed system, can be written

$$dE = T\,dS - p\,dV \tag{1}$$

Thus, for a reversible process at constant E and V

$$(dS)_{E,\,V} = 0 \quad \text{(reversible)} \tag{2}$$

We have seen that a heat engine working in a cycle which has an irreversible step is less efficient than a Carnot engine working between the same two temperatures. Hence we have

$$(dS)_{E,\,V} > 0 \quad \text{(irreversible)} \tag{3}$$

Since spontaneous irreversible processes are moving toward equilibrium, we have from Eqs. (2) and (3) our first criterion of equilibrium, that for a closed system at constant internal energy and volume, the entropy is a maximum at equilibrium.

Since E is a state function and its differential is exact, we can write

$$dE = (\partial E/\partial S)_V\,dS + (\partial E/\partial V)_S\,dV \tag{4}$$

[1] G. N. Lewis and M. Randall, *op. cit.*, p. 130.

Thus, from Eqs. (1) and (4) we obtain the following relations,

$$(\partial E/\partial S)_V = T \tag{5}$$

and

$$(\partial E/\partial V)_S = -p \tag{6}$$

If we choose T and V as independent variables rather than S and V, we then have

$$dE = (\partial E/\partial T)_V \, dT + (\partial E/\partial V)_T \, dV \tag{7}$$

From Eq. (3.4), the heat capacity at constant volume is

$$C_V \equiv (\partial E/\partial T)_V \tag{8}$$

and we define the internal pressure as

$$p_i \equiv (\partial E/\partial V)_T \tag{9}$$

so that

$$dE = C_V \, dT + p_i \, dV \tag{10}$$

Similarly we have

$$dS = (\partial S/\partial T)_V \, dT + (\partial S/\partial V)_T \, dV \tag{11}$$

Substitution of Eq. (11) into Eq. (1) gives

$$dE = T(\partial S/\partial T)_V \, dT + [T(\partial S/\partial V)_T - p] \, dV \tag{12}$$

which when combined with Eq. (10) leads to the expressions for C_V and p_i in the fundamental quantities T, V, p, and S. They are

$$C_V = T(\partial S/\partial T)_V \tag{13}$$

and

$$p_i = T(\partial S/\partial V)_T - p \tag{14}$$

In the combined statement of the first and second laws, Eq. (1), we have an expression giving the internal energy as a function of entropy and volume. Often pressure and temperature are a more practical choice for independent variables. To achieve greater versatility in expressing the concepts of the first and second laws, we introduce the following three state functions:

the enthalpy,

$$H \equiv E + pV \tag{15}$$

the Helmholtz free energy,

$$A \equiv E - TS \tag{16}$$

the Gibbs' free energy,

$$G \equiv H - TS = E + pV - TS \tag{17}$$

All three are necessarily extensive properties. From Eqs. (15) and (1),

$$dH = dE + p \, dV + V \, dp = T \, dS + V \, dp \tag{18}$$

Thus for a process occurring at constant pressure, which frequently is the case in the laboratory, the change in enthalpy is the heat absorbed by the system. By definition, the heat capacity at constant pressure is

$$C_p \equiv (\partial H/\partial T)_p = T(\partial S/\partial T)_p \tag{19}$$

From Eq. (18) we see that, for a closed system at constant enthalpy and pressure, the entropy is a maximum at equilibrium.

Next we obtain from Eqs. (16) and (1),

$$dA = dE - T\,dS - S\,dT = -p\,dV - S\,dT \tag{20}$$

For isothermal processes then, the change in the Helmholtz free energy is the negative of the work done. Thus A is also known as the maximum work function. Lastly, from Eqs. (17) and (1) we have

$$dG = dE + p\,dV + V\,dp - T\,dS - S\,dT = V dp - S\,dT \tag{21}$$

If we now consider all kinds of work, then

$$dG = -(dw - p dV) + V\,dp - S\,dT \tag{22}$$

which at constant temperature and pressure becomes

$$dG = -(dw - p\,dV) \quad (T,\ p\ \text{constant}) \tag{23}$$

so that the change in G is the negative of the work done in excess of the pressure–volume work. From Eqs. (20) and (21) and our knowledge of entropy we obtain two additional criteria for equilibrium. In a closed system at constant temperature and volume the Helmholtz free energy is a minimum, and at constant temperature and pressure the Gibbs' free energy is a minimum.

Introduction of the functions H, A, and G has resulted in useful changes of the independent variables. The same basic concepts, however, are expressed by Eqs. (1), (18), (20), and (21). From these four expressions we readily obtain

$$T = (\partial E/\partial S)_V = (\partial H/\partial S)_p \tag{24}$$

$$-p = (\partial E/\partial V)_S = (\partial A/\partial V)_T \tag{25}$$

$$V = (\partial H/\partial p)_S = (\partial G/\partial p)_T \tag{26}$$

$$-S = (\partial A/\partial T)_V = (\partial G/\partial T)_p \tag{27}$$

Since the differentials are exact, the Euler reciprocity relationship, that, if

$$dx = u\,dy + v\,dz \tag{28}$$

then

$$(\partial u/\partial z)_y = (\partial v/\partial y)_z = \partial^2 x/\partial z\,\partial y \tag{29}$$

can be applied to the four preceding equations. Whence we have

$$(\partial T/\partial V)_S = -(\partial p/\partial S)_V \tag{30}$$

$$(\partial T/\partial p)_S = (\partial V/\partial S)_p \tag{31}$$

$$(\partial p/\partial T)_V = (\partial S/\partial V)_T \tag{32}$$

$$(\partial V/\partial T)_p = -(\partial S/\partial p)_T \tag{33}$$

which are known as the Maxwell relations.

Substitution of Eq. (32) into Eq. (14) gives

$$p_i = (\partial E/\partial V)_T = T(\partial p/\partial T)_V - p \tag{34}$$

This thermodynamic equation of state provides a useful relation between internal energy, temperature and pressure. For a mole of a perfect gas, $pV = RT$. Thus, for a perfect gas the internal pressure is zero and the internal energy is a function of temperature only.

Next we derive the relationship between the heat capacity at constant pressure and the heat capacity at constant volume. From Eqs. (19) and (18) we have

$$C_p = (\partial H/\partial T)_p = (\partial E/\partial T)_p + p(\partial V/\partial T)_p \tag{35}$$

We have from Eqs. (7) and (8)

$$(\partial E/\partial T)_p = C_V + (\partial E/\partial V)_T(\partial V/\partial T)_p \tag{36}$$

so that

$$C_p = C_V + [(\partial E/\partial V)_T + p](\partial V/\partial T)_p \tag{37}$$

Substitution of Eq. (34) then gives

$$C_p = C_V + T(\partial p/\partial T)_V(\partial V/\partial T)_p \tag{38}$$

The coefficient of thermal expansion is

$$\alpha = (1/V)(\partial V/\partial T)_p \tag{39}$$

and the coefficient of compressibility is

$$\beta = (-1/V)(\partial V/\partial p)_T \tag{40}$$

so that

$$\alpha/\beta = -(\partial V/\partial T)_p/(\partial V/\partial p)_T = (\partial p/\partial T)_V \tag{41}$$

Introducing Eqs. (39) and (41) into Eq. (38) we obtain

$$C_p = C_V + \frac{\alpha^2 V T}{\beta} \tag{42}$$

which is the relation required in Sect. 1.2, Eq. (1.2.38). Finally, we note that for a perfect gas

$$C_p = C_V + R \tag{43}$$

6. A Method to Determine the Relations between Thermodynamic Derivatives

Because of the very large number of mathematical relations between the thermodynamic properties and their derivatives, it is extremely useful to have a simple method to derive any desired partial derivative. We give a method[1] which can readily be extended to include variables other than the usual ones of thermodynamics. Given these eleven equations, the combined statement of the first and second laws, Eq. (5.1), the definitions of H, A, and G, Eqs. (5.15), (5.16) and (5.17), their differentials, Eqs. (5.18), (5.20) and (5.21), and two of the Maxwell relations, Eqs. (5.32) and (5.33), and the expressions for C_V and C_p of Eqs. (5.8) and (5.19), we can obtain any desired derivative. To illustrate the method we determine $(\partial G/\partial S)_H$, which we indicate as X. Then

$$dG = X\,dS + Y\,dH \tag{1}$$

Next we must specify the independent variables, and in our example we choose the frequently used pair, T and p. Then using the eleven given relations, we express the differentials of Eq. (1) in terms of dT and dp to obtain

$$dG = -S\,dT + V\,dp = X\,dS + Y(T\,dS + V\,dp) \tag{2}$$

Since dS can be written

$$dS = (\partial S/\partial T)_p\,dT + (\partial S/\partial p)_T\,dp$$
$$= (C_p/T)\,dT - (\partial V/\partial T)_p\,dp \tag{3}$$

Eq. (2) becomes

$$-S\,dT + V\,dp = X[(C_p/T)\,dT - (\partial V/\partial T)_p\,dp]$$
$$+ Y[C_p\,dT + (V - T(\partial V/\partial T)_p)\,dp] \tag{4}$$

Since Eq. (4) must hold both for $dT = 0$ and for $dp = 0$, we equate coefficients of dT and dp to obtain two simultaneous equations in X and Y,

$$-S = (C_p/T)X + C_p Y$$
$$V = -(\partial V/\partial T)_p X + [V - T(\partial V/\partial T)_p]Y \tag{5}$$

Equations (5) are then readily solved for X,

$$X = \left(\frac{\partial G}{\partial S}\right)_H = \frac{-V(S + C_p) + ST(\partial V/\partial T)_p}{C_p V/T}$$
$$= -T[C_p + S(1 + \alpha T)]/C_p \tag{6}$$

[1] A. Tobolsky, *J. Chem. Phys.*, **10**, 644 (1942). See G. N. Lewis and M. Randall, *op. cit.*, p. 667, and H. Margenau and G. M. Murphy, *op. cit.*, pp. 15–24, for additional methods.

7. Open Systems and the Chemical Potential

If we vary the mass of the system, the extensive thermodynamic properties must necessarily change. Accordingly, for an open system of one or more components each present in amount n_i, we write the combined statement of the first and second laws as follows:

$$dE = T\,dS - p\,dV + \sum_i \mu_i\,dn_i \tag{1}$$

where the summation is over all chemical species in the phase. Equation (1) serves to define the chemical potential, μ_i, of the ith component, for by the rule for partial differentiation we have

$$\mu_i \equiv (\partial E/\partial n_i)_{S,\,V,\,n_j \neq i} \tag{2}$$

The chemical potentials, as shown by Eq. (1), do not depend on the total amounts but rather on the relative amounts or composition of the system. Hence the μ_i's are intensive properties. Substitution of Eq. (1) into Eqs. (5.18), (5.20), and (5.21) gives the following additional expressions for the chemical potential,

$$\mu_i = (\partial H/\partial n_i)_{S,\,p,\,n_j \neq i} = (\partial A/\partial n_i)_{V,\,T,\,n_j \neq i} = (\partial G/\partial n_i)_{p,\,T,\,n_j \neq i} \tag{3}$$

From the rightmost equality of Eq. (3) we note that the chemical potential is equal to the partial molal free energy. As defined by G. N. Lewis,[1] the partial molal value of any extensive property X is

$$\overline{X}_i = (\partial X/\partial n_i)_{T,\,p,\,n_j \neq i} \tag{4}$$

Using Eq. (1) we can write the open system equivalent of Eq. (5.21) as

$$dG = V\,dp - S\,dT + \sum \mu_i\,dn_i \tag{5}$$

which at constant temperature and pressure becomes

$$dG = \sum \mu_i\,dn_i \quad (T,\ p\ \text{constant}) \tag{6}$$

Since the chemical potentials are intensive properties, Eq. (6) can be integrated, keeping T and p constant, by the device of increasing each n_i by an increment proportional to itself so that, while the total quantity is altered, the composition remains constant. Thus we have

$$G = \sum \mu_i n_i \tag{7}$$

The same result can be obtained from Eq. (1) and the definition of G. Using Euler's theorem that if f is a homogeneous function of order n of a set of variables y_i, then

$$nf = \sum_i y_i(\partial f/\partial y_i)$$

[1] G. N. Lewis and M. Randall, *op. cit.*, p. 203.

and observing that E is homogeneous and first order in the extensive properties S, V, and the n_i's, we have

$$E = (\partial E/\partial S)S + (\partial E/\partial V)V + \sum_i (\partial E/\partial n_i)n_i = TS - pV + \sum_i \mu_i n_i \quad (8)$$

and

$$G = E - TS + pV = \sum_i \mu_i n_i \quad (9)$$

Differentiation of Eq. (9) gives

$$dG = \sum_i \mu_i \, dn_i + \sum_i n_i \, d\mu_i \quad (10)$$

Subtracting this result from Eq. (5) results in the extended Gibbs–Duhem equation

$$V \, dp - S \, dT = \sum_i n_i \, d\mu_i \quad (11)$$

For constant T and p we have the more familiar form of the Gibbs–Duhem equation

$$\sum_i n_i \, d\mu_i = 0 \quad (12)$$

If we wish to describe a system consisting of a single phase and C components in terms of the $C+2$ intensive properties T, p, and $\mu_i \, .. \, \mu_C$, then from Eq. (11) we see that only $C+1$ of these quantities are independently variable. Moreover, if the system consists of several phases the Gibbs–Duhem relation applies to each phase, so that the number of independent variables is

$$f = C + 2 - P \quad (13)$$

where P is the number of phases. This is the Gibbs phase rule to relate the number of degrees of freedom of a system, the number of phases, and the number of components.

In a closed system in which chemical reactions are occurring the degrees of freedom are further reduced by the requirement of conservation of matter. For closed systems the mole fraction

$$x_i = n_i / \sum_j n_j \quad (14)$$

proves to be a convenient way to express composition. Thus for a binary system at constant T and p we have

$$x_1 \, d\mu_1 + (1 - x_1) \, d\mu_2 = 0 \quad (15)$$

By the Euler relation for second derivatives we obtain from Eq. (5)

$$\partial^2 G/\partial p \, \partial n_i = (\partial V/\partial n_i)_p = \bar{v}_i = (\partial \mu_i/\partial p)_{n_i} \quad (T, n_{j \neq i}, \text{ constant}) \quad (16)$$

For a perfect gas the partial molal volume, $\bar{v}_i$, is

$$\bar{v}_i = RT/p_i \quad (17)$$

Substituting Eq. (17) into Eq. (16) and integrating at constant T we obtain

$$\mu_i = \mu_i^0 + RT \ln (p_i/p_i^0) \quad (T \text{ constant}) \tag{18}$$

where μ_i^0 is the chemical potential and p_i^0 is the pressure of the standard state. If we choose $p_i^0 = 1$ atmosphere and note that μ_i^0 is a function of T, then

$$\mu_i = \mu_i^0(T) + RT \ln p_i \tag{19}$$

Thus for a binary system of perfect gases at constant temperature Eq. (15) becomes

$$x_1 \, d \ln p_1 + (1 - x_1) \, d \ln p_2 = 0 \tag{20}$$

which is the Duhem–Margules relation.

To include non-ideal systems we define the fugacity,[2] f_i, by the following equation

$$\mu_i = \mu_i^0(T) + RT \ln (f_i/f_i^0) \quad (T \text{ constant}) \tag{21}$$

and by the requirement that the fugacity of a perfect gas is equal to its pressure. The fugacity of the arbitrarily chosen standard state is denoted by f_i^0. The ratio of the fugacity of any given state to that of the standard state is called the activity, $a_i = f_i/f_i^0$, so that

$$\mu_i = \mu_i^0(T) + RT \ln a_i \tag{22}$$

The absolute activity, λ_i, is defined by [3]

$$\lambda_i = e^{\mu_i/kT} \tag{23}$$

8. Chemical Equilibrium

In Sect. 5 we stated several equivalent criteria of equilibrium. The last one stated, that for a closed system at constant temperature the Gibbs free energy is a minimum, is perhaps the most generally useful criterion. Thus for a system consisting of several components which can undergo chemical reaction we have, for constant T and p,

$$dG = \sum_i \mu_i \, dn_i + \sum_i n_i \, d\mu_i = 0 \tag{1}$$

at equilibrium. Introducing the Gibbs–Duhem relation, Eq. (7.12), reduces Eq. (1) to

$$dG = \sum_i \mu_i \, dn_i = 0 \quad \text{(at equilibrium)} \tag{2}$$

Thus, for the general chemical reaction

$$a\,A + b\,B + \ldots = l\,L + m\,M \ldots \tag{3}$$

occurring in a closed system, so that mass is conserved, we can write

$$dG = (\mu_A \, dn_A + \mu_B \, dn_B + \ldots) - (\mu_L \, dn_L + \mu_M \, dn_M + \ldots) \tag{4}$$

[2] G. N. Lewis and M. Randall, op. cit., p. 153.
[3] R. H. Fowler and E. A. Guggenheim, op. cit., p. 66.

From the stoichiometry of Eq. (3) we can relate the dn_i's of Eq. (4), for each component reacts or is produced in proportion to its stoichiometric number. Accordingly, we have

$$dn_A/a = dn_B/b = -dn_L/l = -dn_M/m \qquad (5)$$

If we denote the common ratio by dx, we obtain

$$dG = (a\mu_A + b\mu_B + \ldots - l\mu_L - m\mu_M - \ldots)\, dx = 0 \qquad (6)$$

at equilibrium. Since the variation in x is arbitrary, we have

$$a\mu_A + b\mu_B + \ldots - l\mu_L - m\mu_M - \ldots = 0 \qquad (7)$$

Next we express the chemical potentials in terms of the activities as defined in Eq. (7.22), and Eq. (7) becomes

$$(a\mu_A^0 + b\mu_B^0 + \ldots - l\mu_L^0 - m\mu_M^0 - \ldots) + RT \ln (a_A^a a_B^b \ldots / a_L^l a_M^m \ldots) = 0 \quad (8)$$

If the standard states chosen for the chemical potentials are the pure substances at a given pressure, the standard free energy change for the reaction is given by

$$\Delta G^0 = l\mu_L^0 + m\mu_M^0 + \ldots - a\mu_A^0 - b\mu_B^0 - \ldots \qquad (9)$$

Combining Eqs. (8) and (9) we have

$$-\Delta G^0/RT = \ln (a_L^l a_M^m \ldots / a_A^a a_B^b \ldots) = \ln K \qquad (10)$$

Thus at equilibrium the product of the activities each raised to the stoichiometrically appropriate power is constant, and by definition is the equilibrium constant

$$K = e^{-\Delta G^0/RT} \qquad (11)$$

For the special case of perfect gases Eq. (7.18) can be used to obtain the equilibrium constant in terms of the partial pressures.

4

CLASSICAL STATISTICAL MECHANICS

1. Phase Space

Consider a system of N molecules each with s degrees of freedom. As we have seen in Chapter 2 the motion of these molecules is described by Hamilton's equations of motion,

$$\dot{q}_i = \frac{\partial H}{\partial p_i} \qquad \dot{p}_i = -\frac{\partial H}{\partial q_i} \qquad i = 1, \ldots, Ns \tag{1}$$

which constitute $2Ns$ first order differential equations in $2Ns$ unknowns. Once all the values of the p_i and q_i are known at any one time the motion of these molecules is completely known for all time. Thus, in principle, the macroscopic properties of any system can be determined by a detailed investigation of the microscopic motion of the molecules constituting the system. However, if the system consists of a large number of molecules such a procedure quickly becomes highly complicated and loses its value. For this reason, in order to obtain a description of the macroscopic properties of such a system, we shall adopt a quite different procedure.

The behavior, in time, of this system can be graphically represented by means of a single trajectory in a $2Ns$ dimensional space which is determined by the $2Ns$ coordinates $p_1, \ldots, p_{Ns}, q_1, \ldots, q_{Ns}$. At any time the instantaneous state of the system is specified by the position of a *representative point* in this space. This space is called the *phase space* or Γ *space* of the system (gamma implying gas). Sometimes a phase space is used to represent the motion of a single molecule contained in the system. Such a phase space is called μ *space* (mu implying molecule). We could describe the system by plotting the orbit of each of N particles in μ space but this would give us an incomplete description of the system because an exchange of identical particles would not result in different orbits in Γ space. For this reason, we shall, in general, not consider μ space and, unless it is otherwise stated, phase space will mean Γ space.

The macroscopic properties of the system are thus time averages over a segment of the trajectory in phase space. Instead of following this procedure, it is much more advantageous to follow the suggestion of Gibbs. He suggested that instead of taking time averages we consider a large number of similar systems, each consisting of N molecules and Ns degrees of freedom, but whose representative points in phase space are suitably random so that every state accessible to the actual system in the course of time is represented by at least one system at any instant of time. Such a collection of similar systems is called an *ensemble*. We assume that there are so many systems in the ensemble that we can speak of the density $D(p_i, q_i, t)$ with which the representative points are distributed in phase space. Gibbs' suggestion was that we replace time averages over a single system by ensemble averages over the ensemble at a *fixed time*. Thus the average value of a function $A(p, q)$ is,

$$\overline{A(p_i, q_i)} = \frac{\int A(p_i, q_i) D(p_i, q_i) \, dq_1 \ldots dq_s}{\int D(p_i, q_i) \, dq_1 \ldots dp_s} \tag{2}$$

The equivalence of these two averages will be discussed in Sect. 3.

2. Liouville's Theorem

We shall now consider how the density of representative points changes with time. In considering how $D(p_i, q_i, t)$ changes with time we must distinguish between its rate of change with respect to a fixed point in phase space, which is $\partial D/\partial t$ since p_i and q_i will not vary, and its rate of change in a coordinate system moving with a particle through phase space, dD/dt. These two rates of change are related by

$$\frac{dD}{dt} = \frac{\partial D}{\partial t} + \sum_i \left(\frac{\partial D}{\partial p_i} \dot{p}_i + \frac{\partial D}{\partial q_i} \dot{q}_i \right) \tag{1}$$

We shall prove that $dD/dt = 0$. This is *Liouville's Theorem*[1] (Joseph Liouville, 1809–1882). Thus the density in phase space remains constant in the neighborhood of a particle which is moving in phase space. An equivalent statement of this theorem is that if $\delta\omega'$ is the volume occupied at time $t + dt$ by the representative points which occupied a volume $\delta\omega$ at time t then

$$\delta\omega = \delta\omega' \tag{2}$$

It is this property of conservation of volume in phase space during the motion that distinguishes phase space from any other space in which the motion of the system could be represented and which makes phase space important in the study of statistical mechanics. As we shall see, the fact that Hamilton's equations hold for the coordinates of phase space gives it this unique property.

---

[1] J. Liouville, *J. de Math.*, **3**, 348 (1838).

We now proceed to prove Liouville's theorem. The number of representative points N in a volume $\delta\omega$ at time t is given by

$$N = D(p_i, q_i, t)\,\delta\omega \tag{3}$$

This number will change with time because the number of representative points entering $\delta\omega$ through any 'face' will, in general, be different from the number which are leaving through the 'opposite face'. The number of representative points entering $\delta\omega$ during unit time through the 'face' at q_i will be

$$D\dot{q}_i\,\frac{\delta\omega}{\delta q_i} \tag{4}$$

and the number of points leaving $\delta\omega$ through the 'opposite face' is

$$\left(D + \frac{\partial D}{\partial q_i}\,\delta q_i\right)\left(\dot{q}_i + \frac{\partial \dot{q}_i}{\partial q_i}\,\delta q_i\right)\frac{\delta\omega}{\delta q_i} \tag{5}$$

where $\delta\omega/\delta q_i$ is the area of the 'face' (i.e. $\delta\omega$ divided by δq_i and not a partial derivative). Hence, the rate of change with time in the number of representative points lying within $\delta\omega$ is,

$$\frac{\partial N}{\partial t} = -\sum_i \left\{ D\left(\frac{\partial \dot{q}_i}{\partial q_i} + \frac{\partial \dot{p}_i}{\partial p_i}\right) + \left(\frac{\partial D}{\partial q_i}\,\dot{q}_i + \frac{\partial D}{\partial p_i}\,\dot{p}_i\right)\right\}\delta\omega \tag{6}$$

neglecting second order terms. From Hamilton's equations

$$\dot{q}_i = \frac{\partial H}{\partial p_i} \qquad \dot{p}_i = -\frac{\partial H}{\partial q_i} \tag{7}$$

we have,

$$\frac{\partial \dot{q}_i}{\partial q_i} = \frac{\partial^2 H}{\partial q_i \partial p_i} = -\frac{\partial \dot{p}_i}{\partial p_i} \tag{8}$$

and hence, substituting Eq. (8) in Eq. (6) yields

$$\frac{\partial N}{\partial t} = -\sum_i \left(\frac{\partial D}{\partial q_i}\,\dot{q}_i + \frac{\partial D}{\partial p_i}\,\dot{p}_i\right)\delta\omega \tag{9}$$

Dividing through by $\delta\omega$ gives

$$\frac{\partial D}{\partial t} = -\sum_i \left(\frac{\partial D}{\partial q_i}\,\dot{q}_i + \frac{\partial D}{\partial p_i}\,\dot{p}_i\right) \tag{10}$$

which combined with Eq. (1) yields

$$\frac{dD}{dt} = 0 \tag{11}$$

which completes the proof of Liouville's theorem.

If the system to be represented by an ensemble is in thermal equilibrium, then the ensemble averages must be independent of time, since the macroscopic properties of a system in thermal equilibrium do not change with time. Therefore, we may reasonably require that the composition of the ensemble be independent of time. In other words,

$$\frac{\partial D}{\partial t} = 0 \tag{12}$$

An ensemble satisfying Eq. (12) is called a *stationary ensemble* and we shall in general be concerned with this type of ensemble.

It can readily be shown that if D is a function of the energy ε alone the ensemble is stationary. To show this we note that

$$\frac{\partial D}{\partial q_j} = \frac{\partial D}{\partial \varepsilon} \frac{\partial \varepsilon}{\partial q_j} \qquad \frac{\partial D}{\partial p_j} = \frac{\partial D}{\partial \varepsilon} \frac{\partial \varepsilon}{\partial p_j} \tag{13}$$

But rewriting Hamilton's equations we have

$$\frac{\partial \varepsilon}{\partial q_j} = \frac{\partial H}{\partial q_j} = -\dot{p}_j \qquad \frac{\partial \varepsilon}{\partial p_j} = \frac{\partial H}{\partial p_j} = \dot{q}_j \tag{14}$$

which gives us:

$$\dot{q}_j \frac{\partial D}{\partial q_j} + \dot{p}_j \frac{\partial D}{\partial p_j} = \frac{\partial D}{\partial \varepsilon}(-\dot{q}_j\dot{p}_j + \dot{q}_j\dot{p}_j) = 0 \tag{15}$$

which combined with Eq. (10) yields the desired result, Eq. (12).

We shall find it convenient to work with a normalized density of representative points

$$\rho(p_i, q_i) = \frac{D(p_i, q_i)}{\int D(p_i, q_i)\,dq_1 \ldots dp_s} \tag{16}$$

3. The Ergodic Hypothesis and the Assumption of Equal *a Priori* Probabilities for Equal Volumes in Phase Space[1]

We have seen in Sect. 1 that our procedure in statistical mechanics is to replace averages over a single system by ensemble averages over the ensemble at a fixed time. In other words we assume that the probability of the system being in a specified state, at a given instant of time, is identical with the probability that a system, chosen at random from the ensemble, is in that state.

Boltzmann sought to justify this procedure by means of a postulate which he called the *ergodic hypothesis* which states that the representative

[1] For a further discussion the reader is referred to R. C. Tolman, *The Principles of Statistical Mechanics*, Oxford University Press, 1938, pp. 59–70.

point of an isolated system visits in succession every point in phase space compatible with the energy of the system before returning to its original position. Any system satisfying this postulate is then said to be *ergodic*. Assuming the ergodic hypothesis, Boltzmann was able to demonstrate the equivalence of time and ensemble averages. It was thought that the ergodic hypothesis was an actual consequence of the laws of mechanics and that it therefore provided a satisfactory basis for statistical mechanics.

Unfortunately, it is easy to construct non-ergodic systems. For example a molecule making perfectly elastic collisions normal to parallel walls and avoiding collisions with other molecules does not visit all phase points compatible with its energy. Further we can show that no mechanical system, except the trivial case with one degree of freedom, could possibly obey the ergodic hypothesis. For a system with Ns degrees of freedom there will be $2Ns$ constants of integration obtained by solving Hamilton's equations. One of these constants can be determined by the energy and another is specified by choosing a time scale. Any points on the trajectory of the representative point for the system with one set of assigned values to the remaining $2Ns - 2$ constants could never be reached from a point on the trajectory of the representative point for a system with even one of these $2Ns - 2$ constants different, since, if there did exist a point common to both trajectories, Hamilton's equations would not have a unique solution there.

Once it was realized that ergodic systems did not exist, attention was focused on the so-called *quasi-ergodic hypothesis* which states that the trajectory would in time come arbitrarily close to any point in phase space whose energy was compatible with that of the system. These studies, principally by von Neumann[2] and Birkhoff,[3] have shown that for nearly all physical systems one can replace a time average of a physical quantity by an ensemble average. However, these studies do not preclude the possibility of a trajectory whose ensemble average is different from its time average. Furthermore, the time averages are to be taken over an infinite period whereas actual measurements are concerned with finite time intervals.

To illustrate the point, we could again consider the solar system where there are orbits off the ecliptic plane which have the same energy as those on it, and hence are energetically possible, but in the 5 billion year history of the solar system only orbits near the ecliptic plane have been visited. Thus we see that it will take a long time indeed for the representative point of the solar system to come even remotely close to all the energetically possible points in phase space.

2 J. von Neumann, *Proc. Natl. Acad. Sci. U.S.*, **18**, 70, 263 (1932).
3 G. D. Birkhoff, *Proc. Natl. Acad. Sci. U.S.*, **17**, 650, 656 (1931).

In this connection it is useful to consider potential surfaces in configuration space. Consider for example the potential energy surface for the reaction

$$2 H_2 + O_2 \rightarrow 2 H_2O$$

Twelve distances between six atoms suffice to fix the relative configuration and therefore the potential energy. The corresponding potential surface will have low valley-like regions corresponding to the reactants $H_2 + O_2$ and lower valleys still corresponding to two H_2O molecules. If one starts with the reactants at room temperature in the absence of catalysts, it will take ages before any products will appear. Thus the system is metastable and is restricted to the part of phase space corresponding to reactants providing the period of observation is short compared to the duration of the characteristic time $1/V$, where V is the velocity of reaction, under the conditions of the experiment, per mole of product. In this case the ensemble representing the system should only embrace the phase space corresponding to reactants. On the other hand if the observation is made after a time large compared to $1/V$ the ensemble should embrace the phase space of both reactants and products. For intermediate times the degree of reaction must be taken into account in describing the intermediate state of the system. Similarly when sound is passed through a medium the degree of equilibration of internal degrees of freedom with the pressure wave must be considered in any useful statistical mechanical treatment. Thus for all experiments we have duration times, of the experiment, τ_i, which must be compared with the relaxation times of the system, $1/\mu_i$, under the conditions of the experiment, to decide what parts of phase space will be accessible and therefore what parts of phase space we should average over in calculating the properties and behavior of the system in question.

Because of the difficulties involved in basing statistical mechanics on the ergodic theorem, the modern approach (as discussed especially by Tolman) is to regard *without proof*, as a *fundamental postulate*, that *all accessible regions of phase space have equal* a priori *probabilities for equal volumes*. That is, the representative point of a system is equally likely to be in any region of phase space which it visits.

Since, as we shall see in Sect. 6, we can associate an equal area in phase space with each quantum state, this fundamental postulate implies that every allowed state of the system is equally probable. We have already used this postulate in Sect. 1.1 to derive Eq. (1.1.10).

This is the only possible non-arbitrary postulate, since we have seen in Sect. 2 that the laws of mechanics do not indicate any tendency for the representative points to favor any part of phase space visited, and hence crowd together there. In spite of the reasonableness of this procedure, it is to be emphasized that the justification for this postulate is the complete agreement of its applications with experimental findings.

Having considered the theoretical basis of our procedure we shall now obtain the Maxwell–Boltzmann distribution.

4. The Maxwell–Boltzmann Distribution

Before embarking on a study of statistical mechanics from the point of view of ensembles, we shall derive the Maxwell–Boltzmann distribution by a more elementary method for both historical reasons and to serve as an introduction to the more powerful procedures.

We consider a system consisting of N molecules, each molecule having s degrees of freedom. Each molecule will then have a representative point in the $2s$ dimensional μ space. We divide μ space into a number of cells each of whose volume is extremely small so that all molecules in the ith cell have the same energy ε_i. Let the number of allowed states associated with the energy ε_i (i.e. the degeneracy of ε_i) be g_i. Further we suppose that the state of the system is such that there are n_i molecules whose representative points lie in the ith cell.

We now calculate the number of ways of realizing this situation. In order to make this calculation, let us first calculate the number of ways of putting n_1 objects of N objects in one box, then n_2 objects out of $N-n_1$ in a second box, and so on until we have exhausted all of the objects. The number of ways of choosing n_1 objects out of N objects is given by

$$\frac{N!}{(N-n_1)!\, n_1!} \tag{1}$$

and the number of ways of choosing n_2 objects out of $N-n_1$ objects is

$$\frac{(N-n_1)!}{(N-n_1-n_2)!\, n_2!} \tag{2}$$

And so the number of ways of achieving this arrangement is

$$\frac{N!}{(N-n_1)!\, n_1!} \frac{(N-n_1)!}{(N-n_1-n_2)!\, n_2!} \cdots = \frac{N!}{n_1!\, n_2! \ldots} \tag{3}$$

If all the $g_i = 1$ this would be the number of ways that the system can be in a macroscopic state such that there are n_i molecules whose representative points are in the ith cell. But if g_i is different from unity then we must multiply Eq. (3) by $g_i^{n_i}$. Hence the number of ways of achieving a macroscopic state of the system such that n_i molecules have representative points in the ith cell is

$$W = N! \prod_i \frac{g_i^{n_i}}{n_i!} \tag{4}$$

We shall assume that the total number of molecules in the system is extremely large so that the number of molecules n_i whose representative points are in each cell is also large. Under these conditions we can regard W as a continuous function of the n_i.

We seek the most probable distribution of the n_i which we assume to be overwhelmingly more probable than any other distribution. To do this we must determine the values of n_i which make Eq. (4) a maximum subject to the constraining conditions:

$$\sum_i n_i = N \qquad \sum_i n_i \varepsilon_i = E \tag{5}$$

Since the set of n_i which gives W its maximum value also gives $\ln W$ its maximum value, we shall for convenience maximize $\ln W$,

$$\ln W = \ln N! + \sum_i (n_i \ln g_i - \ln n_i!) \tag{6}$$

subject to the constraining conditions Eq. (5). Since both N and all the n_i are very large compared to unity we can apply Stirling's approximation in the form,

$$\ln n! = n \ln n - n \tag{7}$$

which considerably simplifies Eq. (6) giving

$$\ln W = N \ln N - N + \sum_i (n_i \ln g_i - n_i \ln n_i + n_i)$$

$$= N \ln N + \sum_i (n_i \ln g_i - n_i \ln n_i) \tag{8}$$

To obtain the most probable distribution, we maximize Eq. (8) obtaining for the variation:

$$\delta \ln W = \sum_i \left(\ln g_i - \ln n_i - \frac{n_i}{n_i} \right) \delta n_i = 0 \tag{9}$$

$$\delta \ln W = \sum_i (\ln g_i - \ln n_i - 1) \delta n_i = 0 \tag{10}$$

and for the variation of Eq. (5)

$$\delta N = \sum_i \delta n_i = 0 \tag{11}$$

$$\delta E = \sum_i \varepsilon_i \delta n_i = 0 \tag{12}$$

If we multiply Eq. (11) by $\alpha + 1$ and Eq. (12) by $-\beta$ and add the resulting equations to Eq. (10) we have

$$\sum_i (\ln g_i - \ln n_i + \alpha - \beta \varepsilon_i) \delta n_i = 0 \tag{13}$$

We have two constraining conditions so all but two of the n_i can vary independently, and thus we can require

$$\ln g_i - \ln n_i + \alpha - \beta \varepsilon_i = 0 \tag{14}$$

for all but two values of i. However we can certainly choose the values of the two arbitrary parameters α and β so that Eq. (14) also holds true for the remaining two values of i. Solving for n_i we obtain

$$n_i = g_i \, e^{\alpha - \beta \varepsilon_i} \tag{15}$$

We can determine α from the condition

$$N = \sum_i n_i = e^{\alpha} \sum_i g_i \, e^{-\beta \varepsilon_i}$$

$$e^{\alpha} = \frac{N}{\sum_i g_i \, e^{-\beta \varepsilon_i}} \tag{16}$$

Referring back to Eq. (1.10.10) we note that $e^{\alpha} = e^{\mu/kT} = \lambda$, where λ is the absolute activity of a particle. Thus, Eq. (15) becomes

$$n_i = \frac{N g_i \, e^{-\beta \varepsilon_i}}{\sum_i g_i \, e^{-\beta \varepsilon_i}} \tag{17}$$

Since we have divided μ space into regions of extremely small volume to insure that every molecule in each cell has the same energy ε_i, it is more convenient to express this result in differential form. We do this by making the transitions,[1]

$$\varepsilon_i \rightarrow \varepsilon(p, q)$$

$$g_i \rightarrow dq_1 \ldots dp_s = d\omega \tag{18}$$

since g_i is proportional to the volume of the ith cell. Hence, we obtain for the number of molecules, dn, whose representative points lie in the region of μ space defined by the intervals $(q_i, q_i + dq_i)$, $(p_i, p_i + dp_i)$ the following,

$$dn = \frac{N \, e^{-\beta \varepsilon(p, q)} \, dq_1 \ldots dp_s}{\int e^{-\beta \varepsilon(p, q)} \, dq_1 \ldots dp_s} \tag{19}$$

We can calculate the value of β by finding the pressure that a perfect gas exerts on a wall of its container. Since a perfect gas has only kinetic energy, it follows from Eq. (19) that the number of molecules whose momenta lie in the interval bounded by p_x, p_y, p_z and $p_x + dp_x$, $p_y + dp_y$, $p_z + dp_z$ is

$$dn = \frac{N \, e^{-\beta(p_x^2 + p_y^2 + p_z^2)/2m} \, dx \, dy \, dz \, dp_x \, dp_y \, dp_z}{\int e^{-\beta(p_x^2 + p_y^2 + p_z^2)/2m} \, dx \, dy \, dz \, dp_x \, dp_y \, dp_z} \tag{20}$$

If a molecule moving in the x-direction with a velocity x strikes the wall perpendicular to the x-direction the total transfer of momentum will be

$$2m\dot{x} \tag{21}$$

---

[1] A further discussion of this transition will be found in Sect. 6.

Since all the molecules with velocity $\dot{x}$ in a cylinder of unit cross section and height $\dot{x}$ will collide with a unit area of the wall in unit time, then

$$\dot{x}\,dn/V \tag{22}$$

is the number of molecules of velocity $\dot{x}$ which collide with a unit area of the wall. The rate of transfer of momentum of these molecules is

$$2m\dot{x}^2\,dn/V = (2p_x^2/m)\,dn/V \tag{23}$$

Thus the total rate of transfer of momentum per unit area of the wall, which is the pressure exerted by the gas on the wall, is then

$$p = \frac{\dfrac{2N}{mV}\displaystyle\int p_x^2\,e^{-\beta(p_x{}^2+p_y{}^2+p_z{}^2)/2m}\,dx\,dy\,dz\,dp_x\,dp_y\,dp_z}{\displaystyle\int e^{-\beta(p_x{}^2+p_y{}^2+p_z{}^2)/2m}\,dx\,dy\,dz\,dp_x\,dp_y\,dp_z} \tag{24}$$

In the integrals of Eq. (24), the positional coordinates range over all values consistent with the dimensions of the container and the momenta range over all positive and negative values. Since total momentum transfer, Eq. (21), has been introduced in the numerator, integration of that integral from $p_x = 0$ to $p_x \to +\infty$ covers all possible values of p_x. Integrating over the positional coordinates and over p_y and p_z yields

$$p = \frac{\dfrac{2N}{mV}\displaystyle\int_0^\infty p_x^2\,e^{-\beta p_x{}^2/2m}\,dp_x}{\displaystyle\int_{-\infty}^\infty e^{-\beta p_x{}^2/2m}\,dp_x} \tag{25}$$

$$= \frac{4N}{\beta V}\frac{\displaystyle\int_0^\infty y^2\,e^{-y^2}\,dy}{\displaystyle\int_{-\infty}^\infty e^{-y^2}\,dy} = \frac{4N}{\beta V}\frac{\tfrac{1}{4}\sqrt{\pi}}{\sqrt{\pi}} \tag{26}$$

or
$$p = N/\beta V \tag{27}$$

Integral (2) of Appendix 2 has been used to obtain Eq. (26). But the perfect gas law is

$$pV = NkT \tag{28}$$

where k is *Boltzmann's constant* $(1.38 \times 10^{-16}$ ergs/degree). Thus we can make the identification

$$\beta = 1/kT \tag{29}$$

and Eq. (19) becomes

$$dn = \frac{N\,e^{-\varepsilon(p,\,q)/kT}\,d\omega}{\displaystyle\int e^{-\varepsilon(p,\,q)/kT}\,d\omega} \tag{30}$$

which is the famous *Maxwell–Boltzmann distribution function* [compare Eq. (1.1.10)].

5. Entropy in Statistical Mechanics

As a preliminary to this discussion let us calculate the entropy of one mole of a perfect gas from the combined first and second laws of thermodynamics

$$T \, dS = dE + p \, dV \tag{1}$$

But for one mole of a perfect gas

$$E = C_V T \qquad pV = RT \tag{2}$$

Hence,

$$S = C_V \ln T + R \ln V + C \tag{3}$$

where C is a constant. If we have one mole each of two different perfect gases contained in vessels of equal volume at the same temperature and pressure, but separated by a partition, then the entropies of the two gases are

$$S_A = C_V \ln T + R \ln V + C$$

$$S_B = C_V \ln T + R \ln V + C \tag{4}$$

If the partition is removed and the gases allowed to diffuse into one another, then the entropy of the mixture is

$$S_{A+B} = 2C_V \ln T + 2R \ln 2V + 2C$$

$$= 2C_V \ln T + 2R \ln 2 + 2R \ln V + 2C \tag{5}$$

$$S_{A+B} = S_A + S_B + 2R \ln 2 \tag{6}$$

Thus, from purely thermodynamic reasoning we see that the entropy of the mixture is greater than the combined entropy of the separated gases.

As a result of the diffusion of the different perfect gases we have lost a certain degree of knowledge about the gases, since before the partition was removed, knowledge of the position of a molecule also gave knowledge of its species whereas this is no longer true after the partition is removed. In other words, an element of randomness has been introduced into the system. Because of this it is reasonable to postulate a relationship between the entropy of a system and the randomness or degree of disorder of the system in the given state. Thus,

$$S = f(W) \tag{7}$$

where W is the number of *a priori* equally probable states accessible to the system, which is proportional to the total volume of accessible phase space.

If we consider two separate systems with entropies S_1 and S_2 then,

$$S_1 = f(W_1)$$
$$S_2 = f(W_2) \tag{8}$$

Thermodynamics tells us that the entropy of the combined system is

$$S = S_1 + S_2 \tag{9}$$

But, since the systems are independent, the number of *a priori* equally probable states is

$$W_1 W_2 \tag{10}$$

Thus

$$S_1 + S_2 = f(W_1 W_2) \tag{11}$$

The only functional relationship that can exist between S and W satisfying Eq. (11) is

$$S = k' \ln W + C \tag{12}$$

where k' and C are some constants. But if as in Sect. 1.2 we assume that W is one at absolute zero, then the third law of thermodynamics allows us to set C equal to zero. Let us now evaluate k'. From Eq. (4.4) we have

$$W = \sum_{\{n_i\}} W\{n_i\} = \sum_{\{n_i\}} N! \prod_i \frac{g_i^{n_i}}{n_i!} \tag{13}$$

the summation being over all possible sets of the n_i. But since the most probable distribution of the n_i is overwhelmingly more probable than any other, only the most probable distribution of the n_i will contribute to W so that

$$W = N! \prod_i \frac{g_i^{n_i}}{n_i!} \tag{14}$$

where

$$n_i = \frac{N g_i e^{-\varepsilon_i/kT}}{\sum_i g_i e^{-\varepsilon_i/kT}} \tag{15}$$

Thus

$$S = k' \ln W = k'[\ln N! + \sum_i (n_i \ln g_i - \ln n_i!)] \tag{16}$$

Applying Stirling's approximation

$$S = k'[N \ln N - N + \sum_i (n_i \ln g_i - n_i \ln n_i + n_i)]$$

$$= k'[N \ln N + \sum_i (n_i \ln g_i - n_i \ln n_i)]$$

$$= k'[N \ln N + \sum_i \{n_i \ln g_i - n_i(\ln N + \ln g_i - \varepsilon_i/kt$$
$$- \ln \sum_i g_i e^{-\varepsilon_i/kT})\}]$$

$$= k' \left[N \ln \sum_i g_i e^{-\varepsilon_i/kT} + \sum_i \frac{n_i \varepsilon_i}{kT} \right]$$

$$S = k' \left[N \ln \sum_i g_i e^{-\varepsilon_i/kT} + \frac{E}{kT} \right] \tag{17}$$

Thus

$$\left(\frac{\partial S}{\partial E}\right)_V = \frac{k'}{kT} \tag{18}$$

But thermodynamics, Eq. (3.5.5), informs us that

$$\left(\frac{\partial S}{\partial E}\right)_V = \frac{1}{T} \tag{19}$$

and hence we have that k' is Boltzmann's constant, and this gives the famous *Boltzmann relation*

$$S \equiv k \ln W \tag{20}$$

which provides us with a bridge between thermodynamics and statistical mechanics.[1]

6. The Partition Function; Thermodynamic Properties

Combining Eqs. (5.17) and (5.20) we have

$$S = Nk \ln \sum_i g_i e^{-\varepsilon_i/kT} + \frac{E}{T} \tag{1}$$

and so,

$$A = E - TS = -NkT \ln \sum_i g_i e^{-\varepsilon_i/kT} \tag{2}$$

or,

$$\frac{A}{N} = -kT \ln f \tag{3}$$

where

$$f = \sum_i g_i e^{-\varepsilon_i/kT} \tag{4}$$

[1] We shall defer a section on the law of increasing entropy until later.

is called the *partition function*. Equation (3) is the same as Eq. (1.2.23), which was derived in a somewhat different manner. With the aid of the partition function we can derive all of the ten thermodynamic functions (as was done in Sect. 1.2).

We might be inclined, as was historically the case, to make the transition to an integral by the transitions used in obtaining Eq. (4.19), i.e.

$$\varepsilon_i \to \varepsilon(p, q)$$
$$g_i \to d\omega$$

However, this would yield a partition function with the dimensions of $(\text{gram-cm}^2\text{-sec}^{-1})^s = (\text{erg-sec})^s$ whereas Eq. (4) is dimensionless. In order to investigate this anomaly further we consider the case of a single one-dimensional harmonic oscillator, defined by the potential,

$$V = \tfrac{1}{2}aq^2 \tag{5}$$

The total energy of the oscillator is then

$$\varepsilon(p, q) = \frac{p^2}{2m} + \tfrac{1}{2}aq^2 \tag{6}$$

and so the curves of constant energy are ellipses in μ space as is illustrated in Figure 1.

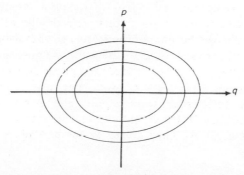

Figure 1. Constant energy paths in μ space for a one-dimensional harmonic oscillator.

The area of the ellipse is given by

$$I = \oint p \, dq \tag{7}$$

The integration is carried out over one complete period of the oscillator.

Classically any ellipse in μ space would represent a state of the oscillator, but in quantum mechanics, the Wilson–Sommerfeld quantization rule[1] requires that

$$\oint p \, dq = nh \tag{8}$$

[1] A. Sommerfeld, *Münchener Ber.*, **1915**, 425, 459; **1916**, 131; W. Wilson, *Phil. Mag.*, **29**, 795 (1915).

where h is Planck's constant $(6.62 \times 10^{-27}$ erg-sec$)$ and n is some integer. The allowed energy surfaces then subdivide μ phase into regions of area h.

This result can be generalized to include systems with many degrees of freedom. We can say that for a system of s degrees of freedom the energy surfaces corresponding to allowed states subdivide μ space into regions of volume h^s. In other words we can associate a volume h^s with each quantum state. Therefore, we would expect that,[2]

$$\varepsilon_i \to \varepsilon(p, q)$$
$$g_i \to d\omega/h^s \tag{9}$$

in making the transition to an integral.

Thus, the partition function becomes

$$f = \sum_i g_i \, e^{-\varepsilon_i/kT} \qquad \text{(quantum)} \tag{10}$$

$$f = \frac{1}{h^s} \int e^{-\varepsilon/kT} \, d\omega \quad \text{(classical)} \tag{11}$$

and is dimensionless in both cases.

There is another quantum mechanical effect which we must discuss. In quantum mechanics a system is described by means of different states each of which is designated by means of quantum numbers. If the N particles of the system are identical then interchange of two or more particles will not change the state of the system so that these are different micro-situations all corresponding to the same macroscopic state of the system. For the case of a system of localized particles, such as a crystal, this indistinguishability of particles does not affect what we have done thus far since there are $N!$ ways of putting the particles onto the distinguishable lattice sites. However, in the case of a system of non-localized particles, such as a gas, we must divide W by $N!$. This is equivalent to replacing $(f)^N$ by

$$\frac{(f)^N}{N!} \tag{12}$$

which would lead to replacing our former expressions for A and S by

$$A = -NkT \ln \sum_i g_i \, e^{-\varepsilon_i/kT} + kT \ln N! \tag{13}$$

$$S = Nk \ln \sum_i g_i \, e^{-\varepsilon_i/kT} - k \ln N! + \frac{E}{T} \tag{14}$$

It is to be emphasized that the introduction of the factors h^s, and $N!$ for identical particles, to our results is wholly a result of quantum mech-

[2] For a more detailed discussion of this transition the reader is referred to D. ter Haar, *Elements of Statistical Mechanics*, Rinehart, New York, 1954, pp. 59–60.

anics and Eqs. (9) to (14) are really quasi-classical results. Historically, classical statistical mechanics was based on a partition function which lacked these factors. In many cases the factors h^s and $N!$ do not affect the expressions for the thermodynamic functions since a ratio of partition functions or a derivative of the logarithm of a partition function is involved. However, in the case of A and S the introduction of these factors is significant and for this reason classical statistical mechanics leads to paradoxes, such as Gibbs' paradox which we shall discuss in the next section, and also is incapable of dealing with such concepts as absolute entropy. Henceforth our discussion of classical statistical mechanics would be more correctly described as quasi-classical statistical mechanics.

7. Application—Perfect Monatomic Gas; Gibbs' Paradox

We consider a perfect monatomic gas enclosed in a volume V. The energy of one atom of this perfect monatomic gas is given by

$$\varepsilon = \frac{p_x^2 + p_y^2 + p_z^2}{2m} + U \tag{1}$$

where

$$U = 0, \quad \text{inside } V$$

$$U = \infty, \text{ outside } V \tag{2}$$

The partition function becomes

$$f = \frac{1}{h^3} \int_{-\infty}^{\infty} e^{-(p_x^2 + p_y^2 + p_z^2)/2mkT} dp_x\, dp_y\, dp_z \int_V dx\, dy\, dz$$

$$= \frac{V}{h^3} \int_{-\infty}^{\infty} e^{-p_x^2/2mkT} dp_x \int_{-\infty}^{\infty} e^{-p_y^2/2mkT} dp_y \int_{-\infty}^{\infty} e^{-p_z^2/2mkT} dp_z$$

$$f = \left(\frac{2\pi mkT}{h^2}\right)^{\frac{3}{2}} V \tag{3}$$

where integral (2) of Appendix 2 has been used. And so the Helmholtz function for N molecules is

$$A = -NkT \ln\left(\frac{2\pi mkT}{h^2}\right)^{\frac{3}{2}} V + kT \ln N! \tag{4}$$

or using Stirling's formula

$$A = -NkT \ln\left(\frac{2\pi mkT}{h^2}\right)^{\frac{3}{2}} V + NkT \ln N - NkT \tag{5}$$

and some of the other thermodynamic properties are:

$$E = NkT^2 \frac{\partial}{\partial T} \ln \left(\frac{2\pi mkT}{h^2}\right)^{\frac{3}{2}} \frac{V}{N!} = \tfrac{3}{2}NkT \tag{6}$$

$$C_V = \tfrac{3}{2}Nk \tag{7}$$

$$p = -\left(\frac{\partial A}{\partial V}\right)_T = \frac{NkT}{V} \tag{8}$$

$$S = \frac{E-A}{T} = \tfrac{5}{2}Nk + Nk \ln \left(\frac{2\pi mkT}{h^2}\right)^{\frac{3}{2}} V - Nk \ln N \tag{9}$$

which is called the *Sackur–Tetrode equation*.[1]

At this point we should discuss a famous paradox, called Gibbs' paradox since it was first pointed out by Willard Gibbs. Consider two separated volumes containing different gas molecules. For simplicity we consider the volumes as equal and as containing equal numbers of molecules. Hence they are at equal pressures. Thus, the entropy of each of the two volumes of molecules is

$$S_A = \tfrac{5}{2}Nk + Nk \ln \left(\frac{2\pi m_A kT}{h^2}\right)^{\frac{3}{2}} V - Nk \ln N$$

$$S_B = \tfrac{5}{2}Nk + Nk \ln \left(\frac{2\pi m_B kT}{h^2}\right)^{\frac{3}{2}} V - Nk \ln N \tag{10}$$

If the two systems are placed in contact, the pressure remaining the same, then, since the volume of the mixture is $2V$, we gain on application of Eq. (5.6).

$$S_{A+B} = \tfrac{5}{2}Nk + \tfrac{5}{2}Nk + Nk \ln \left(\frac{2\pi m_A kT}{h^2}\right)^{\frac{3}{2}} (2V)$$

$$+ Nk \ln \left(\frac{2\pi m_B kT}{h^2}\right)^{\frac{3}{2}} (2V) - Nk \ln N - Nk \ln N$$

$$= S_A + S_B + 2Nk \ln 2 \tag{11}$$

So that the entropy of the mixture exceeds the combined entropy of the separated gases by the factor

$$2Nk \ln 2$$

as we have seen in Sect. 5. If two equal volumes containing equal numbers of *identical* molecules were mixed then application of Eq. (5.6) would lead us to expect an increase of entropy by the above factor. On the other hand no element of randomness has been introduced by the mixing so

[1] O. Sackur, *Ann. Physik*, [4], **36**, 598 (1911); **40**, 67 (1913); H. Tetrode, *ibid.* [4], **38**, 434 (1912).

that no increase of entropy should occur. How are we to resolve this paradox? Central to our problem is the fact that Eq. (5.6) is based on the presence of N identical molecules whereas we have, on mixing the two volumes, $2N$ identical molecules. In other words instead of replacing $(f)^N$ by $(f)^N/N!$ we should replace it by $(f)^{2N}/(2N)!$ or instead of Eq. (6.13) we have,

$$A = -2NkT \ln \sum_i g_i e^{-\varepsilon_i/kT} + kT \ln(2N)!$$

Thus,

$$A = -2NkT \ln \left(\frac{2\pi mkT}{h^2}\right)^{\frac{3}{2}} 2V + 2NkT \ln 2N - 2NkT \tag{12}$$

and

$$E = \tfrac{3}{2}(2N)kT \tag{13}$$

so that

$$S = \frac{E-A}{T} = \tfrac{5}{2}(2N)kT + 2NkT \ln \left(\frac{2\pi mkT}{h^2}\right)^{\frac{3}{2}} V - 2NkT \ln N$$

$$S = S_A + S_B \tag{14}$$

The resolution of this paradox, which puzzled as brilliant a man as Gibbs, provides us with an excellent example of the success of quantum mechanics in eliminating some of the unsolved problems of classical physics.

8. The Principle of Equipartition of Energy

In Sect. 2.5 we observed that the kinetic energy, $\mathcal{T}$[1] was a quadratic homogeneous function of the $\dot{q}_i$.

$$\mathcal{T} = \sum_{ij} a_{ij} \dot{q}_i \dot{q}_j \tag{1}$$

The generalized momentum, p_i, conjugate to q_i is

$$p_i = \frac{\partial \mathcal{T}}{\partial \dot{q}_i} = 2 \sum_j a_{ij} \dot{q}_j \tag{2}$$

If we solve these equations for the $\dot{q}_j$ in terms of the generalized momenta and express $\mathcal{T}$ as a function of the p_i, $\mathcal{T}$ will be a homogeneous quadratic function of the p_i and Euler's Theorem can be applied to $\mathcal{T}$ yielding

$$\sum_{i=1}^{s} p_i \frac{\partial \mathcal{T}}{\partial p_i} = 2\mathcal{T} \tag{3}$$

The average value of the kinetic energy of a molecule is then

$$\bar{\mathcal{T}} = \frac{\int \mathcal{T} e^{-\varepsilon/kT} d\omega}{\int e^{-\varepsilon/kT} d\omega} \tag{4}$$

---

[1] In order to avoid confusion with temperature, which has been denoted by the symbol T, in this section the symbol $\mathcal{T}$ is used to denote kinetic energy.

Applying Euler's Theorem as in Eq. (3) gives

$$\bar{\mathscr{T}} = \frac{\displaystyle\sum_{i=1}^{s} \frac{1}{2} \int \frac{\partial \mathscr{T}}{\partial p_i} p_i e^{-\varepsilon/kT} \, d\omega}{\displaystyle\int e^{-\varepsilon/kT} \, d\omega}$$

$$= \frac{\displaystyle\sum_{i=1}^{s} \frac{kT}{2} \int p_i \frac{d}{dp_i} (-e^{-\varepsilon/kT}) \, d\omega}{\displaystyle\int e^{-\varepsilon/kT} \, d\omega} \tag{5}$$

since $\varepsilon = \mathscr{T} + V$ with only $\mathscr{T}$ depending on p_i. Integrating by parts gives

$$\bar{\mathscr{T}} = \frac{\displaystyle\sum_{i=1}^{s} \frac{kT}{2} \int{}' \left[-p_i e^{-\varepsilon/kT} \Big|_{p_i=-\infty}^{\infty} + \int e^{-\varepsilon/kT} \, dp_i \right] d\omega'}{\displaystyle\int e^{-\varepsilon/kT} \, d\omega} \tag{6}$$

where $d\omega' = dq_1 \ldots dq_s, dp_1 \ldots dp_{i-1}, dp_{i+1} \ldots dp_s$. The integrated parts are zero so,

$$\bar{\mathscr{T}} = \frac{\displaystyle\sum_{i=1}^{s} \frac{kT}{2} \int e^{-\varepsilon/kT} \, d\omega}{\displaystyle\int e^{-\varepsilon/kT} \, d\omega} = s \frac{kT}{2} \tag{7}$$

For every degree of freedom we get a contribution of $\frac{1}{2}kT$ to the average kinetic energy of the molecule.

In certain cases, for example harmonic vibration, the potential energy will contain t squared coordinates. If this is so, then,

$$\bar{U} = t \cdot \tfrac{1}{2}kT \tag{8}$$

using reasoning similar to that used in obtaining Eq. (7). We can say that every degree of freedom contributing to the kinetic energy and every degree of freedom contributing a quadratic term to the potential energy of a molecule contributes

$$\tfrac{1}{2}kT \tag{9}$$

to the total energy of the molecule.

A monatomic molecule will have three degrees of freedom contributing to its kinetic energy and no quadratic terms contributing to its potential energy, giving for the average energy of such a molecule

$$\bar{E} = \tfrac{3}{2}kT \tag{10}$$

which is in accord with Eq. (7.6).

9. The Microcanonical Ensemble

Let us consider an isolated system composed of a large number, N, of molecules having total energy $\mathscr{E}_0$. Since the system is isolated, the energy $\mathscr{E}_0$ is a constant, independent of time. In order to obtain the macroscopic properties of this system, we must find an appropriate ensemble of similar systems. The representative points of such an ensemble must be uniformly distributed in the accessible regions of phase space (to give equal *a priori* probabilities to equal volumes of phase space). The ensemble described by the density

$$\rho(\mathscr{E}) = \text{constant} \qquad \mathscr{E}_0 \leqslant \mathscr{E} \leqslant \mathscr{E}_0 + \delta\mathscr{E} \tag{1}$$

$$\rho(\mathscr{E}) = 0 \qquad\qquad \text{elsewhere}$$

satisfies these requirements. Such an ensemble is called a *microcanonical ensemble*. Since ρ is a function of $\mathscr{E}$ alone the microcanonical is a stationary ensemble. Thus the microcanonical ensemble is appropriate to represent a system of known energy in a macroscopically steady state.

Since the meaning of Eq. (1) is that the energy of the system is a constant and that equal volumes of accessible phase space have equal *a priori* probabilities, the microcanonical ensemble yields no more information than we obtained by more elementary means in Sects. 4 to 8. Nevertheless Eq. (1) will prove useful in deriving the density for the *canonical ensemble*, which allows for a relaxation of the condition of $\mathscr{E}$ being constant.

10. The Canonical Ensemble

Following Gibbs, the canonical ensemble is defined by the density,

$$\rho(\mathscr{E}) = C\, e^{-\mathscr{E}/kT} \tag{1}$$

$\mathscr{E}$ being the energy of the entire system. As we shall see the canonical ensemble can be used to represent a system in thermal contact with a heat reservoir.

In order to prove this point we follow the interesting argument of Kittel,[1] which is similar to the method of compounding an unknown with a known system discussed in Sect. 1.1. Let us consider a microcanonical ensemble representing a very large isolated system. We wish to consider the behavior of a constituent subsystem of this isolated system which is in thermal equilibrium with the rest of the system. We shall denote the properties of the subsystem by the subscript s, properties of the remainder of the total system (which acts as a heat reservoir) by the subscript r, and the properties of the total system by the subscript t. Since the total system is

---

[1] C. Kittel, *Elementary Statistical Physics*, Wiley, New York, 1958, pp. 45–57.

isolated its energy, $\mathcal{E}_t = \mathcal{E}_s + \mathcal{E}_r$, is constant. As the total system is part of a microcanonical ensemble, the probability dp_t that the representative point of the total system is in an element $d\Omega_t$ of phase space is

$$dp_t = C' \, d\Omega_t \tag{2}$$

for $\mathcal{E}_t \leqslant \mathcal{E} \leqslant \mathcal{E}_t + d\mathcal{E}_t$ and

$$dp_t = 0 \tag{3}$$

otherwise, C' being a constant. We may write

$$d\Omega_t = d\Omega_s \, d\Omega_r \tag{4}$$

where $d\Omega_s$ contains only the coordinates and momenta belonging to the subsystem and $d\Omega_r$ contains only the coordinates and momenta of the reservoir. Hence

$$dp_t = C' \, d\Omega_s \, d\Omega_r \tag{5}$$

for $\mathcal{E}_t \leqslant \mathcal{E} \leqslant \mathcal{E}_t + d\mathcal{E}_t$ and

$$dp_t = 0 \tag{6}$$

otherwise.

We seek the probability dp_s that the representative point of the subsystem is in the volume element $d\Omega_s$, without specifying the condition of the reservoir but still requiring that $\mathcal{E}_t$ be a constant. Thus,

$$dp_s = C' \, d\Omega_s \, \Delta\Omega_r \tag{7}$$

where $\Delta\Omega_r$ is the volume of phase space accessible to the representative point of the reservoir if the representative point of the subsystem is in $d\Omega_s$. Let us evaluate $\Delta\Omega_r$.

Since each accessible state of the reservoir is associated with a volume h^m, the entropy of the reservoir is

$$S_r = k \ln \frac{\Delta\Omega_r}{h^m} \tag{8}$$

where m is the number of degrees of freedom of the reservoir, and thus,

$$\Delta\Omega_r = h^m \, e^{S_r/k} \tag{9}$$

Since the subsystem is small in comparison with the total system we have that $\mathcal{E}_r \ll \mathcal{E}_t$ and so, using a Taylor's expansion, we have

$$S_r(\mathcal{E}_r) = S_r(\mathcal{E}_t - \mathcal{E}_s) = S_r(\mathcal{E}_t) - \left(\frac{\partial S_r}{\partial \mathcal{E}_r}\right)_{\mathcal{E}_r = \mathcal{E}_t} \mathcal{E}_s + \dots \tag{10}$$

Thus, from (9)

$$\Delta\Omega_r = h^m \, e^{S_r/k} \exp\left[-(\partial S_r/\partial \mathcal{E}_r)_{\mathcal{E}_r = \mathcal{E}_t} \mathcal{E}_s/k\right] \tag{11}$$

But from thermodynamics, Eq. (3.5.5), we have, since $\mathcal{E}_r \sim \mathcal{E}_t$,

$$\frac{\partial S_r}{\partial \mathcal{E}_r} = \frac{1}{T} \tag{12}$$

where T is the absolute temperature of every part of the system. Then,

$$\Delta\Omega_r = h^m \, e^{S_r/k}(e^{-\mathscr{E}_s/kT}) \tag{13}$$

and hence the probability that the representative point of the subsystem be in the volume $d\Omega_s$ is

$$dp_s = C \, e^{-\mathscr{E}_s/kT} \, d\Omega_s \tag{14}$$

where C is a constant determined by the normalization condition

$$C \int e^{-\mathscr{E}_s/kT} \, d\Omega_s = 1 \tag{15}$$

Equation (14) justifies our statement that the canonical ensemble represents a system in thermal contact with a heat reservoir.

The average value of a property $P(p, q)$ over a canonical distribution is then

$$\bar{P} = \frac{\int P(p, q) \, e^{-\mathscr{E}(p, q)/kT} \, d\Omega}{\int e^{-\mathscr{E}(p, q)/kT} \, d\Omega} \tag{16}$$

The strong resemblance between the canonical ensemble and the Maxwell–Boltzmann distribution function, Eq. (4.30), should be noted. Indeed, we could look upon the canonical ensemble as consisting of a system of 'molecules' which are weakly interacting.

In the case where the system of interest contains a large number of particles then nearly all the systems in the ensemble have energies which differ only slightly from the average of the ensemble. This makes it possible to use canonical ensembles to represent systems of interest which have defined energies. We shall discuss this point in more detail in Sect. 13.

One further property of the canonical ensemble is of interest. If two canonical ensembles, representing two systems in thermal contact, are coupled together, the resulting ensemble is again a canonical ensemble. Let the properties of the first system be denoted by the index 1 and the corresponding properties of the second system by the index 2. Then,

$$\ln \rho_1 = \ln C_1 - (\mathscr{E}_1/kT)$$
$$\ln \rho_2 = \ln C_2 - (\mathscr{E}_2/kT) \tag{17}$$

and adding

$$\ln \rho_1 \rho_2 = \ln C_1 C_2 - [(\mathscr{E}_1 + \mathscr{E}_2)/kT] \tag{18}$$

so that with $\quad \rho = \rho_1 \rho_2, \quad C = C_1 C_2 \quad$ and $\quad \mathscr{E} = \mathscr{E}_1 + \mathscr{E}_2$

we have

$$\ln \rho = \ln C - (\mathscr{E}/kT) \tag{19}$$

showing that the coupled ensemble is also canonical.

11. Thermodynamic Functions from the Canonical Ensemble

We can extend our definition of entropy to the case of the canonical ensemble by defining the entropy of a canonical ensemble whose mean energy is E as being equal to the entropy of a microcanonical ensemble with energy E. We may do this because from thermodynamics we know that the entropy is quite independent of whether the system is isolated or in thermal contact with a heat reservoir.

By definition of the entropy, S, we have

$$S = k \ln \frac{\delta\Omega}{h^{Ns}} \tag{1}$$

N being the number of particles in the system, s the number of degrees of freedom of each particle, and $\delta\Omega$ the volume of phase space corresponding to energies between E and $E+\delta E$. We can gain an estimate for $\delta\Omega$ by requiring that δE be equal to the range of reasonably probable values of the energy of the canonical ensemble, i.e. by requiring that

$$\rho(E)\delta\Omega = 1 \tag{2}$$

Equation (2) follows from the fact that we know that the particles of the microcanonical ensemble must lie in $\delta\Omega$ and their density $\rho(E)$ in $\delta\Omega$ is a constant. Hence,

$$\delta\Omega = 1/\rho(E) = e^{E/kT}/C \tag{3}$$

and

$$S = k \ln (e^{E/kT}/h^{Ns}C) = -k \ln h^{Ns}C + E/T \tag{4}$$

Thus,

$$A = E - TS = kT \ln Ch^{Ns} \tag{5}$$

But we have the normalization condition,

$$\int C\, e^{-\mathscr{E}/kT}\, d\Omega = 1$$

and so since C is a constant,

$$\frac{1}{C} = \int e^{-\mathscr{E}/kT}\, d\Omega \tag{6}$$

Hence we have

$$A = -kT \ln f_N \tag{7}$$

where

$$f_N = \frac{1}{h^{Ns}} \int e^{-\mathscr{E}/kT}\, d\Omega \tag{8}$$

f_N is called the *system partition function* and plays a role similar to the partition function, f, for one particle, except that

$$f_N = (f)^N \tag{9}$$

for a system of localized particles.

For the case of non-localized particles we have

$$f_N = (f)^N/N! \tag{10}$$

12. Application—Perfect Monatomic Gas

In Sect. 7 we treated the perfect monatomic gas, enclosed in a volume V, by means of the microcanonical ensemble. We shall now return to this example and apply the method of the canonical ensemble.

We must evaluate

$$f_N = \frac{1}{h^{3N}N!} \int e^{-\mathscr{E}/kT} \, d\Omega \tag{1}$$

The energy of the system is

$$\mathscr{E} = \sum_{i=1}^{3N} \frac{p_i^2}{2m} + U \tag{2}$$

where

$$U = 0 \qquad \text{inside } V$$
$$U = \infty \qquad \text{outside } V \tag{3}$$

Now

$$d\Omega = \prod_{i=1}^{3N} dq_i \, dp_i \tag{4}$$

Thus,

$$f_N = \frac{V^N}{h^{3N}N!} \int e^{-\sum_i p_i^2/2mkT} \prod_i dp_i$$

$$= \frac{V^N}{h^{3N}N!} \prod_i \int_{-\infty}^{\infty} e^{-p_i^2/2mkT} \, dp_i$$

Hence, using Integral (2) of Appendix 2, we have

$$f_N = \frac{V^N}{N!} \left(\frac{2\pi mkT}{h^2} \right)^{\frac{3}{2}N} \tag{5}$$

Thus, the Helmholtz function for N particles is

$$A = -NkT \ln \left(\frac{2\pi mkT}{h^2} \right)^{\frac{3}{2}} V + NkT \ln N - NkT \tag{6}$$

where Stirling's approximation, $\ln N! = N \ln N - N$, has been used.

$$E = NkT^2 \frac{\partial}{\partial T} \ln \left(\frac{2\pi mkT}{h^2}\right)^{\frac{3}{2}} \frac{V}{N!}$$

$$= \tfrac{3}{2}NkT \tag{7}$$

and thus

$$C_V = \tfrac{3}{2}Nk \tag{8}$$

Also

$$p = -\left(\frac{\partial A}{\partial V}\right)_T = \frac{NkT}{V} \tag{9}$$

which is the perfect gas law. We also have the *Sackur–Tetrode equation*

$$S = (E-A)/T = \tfrac{5}{2}Nk + Nk \ln (2\pi mkT/h^2)^{\frac{3}{2}}V - Nk \ln N \tag{10}$$

13. Energy Fluctuations in a Canonical Ensemble

In the preceding section an expression has been derived for the average value of the energy of a system which can be represented by a canonical ensemble. It is of interest to inquire as to what the chance is of finding the system with an energy different from the average energy of the ensemble. If the theory that has been developed thus far is at all self consistent, then it is to be expected that fluctuations in the value of the energy are insignificant.

In this section we shall find that in a canonical ensemble the distribution of energies is so peaked about the average energy of the ensemble that the ensemble is virtually a microcanonical ensemble.

It is not to be concluded from the following discussion that fluctuations are always negligible. For example, it will be shown in Sect. 5.8 that fluctuations can, in certain circumstances, be large for a gas obeying quantum statistics.

We have from Eq. (11.5) that

$$C = \frac{1}{h^{Ns}} e^{A/kT} \tag{1}$$

so that the normalization condition becomes

$$\int e^{(A-\mathscr{E})/kT} \, d\Omega = h^{Ns} \tag{2}$$

Let us differentiate Eq. (2) with respect to $1/kT$, getting,

$$\int \left[\left(\frac{\partial(A/kT)}{\partial(1/kT)}\right)_V - \mathscr{E} \right] e^{(A-\mathscr{E})/kT} \, d\Omega = 0 \tag{3}$$

and so since $\left(\dfrac{\partial(A/kT)}{\partial(1/kT)}\right)_V$ is independent of the p_i and q_i we have

$$\left(\frac{\partial(A/kT)}{\partial(1/kT)}\right)_V - \frac{1}{h^{Ns}}\int \mathscr{E} \, e^{(A-\mathscr{E})/kT} \, d\Omega = 0$$

or

$$E = \left(\frac{\partial(A/kT)}{\partial(1/kT)}\right)_V \tag{4}$$

which is in accordance with our previous knowledge since $A = -kT \ln f_N$. Now differentiate Eq. (3) with respect to $1/kT$:

$$\int \left[\left(\frac{\partial^2(A/kT)}{\partial(1/kT)^2}\right)_V + \left\{\left(\frac{\partial(A/kT)}{\partial(1/kT)}\right)_V - \mathscr{E}\right\}^2\right] e^{(A-\mathscr{E})/kT} \, d\Omega = 0 \tag{5}$$

which combined with Eq. (4) gives

$$\int \left[\left(\frac{\partial^2(A/kT)}{\partial(1/kT)^2}\right)_V + \{E - \mathscr{E}\}^2\right] e^{(A-\mathscr{E})/kT} \, d\Omega = 0 \tag{6}$$

and so

$$\overline{(E-\mathscr{E})^2} = -\left(\frac{\partial^2(A/kT)}{\partial(1/kT)^2}\right) = -\left(\frac{\partial E}{\partial(1/kT)}\right)_V = kT^2\left(\frac{\partial E}{\partial T}\right)_V$$

$$\frac{\overline{(E-\mathscr{E})^2}}{E^2} = \frac{kT^2 C_V}{E^2} \tag{7}$$

Now C_V and E will be proportional to the number of particles in the system. Thus,

$$\frac{\overline{(E-\mathscr{E})^2}}{E^2} \sim \frac{1}{N} \tag{8}$$

Our statement that nearly all members of an ensemble representing a system with a large number of particles have energies differing only slightly from the average energy of the ensemble is thus justified.

14. The Grand Canonical Ensemble[1]

In Sect. 10 we imagined the system under consideration to be embedded in a heat reservoir and eliminated the restriction that the energy of the system be a constant. In so doing we made the transition from the micro-canonical ensemble to the canonical ensemble. In many physical problems, such as chemical reactions, the restriction that the number of particles of the system be a constant is inconvenient. Reasoning analogously to Sect. 10 we imagine the system under consideration to be embedded not only in a heat bath but also in a 'particle bath' and ridding ourselves of the restriction of a constant number of particles we shall obtain the *grand canonical ensemble*.

We consider a large isolated system t, whose total number of particles and energy is a constant, which is represented by a microcanonical en-

---

[1] Grand canonical ensembles were first introduced by J. W. Gibbs, *Elementary Principles of Statistical Mechanics*, Yale University Press, New Haven, Conn., 1948, Chap. 15.

semble. Let s be a subsystem of the large system which can exchange particles and energy with the remainder, r, of the total system. We have,

$$\mathcal{E}_t = \mathcal{E}_s + \mathcal{E}_r$$
$$N_t = N_s + N_r \tag{1}$$

As in our treatment of the canonical ensemble we have for the probability, dp_s, that a representative point of the subsystem is in a volume $d\Omega_s$ of *its own phase space* without specifying the condition of the reservoir

$$dp_s = C' \, d\Omega_s \, \Delta\Omega_r \tag{2}$$

where $\Delta\Omega_r$ is again the volume of phase space accessible to the representative point of the reservoir when the representative point of the subsystem is in $d\Omega_s$. The entropy of the reservoir is

$$S_r = k \ln (\Delta\Omega_r / h^m) \tag{3}$$

m being the number of degrees of freedom of the reservoir. We note that since $N_s \ll N_r$, m is well defined. Thus,

$$\Delta\Omega_r = h^m \, e^{S_r/k} \tag{4}$$

But expanding in a Taylor's series using the fact that the subsystem is small compared to the total system, i.e. $N_s \ll N_t$ and $E_s \ll E_t$, we have

$$S_r(\mathcal{E}_r, N_r) = S_r(\mathcal{E}_t - \mathcal{E}_s, N_t - N_s)$$
$$= S_r(\mathcal{E}_t, N_t) - \mathcal{E}_s \left(\frac{\partial S_r}{\partial \mathcal{E}_r}\right)_{\mathcal{E}_t, N_t} - N_s \left(\frac{\partial S_r}{\partial N_r}\right)_{\mathcal{E}_t, N_t} \tag{5}$$

In Eq. (5) $\mathcal{E}_s$ and N_s behave as differential quantities because of the small size of the subsystem. But from thermodynamics we have, Eq. (3.5.5)

$$\left(\frac{\partial S_r}{\partial \mathcal{E}_r}\right)_V = \frac{1}{T} \tag{6}$$

Defining the chemical potential μ by Eq (3.7.1) we have

$$T \, dS = dE + p \, dV - \mu \, dN$$

Thus,

$$\partial S / \partial N = -\mu / T \tag{7}$$

and we get for dp_s,

$$dp_s = C \, e^{(\mu N_s - \mathcal{E}_s)/kT} \, d\Omega_s \tag{8}$$

where C is a normalization constant. We are therefore led to the *grand canonical ensemble*, which is defined by

$$\rho(N, \mathcal{E}) = C \, e^{(N\mu - \mathcal{E})/kT} \tag{9}$$

The normalization is given by

$$\sum_{N=0}^{\infty} \int \rho \, d\Omega = 1 \tag{10}$$

and the average value of a quantity $A(p, q)$ over a grand canonical ensemble is defined by

$$\bar{A} = \sum_{N=0}^{\infty} \int A(p, q)\rho \, d\Omega \tag{11}$$

If more than one molecular species is present we replace $N\mu$ by $\sum_i N_i \mu_i$.

Suppose two grand canonical ensembles, representing two systems engaged in thermal and particle exchange, are coupled together, then, if we represent the two systems by the indices 1 and 2 and assuming, for convenience, that only one molecular species is present in each system, we have,

$$\ln \rho_1 = \ln C_1 + \frac{N_1 \mu_1}{kT} - \frac{\mathscr{E}_1}{kT}$$

$$\ln \rho_2 = \ln C_2 + \frac{N_2 \mu_2}{kT} - \frac{\mathscr{E}_2}{kT} \tag{12}$$

Adding,

$$\ln \rho_1 \rho_2 = \ln C_1 C_2 + \frac{N_1 \mu_1 + N_2 \mu_2}{kT} - \frac{\mathscr{E}_1 + \mathscr{E}_2}{kT} \tag{13}$$

so that with $\rho = \rho_1 \rho_2$, $C = C_1 C_2$, and $\mathscr{E} = \mathscr{E}_1 + \mathscr{E}_2$ the resulting ensemble is a grand canonical ensemble. If both systems have the same species of molecule, then the resulting ensemble is a grand canonical ensemble only if $\mu_1 = \mu_2$, which is another way of arriving at the well known equilibrium condition.

From the above considerations we can conclude that the grand canonical ensemble is appropriate to represent an open system in equilibrium and at constant temperature.

15. Thermodynamic Properties from the Grand Canonical Ensemble

We follow the reasoning of Sect. 11 and define the entropy of a grand canonical ensemble as being equal to the entropy of a microcanonical ensemble whose energy and number of particles is equal to the average energy and average number of particles of the grand canonical ensemble. This is a necessary definition since any other would imply that the entropy of a system depended upon its surroundings.

$$S = k \ln (\delta\Omega / h^{\bar{N}s}) \tag{1}$$

where $\delta\Omega$ is the volume of phase space corresponding to energies between E and $E + \delta E$ and s is the number of degrees of freedom of a particle. We can obtain an estimate of $\delta\Omega$ by requiring that

$$\rho(E, \bar{N}) \delta\Omega = 1 \tag{2}$$

Hence,

$$S = k \ln \left(e^{E/kT} / h^{\bar{N}s} C \, e^{\mu \bar{N}/kT} \right)$$
$$= E/T - \mu \bar{N}/T - k \ln' Ch^{\bar{N}s} \tag{3}$$

But,

$$E - TS = A = \mu \bar{N} + kT \ln Ch^{\bar{N}s} \tag{4}$$

Following Gibbs we define the *grand partition function* Ξ by

$$C = 1/h^{\bar{N}s} \Xi \tag{5}$$

But

$$\frac{1}{h^{\bar{N}s}} = \sum_{N=0}^{\infty} \frac{1}{h^{Ns}} \int \rho(N, \mathscr{E}) \, d\Omega$$

and so

$$\Xi = \sum_{N=0}^{\infty} \frac{e^{\mu N/kT}}{h^{Ns}} \int e^{-\mathscr{E}/kT} \, d\Omega \tag{6}$$

Thus Eq. (4) becomes

$$A = \mu \bar{N} - kT \ln \Xi \tag{7}$$

Also

$$G = A + pV \tag{8}$$

but Eq. (3.7.7) states that

$$G = \mu \bar{N} \tag{9}$$

so we have

$$pV = kT \ln \Xi \tag{10}$$

Since

$$-kT \ln \Xi = E - TS - \mu \bar{N}$$

we have

$$d(-kT \ln \Xi) = dE - T \, dS - S \, dT - \mu \, d\bar{N} - \bar{N} \, d\mu \tag{11}$$

which combined with Eq. (3.7.1)

$$d(-kT \ln \Xi) = -p \, dV - S \, dT - \bar{N} \, d\mu \tag{12}$$

Hence we have

$$p = kT \left(\frac{\partial \ln \Xi}{\partial V} \right)_{T, \mu} \tag{13}$$

$$S = k \left(\frac{\partial T \ln \Xi}{\partial T} \right)_{V, \mu}$$

$$S = k \ln \Xi + kT \left(\frac{\partial \ln \Xi}{\partial T} \right)_{V, \mu} \tag{14}$$

$$\bar{N} = kT \left(\frac{\partial \ln \Xi}{\partial \mu} \right)_{V, T} \tag{15}$$

Also, combining Eqs. (7) and (14), we have

$$E = A + TS = \mu\bar{N} + kT^2 \left(\frac{\partial \ln \Xi}{\partial T}\right)_{V,\mu} \tag{16}$$

16. Perfect Monatomic Gas and the Grand Canonical Ensemble

We have

$$\Xi = \sum_{N=0}^{\infty} \frac{e^{\mu N/kT}}{N!\,h^{3N}} \int e^{-E/kT}\,d\Omega = \sum_{N=0}^{\infty} e^{\mu N/kT} f_N \tag{1}$$

where we have inserted the factor $N!$ to account for the fact that the particles are non-localized. This equation is quite general and may therefore be applied also to imperfect gases. We have seen, Eq. (12.5), that

$$f_N = \frac{V^N}{N!} \left(\frac{2\pi mkT}{h^2}\right)^{\frac{3}{2}N} \tag{2}$$

Hence

$$\Xi = \sum_{N=0}^{\infty} \frac{1}{N!} \left[e^{\mu/kT} V \left(\frac{2\pi mkT}{h^2}\right)^{\frac{3}{2}} \right]^N$$

$$= \exp \left[e^{\mu/kT} V \left(\frac{2\pi mkT}{h^2}\right)^{\frac{3}{2}} \right] \tag{3}$$

So we have

$$\bar{N} = kT \left[\frac{\partial}{\partial \mu} \left\{ e^{\mu/kT} V \left(\frac{2\pi mkT}{h^2}\right)^{\frac{3}{2}} \right\} \right]_{V,T}$$

$$= e^{\mu/kT} V \left(\frac{2\pi mkT}{h^2}\right)^{\frac{3}{2}} \tag{4}$$

or

$$\mu = kT \ln \left\{ \bar{N} \Big/ \left[V \left(\frac{2\pi mkT}{h^2}\right)^{\frac{3}{2}} \right] \right\} \tag{5}$$

Also

$$pV = kT \ln \Xi = kT\, e^{\mu/kT} V \left(\frac{2\pi mkT}{h^2}\right)^{\frac{3}{2}}$$

which combined with Eq. (4) yields the perfect gas law

$$pV = \bar{N}kT \tag{6}$$

We can also obtain the Sackur–Tetrode equation

$$S = k \ln \Xi + kT \frac{\partial}{\partial T} \ln \Xi$$

$$= k \, e^{\mu/kT} \, V \left(\frac{2\pi mkT}{h^2}\right)^{\frac{3}{2}} - \frac{\mu}{T} \, e^{\mu/kT} \, V \left(\frac{2\pi mkT}{h^2}\right)^{\frac{3}{2}}$$

$$+ \tfrac{3}{2} k \, e^{\mu/kT} \, V \left(\frac{2\pi mkT}{h^2}\right)^{\frac{3}{2}}$$

$$S = \tfrac{5}{2}\bar{N}k + \bar{N}k \ln \left(\frac{2\pi mkT}{h^2}\right)^{\frac{3}{2}} V - \bar{N}k \ln \bar{N} \tag{7}$$

17. Fluctuations in a Grand Canonical Ensemble

We adopt a procedure exactly analogous to our discussions of the fluctuation in a canonical ensemble and differentiate the normalizing condition [cf. Eq. (15.6)]

$$\sum_{N=0}^{\infty} \frac{1}{h^{Ns}} \int e^{-\ln \Xi + (\mu N - \mathscr{E})/kT} \, d\Omega = 1$$

with respect to $1/kT$ and μ/kT and then differentiate again with respect to these variables. Thus for these two cases differentiating once yields

$$\sum_{N=0}^{\infty} \frac{1}{h^{Ns}} \int \left[-\left(\frac{\partial \ln \Xi}{\partial (1/kT)}\right)_{V,\,\mu/kT} - \mathscr{E} \right] e^{-\ln \Xi + [(\mu N - \mathscr{E})/kT]} \, d\Omega = 0 \tag{1}$$

$$\sum_{N=0}^{\infty} \frac{1}{h^{Ns}} \int \left[-\left(\frac{\partial \ln \Xi}{\partial (\mu/kT)}\right)_{V,\,T} + N \right] e^{-\ln \Xi + [(\mu N - \mathscr{E})/kT]} d\Omega = 0 \tag{2}$$

Since the derivatives of $\ln \Xi$ are independent of the p_i and q_i, Eqs. (1) and (2) yield Eqs. (15.16) and (15.15) respectively providing we recall the definition of the average over an ensemble, Eq. (14.11). Differentiating again we obtain

$$\sum_{N=0}^{\infty} \frac{1}{h^{Ns}} \int \left[-\left(\frac{\partial^2 \ln \Xi}{\partial (1/kT)^2}\right)_{V,\,\mu/kT} + \left\{ -\left(\frac{\partial \ln \Xi}{\partial (1/kT)}\right)_{V,\,\mu/kT} - \mathscr{E} \right\}^2 \right]$$
$$\times e^{-\ln \Xi + [(\mu N - \mathscr{E})/kT]} d\Omega = 0 \tag{3}$$

$$\sum_{N=0}^{\infty} \frac{1}{h^{Ns}} \int \left[-\left(\frac{\partial^2 \ln \Xi}{\partial (\mu/kT)^2}\right)_{V,\,T} + \left\{ -\left(\frac{\partial \ln \Xi}{\partial (\mu/kT)}\right)_{V,\,T} + N \right\}^2 \right]$$
$$\times e^{-\ln \Xi + [(\mu N - \mathscr{E})/kT]} d\Omega = 0 \tag{4}$$

or

$$\sum_{N=0}^{\infty} \frac{1}{h^{Ns}} \int \left[-\left(\frac{\partial^2 \ln \Xi}{\partial (1/kT)^2}\right)_{V,\,\mu/kT} + \{E - \mathscr{E}\}^2 \right] e^{-\ln \Xi + [(\mu N - \mathscr{E})/kT]} \, d\Omega = 0 \tag{5}$$

$$\sum_{N=0}^{\infty} \frac{1}{h^{Ns}} \int \left[-\left(\frac{\partial^2 \ln \Xi}{\partial (\mu/kT)^2}\right)_{V,\,T} + \{\bar{N} - N\}^2 \right] e^{-\ln \Xi + [(\mu N - \mathscr{E})/kT]} \, d\Omega = 0 \tag{6}$$

From the same considerations used in deriving Eqs. (3) and (4) we have

$$\overline{(E-\mathscr{E})^2} = \left(\frac{\partial^2 \ln \Xi}{\partial(1/kT)^2}\right)_{V,\,\mu/kT} \tag{7}$$

$$\overline{(\overline{N}-N)^2} = \left(\frac{\partial^2 \ln \Xi}{\partial(\mu/kT)^2}\right)_{V,\,T} \tag{8}$$

In general $\ln \Xi$ and its derivatives in Eqs. (7) and (8) will be proportional to N so that we have

$$\frac{\overline{(E-\mathscr{E})^2}}{E^2} \sim \frac{1}{N}, \quad \frac{\overline{(\overline{N}-N)^2}}{\overline{N}^2} \sim \frac{1}{N} \tag{9}$$

so that both the energy and the number of particles of a grand canonical ensemble representing a system with a large number of particles are well defined.

18. Boltzmann's *H*-theorem

Boltzmann's *H*-theorem is concerned with the tendency of a system, not in equilibrium, to return to equilibrium, and with the rate at which it does so. A complete discussion of the *H*-theorem involves greater detail and length than we shall attempt and we recommend to the interested reader the excellent works of Tolman[1] and ter Haar.[2] To begin we shall consider a gas composed of perfectly elastic spheres and investigate, as did Boltzmann, collisions as a mechanism for time changes. Then after having obtained a physical feeling for the processes involved we shall consider the more general techniques using ensembles.

Consider a gas, enclosed in a volume V, of N molecules which can be regarded as elastic spheres and define a distribution function $f(\mathbf{p})$ such that $f(\mathbf{p})dp_x dp_y\, dp_z$ is the number of molecules per unit volume with momenta in the interval $(\mathbf{p}, \mathbf{p}+d\mathbf{p})$. If there are collisions then there will be molecules whose momenta leave the volume $d\mathbf{p} \equiv dp_x dp_y dp_z$, and molecules whose momenta enter the volume $d\mathbf{p}$. The time rate of change in the number of molecules per unit volume whose momenta are in $d\mathbf{p}$ we shall denote by

$$\left(\frac{\partial f}{\partial t}\right)_{\text{coll}} d\mathbf{p} \tag{1}$$

We have used the partial derivative because other processes may also cause changes with time. It now remains to calculate this factor. Let us consider a collision between two molecules whose momenta before col-

[1] R. C. Tolman, *op. cit.*, pp. 99–179.
[2] D. ter Haar, *op. cit.*, pp. 10–25; 331–354; 361–368.

lision are $\mathbf{p}_1$ and $\mathbf{p}_2$ and after collision are $\mathbf{p}_1'$ and $\mathbf{p}_2'$. If we wished we could make a detailed calculation about the collision using:

(1) conservation of energy

$$\frac{p_1^2}{2m_1} + \frac{p_2^2}{2m_2} = \frac{p_1'^2}{2m_1} + \frac{p_2'^2}{2m_2} \tag{2}$$

(2) conservation of momentum

$$\mathbf{p}_1 + \mathbf{p}_2 = \mathbf{p}_1' + \mathbf{p}_2' \tag{3}$$

which provide four of the six equations needed. Since the collisions are elastic, changes in velocity must lie along the line of centers. Specification of the orientation of the line of centers provides two additional independent equations. The unit vector in the direction of the line of centers is defined by

$$\mathbf{e} = \frac{\Delta \mathbf{p}_1}{|\Delta \mathbf{p}_1|} = \frac{\mathbf{p}_1 - \mathbf{p}_1'}{|\mathbf{p}_1 - \mathbf{p}_1'|} = -\frac{\Delta \mathbf{p}_2}{|\Delta \mathbf{p}_2|} \tag{4}$$

Thus, we have the configuration depicted in Figure 1.

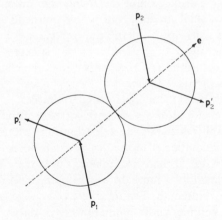

Figure 1. A perfect elastic collision of spherical gas molecules 1 and 2. $\mathbf{p}_1$, $\mathbf{p}_2$, and $\mathbf{p}_1'$, $\mathbf{p}_2'$ are the respective momenta before and after the collision, and $\mathbf{e}$ is the unit vector in the direction of the line of centers.

If $\mathbf{c}$ is the relative velocity of molecule 2 with respect to molecule 1 and D is the diameter of the molecules, then all the molecules within a cylinder of slant height $|\mathbf{c}|\, dt$ and base $D^2 d\mathbf{e}$ collide with molecule 1 in a time dt. This is schematically illustrated in Figure 2.

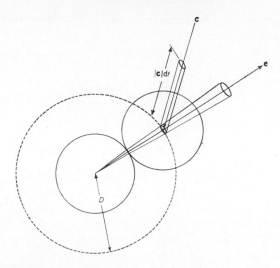

Figure 2. Determination of the number of molecules which collide with molecule 1 during the interval d*t*. *D* is the diameter of the molecules, and **c** is the velocity relative to that of molecule 1.

Thus, since the volume of the cylinder is $(|\mathbf{c}|\mathrm{d}t)\,(D^2\mathrm{d}\mathbf{e})\cos\theta$, the number of collisions per unit time between molecules with momenta in the volume $\mathrm{d}\mathbf{p}_2$ whose line of centers lies within the solid angle about **e** is,

$$af_1 f_2\,\mathrm{d}\mathbf{p}_1\,\mathrm{d}\mathbf{p}_2\,\mathrm{d}\mathbf{e} \tag{5}$$

where $\qquad f_1 = f(\mathbf{p}_1), \qquad a - |\mathbf{c}|D^2\cos\theta \qquad \pi/2 \leqslant \theta \leqslant \pi/2$

provided that we assume that there is no correlation between positions and momenta of different molecules so that $f_2\mathrm{d}\mathbf{p}_2\mathrm{d}V$ is the number of molecules in any volume $\mathrm{d}V$ and at any time with momenta between $\mathbf{p}_2$ and $\mathbf{p}_2 + \mathrm{d}\mathbf{p}_2$ whether the volume is selected at random or a particular volume element is used as was done above. This assumption is generally referred to as *Stosszahlensatz* (collision number theorem).

If the molecules are not elastic spheres then Eq. (5) is still true but the dependence of a on $|\mathbf{c}|$ and θ is much more complicated.

Integrating over $\mathbf{p}_2$ and **e** yields the number of molecules whose representative points leave the volume $\mathrm{d}\mathbf{p}_1$ of momentum space in unit time:

$$f_1\,\mathrm{d}\mathbf{p}_1 \int f_2\,\mathrm{d}\mathbf{p}_2 \int a\,\mathrm{d}\mathbf{e} \tag{6}$$

Now we must calculate the number of collisions in which molecule 1 has momentum $\mathbf{p}_1'$ before and $\mathbf{p}_1$ after, and molecule 2 has momentum $\mathbf{p}_2'$ before and $\mathbf{p}_2$ after while the line of centers is within a small solid angle

$d\mathbf{e}'$ about $\mathbf{e}' = (\mathbf{p}'_1 - \mathbf{p}_1)/(|\mathbf{p}'_1 - {}_1\mathbf{p}|) = -\mathbf{e}$.[3] The inverse collision is illustrated in Figure 3.

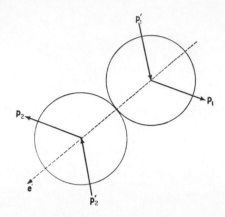

Figure 3. Inverse of the perfect elastic collision shown in Figure 1.

This is,

$$a' f'_1 f'_2 \, d\mathbf{p}_1 \, d\mathbf{p}_2 \, d\mathbf{e}' \tag{7}$$

where

$$a' = D^2 |c| \cos \theta'$$

$\mathbf{c}'$ being the relative velocity of approach of 1 with respect to 2. We can easily see that $a' = a$, since $\theta' = \theta$ and $|\mathbf{c}'| = |\mathbf{c}|$ as the collision is elastic. Hence the number of molecules whose representative point enters the volume $d\mathbf{p}_1$ in unit time is

$$\int' f'_1 f'_2 \, d\mathbf{p}'_1 \, d\mathbf{p}'_2 \int a \, d\mathbf{e}' \tag{8}$$

The prime on the integral sign indicates that only those values of $\mathbf{p}'_1$, $\mathbf{p}'_2$, and $\mathbf{e}'$ such that after the collision one of the molecules has momenta in the volume $d\mathbf{p}_1$ are included. On changing variables of integration we have

$$d\mathbf{p}_1 \int f'_1 f'_2 |J| \, d\mathbf{p}_2 \int a \, d\mathbf{e} \tag{9}$$

where

$$J = \frac{\partial(\mathbf{p}'_1, \mathbf{p}'_2, \mathbf{e}')}{\partial(\mathbf{p}_1, \mathbf{p}_2, \mathbf{e})} = \frac{\partial(p'_{1x}, p'_{1y}, p'_{1z}, p'_{2x}, p'_{2y}, p'_{2z}, \mathbf{e}')}{\partial(p_{1x}, p_{1y}, p_{1z}, p_{2x}, p_{2y}, p_{2z}, \mathbf{e})}$$

is the Jacobian of the transformation. The momentum condition Eq. (3) is

---

[3] Although for our special case of spherically symmetric molecules we can find such an inverse collision in more general cases, it is not always possible to find an inverse collision for an arbitrarily chosen collision. Nonetheless, one can still prove an *H*-theorem by considering cycles of collisions (see R. C. Tolman, *op. cit.*, pp. 140–141).

linear in the momenta and symmetric with respect to primed and un-primed variables. Also we have noted that $e = e'$ and so

$$|J'| = \left| \frac{\partial(\mathbf{p}_1, \mathbf{p}_2, e)}{\partial(\mathbf{p}'_1, \mathbf{p}'_2, e')} \right|$$

is equal to $|J|$. But also $JJ' = 1$ and so $|J| = 1$. Thus subtracting Eq. (6) from Eq. (9) and equating the resulting equation to Eq. (1) we have, on dividing out the factor $d\mathbf{p}_1$,

$$\frac{\partial f_1}{\partial t} = \int (f'_1 f'_2 - f_1 f_2)\, d\mathbf{p}_2\, a\, de \tag{10}$$

If the gas is in an equilibrium state, then $\partial f/\partial t = 0$ and it is sufficient[4] that

$$f'_1 f'_2 = f_1 f_2 \tag{11}$$

This equation means that there are as many inverse collisions as original collisions. This is a special case of the *principle of detailed balancing* which has been discussed in Sect. 1.9. Thus,

$$\ln f'_1 + \ln f'_2 = \ln f_1 + \ln f_2$$

In other words $\ln f$ is conserved and since only energy and momentum are conserved on collision we have

$$\ln f - a + b_1 p_x + b_2 p_y + b_3 p_z + c\,(p_x^2 + p_y^2 + p_z^2)/2m \tag{12}$$

which can be expressed as

$$\ln f = \ln \alpha + \beta(p - p_0)^2/2m$$
$$f = \alpha\, e^{\beta(p - p_0)^2/2m} \tag{13}$$

The constant α is to be regarded as a normalizing factor. We can choose our arbitrary zero of energy so that,

$$f = \alpha\, e^{\beta p^2/2m} \tag{14}$$

Reasoning as in Sect. 4 we can show that $\beta = -1/kT$ so that as we would expect the equilibrium distribution is the Boltzmann distribution. Had we considered a gas in which the molecules exert on each other repulsive forces derivable from the potential function $V(\mathbf{r})$ then our calculations would have been much more complicated but, because the total energy is conserved, would have yielded,[5]

$$f = \alpha\, e^{-\varepsilon/kT} \tag{15}$$

---

[4] This condition can also be shown to be necessary. See, for example, D. ter Haar, *op. cit.*, p. 20.

[5] S. Chapman and T. G. Cowling, *The Mathematical Theory of Non-uniform Gases*, 2nd Ed., Cambridge University Press, 1952, Chap. 4.

where $f \, d\omega$ is the number of molecules in the volume $d\omega$ of μ space. We must integrate over both momenta and coordinates because of the inclusion of coordinates in the total energy ε.

By means of Eq. (10) non-equilibrium behavior can be discussed. Following Boltzmann[6] we can define a quantity H

$$H = \int f \ln f \, d\mathbf{p} \tag{16}$$

where, for reasons of simplicity only, we are still considering a gas of elastic spheres. This quantity will be a function of the time only since the integration is over the whole range of momentum space. Differentiating with respect to the time,

$$\frac{dH}{dt} = \int (\ln f_1 + 1) \frac{\partial f_1}{\partial t} \, d\mathbf{p}_1 \tag{17}$$

If we use Eq. (10)

$$\frac{dH}{dt} = \int (\ln f_1 + 1)(f_1' f_2' - f_1 f_2) a \, d\varepsilon \, d\mathbf{p}_1 \, d\mathbf{p}_2 \tag{18}$$

Interchanging indices gives,

$$\frac{dH}{dt} = \int (\ln f_2 + 1)(f_1' f_2' - f_1 f_2) a \, d\varepsilon \, d\mathbf{p}_1 \, d\mathbf{p}_2 \tag{19}$$

Interchanging primed and unprimed variables in Eqs. (18) and (19) gives, since $|J| = 1$,

$$\frac{dH}{dt} = \int (\ln f_1' + 1)(f_1 f_2 - f_1' f_2') a \, d\varepsilon \, d\mathbf{p}_1 \, d\mathbf{p}_2 \tag{20}$$

$$\frac{dH}{dt} = \int (\ln f_2' + 1)(f_1 f_2 - f_1' f_2') a \, d\varepsilon \, d\mathbf{p}_1 \, d\mathbf{p}_2 \tag{21}$$

If we add Eqs. (18) to (21) we obtain

$$\frac{dH}{dt} = -\frac{1}{4} \int (f_1' f_2' - f_1 f_2) \ln \frac{f_1' f_2'}{f_1 f_2} a \, d\varepsilon \, d\mathbf{p}_1 \, d\mathbf{p}_2 \tag{22}$$

The expression $(a-b) \ln (a/b)$ is positive if $a \neq b$ and zero if $a = b$. Thus

$$\frac{dH}{dt} \leqslant 0 \tag{23}$$

where the equality holds for the case of equilibrium. This is the famous Boltzmann's H-theorem. For a discussion of the validity of this result if mechanisms for time change other than collisions are present the reader is referred to Tolman.[7]

[6] L. Boltzmann, *Wien. Ber.*, **66**, 275 (1872).
[7] R. C. Tolman, *op. cit.*, pp. 142–145.

19. Discussion of the H-theorem

We have found, on the basis of the H-theorem, that for a system not in equilibrium H will always decrease until it reaches its equilibrium value and that thereafter it will maintain this value. However, we shall shortly find that this bald statement is not true and needs some qualification.

We know that the laws of classical mechanics are reversible in time. Consider a system of molecules moving in such a manner that $(dH/dt) < 0$. Suppose that at a certain instant the velocity of every molecule is reversed. This can be done without changing the value of H. As a result each molecule retraces its previous path and so $(dH/dt) > 0$ after this change. This is in contradiction to our discussion of the previous section. This is the famous reversibility paradox first pointed out by Loschmidt.[1]

Some years later Zermelo,[2] using a theorem of Poincaré, was able to show that a system can exhibit increases as well as decreases in the value of H. Poincaré had shown[3] that an isolated system if left to itself would repeat its previous motion as accurately as we required provided we waited a sufficiently long (but still finite) length of time. As a result of Poincaré's theorem any decreases in H that occurred during a certain time interval would eventually have to be balanced by increases in H.

We can resolve our problems by recalling that the main reason for embarking on a study of statistical mechanics was that we did not have, even classically, a precise knowledge of the paths of all the particles in the system. In any case, the Heisenberg uncertainty relation of quantum mechanics requires that we give up the idea of particles moving in sharply defined paths. Thus, our hypothetical exact reversal of the motion of each particle with a corresponding increase in H is quite inconsistent with our assumed lack of precise knowledge of the paths of the particles of the system and, though not impossible, is highly improbable. The H-theorem is to be regarded as being statistical in nature and the best that we can say is that, first, the most probable state of a system in equilibrium is the one for which H is a minimum, and second, for a system with a value of H greater than the minimum there is an overwhelming probability that H will decrease although increases are not impossible.

20. The Relation Between H and Entropy; Law of Increasing Entropy

We have seen that we may define H by

$$H = \int f \ln f \, d\omega \qquad (1)$$

[1] J. Loschmidt, *Wien. Ber.*, **73**, 139 (1876); **75**, 67 (1877).
[2] E. Zermelo, *Ann. Physik*, **57**, 485 (1896).
[3] H. Poincaré, *Acta Math.*, **13**, 167 (1890).

where $f \, d\omega$ is the number of molecules whose representative points are in the volume $d\omega$ of μ space. If as in Sect. 4 we divide μ space into a number of small cells such that all the n_i molecules whose representative points are in the ith cell have energy ε_i and g_i is the number of allowed states associated with ε_i, then Eq. (1) becomes

$$H = \sum_i n_i \ln \frac{n_i}{g_i} + \text{constant} \tag{2}$$

The number of accessible states W is given by

$$W = \prod_i \frac{g_i^{n_i}}{n_i!} \tag{3}$$

If we take the logarithm of this relation and apply Stirling's approximation we have

$$\ln W = -\sum_i n_i \ln \frac{n_i}{g_i} + \text{constant} \tag{4}$$

Thus, to within an additive constant

$$S = k \ln W = -kH \tag{5}$$

so that $-kH$ is the entropy of the system. It is to be noted that this provides a definition of entropy in non-equilibrium situations.

Therefore we can conclude that the most probable value of S for a system in equilibrium is the one for which S is a maximum, and for a system not in equilibrium there is an overwhelming probability of S increasing although decreases are not to be excluded.

21. The H-theorem for Ensembles

Consider an ensemble of density $\rho\,(p, q)$. Since $\rho\,(p, q)$ is the probability of finding the representative point of a given system in the ensemble within a volume $d\Omega$ of Γ space, we would expect, because of the discussion of the previous section, to be able to define a function, $\overline{H}$, by the expression,

$$\overline{\ln \rho} = \int \rho \ln \rho \, d\Omega \tag{1}$$

However, we cannot do this because this function is independent of time. To see this we recall Liouville's theorem which states that

$$\frac{d\rho}{dt} = 0 \tag{2}$$

Thus,

$$\frac{d}{dt}(\overline{\ln \rho}) = \int (\ln \rho + 1) \frac{d\rho}{dt} \, d\Omega = 0 \tag{3}$$

This is not quite the catastrophe that it at first appears to be. Although $\overline{\ln \rho}$ is constant there is still an approach to equilibrium. Perhaps this can be made clear by referring to an analogy first introduced by Gibbs.[1] Consider a vessel containing, in an unmixed condition, water and a non-diffusible black ink, consisting of colloidal particles. If the mixture is stirred then we would expect as an equilibrium state what would appear to the eye as a homogeneous grey liquid. However from a microscopic view the situation would be unchanged with part of the space occupied by water and part occupied by the ink particles. Because of this analogy we introduce a *coarse grained density* P by dividing phase (Γ) space into small but finite cells of volume $\delta\Omega_i$ and letting P be the average of ρ taken over $\delta\Omega_i$

$$P(p,q) = \frac{1}{\delta\Omega_i} \int_i \rho \, d\Omega \tag{4}$$

The normalization condition becomes

$$\int P \, d\Omega = 1 \tag{5}$$

Instead of Eq. (1) we define $\overline{H}$ by

$$\overline{H} = \int P \ln P \, d\Omega = \int \rho \ln P \, d\Omega \tag{6}$$

and identify $-k\overline{H}$ with the entropy of the system under consideration.

Let us consider how $\overline{H}$ changes with time. Suppose that at t_1 an experimental observation on the state of the system is made. We can construct an ensemble representing the system at time t_1 by dividing phase space into small volumes, chosen in accord with the limitations of the experiment, and, in accord with the assumption of equal *a priori* probabilities for equal volumes of phase space, by taking uniform distributions of representative points throughout these cells. Thus

$$\rho_1 = P_1 \tag{7}$$

and

$$\overline{H}_1 = \int P_1 \ln P_1 \, d\Omega = \int \rho_1 \ln \rho_1 \, d\Omega \tag{8}$$

Assuming that the system is in a non-equilibrium state at time t_1 then at some later time t_2 we shall have, in general,

$$\rho_2 \neq P_2 \tag{9}$$

and

$$\overline{H}_2 = \int P_2 \ln P_2 \, d\Omega \tag{10}$$

[1] J. W. Gibbs, *op. cit.*, Chap. 12, p. 144.

Thus,

$$\bar{H}_1 - \bar{H}_2 = \int (\rho_1 \ln \rho_1 - P_2 \ln P_2) \, d\Omega \tag{11}$$

Because of Eqs. (5) and (6) we have

$$\bar{H}_1 - \bar{H}_2 = \int (\rho_2 \ln \rho_2 - \rho_2 \ln P_2) \, d\Omega \tag{12}$$

$$= \int (\rho_2 \ln \rho_2 - \rho_2 \ln P_2 + P_2 - \rho_2) \, d\Omega \tag{13}$$

If we set $\rho_2 = P_2 \, e^\Delta$, we have

$$\bar{H}_1 - \bar{H}_2 = \int P_2(\Delta e^\Delta + 1 - e^\Delta) \, d\Omega \tag{14}$$

If $I = \Delta e^\Delta + 1 - e^\Delta$ then $dI/d\Delta = \Delta e^\Delta$ is positive or negative as Δ is positive or negative so that $I > 0$ if $\Delta \neq 0$. Thus if the system is in a non-equilibrium situation

$$\bar{H}_1 > \bar{H}_2 \tag{15}$$

and if the system is in an equilibrium situation $\rho_2 = P_2$, which together with Eq. (12) gives

$$\bar{H}_1 = \bar{H}_2 \tag{16}$$

which is the H-theorem for an ensemble.

5

QUANTUM STATISTICAL MECHANICS

1. Historical Introduction

During the nineteenth century, a wide range of phenomena had been explained by classical physics. However, by the close of the nineteenth century there was a hard core of results, such as the spectral distribution of thermal radiation from a black body and the low temperature specific heats of solids, which, it was felt, should have been understood on the basis of classical physics but were not.

In 1900, Planck[1] succeeded in explaining the black body spectrum by assuming that electromagnetic radiation was emitted in discrete quanta each of which contained an energy ε given by

$$\varepsilon = h\nu \tag{1}$$

where ν is the frequency of the radiation and h is Planck's constant.

A few years later Einstein[2] explained the emission of electrons due to light falling on a metal surface by assuming that electromagnetic radiation was absorbed in discrete quanta of magnitude $h\nu$. In 1907, Einstein[3] and in 1912, Debye[4] were able, by using Planck's hypothesis, to explain the specific heats of solids. We shall discuss their theories in detail in Chapter 7. The crowning achievement of what is now called the old quantum theory came when Bohr[5] was able to predict the spectrum of hydrogen by postulating that the hydrogen atom consisted of a positive nucleus and an orbiting electron which could only exist in certain states where the orbital angular momentum was an integral multiple of $h/2\pi$. Later Wilson[6] and Sommerfeld[7] were able to extend Bohr's procedure to explain a wide variety of atomic systems. However, in certain more complicated problems, such as the rotational spectra of diatomic molecules, the old quantum theory did not give quantitatively correct results and was finally replaced by what is now known as quantum mechanics.

[1] M. Planck, *Ann. Physik*, **4**, 553 (1901).
[2] A. Einstein, *Ann. Physik*, **17**, 132 (1905).
[3] A. Einstein, *Ann. Physik*, **22**, 180 (1907); **34**, 170 (1911).
[4] P. Debye, *Ann. Physik*, **39**, 789 (1912).
[5] N. Bohr, *Phil. Mag.*, **26**, 1 (1913).
[6] W. Wilson, *Phil. Mag.*, **29**, 795 (1915).
[7] A. Sommerfeld, *Münchener Ber.*, **1915**, 425, 459; **1916**, 131.

The dualism of the wave and particle aspects of radiation led de Broglie[8] to suggest that particles exhibited a similar dualism. This dualism of matter was confirmed by the experiments of Davisson and Germer[9] who observed the diffraction of electrons by a nickel crystal, and by those of Thomson[10] who observed the diffraction of electrons by extremely thin metallic films. These results became physically more clear when Heisenberg[11] developed the uncertainty principle, according to which it is impossible, because of the interaction of a particle with the measuring system, to determine simultaneously with precision the values of two conjugate variables, such as the momentum and position, of a particle, and that the product of the uncertainties, Δp and Δq, in the determination of their values is given by

$$\Delta p \cdot \Delta q \geq h/4\pi \qquad (2)$$

2. The Formulation of Quantum Mechanics

We shall give merely an outline of the basic concepts of quantum mechanics without attempting to give a full discussion of their physical foundations.

A—In classical mechanics a complete description of a physical system is given by the specification of values of all its coordinates and conjugate momenta. However, in quantum mechanics this is not possible and a description of the state of a system is given by a *probability function* of the coordinates and time, Ψ, which is, in general, complex, such that $\Psi^* \Psi \, d\tau$ is the probability of finding the system in the element $d\tau$ of configuration space, where Ψ^* is the complex conjugate of Ψ. The total probability of finding the system somewhere in configuration space must be unity and therefore Ψ must be normalized, i.e.

$$\int \Psi^* \Psi \, d\tau = 1 \qquad (1)$$

Ψ is often called the *wave function*. Unless otherwise stated, all wave functions will be considered as normalized.

B—To any observable quantity, *A*, in classical mechanics there corresponds a linear operator, **A**, such that if *a* is the value of *A* in the state represented by φ then the operation of **A** on the function ϕ is the equivalent of multiplying φ by *a*, that is,

$$\mathbf{A}\varphi = a\varphi \qquad (2)$$

φ is called an *eigenstate* or *eigenfunction* and *a* an *eigenvalue* of **A**. If

[8] L. de Broglie, *Ann. Phys.*, **3**, 22 (1925).
[9] C. Davisson and L. Germer, *Phys. Rev.*, **30**, 705 (1927).
[10] G. Thomson, *Proc. Roy. Soc. (London)*, **117**, 600 (1928).
[11] W. Heisenberg, *Z. Physik*, **43**, 172 (1927).

more than one eigenstate corresponds to a given eigenvalue the state is said to be *degenerate*. The form of **A** may be found by means of the following rules:

(a) If A is one of the coordinates, q_j, or the time, t, the operator is the variable itself.

(b) If A is one of the momenta, p_j, then the operator is $\dfrac{\hbar}{i}\dfrac{\partial}{\partial q_j}$, where q_j is conjugate to p_j and $\hbar = h/2\pi$.

For this formulation to be meaningful we require that the eigenvalues of an operator be real. In other words,

$$a = \int \varphi^* A\varphi \, d\tau = \int (A\varphi)^*\varphi \, d\tau = a^* \tag{3}$$

Generalizing the above requirement slightly, we arrive at the concept of a *Hermitian operator*. An operator **A** is Hermitian if, for any pair of functions χ and ϕ, we have,

$$\int \chi^* A\phi \, d\tau = \int (A\chi)^*\phi \, d\tau \tag{4}$$

The only operators with which we shall be concerned will be Hermitian.

C—Ψ satisfies the *time-dependent Schrödinger equation*[1]

$$\mathbf{H}\Psi = -\frac{\hbar}{i}\frac{\partial \Psi}{\partial t} \tag{5}$$

We separate out the time dependence by letting

$$\Psi(q, t) = \psi(q)\, e^{-i(\mathscr{E}/\hbar)t} \tag{6}$$

obtaining the *time-independent Schrödinger equation*

$$\mathbf{H}\psi = \mathscr{E}\psi \tag{7}$$

D—Two functions ϕ and φ are said to be *orthogonal* provided that,

$$\int \phi^*\varphi \, d\tau = 0 \tag{8}$$

The eigenfunctions φ_j of any Hermitian operator **A** are orthogonal. To see this we first consider two non-degenerate eigenfunctions φ_i and φ_j,

$$\mathbf{A}\varphi_i = a_i\varphi_i, \qquad \mathbf{A}\varphi_j = a_j\varphi_j \tag{9}$$

Hence,

$$a_i \int \varphi_j^*\varphi_i \, d\tau = \int \varphi_j^* \mathbf{A}\varphi_i \, d\tau = \int (A\varphi_j)^*\varphi_i \, d\tau$$
$$= a_j \int \varphi_j^*\varphi_i \, d\tau \tag{10}$$

---

[1] E. Schrödinger, *Ann. Physik*, **79**, 361, 478 (1926); **80**, 437 (1926); **81**, 109 (1926).

where the Hermitian property of **A** has been used in obtaining both the third and the fourth equality. Thus,

$$(a_i - a_j) \int \varphi_j^* \varphi_i \, d\tau = 0 \tag{11}$$

and since $a_i \neq a_j$ we must have $\int \varphi_j^* \varphi_i \, d\tau = 0$ and the eigenfunctions are orthogonal. If two or more eigenfunctions have the same eigenvalue then the above argument is not applicable. However, we can find linear combinations of the eigenfunctions that are orthogonal. For example, suppose that

$$\mathbf{A}\varphi_i = a\varphi_i, \qquad \mathbf{A}\varphi_j = a\varphi_j \tag{12}$$

then if $\varphi_j' = \varphi_j - \varphi_i \int \varphi_i^* \varphi_j \, d\tau$, then multiplying by φ_j^* and integrating

$$\int \varphi_i^* \varphi_j' \, d\tau = \int \varphi_i^* \varphi_j \, d\tau - \int \varphi_i^* \varphi_j \, d\tau = 0 \tag{13}$$

and φ_i and φ_j' are orthogonal. φ_j' is an eigenfunction of A with eigenvalue a since

$$\mathbf{A}\varphi_j' = \mathbf{A}\varphi_j - \mathbf{A}\varphi_i \int \varphi_j^* \varphi_i \, d\tau$$

$$= a\varphi_j - a\varphi_i \int \varphi_j^* \varphi_i \, d\tau = a\varphi_j' \tag{14}$$

The above process by which φ_j' was obtained from φ_j is called the *Schmidt orthogonalization procedure*.[2]

E—Now suppose that the set of functions φ_j are the eigenfunctions of some operator **A** (which will be Hermitian). The above considerations on orthogonal functions make possible an expansion of the wave function in terms of φ_j

$$\varphi = \sum_j c_j \varphi_j \tag{15}$$

A set of functions in terms of which such an expansion can be made is called a *closed* (or sometimes a *complete*) *set*. We shall assume that the eigenfunctions of any operator in quantum mechanics form a closed set and hence that such expansions are possible. Multiply both sides of Eq. (15) by φ_k^* and integrate. Taking into consideration the orthogonality and normality of the φ_j, we have,

$$c_k = \int \varphi_k^* \varphi \, d\tau \tag{16}$$

F—There is one final concept that will be of value. If φ_j is an eigenfunction of the operator **A** with eigenvalue a_j the state represented by

$$\varphi = \sum_j c_j \varphi_j \tag{17}$$

is the state in which the probability of finding the observed value of A to be

2 E. Schmidt, *Math. Ann.*, **63**, 433 (1907).

a_i is $c_i^* c_i$. This is called the *superposition principle*. From this we can show that the *mean value* or *expectation value* $\langle A \rangle$ of A in the state φ is

$$\langle A \rangle = \int \varphi^* \mathbf{A} \varphi \, d\tau \tag{18}$$

since if φ_j is the set of eigenfunctions of $\mathbf{A}$ with eigenvalue a_i we expand φ in terms of the φ_j

$$\varphi = \sum_j c_j \varphi_j$$

and so

$$\int \varphi^* \mathbf{A} \varphi \, d\tau = \int \left(\sum_j c_j^* \varphi_j^* \right)' \mathbf{A} \left(\sum_k c_k \varphi_k \right) d\tau$$

$$= \int \left(\sum_j c_j^* \varphi_j^* \right) \left(\sum_k c_k a_k \varphi_k \right) d\tau$$

$$= \sum_j a_j c_j^* c_j \tag{19}$$

the last equality being due to the orthogonality and normality of the φ_j. Because of the superposition principle $\sum_j a_j c_j^* c_j$ is the average value of A in the state φ.

The above discussion of wave mechanics is very brief but will suffice for our purposes. However, the reader with no previous knowledge of quantum mechanics is advised to refer to any good book on the subject[3] for more details and applications so that he may gain more familiarity with quantum mechanics.

3. The Matrix Formulation of Quantum Mechanics

We now consider a different formulation of quantum mechanics due originally to Heisenberg[1] in which the dynamical variables appear explicitly without having to differentiate a wave function. The classical equations are of this form so that we would expect a closer resemblance to classical mechanics here than in the Schrödinger formulation.[2] We shall, however, not stress this similarity as it presumes a rather deep understanding of classical mechanics, in particular a knowledge of Poisson brackets and contact transformations.[3]

[3] See for example *Q.C.*, Chapter 3; L. I. Schiff, *Quantum Mechanics*, 2nd Ed., McGraw-Hill, New York, Chapters 2 and 3.

[1] W. Heisenberg, *Z. Physik*, **33**, 879 (1925); M. Born, W. Heisenberg, and P. Jordan, *Z. Physik*, **35**, 557 (1925).

[2] The connection between matrix mechanics and wave mechanics was established by E. Schrödinger, *Ann. Physik*, **79**, 734 (1926), and C. Eckart, *Phys. Rev.*, **29**, 711 (1926).

[3] The Poisson bracket of two functions u and v of the coordinates and momenta, $[u, v]$, is defined as

$$[u, v] = \sum \left(\frac{\partial u}{\partial q_i} \frac{\partial v}{\partial p_i} - \frac{\partial u}{\partial p_i} \frac{\partial v}{\partial q_i} \right)$$

and a contact transformation is a transformation from one set of variables satisfying Hamilton's equations to another set of variables satisfying Hamilton's equations. See H. Goldstein, *Classical Mechanics*, Addison-Wesley, Reading, Mass., 1950, Chap. 8, and R. C. Tolman, *The Principles of Statistical Mechanics*, Oxford University Press, 1938, §11, 14.

A—Consider an arbitrary orthogonal, normalized, and closed set, ϕ_m, and then form φ_m such that

$$\varphi_m = \mathbf{A}\phi_m \tag{1}$$

where A is some operator. Expanding φ_m in terms of the ϕ_m we get

$$\varphi_m = \mathbf{A}\phi_m = \sum_k A_{km}\phi_k \tag{2}$$

and multiplying both sides by ϕ_n^* and integrating gives

$$A_{nm} = \int \phi_n^* \mathbf{A}\phi_m \, d\tau \tag{3}$$

A_{nm} is called the *matrix element* of $\mathbf{A}$ in the ϕ representation and the set of quantities A_{nm} is called the *matrix* of $\mathbf{A}$ in the ϕ representation and is usually written in the form

$$\begin{pmatrix} a_{11} & a_{12} & a_{13} & \cdots \\ a_{21} & a_{22} & a_{23} & \cdots \\ a_{31} & a_{32} & a_{33} & \cdots \\ \vdots & \vdots & \vdots & \end{pmatrix}$$

We shall indicate the matrix of an operator, $\mathbf{A}$, by enclosing the operator in parentheses, i.e. $(\mathbf{A})$.

B—At this point it is convenient to give a resumé of the algebraic properties of matrices

    (*a*) Addition: $C_{ij} = A_{ij} + B_{ij}$ if $\mathbf{C} = \mathbf{A} + \mathbf{B}$ (4)

    (*b*) Multiplication: $C_{ij} = \sum_k A_{ik} B_{kj}$ if $\mathbf{C} = \mathbf{AB}$ (5)

We wish to find the matrix C_{ij} of the operator $\mathbf{C} = \mathbf{AB}$. Now,

$$\mathbf{AB}\phi_j = \mathbf{A}\sum_k B_{kj}\phi_k = \sum_k B_{kj}\mathbf{A}\phi_k = \sum_k \sum_i B_{kj}A_{ik}\phi_i$$

$$= \sum_i \left(\sum_k A_{ik}B_{kj}\right)\phi_i = \sum_i C_{ij}\phi_i$$

so that,[4]

$$C_{ij} = \sum_k A_{ik}B_{kj}$$

We should note that matrix multiplication is non-commutative, i.e. $(\mathbf{AB})$ and $(\mathbf{BA})$ are usually not equal.

    (*c*) The *unit matrix* $(\mathbf{I}) = \delta_{ij}\begin{Bmatrix} = 1 & \text{if } i = j \\ = 0 & \text{if } i \neq j \end{Bmatrix}$ has the property

$$(\mathbf{I})(\mathbf{A}) = (\mathbf{A})(\mathbf{I}) = (\mathbf{A}) \tag{6}$$

---

[4] The matrices that arise in quantum mechanics usually contain an infinite number of columns and rows whereas the matrices that the student has encountered in algebra courses are finite in size. We shall not concern ourselves with this added complication. However, a few points might be made. The multiplication law is only true provided the sum converges. In some cases the matrix will have a non-denumerable number of columns or rows or both in which case the summation is replaced by integration. We shall assume throughout that we can interchange orders of summation.

for arbitrary (A)

(d) The *inverse* $(\mathbf{A}^{-1})$ of a square matrix (A) is defined by

$$(\mathbf{A})(\mathbf{A}^{-1}) = (\mathbf{A}^{-1})(\mathbf{A}) = (\mathbf{I}) \tag{7}$$

(e) The *trace* of a square matrix (A) is defined by

$$\text{trace } (\mathbf{A}) = \sum_i A_{ii} \tag{8}$$

(f) A *similarity transformation* of a square matrix (A) into a square matrix (A)′ by a matrix (S) is defined by the following equation

$$(\mathbf{A})' = (\mathbf{SAS}^{-1}) \tag{9}$$

A similarity transformation has the property of leaving matrix equations unchanged. The trace is also invariant under a similarity transformation since

$$\text{trace } (\mathbf{A}) = \sum_i A_{ii}$$

$$\text{trace } (\mathbf{A})' = \sum_i \sum_{mn} S_{im} A_{mn} (S^{-1})_{ni}$$

But,

$$\sum_i S_{im} (S^{-1})_{ni} = \delta_{mn}$$

so,

$$\text{trace } (\mathbf{A})' = \sum_m A_{mm} = \text{trace } (\mathbf{A}) \tag{10}$$

(g) A square matrix is *diagonal* if it has non-zero elements only along its principal diagonal $(i = j)$. The matrix is said to be *diagonalized* by the matrix (S) if $(\mathbf{A})' = (\mathbf{SAS}^{-1})$ is diagonal.

Let us find the form of (A)′. Multiplying on the right by (S) yields

$$(\mathbf{S})(\mathbf{A}) = (\mathbf{A})'(\mathbf{S})$$

Hence if λ_i are the diagonal elements of (A)′ we have

$$\sum_k S_{ik} A_{kj} = \lambda_i S_{ij}$$

A non-trivial solution is only possible if the determinant of the coefficients is zero. Hence

$$\left| A_{kj} - \lambda_i \delta_{kj} \right| = 0 \tag{11}$$

The solutions, λ_i, of this equation are called the *eigenvalues* of the matrix (A) and are the same as the eigenvalues of the operator A. A similarity transformation has the property of leaving the eigenvalues of a matrix unchanged.

C—(a) If A is Hermitian then $A_{ij} = A_{ji}^*$ and conversely.

$$A_{ij} = \int \phi_i^* \mathbf{A} \phi_j \, d\tau = \int \phi_j (\mathbf{A}\phi_i)^* \, d\tau = A_{ji}^* \tag{12}$$

(b) The *adjoint matrix* ($A^\dagger$) of A is defined by

$$(A^\dagger)_{ij} = A^*_{ji} \tag{13}$$

so that a Hermitian matrix is equal to its adjoint.

(c) A square matrix is *unitary* if

$$(\mathbf{A}^\dagger) = (\mathbf{A}^{-1}) \tag{14}$$

D—(a) A wave function φ can be represented as a column matrix. Suppose that in a particular representation

$$\varphi = \sum_n c_n \phi_n \tag{15}$$

φ is completely specified by the c_i which may be arranged in a column thus,

$$\begin{pmatrix} c_1 \\ c_2 \\ \vdots \end{pmatrix} \tag{16}$$

As we shall see this is a generalization of the concept of a vector to an infinite dimensional space.

If φ is normalized: $\displaystyle\int \varphi^*\varphi \, d\tau = \sum_n c_n^* c_n = 1$ (17)

If $\varphi_a = \sum c_{an}\phi_n$ and $\varphi_b = \sum_n c_{bn}\phi_n$ are orthogonal:

$$\int \varphi_a^*\varphi_b \, d\tau = \int \sum_{n,m} c_{am}^* c_{bn} \phi_m^* \phi_n \, d\tau = \sum_m c_{am}^* c_{bm} = 0 \tag{18}$$

(b) Any Hermitian matrix (A) can be diagonalized by a unitary similarity transformation.

To prove this we take the first eigenvalue a_1 and its associated eigenfunction φ_1. In the representation used

$$\varphi_1 = \sum c_n^{(1)} \phi_n$$

Form any unitary matrix $U^{(1)}$ with the $c_j^{(1)}$ as its first column.

$$\begin{pmatrix} c_1^{(1)} & \cdots \\ c_2^{(1)} & \\ \vdots & \end{pmatrix}$$

Thus

$$(U^{(1)*}AU^{(1)})_{m1} = \sum_i U_{im}^{(1)*} \sum_j A_{ij} U_{j1}^{(1)}$$

$$= \sum_i U_{im}^{(1)*} a_1 U_{i1}^{(1)} = a_1 \delta_{m1}$$

Because of the Hermitian property of (A), the first row will also consist of zero except in the (1,1) position.

Hence,

$$(\mathbf{U}^{(1)*}\mathbf{A}\mathbf{U}^{(1)}) = \begin{pmatrix} a_1 & 0 & 0 & . & . & . \\ 0 & & & & & \\ 0 & & \mathbf{A}^{(2)} & & & \\ \vdots & & & & & \end{pmatrix}$$

By noting first that,

$$\begin{pmatrix} 1 & 0 \\ 0 & \mathbf{U}^{(2)*} \end{pmatrix}\begin{pmatrix} a_1 & 0 \\ 0 & \mathbf{A}^{(2)} \end{pmatrix}\begin{pmatrix} 1 & 0 \\ 0 & \mathbf{U}^{(2)} \end{pmatrix} = \begin{pmatrix} a_1 & 0 \\ 0 & \mathbf{U}^{(2)*}\mathbf{A}^{(2)}\mathbf{U}^{(2)} \end{pmatrix}$$

and second that

$$\begin{pmatrix} 1 & 0 \\ 0 & \mathbf{U}^{(2)} \end{pmatrix}(\mathbf{U}^{(1)})$$

is unitary, we see by repeating the argument that $(\mathbf{A})$ is diagonalized by the unitary matrix $(\mathbf{U}\dagger)$ where

$$(\mathbf{U}) = \ldots \begin{pmatrix} 1 & 0 \\ 0 & \mathbf{U}^{(2)} \end{pmatrix}(\mathbf{U}^{(1)})$$

E—Changes from one representation to another representation can now be affected. Suppose that we have the matrix of an operator $\mathbf{A}$ in the ϕ representation and we wish to change to some other orthogonal and normalized set of functions φ_i. Thus

$$A_{ij} = \int \phi_i^* \mathbf{A}\phi_j \, d\tau \tag{19}$$

$$A'_{mn} = \int \varphi_m^* \mathbf{A}\varphi_n \, d\tau \tag{20}$$

We wish to find the relationship between A_{ij} and A'_{mn}. Let

$$\varphi_m = \sum_i S_{im} \phi_i \tag{21}$$

S_{ij} is called the *transformation matrix*.
Hence,

$$A'_{mn} = \int \sum_{ij} S_{im}^* S_{jn} \phi_i \mathbf{A}\phi_j \, d\tau$$

$$= \sum_{ij} S_{im}^* A_{ij} S_{jn} = (S^\dagger A S)_{mn} \tag{22}$$

$(\mathbf{S})$ is a unitary matrix since

$$S_{mn} = \int \varphi_m^* \varphi_n \, d\tau = \int \sum_{ij} S_{im}^* S_{jn} \phi_i^* \phi_j \, d\tau$$

$$= \sum_i S_{im}^* S_{in} \tag{23}$$

Thus, from any given representation, an equivalent representation of all quantum mechanical relationships can be obtained by means of unitary similarity transformation.[5]

F—As a conclusion to this section we obtain Schrödinger's equation in matrix notation. Consider the representation,

$$\Psi = \sum_n c_n \varphi_n \tag{24}$$

Substituting this into Schrödinger's time-dependent equation, Eq. (2.5), we obtain

$$i\hbar \sum_n \frac{\partial c_n}{\partial t} \varphi_n = \sum_i c_n \mathbf{H} \varphi_n \tag{25}$$

and on multiplying by φ_m^* and integrating we have, because of the orthogonality and normality of the φ_n,

$$i\hbar \frac{\partial c_m}{\partial t} = \sum_n c_n H_{mn} \tag{26}$$

which is Schrödinger's equation in the φ representation.

4. The Density Matrix

Suppose we have an ensemble consisting of a large number, N, of identical systems and let $\Psi^{(k)}$ be the wave function of the kth system. Consider the representation

$$\Psi^{(k)} = \sum_n c_n^{(k)} \varphi_n \tag{1}$$

Define the density matrix[1] by

$$\rho_{nm} = \frac{1}{N} \sum_{k=1}^{N} c_m^{(k)*} c_n^{(k)} \tag{2}$$

We can obtain an interpretation of the diagonal elements of the density matrix,

$$\rho_{nn} = \frac{1}{N} \sum_{k=1}^{N} c_n^{(k)*} c_n^{(k)} \tag{3}$$

ρ_{nn} is thus the probability that a system chosen at random from the ensemble will be in the state n. The density matrix is the quantum analogue of the density function $\rho(p, q)$ in classical statistical mechanics.

---

[5] It can be shown (P. A. M. Dirac, *The Principles of Quantum Mechanics*, 3rd Ed., Oxford University Press, 1947, pp. 125–130) that in the classical limit a unitary similarity transformation of the wave functions produces a contact transformation of the classical conjugate variables p and q.

[1] J. von Neumann, *Gottinger Nachrichten*, **1927**, 245.

The density matrix has the following important properties:

A—

$$\text{trace } (\rho) = 1 \tag{4}$$

This follows from the normalization of each of the $\Psi^{(k)}$

$$1 = \frac{1}{N} \sum_{k=1}^{N} \int \Psi^{(k)*}\Psi^{(k)} \, d\tau = \frac{1}{N} \sum_{k=1}^{N} \sum_{n} c_n^{(k)*} c_n^{(k)}$$

$$= \sum_{n} \rho_{nn} = \text{trace } (\rho) \tag{5}$$

In other words the probability of finding a system chosen at random from the ensemble in some state is unity. Also we note that summing over the diagonal elements of the density matrix is the quantum analogue of integrating $\rho(p, q)$ over all of phase space.

B—The ensemble average $\overline{\langle A \rangle}$ of a physical quantity A is given by

$$\overline{\langle A \rangle} = \text{trace } (\mathbf{A}\rho) \tag{6}$$

Because the trace is independent of the representation so also is $\overline{\langle A \rangle}$.

$$\overline{\langle \mathbf{A} \rangle} = \frac{1}{N} \sum_{k=1}^{N} \int \Psi^{(k)*} \mathbf{A} \Psi^{(k)} d\tau$$

$$= \frac{1}{N} \sum_{k=1}^{N} \int \left(\sum_m c_m^{(k)*}\varphi_m^*\right) \mathbf{A} \left(\sum_n c_n^{(k)}\varphi_n\right) d\tau$$

$$= \frac{1}{N} \sum_{k=1}^{N} \sum_{m,n} A_{mn} c_m^{(k)*} c_n^{(k)} = \sum_{m,n} A_{mn} \rho_{nm}$$

$$\overline{\langle \mathbf{A} \rangle} = \sum_m (A\rho)_{mm} = \text{trace } (\mathbf{A}\rho) \tag{7}$$

Again we see the correspondence between the trace of a quantum mechanical matrix and the integral of the classical quantity over phase space.

C—

$$i\hbar \frac{\partial \rho_{mn}}{\partial t} = \sum_j (H_{mj}\rho_{jn} - \rho_{mj}H_{jn}) \tag{8}$$

This is the quantum analogue to Liouville's theorem [see Eqs. (4.2.10) and (4.1.1)] in classical statistical mechanics.[2] We prove Eq. (8) by means of the matrix-Schrödinger equation, Eq. (3.26), and its complex conjugate,

$$i\hbar \frac{\partial c_m^{(k)}}{\partial t} = \sum_j c_j^{(k)} H_{mj}, \qquad i\hbar \frac{\partial c_n^{(k)*}}{\partial t} = -\sum_j c_j^{(k)*} H_{nj}^* \tag{9}$$

[2] This correspondence is a special case of the correspondence between Poisson brackets in classical mechanics and commutator brackets in quantum mechanics. See L. I. Schiff, *op. cit.*, pp. 133–135.

Thus, multiplying the first equation by $c_n^{(k)*}$ and the second by $c_m^{(k)}$ and adding the resulting two equations, we have, since $d(uv) = udv + vdu$,

$$i\hbar \frac{\partial}{\partial t} (c_n^{(k)*} c_m^{(k)}) = \sum_j (c_n^{(k)*} c_j^{(k)} H_{mj} - c_j^{(k)*} c_m^{(k)} H_{nj}^*)$$

$$= \sum_j (c_n^{(k)*} c_j^{(k)} H_{mj} - c_j^{(k)*} c_m^{(k)} H_{jn}) \qquad (10)$$

since $\mathbf{H}$ is Hermitian. Summing Eq. (10) over k, dividing by N, and taking into account Eq. (2) yields Eq. (8).

D—Consider the ϕ representation, such that

$$\varphi_j = \sum_i S_{ij} \phi_i \qquad (11)$$

where $(\mathbf{S})$ is unitary, then if $(\rho)'$ is the density matrix in the ϕ representation and (ρ) the density matrix in the φ representation, we have

$$(\rho)' = (\mathbf{S}^\dagger \rho \mathbf{S}) \qquad (12)$$

since

$$\Psi^{(k)} = \sum_m b_m^{(k)} \phi_m = \sum_n c_n^{(k)} \varphi_n$$

$$= \sum_{n,m} c_n^{(k)} S_{mn} \phi_m \qquad (13)$$

so that

$$b_m^{(k)} = \sum_n c_n^{(k)} S_{mn} \qquad (14)$$

Thus,

$$\rho'_{ij} = \frac{1}{N} \sum_{k=1}^N b_j^{(k)*} b_i^{(k)}$$

$$= \frac{1}{N} \sum_{k=1}^N \left[\sum_{m,n} c_m^{(k)*} S_{jm}^* c_n^{(k)} S_{in} \right]$$

$$\rho'_{ij} = \sum_{m,n} S_{jm}^* \rho_{nm} S_{in} = \sum_{m,n} S_{ni}^* \rho_{nm} S_{mj} \qquad (15)$$

$$(\rho)' = (\mathbf{S}^\dagger \rho \mathbf{S}) \qquad (16)$$

5. The Fundamental Postulates of Equal *a Priori* Probabilities and Random *a Priori* Phases for the Quantum Mechanical States of a System

Because the postulates of classical mechanics are insufficient to form a foundation for classical statistical mechanics it was necessary to introduce in Sect. 4.3 the additional postulate of equal *a priori* probabilities for equal volumes in phase space.

In quantum statistical mechanics, because of the lack of precise knowledge of the state of a system, it is necessary to introduce a postulate, in addition to those of quantum mechanics, so that we are able to choose the probabilities and phases of the eigenfunctions for the different states that agree equally well with that partial knowledge of the system.

We take as the *fundamental postulate* of quantum statistical mechanics the assumption of *equal* a priori *probabilities and random* a priori *phases for the quantum mechanical states of a system having the same energy.* The justification of this postulate is the complete agreement of its consequences with experiment.

In order to understand the meaning of the assumption of random *a priori* phases we consider the following example due to Tolman.[1] Consider the uniform ensemble

$$\rho_{ij} = \rho_0 \delta_{ij} \tag{1}$$

where ρ_0 is a constant real number. In other words the density matrix is diagonal with all elements equal in some representation. Equation (1) is in fact true for all representations since by Eq. (4.16) we have

$$\rho'_{mn} = \sum_{i,j} S^*_{im} \rho_{ij} S_{jn} = \rho_0 \sum_j S^*_{jm} S_{jn} = \rho_0 \delta_{mn} \tag{2}$$

The last equality is true since (S) is unitary.

Now by the definition of the density matrix we have

$$\rho_{nm} = \frac{1}{N} \sum_{k=1}^{N} c_m^{(k)*} c_n^{(k)} \tag{3}$$

The $c_j^{(k)}$ are, in general, complex quantities so that

$$c_j^{(k)} = r_j^{(k)} e^{i\theta_j^{(k)}}$$

and thus

$$\rho_{mn} = \frac{1}{N} \sum_{k=1}^{N} r_m^{(k)} r_n^{(k)} e^{i(\theta_n^{(k)} - \theta_m^{(k)})} \tag{4}$$

The only non-arbitrary way of insuring the simultaneous validity of Eqs. (1) and (4) is to assume that the phases $\theta_j^{(k)}$ are random. In other words *the assumption of random* a priori *phases insures that the density matrix will be diagonal.*

6. Ensemble in Quantum Statistics

We define the *canonical ensemble* in quantum statistical mechanics by means of

$$\rho = C e^{-H/kT} \tag{1}$$

where ρ and H are operators. Equation (1) is to be regarded as an abbreviation for

$$\rho = C \sum_{m=0}^{\infty} \frac{1}{m!} [-H/kT]^m \tag{2}$$

---

[1] R. C. Tolman, *op. cit.*, pp. 343–344.

Also, if $\mathscr{E}_m$ is the energy eigenvalue for the mth state of the system, we have for the *partition function*,

$$f_N = \sum_m e^{-\mathscr{E}_m/kT} = \text{trace}\,(e^{-H/kT}) \tag{3}$$

Since the trace is invariant under similarity transformations, the partition function is independent of the representation used.

The grand canonical ensemble in quantum statistical mechanics is defined by the density matrix

$$\rho = C\,e^{(N\mu - H)/kT} \tag{4}$$

where ρ and H are operators. If $\mathscr{E}_m$ is the energy eigenvalue for the mth state of the system then the *grand partition function* is

$$\Xi = \sum_{N,\,m} e^{(N\mu - \mathscr{E}_m)/kT} = \text{trace}\,(e^{(N\mu - H)/kT}) \tag{5}$$

The grand partition function is thus independent of the representation.

7. Symmetric and Antisymmetric Wave Functions; the Pauli Principle

As was discussed in Sect. 4.6 the interchange of two identical particles in a system does not give rise to a different state of the system. Because of the Heisenberg uncertainty relations, the concept of the path of a system ceases to have meaning. Thus, in quantum mechanics identical particles are said to be *indistinguishable*.

Consider a system of two particles and let $\Psi\,(1, 2)$, where the integers 1 and 2 represent the coordinates of the two particles, be the wave function of the system. Interchanging the two particles yields the same state and thus $|\Psi\,(2, 1)| = |\Psi\,(1, 2)|$. This means that the two wave functions can only differ by a phase factor,

$$\Psi(2, 1) = e^{i\theta}\,\Psi(1, 2) \tag{1}$$

Interchanging the two identical particles again yields

$$\Psi(1, 2) = e^{i\theta}\,\Psi(2, 1) = e^{i2\theta}\,\Psi(1, 2) \tag{2}$$

so that $e^{i2\theta} = 1$, or $e^{i\theta} = \pm 1$ and hence,

$$\Psi(2, 1) = \pm\,\Psi(1, 2) \tag{3}$$

This result can be generalized to systems containing any number of identical particles. Wave functions which do not change sign on the interchange of two identical particles are called *symmetric* wave functions and wave functions which do change sign are called *antisymmetric*.

It is observed that the wave functions which describe either a proton, a neutron, or an electron are antisymmetric whereas the wave function which describes a photon is symmetric. Atomic nuclei composed of an odd number of neutrons and protons are described by antisymmetric wave functions and nuclei with an even number of neutrons and protons are described by symmetric wave functions.

Consider a system of N identical particles such that the Hamiltonian of the system can be considered to be the sum of the Hamiltonians for the particles to a sufficient degree of approximation

$$\mathbf{H} = \sum_i \mathbf{H}(i) \tag{4}$$

The time-independent Schrödinger equation is

$$\mathbf{H}\psi = \mathscr{E}\psi \tag{5}$$

We can separate the variables,

$$\psi = \psi_\alpha(1)\psi_\beta(2)\ldots, \quad \mathscr{E} = \varepsilon_\alpha + \varepsilon_\beta + \ldots$$
$$\mathbf{H}(i)\psi_\mu(i) = \varepsilon_\mu\psi_\mu(i) \tag{6}$$

If the particles have symmetric wave functions then we have as the wave function for the system,

$$\psi = \frac{1}{\sqrt{N!}} \sum_P P\psi_\alpha(1)\psi_\beta(2)\ldots \tag{7}$$

where $P\psi_\alpha(1)\psi_\beta(2)\ldots$ is obtained from $\psi_\alpha(1)\psi_\beta(2)\ldots$ by a permutation of the arguments of the particle wave functions.

On the other hand if the particles have antisymmetric wave functions then we have as the wave function for the system,

$$\psi = \frac{1}{\sqrt{N!}} \begin{vmatrix} \psi_\alpha(1) & \psi_\alpha(2) & \cdots \\ \psi_\beta(1) & \psi_\beta(2) & \cdots \\ \cdot & \cdot & \\ \cdot & \cdot & \\ \cdot & \cdot & \end{vmatrix} \tag{8}$$

Should two of the particles occupy the same state then two columns of the above determinant would be equal and $\psi = 0$. In other words two particles with antisymmetric wave functions cannot occupy the same state. This is the *Pauli exclusion principle*.[1]

We shall now incorporate the above considerations about indistinguishable particles into statistical mechanics. We shall find that particles which have symmetric wave functions obey *Bose–Einstein statistics* and particles which have antisymmetric wave functions obey *Fermi–Dirac statistics*. We have already encountered these statistics in Sects. 1.13 and 14. These formulae can also be obtained by the method of the most probable distribution[2] but

[1] W. Pauli, *Z. Physik*, **31**, 776 (1925).
[2] See, for example, *Q.C.*, pp. 285–288.

this is not entirely satisfactory[3] so instead we shall obtain these results by two rigorous methods. First we shall use the method of the grand partition function, and then, in the next chapter, the method of Darwin and Fowler.

8. Bose–Einstein[1] and Fermi–Dirac[2] Statistics

A. Bose–Einstein statistics

Consider a gas of identical independent particles, each particle having a symmetric wave function. If n_i is the number of particles occupying the energy level ε_i then

$$N = \sum_i n_i, \qquad \mathscr{E} = \sum_i n_i \varepsilon_i \tag{1}$$

There is no restriction on the values of the n_i since any number of particles can occupy a given energy level. The grand partition function is

$$\Xi = \sum_{N=0}^{\infty} e^{(\mu N - \mathscr{E})/kT} = \sum_{\sum n_i = 0}^{\infty} e^{(\mu \sum_i n_i - \sum_i n_i \varepsilon_i)/kT} \tag{2}$$

The symbol $\sum_{\sum n_i = 0}^{\infty}$ means that the summation is to run over all values of n_i such that $\sum n_i = 0, 1, 2 \ldots$. Thus[3]

$$\Xi = \sum_{\sum n_i = 0}^{\infty} \prod_i e^{(\mu - \varepsilon_i)n_i/kT} = \prod_i \sum_{n_i=0}^{\infty} e^{(\mu - \varepsilon_i)n_i/kT}$$

$$= \prod_i \frac{1}{1 - e^{(\mu - \varepsilon_i)/kT}} \tag{3}$$

---

[3] Briefly, an objection to this method is that in deriving Fermi–Dirac statistics $g_k - n_k$ must be assumed large, where g_k is the degeneracy of the energy level ε_k and n_k the number of particles which occupy the level. Then $(g_k - n_k)!$ may be expanded by Stirling's approximation which enables one to obtain the result

$$n_k = \frac{g_k}{e^{\alpha}e^{\beta \varepsilon_k} + 1}$$

But for the case $e^{\alpha} e^{\beta \varepsilon_k} \ll 1$ we see that $n_k \simeq g_k$, contradicting the assumption that $g_k - n_k$ is large.

[1] S. Bose, *Z. Physik*, **26**, 178 (1924); A. Einstein, *Berliner Ber.*, **1924**, 261; **1925**, 3, 18.

[2] E. Fermi, *Z. Physik*, **36**, 902 (1926); P. A. M. Dirac, *Proc. Roy. Soc. (London)*, **A112**, 661 (1926).

[3] The validity of the operation of interchanging the order of summation and multiplication used in obtaining Eq. (3) is clearer using the following simplified notation

$$\prod_i \sum_{n_i=0}^{\infty} a_i{}^{n_i} = (1 + a_1 + a_1{}^2 + \ldots)(1 + a_2 + a_2{}^2 + \ldots)(1 + a_3 + a_3{}^2 + \ldots)\ldots$$

$$= 1 + a_1 + a_2 + a_3 + \ldots + a_1{}^2 + a_1 a_2 + a_2{}^2 + a_1 a_3 + a_2 a_3 + a_3{}^2 + \ldots$$

$$= \sum_{\sum n_i = 0}^{\infty} a_1{}^{n_1} a_2{}^{n_2} a_3{}^{n_3} \ldots = \sum_{\sum n_i = 0}^{\infty} \prod_i a_i{}^{n_i}$$

Whence, if we let

$$\Xi_i = \frac{1}{1 - e^{(\mu - \varepsilon_i)/kT}} \tag{4}$$

we have for the mean number of particles in the system

$$\bar{N} = kT \frac{\partial \ln \Xi}{\partial \mu} = kT \sum_i \frac{\partial \ln \Xi_i}{\partial \mu} \tag{5}$$

Since $\bar{N} = \sum_i \bar{n}_i$ we have

$$\bar{n}_i = kT \frac{\partial \ln \Xi_i}{\partial \mu} = \frac{e^{(\mu - \varepsilon_i)/kT}}{1 - e^{(\mu - \varepsilon_i)/kT}} \tag{6}$$

$$\bar{n}_i = \frac{1}{e^{(\varepsilon_i - \mu)/kT} - 1} \tag{7}$$

All the $\bar{n}_i$ are positive numbers and thus we require that $e^{(\varepsilon_i - \mu)/kT} \geq 1$ for all i. It is to be noted that the Bose–Einstein formulae will reduce to the Boltzmann formulae if

$$e^{-\mu/kT} \gg 1 \tag{8}$$

It is of interest to investigate the fluctuations in $\bar{n}_i$ for the Bose–Einstein case. Applying Eq. (4.17.8) to Eq. (4) gives

$$\overline{(n_i - \bar{n}_i)^2} = \frac{\partial^2 \ln \Xi_i}{\partial (\mu/kT)^2} = \frac{e^{(\varepsilon_i - \mu)/kT}}{(e^{(\varepsilon_i - \mu)/kT} - 1)^2}$$

$$= \bar{n}_i + \bar{n}_i^2 \tag{9}$$

Hence

$$\frac{\overline{(n_i - n_i)^2}}{n_i^2} = \frac{1}{\bar{n}_i} + 1 \tag{10}$$

If the gas is strongly degenerate, then as is seen from Eq. (7), $\bar{n}_0 \simeq N$ and so we would expect large fluctuations in the value of n_0.

B. Fermi–Dirac Statistics

Consider a gas of identical particles, each particle having an antisymmetric wave function. Again let n_i be the number of particles occupying the energy level ε_i. Because of the Pauli exclusion principle, n_i can only have the values zero or one. The grand partition function is particularly easy to evaluate:

$$\Xi = \sum_{\substack{\sum n_i = 0 \\ n_i = 0, 1}}^{\infty} \prod_i e^{n_i(\mu - \varepsilon_i)/kT} = \prod_i \sum_{n_i = 0, 1} e^{n_i(\mu - \varepsilon_i)/kT}$$

$$= \prod_i (1 + e^{(\mu - \varepsilon_i)/kT}) \tag{11}$$

Thus if

$$\Xi_i = 1 + e^{(\mu - \varepsilon_i)/kT} \tag{12}$$

we have

$$\bar{n}_i = kT \frac{\partial \ln \Xi_i}{\partial \mu} = \frac{e^{(\mu - \varepsilon_i)/kT}}{1 + e^{(\mu - \varepsilon_i)/kT}} \tag{13}$$

$$\bar{n}_i = \frac{1}{e^{(\varepsilon_i - \mu)/kT} + 1} \tag{14}$$

In this case μ can take on any value.

Fluctuations in n_i are given by

$$\overline{(n_i - \bar{n}_i)^2} = \frac{\partial^2 \ln \Xi_i}{\partial(\mu/kT)^2} = \frac{e^{(\varepsilon_i - \mu)/kT}}{(e^{(\varepsilon_i - \mu)/kT} + 1)^2}$$

$$= \bar{n}_i - \bar{n}_i^2 \tag{15}$$

$$\frac{\overline{(n_i - \bar{n}_i)^2}}{\bar{n}_i^2} = \frac{1}{\bar{n}_i} - 1 \tag{16}$$

Since the n_i can only be zero or one, the fluctuations given by Eq. (15) are not large. However, the relative fluctuations given by (16) will not, in general, be small unless $\bar{n}_i$ is virtually one.

From Eqs. (7) and (14) we see that Bose–Einstein and Fermi–Dirac formulae reduce to the Boltzmann formula in the case,

$$e^{(\varepsilon_i - \mu)/kT} \gg 1 \tag{17}$$

This will certainly be the case if ε_i is sufficiently large. The condition for the validity of Boltzmann statistics will be

$$e^{-\mu/kT} \gg 1 \tag{18}$$

But for the classical limit Eq. (4.16.4) gives

$$e^{\mu/kT} = \frac{N}{V} \left(\frac{h^2}{2\pi m kT} \right)^{\frac{1}{2}}$$

The de Broglie wave length for a particle is

$$\lambda = h/p = h/(2m\varepsilon)^{\frac{1}{2}} = (h^2/3mkT)^{\frac{1}{2}} \tag{19}$$

so that

$$e^{\mu/kT} = \left(\frac{3}{2\pi} \right) \frac{N}{V} \lambda^3 \tag{20}$$

Thus Eq. (18) requires that for classical behavior the de Broglie wavelength must be small compared to the average distance between particles. This can be achieved at *low densities* or at *high temperatures*, Eq. (19). Whenever there are departures from classical behavior the gas is said to be *degenerate*.

9. Density of States; Black Body Radiation

We wish to calculate the number of states in an energy range $d\varepsilon$ for a particle enclosed in a volume V. For convenience the volume is assumed to be a cube of edge L. The energy levels of a particle in a box were obtained in Sect. 1.4. Referring to Eq. (1.4.4) the energy levels for a particle in a cube of edge L are given by

$$\varepsilon(k_x, k_y, k_z) = \frac{h^2}{8mL^2}(k_x^2 + k_y^2 + k_z^2) \tag{1}$$

where k_x, k_y, k_z are positive integers. Equation (1) is the equation of a sphere in k_x, k_y, k_z space.

Each state is specified by a 'lattice point' in the positive octant of k_x, k_y, k_z space and, therefore, there is one state per unit volume of this space. Thus if we define

$$k^2 = k_x^2 + k_y^2 + k_z^2 \tag{2}$$

then the number of states with k in the range dk is given by the volume of a spherical shell of radius k lying in the positive octant of k_x, k_y, k_z space,

$$g(k)\,dk = \tfrac{1}{8} \cdot 4\pi k^2\,dk \tag{3}$$

Usually it is more convenient to know the number of states with energy ε in the range $d\varepsilon$. Making use of Eqs. (1) and (2) we have

$$g(\varepsilon)\,d\varepsilon = 2\pi(2m/h^2)^{\frac{3}{2}}V\varepsilon^{\frac{1}{2}}\,d\varepsilon \tag{4}$$

The above expressions are correct only for particles of spin zero. For a particle of spin s we must multiply the above expressions by $2s+1$ to take into account that $2s+1$ states will correspond to one energy state defined by Eq. (1).

We are now able to discuss the spectral distribution of black body radiation, which we regard as being a photon gas, enclosed in volume V, which is in thermal equilibrium with matter (the black body). The system is isolated and, hence, has a definite energy E. However, photons absorbed at one frequency might be emitted at another frequency and in different numbers so as to conserve the energy. Hence the number of particles in the system is not conserved. In other words we have the 'reaction' $aA \rightleftharpoons bA$. At equilibrium we have the condition (recall Sect. 3.7)

$$0 = a\mu - b\mu = (a-b)\mu$$
$$\mu = 0 \tag{5}$$

since $a \neq b$.

Since a photon has no rest mass, Eqs. (3) and (4) are not directly applicable. We write $\varepsilon = p^2/2m$ and substitute this into Eq. (1) obtaining

$$p = \frac{hk}{2L} \tag{6}$$

However, for a photon emitted at a frequency v,

$$p = hv/c \tag{7}$$

Thus, the number of states with frequency in the range dv is

$$g(v)\, dv = 2 \cdot \frac{4\pi v^2 V}{c^3}\, dv \tag{8}$$

The factor 2 has been inserted because transverse electromagnetic radiation has two degrees of freedom.

Since $\mu = 0$ the probability of a photon having energy $\varepsilon = hv$ is

$$\frac{1}{e^{hv/kT} - 1} \tag{9}$$

so that the number of photons with frequency in the range dv is

$$dn = \frac{8\pi v^2}{c^3}\, V \frac{dv}{e^{hv/kT} - 1} \tag{10}$$

The energy, per unit volume, of the photons whose frequency is in the interval dv is obtained by multiplying dn/V by hv. Thus,

$$\rho(v)\, dv = \frac{8\pi h v^3}{c^3}\, \frac{dv}{e^{hv/kT} - 1} \tag{11}$$

This is the famous *Planck radiation law*.[1] We shall return to the subject of black body radiation in more detail in Chapter 7.

10. Perfect Bose–Einstein Gas; Einstein Condensation

We shall now discuss a gas composed of Bose–Einstein particles with spin s with a non-zero rest mass. From Eq. (8.3) we have

$$\ln \Xi = - \sum_{i=0}^{\infty} \ln\left(1 - e^{(\mu - \varepsilon_i)/kT}\right) \tag{1}$$

Replacing this sum by an integral and noting that the number of states with energy in the range $d\varepsilon$ is

$$(2s+1)2\pi(2m/h^2)^{\frac{3}{2}} V \varepsilon^{\frac{1}{2}}\, d\varepsilon$$

we have

$$\ln \Xi = -2\pi(2s+1)\left(\frac{2m}{h^2}\right)^{\frac{3}{2}} V \int_0^{\infty} \varepsilon^{\frac{1}{2}} \ln\left(1 - e^{(\mu - \varepsilon)/kT}\right) d\varepsilon \tag{2}$$

Equation (2) can only be evaluated in the limiting cases of *weak degeneracy* $e^{\mu/kT} \ll 1$ and *strong degeneracy* $e^{\mu/kT} \simeq 1$ (if the zero of energy has

[1] M. Planck, *Ann. Physik*, **4**, 553 (1901).

been taken at the lowest energy level). Before embarking on an investigation of these cases we can prove a general result. We have

$$E = \mu\overline{N} + kT^2 \frac{\partial \ln \Xi}{\partial T} = kT^2 \frac{\partial}{\partial T}\left(-\frac{\mu\overline{N}}{kT} + \ln \Xi\right)$$

$$p = kT \frac{\partial \ln \Xi}{\partial V} = kT \frac{\partial}{\partial V}\left(-\frac{\mu\overline{N}}{kT} + \ln \Xi\right) \tag{3}$$

If we introduce the new variable $x^2 = \varepsilon/kT$ we obtain

$$\ln \Xi = -4\pi(2s+1)\left(\frac{2mkT}{h^2}\right)^{\frac{3}{2}} V \int_0^\infty x^2 \ln\left(1 - e^{\mu/kT - x^2}\right) dx \tag{4}$$

Also

$$\overline{N} = \sum_{i=0}^\infty \frac{1}{e^{(\varepsilon_i - \mu)/kT} - 1} = 4\pi(2s+1)\left(\frac{2mkT}{h^2}\right)^{\frac{3}{2}} V \int_0^\infty \frac{x^2 \, dx}{e^{-\mu/kT + x^2} - 1} \tag{5}$$

Thus $e^{\mu/kT}$ and μ/kT are functions of $VT^{\frac{3}{2}}$ (see Eqs. 8.19, 8.20 and 5), from which we can infer that $\ln \Xi$ and $-(\mu/kT)\overline{N} + \ln \Xi$ are functions of $VT^{\frac{3}{2}}$. Thus if we denote $-(\mu\overline{N}/kT) \div \ln \Xi$ by F we see that

$$\frac{\partial F}{\partial T} = \tfrac{3}{2}VT^{\frac{1}{2}} \frac{\partial A}{\partial(VT^{\frac{3}{2}})}$$

$$\frac{\partial F}{\partial V} = T^{\frac{3}{2}} \frac{\partial A}{\partial(VT^{\frac{3}{2}})} \tag{6}$$

Thus

$$E = kT^2 \frac{\partial A}{\partial T} = \tfrac{3}{2}VkT^{\frac{5}{2}} \frac{\partial A}{\partial(VT^{\frac{3}{2}})}$$

$$p = kT \frac{\partial A}{\partial V} = kT^{\frac{5}{2}} \frac{\partial A}{\partial(VT^{\frac{3}{2}})} \tag{7}$$

and so

$$pV = \tfrac{2}{3}E \tag{8}$$

This result is also true for a perfect gas since $E = \tfrac{3}{2}NkT$ and $pV = NkT$. This is to be expected since Bose–Einstein statistics become Boltzmann statistics in the classical case. We shall also find this result true for a perfect Fermi–Dirac gas. We shall now investigate the two limiting cases.

A. Weak degeneracy

We must evaluate $\ln \Xi$ for the case $e^{\mu/kT} \ll 1$. Before doing this it is convenient to obtain a series expansion for $e^{\mu/kT}$ by successive approximations. To a first approximation Eq. (5) becomes

$$\overline{N} = 4\pi(2s+1)\left(\frac{2mkT}{h^2}\right)^{\frac{3}{2}} V e^{\mu/kT} \int_0^\infty x^2 e^{-x^2} dx$$

$$= 4\pi(2s+1)\left(\frac{2mkT}{h^2}\right)^{\frac{3}{2}} V e^{\mu/kT} \frac{\pi^{\frac{1}{2}}}{4} \tag{9}$$

where we have used Integral (2) in Appendix 2. Thus, to a first approximation,

$$e^{\mu/kT} = \frac{1}{2s+1} \frac{\bar{N}}{V} \left(\frac{h^2}{2\pi mkT} \right)^{\frac{3}{2}} \tag{10}$$

To obtain a second approximation we expand the denominator of the integrand in Eq. (5):

$$\bar{N} = 4\pi(2s+1) \left(\frac{2mkT}{h^2} \right)^{\frac{3}{2}} V \int_0^\infty \frac{x^2 \, dx}{e^{-\mu/kT+x^2} - 1}$$

$$= 4\pi(2s+1) \left(\frac{2mkT}{h^2} \right)^{\frac{3}{2}} V \int_0^\infty \frac{x^2 \, e^{\mu/kT-x^2}}{1 - e^{\mu/kT-x^2}} \, dx$$

$$= 4\pi(2s+1) \left(\frac{2mkT}{h^2} \right)^{\frac{3}{2}} V \int_0^\infty x^2 \, e^{\mu/kT-x^2}$$

$$\times (1 + e^{\mu/kT-x^2} + e^{2\mu/kT-2x^2} + \ldots) \, dx$$

$$\bar{N} = 4\pi(2s+1) \left(\frac{2mkT}{h^2} \right)^{\frac{3}{2}} V \frac{\pi^{\frac{1}{2}}}{4} \left[e^{\mu/kT} + \frac{e^{2\mu/kT}}{2^{\frac{3}{2}}} + \frac{e^{3\mu/kT}}{3^{\frac{3}{2}}} + \ldots \right] \tag{11}$$

If we introduce the notation

$$y = \frac{1}{2s+1} \frac{\bar{N}}{V} \left(\frac{h^2}{2\pi mkT} \right)^{\frac{3}{2}} \tag{12}$$

and substitute the first approximation for $e^{\mu/kT}$ into the second term of the series in Eq. (11), we have

$$y = e^{\mu/kT} + \frac{y^2}{2^{\frac{3}{2}}} + \ldots \tag{13}$$

Thus, to a second approximation, we have

$$e^{\mu/kT} = y - \frac{y^2}{2^{\frac{3}{2}}} + \ldots \tag{14}$$

We are now able to evaluate the thermodynamic functions for this case. If we note that

$$-\ln(1-t) = \sum_{n=1}^\infty \frac{t^n}{n}$$

we have

$$\ln \Xi = -4\pi(2s+1) \left(\frac{2mkT}{h^2} \right)^{\frac{3}{2}} V \int_0^\infty x^2 \ln(1 - e^{\mu/kT-x^2}) \, dx$$

$$= \frac{4\bar{N}}{y\pi^{\frac{1}{2}}} \sum_{n=1}^\infty \frac{e^{\mu n/kT}}{n} \int_0^\infty x^2 \, e^{-nx^2} \, dx$$

$$\ln \Xi = \frac{\bar{N}}{y} \sum_{n=1}^\infty \frac{e^{\mu n/kT}}{n^{\frac{5}{2}}} \tag{15}$$

where we have again used Integral (2) in Appendix 2. Thus using Eq. (14) we have

$$\ln \Xi = \frac{\bar{N}}{y}\left[e^{\mu/kT} + \frac{e^{2\mu/kT}}{2^{\frac{5}{2}}} + \cdots\right]$$

$$= \frac{\bar{N}}{y}\left[y - \frac{y^2}{2^{\frac{3}{2}}} + \frac{y^2}{2^{\frac{5}{2}}} + \cdots\right] \tag{16}$$

$$\ln \Xi = \bar{N}\left[1 - \frac{y}{2^{\frac{5}{2}}} + \cdots\right] \tag{17}$$

Now

$$pV = kT \ln \Xi$$

$$pV = \bar{N}kT\left[1 - \frac{y}{2^{\frac{5}{2}}} + \cdots\right] \tag{18}$$

Thus from Eq. (8) we obtain

$$E = \tfrac{3}{2}\bar{N}kT\left[1 - \frac{y}{2^{\frac{5}{2}}} + \cdots\right] \tag{19}$$

and so

$$C_V = \tfrac{3}{2}\bar{N}k\left[1 + \frac{y}{2^{\frac{7}{2}}} + \cdots\right] \tag{20}$$

Also from Eq. (4.15.7) we have

$$S = \frac{E-A}{T} = \frac{E-\mu\bar{N}}{T} + k\ln\Xi$$

$$= \bar{N}k\left[\frac{5}{2} - \ln y - \frac{y}{2^{\frac{5}{2}}} + \cdots\right] \tag{21}$$

All the above series converge since $y \ll 1$.

B. Strong degeneracy: Einstein condensation

As we have discussed $e^{\mu/kT}$ is limited to the range of values $0 \leqslant e^{\mu/kT} \leqslant 1$. From Eq. (11) we observe that as $e^{\mu/kT}$ increases from zero to unity $\bar{N}$ increases monotonically from zero to a maximum value,

$$\bar{N} = (2s+1)\left(\frac{2\pi mkT}{h^2}\right)^{\frac{3}{2}} V\left[1 + \frac{1}{2^{\frac{3}{2}}} + \frac{1}{3^{\frac{3}{2}}} + \cdots\right]$$

$$= (2s+1)\left(\frac{2\pi mkT}{h^2}\right)^{\frac{3}{2}} V(2.612) \tag{22}[1]$$

[1] The infinite series is a special case of the *Riemann Zeta function*

$$\xi(x) = \sum_{n=1}^{\infty} \frac{1}{n^x}$$

See E. Jahnke and F. Emde, *Tables of Functions*, 4th Ed., Dover, New York, 1945, pp. 269–274.

However, let us return to the original form of this equation

$$\bar{N} = \frac{1}{e^{-\mu/kT} - 1} + \frac{1}{e^{(\varepsilon_1 - \mu)/kT} - 1} + \cdots \tag{23}$$

As $e^{\mu/kT} \to 1$ the first term will dominate and can become arbitrarily large. Therefore there is no limit to the number of particles that the system can accept.

The discrepancy in our results can be easily resolved for since $g(\varepsilon) \to 0$ as $\varepsilon \to 0$ the contribution from the lowest energy level was omitted in replacing the above sum by an integral. In other words, Eq. (11) represents the number of particles in excited states. For the case of few particles, i.e. weak degeneracy, no error has been made since $e^{\mu/kT} \ll 1$ means that the contribution of the lowest state will be negligible.

Thus if we keep $\bar{N}/V$ ($= \rho/m$) constant, where ρ is the density in gm cm^{-3}, and decrease T then Eq. (11) will be correct until a temperature T_0 defined by

$$\frac{\bar{N}}{V} = \frac{\rho}{m} = (2s+1)\left(\frac{2\pi mkT_0}{h^2}\right)^{\frac{3}{2}} 2.612 \tag{24}$$

is reached. For $T < T_0$ the contribution of the lowest energy level becomes important. Thus,

$$\bar{N} = \frac{1}{e^{-\mu/kT} - 1} + (2s+1)\left(\frac{2\pi mkT}{h^2}\right)^{\frac{3}{2}} V \left[e^{\mu/kT} + \frac{e^{2\mu/kT}}{2^{\frac{3}{2}}} + \frac{e^{3\mu/kT}}{3^{\frac{3}{2}}} + \cdots\right] \tag{25}$$

However, for $T < T_0$, $e^{\mu/kT} \simeq 1$ so that,

$$\bar{N} = -\frac{kT}{\mu} + (2s+1)\left(\frac{2\pi mkT}{h^2}\right)^{\frac{3}{2}} V 2.612 \tag{26}$$

Using Eq. (24) to eliminate V we have

$$\bar{N} = -\frac{kT}{\mu} + \bar{N}\left(\frac{T}{T_0}\right)^{\frac{3}{2}} = n_0 + \bar{N}\left(\frac{T}{T_0}\right)^{\frac{3}{2}} \tag{27}$$

where n_0 is the number of particles in the lowest energy state. Thus, as we see in Figure 1,

$$n_0 = \bar{N}\left[1 - \left(\frac{T}{T_0}\right)^{\frac{3}{2}}\right] \tag{28}$$

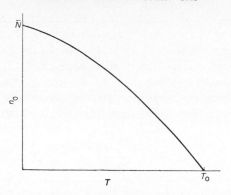

Figure 1. Number of Bose-Einstein particles in the ground state as a function of temperature.

On the other hand we could keep T constant and increase n_0 by decreasing V. Equation (11) would remain true until V reached a value V_0 defined by

$$\overline{N} = (2s+1)\left(\frac{2\pi mkT}{h^2}\right)^{\frac{3}{2}} 2.612\, V_0 \qquad (29)$$

For $V < V_0$ Eq. (26) will be true. Thus,

$$1 = \frac{kT}{\mu \overline{N}} + \frac{V}{V_0} = \frac{n_0}{\overline{N}} + \frac{V}{V_0}$$

$$n_0 = \overline{N}\left[1 - \frac{V}{V_0}\right] \qquad (30)$$

Equation (30) is depicted in Figure 2.

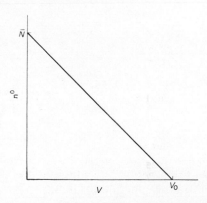

Figure 2. Number of Bose–Einstein particles in the ground state as a function of volume.

This rapid increase in the number of particles in the lowest energy state below T_0 or V_0, as the case may be, is known as the *Einstein condensation*.[2] The analogy between the condensation of a gas and the Einstein condensation was first pointed out by Kahn and Uhlenbeck.[3]

Let us now consider the behavior of the thermodynamic properties as functions of the temperature. The behavior of the gas above T_0 has been obtained in the case of weak degeneracy. For $T < T_0$, $e^{\mu/kT} \simeq 1$ so that since

$$E = \tfrac{3}{2}pV = \tfrac{3}{2}kT \ln \Xi \tag{31}$$

we have from Eq. (15)

$$E = \tfrac{3}{2}(2s+1)kT \left(\frac{2\pi mkT}{h^2}\right)^{\frac{3}{2}} V \left[1 + \frac{1}{2^{\frac{5}{2}}} + \frac{1}{3^{\frac{5}{2}}} + \dots\right]$$

$$= \tfrac{3}{2}(1.341)(2s+1)\left(\frac{2\pi m}{h^2}\right)^{\frac{3}{2}} V(kT)^{\frac{5}{2}} \tag{32}$$

There is no contribution from the lowest energy state since $\varepsilon_0 = 0$. Thus,

$$C_V = \tfrac{15}{4}(1.341)(2s+1)\left(\frac{2\pi m}{h^2}\right)^{\frac{3}{2}} Vk^{\frac{5}{2}}T^{\frac{3}{2}} \tag{33}$$

The value of C_V at $T = T_0$ is

$$C_V = \frac{15}{4}\left(\frac{1.341}{2.612}\right)\bar{N}k = 1.926\,\bar{N}k \tag{34}$$

As is seen in Figure 3 the specific heat rises to a maximum at $T = T_0$.

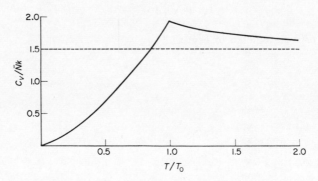

Figure 3. Specific heat of a perfect Bose–Einstein gas.

Because there will be a discontinuity in a plot of $\partial C_V/\partial T$ vs. T the Einstein condensation is a third order phase transition.

[2] A. Einstein, *Berliner Ber.*, **1925**, 3.
[3] B. Kahn and G. Uhlenbeck, *Physica*, **5**, 399 (1938).

For $T < T_0$ the entropy is

$$S = \frac{E - \mu \overline{N}}{T} + k \ln \Xi$$

$$= \frac{E}{T} + k \ln \Xi = \frac{5E}{3T}$$

$$S = \tfrac{5}{2}(1.341)(2s + 1)\left(\frac{2\pi m}{h^2}\right)^{\frac{3}{2}} V k^{\frac{5}{2}} T^{\frac{3}{2}} \tag{35}$$

so that $S \propto T^{\frac{3}{2}}$. Moreover the atoms in the ground state have zero entropy.

Helium, which is almost exclusively ^{4}He, liquifies at $4.21°$K and undergoes a strange transition at $2.19°$K. The high temperature phase is called liquid helium-I and the low temperature phase is called liquid helium-II and appears to persist to absolute zero. Figure 4 is a plot of the specific

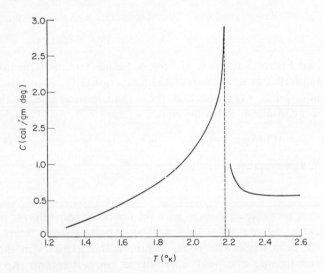

Figure 4. Specific heat of liquid helium under its own vapor pressure.

heat of liquid helium under its own vapor pressure as a function of temperature.[4]

Because of the shape of this curve the transition is called the λ *transition* and is a second order phase transition.

One of the most important properties of liquid helium-II is its very low

[4] W. Keesom and K. Clusius, *Proc. Roy. Acad. Amsterdam*, **35**, 307 (1932); *Leiden Commun.*, **219c**; W. Keesom and A. Keesom, *Proc. Roy. Acad. Amsterdam*, **35**, 736 (1932).

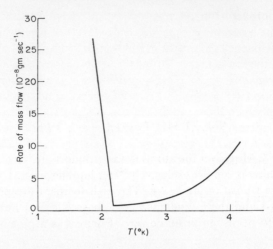

Figure 5. Rate of mass flow of liquid helium through a fine annulus.

viscosity. In Figure 5 the rate of flow of liquid helium-II through a fine annulus is plotted as a function of the temperature.[5]

F. London[6] has suggested that the λ transition is due to the Bose-Einstein condensation. Substituting

$$\rho = 0.146 \text{ gm cm}^{-3}, \ m = 6.55 \times 10^{-24} \text{gm, and } s = 0$$

into Eq. (24) we have

$$T_0 = 3.2°\text{K}$$

which is in reasonable agreement with the observed transition temperature 2.19°K. Closer agreement should not be expected since intermolecular forces have been neglected. Tisza[7] regarded the particles in the excited states as composing one fluid with normal properties and the particles in the lowest energy state as composing another fluid. The particles in the lowest state have zero entropy and are able to move through the normal atoms without viscosity. This phenomenological viewpoint is known as the *two-fluid theory.* Recently Feynman[8] and Chester[9] have succeeded in expanding this point of view to include interactions between the particles.

5 D. Osborne, B. Weinstock and B. Abraham, *Phys. Rev.*, **75**, 988 (1949).
6 F. London, *Phys. Rev.*, **54**, 947 (1938).
7 L. Tisza, *C. R. Acad. Sci.*, *Paris*, **207**, 1035, 1186 (1938).
8 R. P. Feynman, *Phys. Rev.*, **91**, 1291 (1953).
9 G. Chester, *Phys. Rev.*, **100**, 455 (1955).

Another approach, due to Landau[10] and improved upon by Feynman,[11] is based on the assumption that the energy levels of liquid helium (not of the individual particles) consist of two overlapping sets of continuous energy states, the first set representing the levels of the quanta of the sound field (called *phonons*) and the other representing the levels of the quanta of vortex motion (called *rotons*). On this basis Landau obtained a two-fluid theory in which the normal fluid consists of *excitatons* (phonons and rotons) and not excited atoms. This approach seems more closely in accord with experimental results than does Tisza's two-fluid theory and has met with increasing approval in the past few years.

11. Perfect Fermi–Dirac Gas

For this case,

$$\ln \Xi = \sum_{i=0}^{\infty} \ln (1 + e^{(\mu - \varepsilon_i)/kT}) \tag{1}$$

As in our discussion of the perfect Bose–Einstein gas we can show that μ/kT and $\ln \Xi$ are functions of $VT^{\frac{3}{2}}$ and hence

$$pV = \tfrac{2}{3}E \tag{2}$$

This is a general result. However, Eq. (1) can only be conveniently evaluated for the limiting cases of *weak degeneracy*, $e^{\mu/kT} \ll 1$, and *strong degeneracy*, $e^{\mu/kT} \gg 1$.

A. Weak degeneracy

By proceeding in exact analogy to our discussion of a weakly degenerate Bose–Einstein gas we obtain

$$e^{\mu/kT} = y + \frac{y^2}{2^{\frac{3}{2}}} + \cdots \tag{3}$$

where

$$y = \frac{1}{2s+1} \frac{\overline{N}}{V} \left(\frac{h^2}{2\pi mkT} \right)^{\frac{3}{2}} \tag{4}$$

Thus

$$\ln \Xi = \frac{\overline{N}}{y} \left[e^{\mu/kT} - \frac{e^{2\mu/kT}}{2^{\frac{5}{2}}} + \cdots \right] \tag{5}$$

$$= \overline{N} \left[1 + \frac{y}{2^{\frac{5}{2}}} + \cdots \right] \tag{6}$$

[10] L. Landau, *J. Exptl. Theoret. Phys. (U.S.S.R.)*, **11**, 592 (1941).

[11] R. P. Feynman, *Phys. Rev.*, **91**, 1291, 1301 (1953); **94**, 262 (1954); R. P. Feynman and M. Cohen, *Phys. Rev.*, **102**, 1189 (1956).

And

$$pV = \bar{N}kT \left[1 + \frac{y}{2^{\frac{5}{2}}} + \ldots \right] \tag{7}$$

$$E = \tfrac{3}{2}\bar{N}kT \left[1 + \frac{y}{2^{\frac{5}{2}}} + \ldots \right] \tag{8}$$

$$C_V = \tfrac{3}{2}\bar{N}k \left[1 - \frac{y}{2^{\frac{5}{2}}} + \ldots \right] \tag{9}$$

$$S = \bar{N}k \left[\tfrac{5}{2} - \ln y + \frac{y}{2^{\frac{5}{2}}} + \ldots \right] \tag{10}$$

B. Strong degeneracy

It is convenient to introduce the probability $f(\varepsilon)$ that a state at energy ε is occupied,

$$f(\varepsilon) = \frac{1}{e^{(\varepsilon - \mu)/kT} + 1} \tag{11}$$

For the case of a degenerate electron gas μ is often called the Fermi energy, ε_F. A plot of $f(\varepsilon)$ for $T = 0$ and $T > 0$ is given in Figure 1.

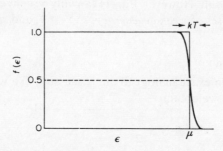

Figure 1. Fermi–Dirac distribution function $f(\varepsilon)$ plotted against ε at absolute zero (solid line) and at a low temperature $kT \ll \mu$ (dotted line).

For $T = 0$ the distribution cuts off abruptly at $\varepsilon = \mu$ but for $T > 0$ the distribution slopes off over a region of width of the order of kT where the distribution has a classical form.

It is of value to prove a theorem due to Sommerfeld.[1] We consider the integral

$$I = \int_0^\infty f(\varepsilon) \frac{dF}{d\varepsilon} \, d\varepsilon \tag{12}$$

[1] A. Sommerfeld, *Z. Physik*, **47**, 1 (1928).

where $F(\varepsilon)$ is such that $F(0) = 0$. Integrating by parts and noting that $F(0) = 0$ and $f(\infty) = 0$ gives

$$I = f(\varepsilon)F(\varepsilon)\Big|_0^\infty - \int_0^\infty F(\varepsilon)\frac{df}{d\varepsilon}\,d\varepsilon$$

$$= -\int_0^\infty F(\varepsilon)\frac{df}{d\varepsilon}\,d\varepsilon \tag{13}$$

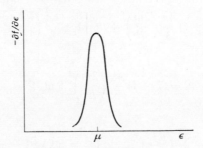

Figure 2. The partial derivation of the Fermi–Dirac distribution function with respect to ε as a function of ε.

In Figure 2 we see that the integrand in Eq. (13) is appreciable only for $\varepsilon \simeq \mu$. Expand $F(\varepsilon)$ in a Taylor's series about μ,

$$F(\varepsilon) = \sum_{n=0}^\infty \frac{(\varepsilon-\mu)^n}{n!}\left(\frac{d^nF}{d\varepsilon^n}\right)\Big|_{\varepsilon=\mu} \tag{14}$$

Now

$$\frac{df}{d\varepsilon} = -\frac{1}{kT}\frac{e^{(\varepsilon-\mu)/kT}}{(e^{(\varepsilon-\mu)/kT}+1)^2} \tag{15}$$

and thus

$$I = \frac{1}{kT}\int_0^\infty \sum_{n=0}^\infty \frac{(\varepsilon-\mu)^n}{n!}\frac{e^{(\varepsilon-\mu)/kT}}{(e^{(\varepsilon-\mu)/kT}+1)^2}\left(\frac{d^nF}{d\varepsilon^n}\right)_\mu d\varepsilon$$

$$= \sum_{n=0}^\infty \frac{(kT)^n}{n!}\left[\frac{d^nF}{d\varepsilon^n}\right]_\mu \int_{-\infty}^\infty y^n\,e^{-y}(1+e^{-y})^{-2}dy \tag{16}$$

since $e^y(1+e^y)^{-2} = e^{-y}(1+e^{-y})^{-2}$. Expanding $(1+e^{-y})^{-2}$ gives

$$I = \sum_{n=0}^\infty \frac{(kT)^n}{n!}\left(\frac{d^nF}{d\varepsilon^n}\right)_\mu \int_{-\infty}^\infty y^n\left(\sum_{k=1}^\infty k(-1)^{k-1}\,e^{-ky}\right)dy$$

$$= F(\mu)+2\sum_{n=1}^\infty (kT)^{2n}\left(\frac{d^{2n}F}{d\varepsilon^{2n}}\right)_\mu\left(\sum_{k=1}^\infty \frac{(-1)^{k-1}}{k^{2n}}\right) \tag{17}$$

Generally one term is sufficient,

$$\int_0^\infty f(\varepsilon)\frac{dF}{d\varepsilon}\,d\varepsilon = F(\mu) + \frac{\pi^2}{6}(kT)^2\left(\frac{d^2F}{d\varepsilon^2}\right)_\mu \tag{18}$$

where we have used Series (1) in Appendix 3.

We can now evaluate some of the thermodynamic functions.

$$\overline{N} = \int_0^\infty g(\varepsilon)f(\varepsilon)\,d\varepsilon = (2s+1)2\pi\left(\frac{2m}{h^2}\right)^{\frac{3}{2}}V\int_0^\infty \varepsilon^{\frac{1}{2}}f(\varepsilon)\,d\varepsilon$$

$$= (2s+1)\frac{4\pi}{3}\left(\frac{2m}{h^2}\right)^{\frac{3}{2}}V\mu^{\frac{3}{2}}\left[1 + \frac{\pi^2}{8}\left(\frac{kT}{\mu}\right)^2 + \ldots\right] \tag{19}$$

Thus at $T = 0$,

$$\overline{N} = (2s+1)\frac{4\pi}{3}\left(\frac{2m}{h^2}\right)^{\frac{3}{2}}V\mu(0)^{\frac{3}{2}} \tag{20}$$

so that,

$$\mu = \mu(0)\left[1 + \frac{\pi^2}{8}\left(\frac{kT}{\mu}\right)^2 + \ldots\right]^{-\frac{2}{3}} = \mu(0)\left[1 - \frac{\pi^2}{12}\left(\frac{kT}{\mu}\right)^2 + \ldots\right]$$

$$= \mu(0)\left[1 - \frac{\pi^2}{12}\left(\frac{kT}{\mu(0)}\right)^2 + \ldots\right] \tag{21}$$

Thus μ is lowered slightly as the temperature is increased.
Also,

$$E = \int_0^\infty \varepsilon\, g(\varepsilon)f(\varepsilon)\,d\varepsilon = (2s+1)2\pi\left(\frac{2m}{h^2}\right)^{\frac{3}{2}}V\int_0^\infty \varepsilon^{\frac{3}{2}}f(\varepsilon)\,d\varepsilon$$

$$= (2s+1)\tfrac{4}{5}\pi\left(\frac{2m}{h^2}\right)^{\frac{3}{2}}V\mu^{\frac{5}{2}}\left[1 + \frac{5\pi^2}{8}\left(\frac{kT}{\mu}\right)^2 + \ldots\right] \tag{22}$$

If we use Eqs. (20) and (21) we obtain

$$E = \tfrac{3}{5}\overline{N}\mu(0)\left[1 - \frac{\pi^2}{12}\left(\frac{kT}{\mu(0)}\right)^2 + \ldots\right]^{\frac{5}{2}}\left[1 + \frac{5\pi^2}{8}\left(\frac{kT}{\mu(0)}\right)^2 + \ldots\right]$$

$$= \tfrac{3}{5}\overline{N}\mu(0)\left[1 + \frac{5\pi^2}{12}\left(\frac{kT}{\mu(0)}\right)^2 + \ldots\right] \tag{23}$$

And so

$$C_V = \frac{dE}{dT} = \frac{\pi^2}{2}\overline{N}k\left(\frac{kT}{\mu(0)}\right) \tag{24}$$

$$S = \int_0^T \frac{C_V\,dT}{T} = \frac{\pi^2}{2}\overline{N}k\left(\frac{kT}{\mu(0)}\right) \tag{25}$$

The primary application of these results is in the free electron theory of metals which we shall discuss in Chapter 9.

12. The *H*-theorem in Quantum Mechanics

Consider an ensemble with density matrix (ρ). We cannot define $\bar{H}$ as trace $(\rho \ln \rho)$ since this function is independent of the time. Instead we introduce a coarse grained density matrix $(\mathbf{P})$ by dividing the energy levels into groups, in accordance with our limited knowledge of the system. If g_i is the number of levels in the ith group, then

$$P_{ij} = \frac{\delta_{ij}}{g_i} \sum \rho_{mm} \tag{1}$$

The summation extends over all the states in the ith group. The normalization condition is then

$$\sum_i P_{ii} = 1 \tag{2}$$

We define $\bar{H}$ by

$$\bar{H} = \overline{\ln P} = \text{trace}\,(\rho \ln \mathbf{P}) = \sum \rho_{ii} \ln P_{ii}$$
$$= \sum_i P_{ii} \ln P_{ii} \tag{3}$$

To see how $\bar{H}$ changes with time we make an experimental observation of the system at time t_1, and then construct an ensemble representing the system at time t_1 by dividing the energy levels of the system into groups in accord with the limitations of the experiment and, in accord with the assumption of equal *a priori* probabilities and random *a priori* phases, by taking

$$(\rho^{(1)}) = (\mathbf{P}^{(1)}) \tag{4}$$

for $0 \leqslant m \leqslant g_i$. Thus,

$$\bar{H}_1 = \sum_i P_{ii}^{(1)} \ln P_{ii}^{(1)} = \sum_i \rho_{ii}^{(1)} \ln \rho_{ii}^{(1)} \tag{5}$$

If at time t_1 the system is in a non-equilibrium state then at some later time

$$(\rho^{(2)}) \neq (\mathbf{P}^{(2)}) \tag{6}$$

and

$$\bar{H}_2 = \sum_i P_{ii}^{(2)} \ln P_{ii}^{(2)} = \sum_i \rho_{ii}^{(2)} \ln P_{ii}^{(2)} \tag{7}$$

Thus

$$\bar{H}_1 - \bar{H}_2 = \sum_i (\rho_{ii}^{(1)} \ln \rho_{ii}^{(1)} - P_{ii}^{(2)} \ln P_{ii}^{(2)}) \tag{8}$$

But $\sum_i \rho_{ii} \ln P_{ii}$ is time-dependent, so using this fact and Eq. (4) we have

$$\bar{H}_1 - \bar{H}_2 = \sum_i (\rho_{ii}^{(2)} \ln \rho_{ii}^{(2)} - \rho_{ii}^{(2)} \ln P_{ii}^{(2)})$$
$$= \sum_i (\rho_{ii}^{(2)} \ln \rho_{ii}^{(2)} - \rho_{ii}^{(2)} \ln P_{ii}^{(2)} + P_{ii}^{(2)} - \rho_{ii}^{(2)}) \tag{9}$$

The last equality is obtained from the fact that $\sum_i P_{ii} = \sum_i \rho_{ii} = 1$. If we set $\rho_{ii}^{(2)} = P_{ii}^{(2)} e^\Delta$, we have

$$\bar{H}_1 - \bar{H}_2 = \sum_i P_{ii}^{(2)}[\Delta e^\Delta + 1 - e^\Delta] \tag{10}$$

But if $I = \Delta e^\Delta + 1 - e^\Delta$ then $dI/d\Delta = \Delta e^\Delta$, which is positive or negative as Δ is positive or negative. Hence $I > 0$ and thus since P_{ii} is positive,

$$\bar{H}_1 > \bar{H}_2 \tag{11}$$

If the system is in equilibrium $(\rho^{(2)}) = (\mathbf{P}^{(2)})$, which means

$$\bar{H}_1 = \bar{H}_2 \tag{12}$$

Thus, the H-theorem is true in quantum statistical mechanics also.

6

THE DARWIN–FOWLER METHOD

1. Introduction

The Darwin and Fowler[1, 2, 3, 4, 5] formulation of statistical mechanics is based on the microcanonical ensemble or distribution in which both the total number of systems and the total energy are fixed. It differs from the method developed previously in which the most probable distribution is calculated, for by the method of Darwin and Fowler the mean distribution is determined. The outcome, we shall see, is that the mean distribution is approached by the most probable distribution when the number of systems becomes very large. In this case, the probability of significant fluctuations is low and the distribution has a sharp maximum.

Briefly, the method of mean values consists of enumerating the number of complexions[6] (accessible states) of an assembly of systems in terms of the allowed energy levels of the systems comprising the assembly. The enumerations must of course be consistent with the requirement that both the number of systems and the total energy of the assembly remain constant. Then, when we have the number of complexions over which the averaging is to be done, the desired averages can be formulated. Specifically we may want the average values of the number of identical systems in a given energy level (occupation number), or, if the assembly consists of two or more kinds of systems, we may want to know the average energy of all the systems of a given kind.

Once the appropriate quantities which characterize the mean distribution

[1] R. H. Fowler, *Statistical Mechanics*, 2nd Ed., Cambridge University Press, 1936, pp. 16–76.

[2] R. H. Fowler and E. A. Guggenheim, *Statistical Thermodynamics*, Cambridge University Press, 1939, pp. 22–69.

[3] E. Schrödinger, *Statistical Thermodynamics*, 2nd Ed., Cambridge University Press, 1957, pp. 25–41.

[4] H. Margenau and G. M. Murphy, *The Mathematics of Physics and Chemistry*, 2nd Ed., Van Nostrand, Princeton, N.J., 1956, pp. 452–465.

[5] D. ter Haar, *Elements of Statistical Mechanics*, Rinehart, New York, 1954, pp. 408–416, 440–443.

[6] We use the term complexion here in keeping with the terminology of the originators of the method.

have been formulated, the problem remains to evaluate them. This is done by first identifying each of these quantities with a coefficient in the multi-nomial expansion of a power series (which itself is identified with the partition function for a given system). The coefficients are then obtained by expressing the power series as contour integrals which can be evaluated by the method of steepest descents.

2. Number of Accessible States of the Assembly

The assembly we choose for consideration consists of N simple systems of which there are N_A identical systems A and N_B identical systems B. Further we specify that A and B both be localized oscillators. Each system could thus be identified with one of the three oscillatory degrees of free-dom of an atom in a solid near its melting point. For each oscillator A the allowed energy levels are $0, \varepsilon, 2\varepsilon, \ldots r\varepsilon, \ldots$, where $\varepsilon = hv_A$ and the lowest energy level has been taken as zero for mathematical convenience (cf. Sect. 1.6). The energy levels are non-degenerate (i.e. of weight unity); later we shall see that the method can readily be extended to include degeneracy. We denote by a_r the number of oscillators A in the state with energy $r\varepsilon$ and call the set of integers $a_0, a_1, a_2, \ldots a_r, \ldots$ the occupation numbers for the respective states. Similarly we designate the energy levels of each oscillator B by $0, \eta, 2\eta, \ldots s\eta, \ldots$ $(\eta = hv_B)$ and the occupation numbers by $b_0, b_1, b_2, \ldots b_s, \ldots$. Also, we choose the unit of energy such that the energy levels have no common factors other than unity. Since the total number of systems, N, and the total energy, E, of the assembly are required to be constant, we can write the following relations:

$$N_A + N_B = N \qquad (1)$$

$$N_A = \sum_r a_r \qquad (2)$$

$$N_B = \sum_s b_s \qquad r, s = 0, 1, 2, \ldots \qquad (3)$$

$$E = \sum_r a_r r\varepsilon + \sum_s b_s s\eta \qquad (4)$$

Thus any specification of the occupation numbers which is consistent with the above equations describes a possible statistical state of the assembly in terms of the energy levels of the component systems, which we have assumed are essentially non-interacting. A particular statistical state of the assembly can be obtained in many ways, for it is determined by how many systems are in each allowed energy level but it does not depend on which ones. If $a_r = 20$, then any twenty of the N_A oscillators can be in the state with energy $r\varepsilon$. The number of ways of obtaining a state of the assembly corresponding to a given set of occupation numbers, which is also referred to as the number of complexions for this statistical state of the assembly, is given by

$$\frac{N_A!}{a_0!\,a_1!\,a_2!\ldots a_r!\ldots} \times \frac{N_B!}{b_0!\,b_1!\,b_2!\ldots b_s!\ldots} \tag{5}$$

The factors in the denominator arise, of course, from the fact that permutation of identical systems within an energy level does not change the complexion. Now if we sum Eq. (5) for all possible statistical states of the assembly we obtain the total number of complexions

$$C = \sum_a \sum_b \frac{N_A!}{a_0!\,a_1!\,a_2!\ldots a_r!\ldots} \frac{N_B!}{b_0!\,b_1!\,b_2!\ldots b_s!\ldots} \tag{6}$$

where the summations are taken over all values of the a's and b's which are consistent with Eqs. (1), (2), (3) and (4). Thus, in the Darwin–Fowler method C is the number of states over which the averaging is to be carried out.

3. Formulation of the Appropriate Averages and their Expression as Contour Integrals

The average value of a quantity (cf. Sect. 1.2) is obtained from the product of the probability of being in a given state and the value of the quantity in that state summed over all possible states. Since each complexion has a weight of unity, the probability that the assembly is in a particular statistical state is the number of complexions corresponding to that state divided by the total number C. Thus, the average value, $\bar{a}_r$, of the number of systems with energy $r\varepsilon$ is given by

$$\bar{a}_r = \frac{1}{C} \sum_a \sum_b \frac{a_r N_A!}{a_0!\,a_1!\,a_2!\ldots a_r!\ldots} \frac{N_B!}{b_0!\,b_1!\,b_2!\ldots b_s!\ldots} \tag{1}$$

Similarly the average energy, $\bar{E}_A$, of the N_A systems A is

$$\bar{E}_A = \frac{1}{C} \sum_a \sum_b \frac{\left(\sum_r a_r r\varepsilon\right) N_A!}{a_0!\,a_1!\,a_2!\ldots a_r!\ldots} \frac{N_B!}{b_0!\,b_1!\,b_2!\ldots b_s!\ldots} \tag{2}$$

Next we consider the partition function for the N_A systems of kind A, which is defined by

$$\frac{1}{(1-z^\varepsilon)^{N_A}} = (1+z^\varepsilon+z^{2\varepsilon}+\ldots+z^{r\varepsilon}+\ldots)^{N_A} = \left(\sum_r z^{r\varepsilon}\right)^{N_A} \qquad r = 0,1,2,\ldots \tag{3}$$

When Eq. (3) is expanded in powers of z by the multinomial theorem,[1] the general term of the expansion is

$$\frac{N_A!}{a_0! a_1! a_2! \ldots a_r! \ldots} z^{\Sigma_r a_r r \varepsilon} \qquad \left(\sum_r a_r = N_A \right) \tag{4}$$

Similarly, for the N_B systems B we define the function

$$\frac{1}{(1-z^\eta)^{N_B}} = (1 + z^\eta + z^{2\eta} + \ldots + z^{s\eta} + \ldots)^{N_B} = \left(\sum_s z^{s\eta} \right)^{N_B}$$

$$s = 0, 1, 2, \ldots \tag{5}$$

and, upon expanding this function, we have for the general term

$$\frac{N_B!}{b_0! b_1! b_2! \ldots b_s! \ldots} z^{\Sigma_s b_s s \eta} \qquad \left(\sum_s b_s = N_B \right) \tag{6}$$

---

[1] The multinomial theorem can be readily obtained from the binomial theorem by mathematical induction. Applying the binomial theorem to the trinomial $(a + b + c)^n$ gives

$$[a + (b + c)]^n = a^n + na^{n-1}(b + c) + \frac{n(n-1)}{2!} a^{n-1}(b + c)^2 + \ldots$$

$$+ \frac{n!}{(n-r)! r!} a^{n-r} (b + c)^r + \ldots \tag{1}$$

Since

$$(b + c)^r = b^r + rb^{r-1}c + \frac{r(r-1)}{2!} b^{r-2}c^2 + \ldots \frac{r!}{(r-s)! s!} b^{r-s}c^s + \ldots \tag{2}$$

the general term of Eq. (1) is

$$\left[\frac{n!}{(n-r)! r!} a^{n-r} \right] \left[\frac{r!}{(r-s)! s!} b^{r-s}c^s \right] = \frac{n! a^{n-r} b^{r-s} c^s}{(n-r)! (r-s)! s!} \tag{3}$$

By similar successive applications of the binomial theorem to a multinomial of m terms, $(a_1 + a_2 + a_3 + \ldots + a_m)^n$, we obtain for the general term

$$\frac{n! a_1^{n-r_1} a_2^{r_1-r_2} a_3^{r_2-r_3} \ldots a_m^{r_{m-1}}}{(n - r_1)! (r_1 - r_2)! (r_2 - r_3)! \ldots r_{m-1}!} \tag{4}$$

Likewise, for $m + 1$ terms we have

$$\frac{n! a_1^{n-r_1} a_2^{r_1-r_2} a_3^{r_2-r_3} \ldots a^r m_{m+1}}{(n - r_1)! (r_1 - r_2)! (r_2 - r_3)! \ldots r_m!} \tag{5}$$

Since m can be any integer and we can derive the general term for a multinomial of $m + 1$ terms by applying the binomial theorem to the result for a multinomial of m terms, we can then write the general term in the expansion of any multinomial as follows:

$$\frac{n! a_1^{b_1} a_2^{b_2} a_3^{b_3} \ldots a_i^{b_i} \ldots}{b_1! b_2! b_3! \ldots b_i! \ldots} \tag{6}$$

where $n = \sum_i b_i$

For the special case of

$$(1 + x^a + x^{2a} + \ldots + x^{ra} + \ldots)^n$$

the general term is

$$\frac{n! x^{0 b_0} x^{ab_1} x^{2ab_2} \ldots x^{rab_r} \ldots}{b_0! b_1! b_2! \ldots b_r! \ldots} = \frac{n! x^{\Sigma_r rab_r}}{b_0! b_1! b_2! \ldots b_r! \ldots} \tag{7}$$

The product of the two series of Eqs. (3) and (5)

$$(1-z^\varepsilon)^{-N_A}(1-z^\eta)^{-N_B} \tag{7}$$

can likewise be expanded in powers of z. Remembering that

$$E = \sum_r a_r r\varepsilon + \sum_s b_s s\eta$$

we see that the coefficient of z^E in the expansion of Eq. (7) is

$$\sum_a \sum_b \frac{N_A!}{a_0!\,a_1!\,a_2!\ldots a_r!\ldots} \frac{N_B!}{b_0!\,b_1!\,b_2!\ldots b_s!\ldots} \tag{8}$$

in which the summations are again carried out over all values of the a's and b's consistent with Eqs. (2.2), (2.3), and (2.4). Further, comparison of Eq. (8) with the expression for C, the total number of complexions of Eq. (2.6), shows that C is the coefficient of z^E in the expansion in powers of z of

$$(1-z^\varepsilon)^{-N_A}(1-z^\eta)^{-N_B}$$

To obtain a similar relation between $C\bar{E}_A$ and a coefficient in a power series we first apply the operator $z\,d/dz$ to Eq. (3), which gives

$$z\frac{d}{dz}(1-z^\varepsilon)^{-N_A} = z\frac{d}{dz}\left[\sum_a \frac{N_A!}{a_0!\,a_1!\,a_2!\ldots a_r!\ldots}z^{\Sigma_r\,a_r r\varepsilon}\right]$$

$$= \sum_a \frac{N_A!\sum_r a_r r\varepsilon\, z^{\Sigma_r\,a_r r\varepsilon}}{a_0!\,a_1!\,a_2!\ldots a_r!\ldots} \tag{9}$$

Multiplication of this result by Eq. (5) yields $(1-z^\eta)^{-N_B}z\dfrac{d}{dz}(1-z^\varepsilon)^{-N_A}$, the general term of which is:

$$\sum_a \sum_b \frac{N_A!\sum_r a_r r\varepsilon}{a_0!\,a_1!\,a_2!\ldots a_r!\ldots} \frac{N_B!}{b_0!\,b_1!\,b_2!\ldots b_s!\ldots}z^E \tag{10}$$

which is to be summed as before. Thus, $C\bar{E}_A$ is the coefficient of z^E in this power series. A useful equivalent form of Eq. (10) is

$$(1-z^\eta)^{-N_B}z\frac{d}{dz}(1-z^\varepsilon)^{-N_A}$$
$$= (1-z^\varepsilon)^{-N_A}(1-z^\eta)^{-N_B}\left[-N_A z\frac{d}{dz}\ln(1-z^\varepsilon)\right] \tag{11}$$

To express $C\bar{a}_r$, we note that

$$\sum_a \sum_b \frac{N_A!\,a_r}{a_0!\,a_1!\,a_2!\ldots a_r!\ldots} \frac{N_B!}{b_0!\,b_1!\,b_2!\ldots b_s!\ldots}$$

$$= \sum_a \sum_b \frac{N_A(N_A-1)!\,a_r}{a_0!\,a_1!\,a_2!\ldots a_r(a_r-1)!\ldots} \frac{N_B!}{b_0!\,b_1!\,b_2!\ldots b_s!\ldots}$$

$$= N_A \sum_a{}' \sum_b \frac{(N_A-1)!}{a_0!\,a_1!\,a_2!\ldots a_r!\ldots} \frac{N_B!}{b_0!\,b_1!\,b_2!\ldots b_s!\ldots} \tag{12}$$

The relations restricting the summations in the rightmost member of Eq. (12) now differ and are

$$\sum_r{}' a_r = N_A - 1 \tag{13}$$

$$\sum_s b_s = N_B \tag{14}$$

$$\sum_r{}' a_r r\varepsilon + \sum_s b_s s\eta = E - r\varepsilon \tag{15}$$

Thus $C\bar{a}_r$ is the coefficient of z^E in the expansion in powers of z of

$$N_A z^{r\varepsilon}(1 - z^\varepsilon)^{-(N_A - 1)}(1 - z^\eta)^{-N_B} \tag{16}$$

A simpler, more familiar example of this method of identification with coefficients in an expansion is encountered in the binomial frequency distribution. If p is the chance that an event will occur and $q = 1 - p$ is the chance it will not, then the chance of observing the event $n - r$ times in n observations is given by the term containing p^{n-r} in the binomial expansion of

$$(p + q)^n = p^n + p^{n-1}q + \ldots + \frac{n!}{(n-r)!\,r!}\, p^{n-r}q^r + \ldots + q^n$$

In this case evaluation of the coefficients is simple arithmetic. To obtain the coefficients with which C, $C\bar{E}_A$, and $C\bar{a}_r$ have been identified we require a more powerful mathematical apparatus; namely, expression of the power series as contour integrals to be solved by the method of steepest descents.

To gain a feeling for contour integrals,[2] consider the function $f(z) = z^n$, where z is a complex variable,

$$z = x + iy = r(\cos\alpha + i\sin\alpha) = re^{i\alpha} \tag{17}$$

By De Moivre's theorem we have

$$z^n = r^n(\cos n\alpha + i\sin n\alpha) = r^n e^{in\alpha} \tag{18}$$

Next we integrate z^n counterclockwise around the circle whose center is the origin and whose radius is unity. Then $dz = ire^{i\alpha}d\alpha$ since r is constant, and we obtain

$$\int_0^{2\pi} z^n \, dz = ir^{n+1}\int_0^{2\pi} e^{i(n+1)\alpha}\, d\alpha = 0; \qquad n \neq -1 \tag{19}$$

and

$$\int_0^{2\pi} z^{-1}\, dz = i\int_0^{2\pi} d\alpha = 2\pi i \tag{20}$$

Thus, if we were to integrate a power series in z around this circle, all terms but that containing z^{-1} would vanish. We have already identified C,

2 For more precise knowledge of contour integration, the reader is referred to mathematical texts such as H. and B. S. Jeffreys, *Methods of Mathematical Physics*, Cambridge University Press, 1946, and E. G. Phillips, *Functions of a Complex Variable*, Oliver and Boyd, Edinburgh (also Interscience Publishers, Inc.), 1947.

$C\bar{E}_A$, and $C\bar{a}_r$ with the coefficients of z^E in three power series, and, if we divide each of the series by z^{E+1} then $C\bar{E}_A$ and $C\bar{a}_r$ will be the coefficients of z^{-1}.

Thus, by Cauchy's residue theorem[3] we obtain the following three integrals:

$$C = \frac{1}{2\pi i} \int_\gamma \frac{dz}{z^{E+1}} (1 - z^\epsilon)^{-N_A}(1 - z^\eta)^{-N_B} \tag{21}$$

$$C\bar{E}_A = \frac{1}{2\pi i} \int_\gamma \frac{dz}{z^{E+1}} \left[z \frac{d}{dz} (1 - z^\epsilon)^{-N_A} \right] (1 - z^\eta)^{-N_B} \tag{22}$$

$$C\bar{a}_r = \frac{1}{2\pi i} N_A \int_\gamma \frac{dz}{z^{E+1}} z^{r\epsilon}(1 - z^\epsilon)^{-(N_A-1)}(1 - z^\eta)^{-N_B} \tag{23}$$

The contour, γ, for these complex integrals can be any path taken once counterclockwise around the origin ($z = 0$) which lies entirely within the circle of convergence ($r = 1$) of the power series.

It is easy to verify the exactness of Eqs. (21), (22), and (23) for small values of N_A, N_B, and E, and, in fact, the integrals are exact for all values of these three parameters. However, we are ultimately interested in an assembly which corresponds to physical reality, i.e. which has a large number of constituent systems. Thus, we need the asymptotic values of Eqs. (21), (22), and (23) as N_A, N_B, and E increase without limit. The relative increase in these quantities must be the same in order to preserve the intensive properties of the assembly as it becomes infinitely large.

4. Evaluation of the Integrals by the Method of Steepest Descents

The method of steepest descents is due to Debye[1] and was adapted for the evaluation of the integrals Eqs. (3.21), (3.22), and (3.23) by Darwin and Fowler. We shall not attempt to develop the general method of steepest descents, but shall merely describe the salient aspects required for the problem at hand. The essence of the method is to locate a saddle-point of the integrand on the positive real axis and then to choose the contour of integration so that it passes through the saddle-point and as a result follows the line of steepest descent on either side of the positive real axis. The result is that the major contribution to the absolute value of the integral comes from the saddle-point and its neighborhood.

Consider the behavior of the integrand of Eq. (3.21) on the positive real axis. The factor $z^{-(E+1)}$ is infinitely large at $z = 0$, decreases monotonically with increasing z, and approaches zero as z increases without limit. The factor $(1 - z^\epsilon)^{-N_A} (1 - z^\eta)^{-N_B}$ on the other hand has the value one at $z = 0$

[3] E. G. Phillips, op. cit., pp. 114–135.
[1] P. Debye, Math. Ann., 67, 535 (1909). See also H. & B. S. Jeffreys, op. cit.

and increases monotonically as z goes from zero to one. Thus the integrand becomes infinite at both $z = 0$ and $z = 1$ and must exhibit a single minimum at some $z = \theta$ where $0 < \theta < 1$, as shown in Figure 1.

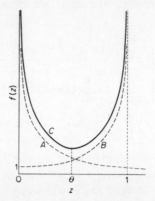

Figure 1. Schematic representation of the integrand of Eq. (3.21) on the positive real axis. $A, f(z) = z^{-(E+1)}$; $B, f(z) = (1 - z^{\varepsilon})^{-N_A} (1 - z^{\eta})^{-N_B}$; $C, f(z) = z^{-(E+1)}$
$$\times (1 - z^{\varepsilon})^{-N_A} (1 - z^{\eta})^{-N_B}.$$

If, as we shall see, the point θ on the positive real axis is a saddle-point of the integrand, then as we move off the real axis keeping θ constant, the absolute value of the integrand decreases and its curvature is opposite to that along the real axis. In Figure 2 we illustrate this behavior of the integrand where $z = \theta e^{i\alpha}$ and $-\pi < \alpha < \pi$.

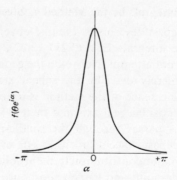

Figure 2. Schematic illustration of the integrand of Eq. (3.21), $z^{-(E+1)} (1 - z^{\varepsilon})^{-N_A}$
$$\times (1 - z^{\eta})^{-N_B} \text{ when } z = \theta e^{i\alpha} \text{ and } -\pi < \alpha < \pi.$$

Thus, if we choose as the contour of integration the circle about the origin of radius θ, with the aid of Figures 1 and 2 we can see that the main contribution to the absolute value of the integral comes from the point $z = \theta$ and its neighborhood. Subsequently, we shall establish the mathematical basis for the foregoing observations on the integral of Eq. (3.21). First, however, let us examine some of the consequences.

With the aid of Eq. (3.11) we combine Eqs. (3.21) and (3.22) to obtain

$$\bar{E}_A = \frac{C\bar{E}_A}{C} = \frac{\int_\gamma \frac{dz}{z^{E+1}} (1-z^\varepsilon)^{-N_A}(1-z^\eta)^{-N_B} \left[-N_A z \frac{d}{dz} \ln(1-z^\varepsilon) \right]}{\int_\gamma \frac{dz}{z^{E+1}} (1-z^\varepsilon)^{-N_A}(1-z^\eta)^{-N_B}} \tag{1}$$

The modulus of the integrand in the numerator likewise exhibits a sharp maximum at the point $z = \theta$, $\alpha = 0$ on the chosen contour, $z = \theta e^{i\alpha}$, and hence the main contribution to both integrals of Eq. (1) comes from near this point. For this reason factors such as $-N_A z \, d \ln(1-z^\varepsilon)/dz$ can be taken outside the integral sign if we substitute θ for z in the factor. The restriction is that these factors not be raised to a high power such as E or N. Substituting $z = \theta$ in $-N_A z \, d \ln(1-z^\varepsilon)/dz$ and taking this factor outside of the integral gives the following result

$$\bar{E}_A = \frac{-N_A \theta \frac{d}{d\theta} \ln(1-\theta^\varepsilon) \int_\gamma \frac{dz}{z^{E+1}} (1-z^\varepsilon)^{-N_A}(1-z^\eta)^{-N_B}}{\int_\gamma \frac{dz}{z^{E+1}} (1-z^\varepsilon)^{-N_A}(1-z^\eta)^{-N_B}}$$

$$= -N_A \theta \frac{d}{d\theta} \ln(1-\theta^\varepsilon) \tag{2}$$

Similarly, if we rewrite Eq. (3.23) in the following manner,

$$C\bar{a}_r = \frac{1}{2\pi i} N_A \int_\gamma \frac{dz}{z^{E+1}} z^{r\varepsilon}(1-z^\varepsilon)(1-z^\varepsilon)^{-N_A}(1-z^\eta)^{-N_B} \tag{3}$$

and proceed as we did above, we obtain

$$\bar{a}_r = N_A \theta^{r\varepsilon}(1-\theta^\varepsilon) \tag{4}$$

Thus the parameter θ plays an important role in our results. We have noted that θ is the unique minimum on the positive real axis between $z = 0$ and $z = 1$ of the integrand of Eq. (3.21); hence the first derivative must vanish at this point and

$$\frac{d}{dz} \{z^{-E}(1-z^\varepsilon)^{-N_A}(1-z^\eta)^{-N_B}\} = 0 \tag{5}$$

From Eq. (5) we then have

$$E = \frac{N_A \varepsilon}{\theta^{-\varepsilon}-1} + \frac{N_B \eta}{\theta^{-\eta}-1} \tag{6}$$

Since the total energy of the assembly is conserved, we have immediately from Eqs. (2) and (6)

$$\bar{E}_B = \frac{N_B \eta}{\theta^{-\eta} - 1} \tag{7}$$

What then is the physical significance of the parameter θ? The average energy of each system of kind A is

$$\frac{\bar{E}_A}{N_A} = \frac{\varepsilon}{\theta^{-\varepsilon} - 1} \tag{8}$$

and in Sect. 1.1 we have seen that the limiting value of the average energy of an oscillator is kT when $h\nu$ becomes very small. Thus, we have that

$$kT = \lim_{\varepsilon \to 0} \frac{\varepsilon}{\theta^{-\varepsilon} - 1} = (-\ln \theta)^{-1} \tag{9}$$

and

$$\theta = e^{-1/kT} \tag{10}$$

Using this result in Eqs. (2) and (4) we obtain the familiar expressions, due to Planck,

$$\bar{E}_A = \frac{N_A \varepsilon}{e^{\varepsilon/kT} - 1} \tag{11}$$

and

$$\bar{a}_r = N_A e^{-r\varepsilon/kT} (1 - e^{-\varepsilon/kT}) \tag{12}$$

5. Further Considerations of the Method of Steepest Descents

We return now to the proof of the method used to obtain the important results of the last section. In the manner of Fowler,[1, 2] we consider the two functions $\phi(z)$ and $F(z)$, both of which must be analytic.[3] Let

$$\phi(z) = z^{-c_0} \{ f_1(z) \}^{c_1} \{ f_2(z) \}^{c_2} \cdots \tag{1}$$

where (1) the $f_i(z)$ are power series in z which begin with non-zero constant terms, continue with positive integral coefficients, and have radii of convergence of unity, (2) unity is the only factor common to all of the exponents of z in these power series, and (3) the product of E and each c_i, Ec_i, is an integer. Except for a possible simple pole at the origin, $F(z)$ must

---

[1] R. H. Fowler, *op. cit.*, pp. 36–38.

[2] C. G. Darwin and R. H. Fowler, *Phil. Mag.*, **44**, 450 (1922).

[3] A function is analytic in a domain if it is single valued and differentiable at every point in the domain.

have no singularities in the unit circle. We must then prove that θ is the unique positive fractional root of

$$\frac{d\phi(z)}{dz} = 0 \tag{2}$$

and

$$\frac{1}{2\pi i} \int_\gamma F(z)[\phi(z)]^E \frac{dz}{z} = [\phi(z)]^E[F(\theta)\{2\pi E\theta^2\phi''(\theta)/\phi(\theta)\}^{-\frac{1}{2}}$$
$$+ G(\theta)(2\pi)^{-\frac{1}{2}}\{E\theta^2\phi''(\theta)/\phi(\theta)\}^{-\frac{3}{2}} + \dots] \tag{3}$$

where the contour of integration is taken once counterclockwise about the origin.

To prove that $\phi(z)$ exhibits a unique minimum on the positive real axis at some point $z = \theta$ in the interval $0 \leqslant z \leqslant 1$ we consider the logarithm of $\phi(z)$. For real positive values of z, we have

$$\ln \phi(z) = -c_0 \ln z + c_1 \ln f_1(z) + c_2 \ln f_2(z) + \dots \tag{4}$$

Differentiating Eq. (4) gives

$$\frac{d \ln \phi(z)}{dz} = \frac{\phi'(z)}{\phi(z)} = -\frac{c_0}{z} + \frac{c_1 f_1'(z)}{f_1(z)} + \frac{c_2 f_2'(z)}{f_2(z)} + \dots \tag{5}$$

The first term of the right side of Eq. (5), $-c_0/z$, increases monotonically from minus infinity to $-c_0$ as z goes from zero to plus one. Thus, if it can be shown that each $f_i'(z)/f(z)$ is zero at $z = 0$ and increases monotonically as z increases to unity, Eq. (5) vanishes at only one point in the interval, $0 \leqslant z \leqslant 1$. By definition, the general form of $f_i(z)$ is

$$f_i(z) = \sum_n \omega_n z^n \tag{6}$$

Next, let

$$y_i = \frac{z f_i'(z)}{f_i(z)} = \frac{\sum_n \omega_n n z^n}{\sum_n \omega_n z^n} \tag{7}$$

From the definition of $f_i(z)$ we have that $y_i = 0$ at $z = 0$ and increases continuously approaching plus infinity as z approaches unity. Differentiating Eq. (7) and multiplying the result by z gives

$$zy_i' = \frac{\sum_n n^2 \omega_n z^n}{\sum_n \omega_n z^n} - \frac{\left(\sum_n n\omega_n z^n\right)^2}{\left(\sum_n \omega_n z^n\right)^2} = \frac{\sum_n \omega_n z^n \sum_n n^2 \omega_n z^n - \left(\sum_n n\omega_n z^n\right)^2}{\left(\sum_n \omega_n z^n\right)^2} \tag{8}$$

If we write the numerator of Eq. (8) as

$$\frac{1}{2} \sum_n \sum_{n'} (n - n')^2 \omega_n \omega_n' z^{n+n'} \tag{9}$$

we see that zy_i' is positive in the interval. Therefore, as z approaches unity, y_i approaches either a finite positive limit or plus infinity. But the first of these possibilities is contrary to the definition of $f_i(z)$ and hence y_i. From this result we see that if we rearrange Eq. (5) as follows

$$\frac{z\,\phi'(z)}{\phi(z)} + c_0 = \frac{c_1\,z f_1'(z)}{f_1(z)} + \frac{c_2\,z f_2'(z)}{f_2(z)} + \ldots \tag{10}$$

the right side of Eq. (10) is zero at $z = 0$ and increases monotonically to plus infinity as z increases to unity, and therefore it can have the value c_0 at only one point in the interval. This point is designated as $z = \theta$, and θ is thus the unique positive fractional root of

$$\frac{d\phi(z)}{dz} = 0 \tag{11}$$

We also have the result that, since zy' is positive in the interval $0 \leqslant z \leqslant 1$, $\phi''(z)$ is positive, too.

We take as the contour of integration for Eq. (3) the circle $z = \theta e^{i\alpha}$. We have shown that θ is the unique minimum in the interval $0 \leqslant z \leqslant 1$ on the positive real axis; as we shall see the method of steepest descents requires that θ be a saddle-point of the integrand on the circle $z = \theta e^{i\alpha}$. Subsequently we shall prove that for large E the main contribution to the integral comes from the points on the contour in the immediate neighborhood of $z = \theta$. First, we consider the integral in this neighborhood. We substitute $z = \theta e^{i\alpha}$ and expand $\ln \phi(z)$ in a Taylor's series about the point $z = \theta$ on the circle $z = \theta e^{i\alpha}$ to obtain

$$\ln \phi(z) = \ln \phi(\theta) + \alpha \left[\frac{d}{d\alpha} \ln \phi(z)\right]_{z=\theta} + \frac{\alpha^2}{2}\left[\frac{d^2}{d\alpha^2} \ln \phi(z)\right]_{z=\theta} + \ldots$$

$$= \ln \phi(\theta) - \frac{\alpha^2 \theta^2}{2} \frac{\phi''(\theta)}{\phi(\theta)} + \ldots \tag{12}$$

since $\phi'(\theta) = 0$ by Eq. (11). From Eq. (12) we have

$$[\phi(z)]^E = [\phi(\theta)]^E \, e^{-\alpha^2 E \theta^2 \phi''(\theta)/2\phi(\theta)} + \ldots \tag{13}$$

We do not need additional terms, because we have shown that $\phi''(\theta)$ is positive and, for large values of E and N, $E\phi''(\theta)$ will be very large. Next we expand $F(z)$ in a Taylor's series to obtain

$$F(z) = F(\theta) + \alpha i \theta F'(\theta) - \frac{\alpha^2}{2}\left[\theta F'(\theta) + \theta^2 F''(\theta)\right] + \ldots \tag{14}$$

Upon substitution of Eqs. (13) and (14), the integral, Eq. (3), becomes

$$\frac{1}{2\pi i} \int_\gamma F(z) [\phi(z)]^E \frac{dz}{z}$$

$$= \frac{1}{2\pi i} [\phi(\theta)]^E \int_{-\infty}^{+\infty} \{F(\theta) + \alpha i \theta F'(\theta) + \alpha^2 G_1 + \alpha^3 G_2 + \ldots\}$$

$$\times e^{-\alpha^2 E \theta^2 \phi''(\theta)/2\phi(\theta)} \, i \, d\alpha \tag{15}$$

where the G_i's are functions of θ. The change of limits from $-\pi$ to $+\pi$ over to $-\infty$ to $+\infty$ introduces no significant error since we are concerned with the case where E is large and α is small. Usually only the leading term of Eq. (15) is needed, although in some problems, e.g. calculation of fluctuations, the first terms cancel and the next non-zero term is needed. Remembering, Appendix 2, that

$$\int_{-\infty}^{+\infty} e^{-ax^2}\,dx = (\pi/a)^{\frac{1}{2}}$$

and

$$\int_{-\infty}^{+\infty} x^2\, e^{-ax^2}\,dx = \tfrac{1}{2}(\pi/a^3)^{\frac{1}{2}}$$

and noting that the terms containing odd powers of α vanish on integration, we obtain

$$\frac{1}{2\pi i}\,[\phi(\theta)]^E \int_{-\infty}^{+\infty} \{F(\theta) + \alpha i\theta F'(\theta) + \alpha^2 G_1 + \ldots\}\, e^{-\alpha^2 E\theta^2 \phi''(\theta)/2\phi(\theta)}\, i\,d\alpha$$

$$= [\phi(\theta)]^E [F(\theta)\{2\pi E\theta^2 \phi''(\theta)/\phi(\theta)\}^{-\frac{1}{2}}$$
$$+ G_1(\theta)(2\pi)^{-\frac{1}{2}}\{E\theta^2 \phi''(\theta)/\phi(\theta)\}^{-\frac{3}{2}} + \ldots] \quad (16)$$

Since $G_1(\theta)$ is independent of E, the second term of the right side of Eq. (16) is of the order of $1/E$ times the first term, which illustrates the sharpness of the maximum for large values of E.

Finally we must show that the main contribution to the integral does come only from points on $z = \theta e^{i\alpha}$ in the neighborhood of $z = \theta$. With the aid of De Moivre's theorem,

$$z^n = r^n(\cos n\alpha + i \sin n\alpha)$$

we see that other maxima could exist for $\alpha \neq 0$ if all of the exponents of z in the several power series of $\phi(z)$ had

$$2\pi/\alpha$$

as a common factor. But we have expressly required that there be no factor other than unity common to all the exponents; hence, the only maximum is that at $\alpha = 0$. Further, it develops that, since the $F(z)$ are constructed of terms from $\phi(z)$, the above restriction is not required. If there were K factors common to all the exponents, then there would be K equal maxima on $z = \theta e^{i\alpha}$, and the integrals C and $C\bar{E}_A$ would be K times as large. This, of course, would not affect the value of $\bar{E}_A$.

The expressions for the partition functions for the N_A systems A and the N_B systems B, Eqs. (3.3), (3.5), fulfil the conditions for the $\{f_i(z)\}^{c_i}$ so that

$$\phi(z) = z^{-1}(1-z^\varepsilon)^{-N_A/E}(1-z^\eta)^{-N_B/E} \quad (17)$$

where N_A/E and N_B/E are constant. Therefore, we can now evaluate C, Eq. (3.21). Noting that $F(z) = 1$ in the case of C, we have from Eq. (16) that

$$C = [\phi(\theta)]^E [2\pi E\theta^2 \phi''(\theta)/\phi(\theta)]^{-\frac{1}{2}} = \frac{\theta^{-E}(1-\theta^\varepsilon)^{-N_A}(1-\theta^\eta)^{-N_B}}{[2\pi E\theta^2 \phi''(\theta)/\phi(\theta)]^{\frac{1}{2}}} \quad (18)$$

The term

$$[2\pi E\theta^2 \phi''(\theta)/\phi(\theta)]^{-\frac{1}{2}}$$

can be simplified using Eq. (4.6) for E, and remembering that $\phi'(\theta) = 0$. We have then that

$$E\theta^2 \phi''(\theta)/\phi(\theta) = E\left(\theta \frac{d}{d\theta}\right)^2 \ln \phi(\theta) = \theta \frac{dE}{d\theta} \quad (19)$$

Substituting this result in Eq. (18) gives

$$C = \frac{\theta^{-E}(1-\theta^\varepsilon)^{-N_A}(1-\theta^\eta)^{-N_B}}{\left(2\pi\theta \dfrac{dE}{d\theta}\right)^{\frac{1}{2}}} \quad (20)$$

For $C\bar{E}_A$, Eq. (4.1), $F(z)$ takes the form

$$-N_A z \frac{d}{dz} \ln(1-z^\varepsilon) \quad (21)$$

and for $C\bar{a}_r$, Eq. (4.3), it is

$$N_A z^{r\varepsilon}(1-z^\varepsilon) \quad (22)$$

We now see from Eq. (16) why we were justified in taking these factors outside the integral sign after replacing z by θ, Eqs. (4.2), (4.4).

The above method can be readily extended to include both degeneracy and systems of more than two kinds.[4]

6. Fluctuations of the Average Occupation Number, $\bar{a}_r$, and the Average Energy, $\bar{E}_A$

In a complete statistical theory it must be shown that fluctuations of a quantity Q about its average value $\bar{Q}$ are not significant. Darwin and Fowler have given a general theory for fluctuations of order n such that all $\overline{(Q - \bar{Q})^n}$ can be calculated.[1] In this section, however, we develop only the second order fluctuations in $\bar{a}_r$ and $\bar{E}_A$, which are

$$\overline{(a_r - \bar{a}_r)^2} = \overline{a_r^2} - (\bar{a}_r)^2 \quad (1)$$

and

$$\overline{(E_A - \bar{E}_A)^2} = \overline{E_A^2} - (\bar{E}_A)^2 \quad (2)$$

[4] R. H. Fowler, *op. cit.*, pp. 38–40.
[1] R. H. Fowler, *op. cit.*, Chap. 20, and C. G. Darwin and R. H. Fowler, *Proc. Cambridge Phil. Soc.*, **21**, 391 (1922).

To obtain $\overline{a_r^2}$, we use the same method used for Eq. (3.1) for $\bar{a}_r$, and thus have

$$\overline{a_r^2} = \frac{1}{C} \sum_a \sum_b \frac{a_r^2 N_A!}{a_0! a_1! a_2! \ldots a_r! \ldots} \frac{N_B!}{b_0! b_1! b_2! \ldots b_s! \ldots} \tag{3}$$

Thus $C\overline{a_r^2}$ is the coefficient of z^E in the power series

$$N_A(N_A - 1)z^{2r\varepsilon}(1 - z^\varepsilon)^{-(N_A-2)}(1 - z^\eta)^{-N_B} \tag{4}$$

and [compare Eqs. (3.16), (3.23), and (4.3) for $\bar{a}_r$],

$$C\overline{a_r^2} = \frac{1}{2\pi i} N_A(N_A - 1) \int_\gamma \frac{dz}{z^{E+1}} z^{2r\varepsilon}(1 - z^\varepsilon)^{-(N_A-2)}(1 - z^\eta)^{-N_B}$$

$$= \frac{1}{2\pi i} N_A(N_A - 1) \int_\gamma \frac{dz}{z^{E+1}} z^{2r\varepsilon}(1 - z^\varepsilon)^2(1 - z^\varepsilon)^{-N_A}(1 - z^\eta)^{-N_B} \tag{5}$$

Evaluating Eq. (5) by Eq. (5.16) and noting again that $F(z) = 1$ for C, we have

$$\overline{a_r^2} = N_A(N_A - 1)\theta^{2r\varepsilon}(1 - \theta^\varepsilon)^2 + (G_{a_r^2})(1/E) \tag{6}$$

where $G_{a_r^2}$ is a function of θ. By Eqs. (5.16) and (4.4) the corresponding expression for $\bar{a}_r$ is

$$\bar{a}_r = N_A \theta^{r\varepsilon}(1 - \theta^\varepsilon) + (G_{\bar{a}_r})(1/E) \tag{7}$$

Combining Eqs. (6) and (7) and dropping the terms in $(1/E)$

$$\overline{a_r^2} \simeq (\bar{a}_r)^2 - \frac{1}{N_A}(\bar{a}_r)^2 \tag{8}$$

and

$$\frac{\overline{a_r^2} - (\bar{a}_r)^2}{(\bar{a}_r)^2} \simeq -\frac{1}{N_A} \tag{9}$$

Thus, for large E and N_A, second order fluctuations in $\bar{a}_r$ are very small. Compare Eq. (4.17.9).

We follow a similar procedure to evaluate Eq. (2). From Eq. (3.2) it follows that

$$\overline{E_A^2} = \frac{1}{C} \sum_a \sum_b \frac{\left(\sum_r a_r r\varepsilon\right)^2 N_A!}{a_0! a_1! a_2! \ldots a_r! \ldots} \frac{N_B!}{b_0! b_1! b_2! \ldots b_s! \ldots} \tag{10}$$

Thus, $C\overline{E_A^2}$ is the coefficient of z^E in the power series [see Eqs. (3.10) and (3.22)]

$$(1 - z^\eta)^{-N_B} \left(z \frac{d}{dz}\right)^2 (1 - z^\varepsilon)^{-N_A} \tag{11}$$

and

$$CE_A^2 = \frac{1}{2\pi i} \int_\gamma \frac{dz}{z^{E+1}} \left[\left(z\frac{d}{dz} \right)^2 (1-z^\varepsilon)^{-N_A} \right] (1-z^\eta)^{-N_B} \qquad (12)$$

It is easily verified that

$$\left(z\frac{d}{dz} \right)^2 (1-z^\varepsilon)^{-N_A}$$

$$= -N_A(1-z^\varepsilon)^{-N_A} \left[\left(z\frac{d}{dz} \right)^2 \ln(1-z^\varepsilon) - N_A \left(z\frac{d}{dz} \ln(1-z^\varepsilon) \right)^2 \right] \qquad (13)$$

so that Eq. (12) becomes

$$CE_A^2 = \frac{1}{2\pi i} \int_\gamma \frac{dz}{z^{E+1}} (1-z^\varepsilon)^{-N_A}(1-z^\eta)^{-N_B} \left[\left\{ -N_A z\frac{d}{dz} \ln(1-z^\varepsilon) \right\}^2 - \right.$$
$$\left. -N_A \left(z\frac{d}{dz} \right)^2 \ln(1-z^\varepsilon) \right] \qquad (14)$$

By Eq. (5.16) and $F(z) = 1$ for C, Eq. (14) becomes

$$\overline{E_A^2} = \left\{ -N_A \theta \frac{d}{d\theta} \ln(1-\theta^\varepsilon) \right\}^2 - N_A \left(\theta\frac{d}{d\theta} \right)^2 \ln(1-\theta^\varepsilon) + (G_{\overline{E_A^2}})(1/E) \qquad (15)$$

and from Eqs. (5.16) and (4.2)

$$\overline{E_A} = -N_A \theta\frac{d}{d\theta} \ln(1-\theta^\varepsilon) + (G_{\overline{E_A}})(1/E) \qquad (16)$$

Combining Eqs. (15) and (16) and dropping the terms in $(1/E)$

$$\overline{E_A^2} - (\overline{E_A})^2 \cong \theta\frac{d\overline{E_A}}{d\theta} \qquad (17)$$

and

$$\frac{\overline{E_A^2} - (\overline{E_A})^2}{(\overline{E_A})^2} \cong -\frac{1}{N_A} \qquad (18)$$

Fluctuations in $\overline{E_A}$ are thus also small for large E and N_A. It is interesting to compare Eq. (18) with Eqs. (4.13.17) and (4.17.7).

7. Fermi–Dirac, Bose–Einstein, and Intermediate Statistics by the Method of Darwin and Fowler

In the preceding sections of this chapter we have concerned ourselves with an assembly consisting of two sets of localized oscillators. Next we turn our attention to an assembly made up of two sets of systems which are contained in a common enclosure, but which are not localized. To express this a little differently, in the former case we thought of our systems as being distinguishable (no symmetry restrictions on the assembly wave function), while now we are considering indistinguishable systems. There are three cases of interest.

1. Fermi–Dirac statistics for which the assembly wave function is antisymmetric with respect to interchange of two systems. By the Pauli exclusion principle, the allowed values of the occupation numbers are

$$a_r = 0, 1 \tag{1}$$

2. Bose–Einstein statistics for which the assembly wave function is symmetric with respect to the interchange of two systems. In this case there is no restriction on the occupation numbers, so that we have

$$a_r = 0, 1, 2, 3, \ldots \tag{2}$$

3. In intermediate statistics the occupation numbers can assume values from zero to d, where d is a positive integer. Thus, we have

$$a_r = 0, 1, \ldots, d \tag{3}$$

Again we consider an assembly of systems of two kinds, A and B, N_A and N_B in number, respectively. We let ε_r and a_r denote the rth energy level and occupation number of each system A, and use η_s and b_s for system B. We first assume the states for A and B to be non-degenerate, and again we invoke the following conditions

$$\sum_r a_r = N_A \tag{4}$$

$$\sum_s b_s = N_B \tag{5}$$

$$\sum_r a_r \varepsilon_r + \sum_s b_s \eta_s = E \tag{6}$$

The number of complexions for a given statistical state of the assembly we write as

$$\prod_r \gamma(a_r) \prod_s \gamma'(b_s) \tag{7}$$

For the three statistics γ is defined so that:

Fermi–Dirac Statistics $\gamma(0) = \gamma(1) = 1; \; \gamma(a) = 0, \; a \geqslant 2$ $\tag{8}$

Bose–Einstein Statistics $\gamma(0) = \gamma(a) = 1, \; a \geqslant 1$ $\tag{9}$

Intermediate Statistics $\gamma(0) = \gamma(a) = 1, \; 1 \leqslant a \leqslant d$;

$$\gamma(a) = 0, \; a > d \tag{10}$$

The total number of complexions is then

$$C = \sum_{a,b} \prod_r \gamma(a_r) \prod_s \gamma'(b_s) \tag{11}$$

where the summation is to be made in accord with Eqs. (4), (5), and (6). In contrast with our use of the multinomial theorem and one selector variable,

z, in Sect. 3, we must now employ three selector variables. Thus, we write the power series

$$\sum_{a,b} \prod_r \gamma(a_r) x^{a_r} z^{a_r \varepsilon_r} \prod_s \gamma'(b_s) y^{b_s} z^{b_s \eta_s} \tag{12}$$

in which the summation is over all positive and zero values of the a_r's and b_s's. In this triple series C, the number of complexions, is seen to be the coefficient of the term $x^{N_A} y^{N_B} z^E$, which is the term selecting values of the a_r's and b_s's in accord with Eqs. (4), (5), and (6). Thus, to obtain C, $C\bar{E}_A$, etc., the procedure will be to apply Cauchy's theorem three times, and evaluate the integrals by the method of steepest descents. The series, Eq. (12), can be partially summed by introducing the following generating functions:

$$g(xz^{\varepsilon_r}) = \sum_{n=0}^{\infty} \gamma(n) x^n z^{n\varepsilon_r} \tag{13}$$

$$g'(yz^{\eta_s}) = \sum_{n=0}^{\infty} \gamma'(n) y^n z^{n\eta_s} \tag{14}$$

Substitution of Eqs. (13) and (14) into Eq. (12) gives

$$\prod_r g(xz^{\varepsilon_r}) \prod_s g'(yz^{\eta_s}) \tag{15}$$

Proceeding in a manner similar to that of Sect. 3, we write

$$C = \frac{1}{(2\pi i)^3} \int \int \int \frac{dx\,dy\,dz}{x^{N_A+1} y^{N_B+1} z^{E+1}} \prod_r g(xz^{\varepsilon_r}) \prod_s g'(yz^{\eta_s}) \tag{16}$$

and require that the radii of convergence of the series be non-zero. To obtain the average value of the occupation number for the rth level of the systems A, we multiply each term of the expression for C, Eq. (11), by a_r. This is the same principle we used to obtain Eq. (3.1), and gives the result

$$C\bar{a}_r = \sum_{a,b} a_r \gamma(a_r) \prod_{t \neq r} \gamma(a_t) \prod_s \gamma'(b_s) \tag{17}$$

From Eq. (17) we form the unrestricted power series

$$\sum_{a,b} a_r \gamma(a_r) x^{a_r} z^{a_r \varepsilon_r} \prod_{t \neq r} \gamma(a_t)\, x^{a_t} z^{a_t \varepsilon_t} \prod_s \gamma'(b_s)\, y^{b_s} z^{b_s \eta_s} \tag{18}$$

Use of the generating functions, Eqs. (13) and (14), leads to

$$\left\{ \sum_{n=0}^{\infty} n\gamma(n) x^n z^{n\varepsilon_r} \right\} \prod_{t \neq r} g(xz^{\varepsilon_t}) \prod_s g'(yz^{\eta_s})$$

$$= \left\{ x \frac{\partial}{\partial x} g(xz^{\varepsilon_r}) \right\} \prod_{t \neq r} g(xz^{\varepsilon_t}) \prod_s g'(yz^{\eta_s}) \tag{19}$$

$C\bar{a}_r$ is then the coefficient of $x^{N_A}y^{N_B}z^E$ in Eq. (19); hence, we have

$$C\bar{a}_r = \frac{1}{(2\pi i)^3}\iiint \frac{dx\,dy\,dz}{x^{N_A+1}y^{N_B+1}z^{E+1}}\left\{x\frac{\partial}{\partial x}g(xz^{\varepsilon_r})\right\}\prod_{t\neq r}g(xz^{\varepsilon_t})\prod_s g'(yz^{\eta_s})$$

$$= \frac{1}{(2\pi i)^3}\iiint \frac{dx\,dy\,dz}{x^{N_A+1}y^{N_B+1}z^{E+1}}\left\{x\frac{\partial}{\partial x}\ln g(xz^{\varepsilon_r})\right\}\prod_r g(xz^{\varepsilon_t})\prod_s g'(yz^{\eta_s}) \tag{20}$$

It can be shown that λ_A, λ_B, θ are the coordinates of the unique minimum of the integrand of the expression for C, Eq. (16), as a function of the real variables x, y, z. The expression for $C\bar{a}_r$ differs from that for C only by the factor

$$x\frac{\partial}{\partial x}\ln g(xz^{\varepsilon_r}) \tag{21}$$

It can also be shown that, as before, factors such as Eq. (21) can be taken outside the integral signs, if we replace x, y, and z with λ_A, λ_B, and θ, respectively. If we do so, we obtain

$$\bar{a}_r = \frac{C\bar{a}_r}{C} = \lambda_A\frac{\partial}{\partial\lambda_A}\ln g(\lambda_A\theta^{\varepsilon_r}) \tag{22}$$

and

$$N_A = \sum_r \bar{a}_r = \lambda_A\frac{\partial}{\partial\lambda_A}\sum_r \ln g(\lambda_A\theta^{\varepsilon_r}) \tag{23}$$

Similarly, we write

$$C\bar{E}_A = \sum_{a,b}\left(\sum_r a_r\varepsilon_r\right)\gamma(a_r)\prod_{t\neq r}\gamma(a_t)\prod_s \gamma'(b_s) \tag{24}$$

We form the unrestricted power series

$$\sum_{a,b}\left(\sum_r a_r\varepsilon_r\right)\gamma(a_r)x^{a_r}z^{a_r\varepsilon_r}\prod_{t\neq r}\gamma(a_t)\,x^{a_t}z^{a_t\varepsilon_t}\prod_s \gamma'(b_s)\,y^{b_s}z^{b_s\eta_s} \tag{25}$$

and, using the generating functions, we have

$$\left\{\sum_{n=0}^{\infty}\left(\sum_r n\varepsilon_r\gamma(n)x^n z^{n\varepsilon_r}\right)\right\}\prod_{t\neq r}g(xz^{\varepsilon_t})\prod_s g'(yz^{\eta_s})$$

$$= \left\{z\frac{\partial}{\partial z}\sum_r g(xz^{\varepsilon_r})\right\}\prod_{t\neq r}g(xz^{\varepsilon_t})\prod_s g'(yz^{\eta_s}) \tag{26}$$

in which $C\bar{E}_A$ is the coefficient of $x^{N_A}y^{N_B}z^E$.

Next, we write

$$C\bar{E}_A = \frac{1}{(2\pi i)^3}\iiint \frac{dx\,dy\,dz}{x^{N_A+1}y^{N_B+1}z^{E+1}}\left\{z\frac{\partial}{\partial z}\sum_r g(xz^{\varepsilon_r})\right\}\prod_{t\neq r}g(xz^{\varepsilon_t})\prod_s g'(yz^{\eta_s})$$

$$= \frac{1}{(2\pi i)^3}\iiint \frac{dx\,dy\,dz}{x^{N_A+1}y^{N_B+1}z^{E+1}}\left\{z\frac{\partial}{\partial z}\sum_r \ln g(xz^{\varepsilon_r})\right\}\prod_r g(xz^{\varepsilon_t})\prod_s g'(yz^{\eta_s}) \tag{27}$$

to obtain

$$\bar{E}_A = \sum_r \bar{a}_r \varepsilon_r = \theta \frac{\partial}{\partial \theta} \sum_r \ln g(\lambda_A \theta^{\varepsilon_r}) \tag{28}$$

Expressions for N_B and E_B are similarly obtained, and the method can readily be extended to assemblies of more than two kinds of systems. For degenerate systems in which there are $\omega_r (\geqslant 1)$ states with energy ε_r, Eqs. (22), (23), and (28) take the form

$$\bar{a}_r = \omega_r \lambda_A \frac{\partial}{\partial \lambda_A} \ln g(\lambda_A \theta^{\varepsilon_r}) \tag{29}$$

$$N_A = \lambda_A \frac{\partial}{\partial \lambda_A} \sum_r \omega_r \ln g(\lambda_A \theta^{\varepsilon_r}) \tag{30}$$

and

$$\bar{E}_A = \theta \frac{\partial}{\partial \theta} \sum_r \omega_r \ln g(\lambda_A \theta^{\varepsilon_r}) \tag{31}$$

This follows since $\bar{a}_r$ and $\bar{E}_A$ were shown to depend on $\ln g(\lambda_A \theta^{\varepsilon_r})$ only.

Next we inquire into the nature of the generating functions for the three statistics of interest to us.

First, consider Fermi–Dirac statistics. From Eqs. (1) and (13) we have

$$g(\lambda_A \theta^{\varepsilon_r}) = 1 + \lambda_A \theta^{\varepsilon_r} \tag{32}$$

Introducing this result in Eq. (29) gives

$$\bar{a}_r = \frac{\omega_r \lambda_A \theta^{\varepsilon_r}}{1 + \lambda_A \theta^{\varepsilon_r}} = \frac{\omega_r}{\lambda_A^{-1} e^{\varepsilon_r/kT} + 1} \tag{33}$$

if we use the previously determined relationship (see also Sect. 8)

$$\theta = e^{-1/kT}$$

Similarly, we have, from Eqs. (30) and (31),

$$N_A = \sum_r \frac{\omega_r}{\lambda_A^{-1} e^{\varepsilon_r/kT} + 1} \tag{34}$$

and

$$\bar{E}_A = \sum_r \frac{\omega_r \varepsilon_r}{\lambda_A^{-1} e^{\varepsilon_r/kT} + 1} \tag{35}$$

For Bose–Einstein statistics, we have no restriction on the occupation numbers, so that, from Eqs. (2) and (13),

$$g(\lambda_A \theta^{\varepsilon_r}) = 1 + \lambda_A \theta^{\varepsilon_r} + (\lambda_A \theta^{\varepsilon_r})^2 + \ldots = (1 - \lambda_A \theta^{\varepsilon_r})^{-1} \tag{36}$$

The average value of the occupation number of the rth state is thus

$$\bar{a}_r = \frac{\omega_r}{\lambda_A^{-1} e^{\varepsilon_r/kT} - 1} \tag{37}$$

and

$$N_A = \sum_r \frac{\omega_r}{\lambda_A^{-1} e^{\varepsilon_r/kT} - 1} \tag{38}$$

$$\bar{E}_A = \sum_r \frac{\omega_r \varepsilon_r}{\lambda_A^{-1} e^{\varepsilon_r/kT} - 1} \tag{39}$$

In the case of intermediate statistics permissible values of the occupation numbers, Eq. (3), result in the following generating function

$$g(\lambda_A \theta^{\varepsilon_r}) = 1 + \lambda_A \theta^{\varepsilon_r} + \ldots + (\lambda_A \theta^{\varepsilon_r})^d = \frac{1 - (\lambda_A \theta^{\varepsilon_r})^{d+1}}{1 - \lambda_A \theta^{\varepsilon_r}} \tag{40}$$

We note that if $d = 1$, Eq. (40) reduces to Eq. (32), and if $d \to \infty$, Eq. (40) becomes the same as Eq. (36). Use of Eq. (40) in Eqs. (29), (30), and (31) gives

$$\bar{a}_r = \omega_r \lambda_A \frac{\partial}{\partial \lambda_A} \ln \left[\frac{1 - (\lambda_A \theta^{\varepsilon_r})^{d+1}}{1 - \lambda_A \theta^{\varepsilon_r}} \right]$$

$$= \frac{\omega_r}{(\lambda_A \theta^{\varepsilon_r})^{-1} - 1} \left[1 - \frac{d+1}{\sum\limits_{m=0}^{d} (\lambda_A \theta^{\varepsilon_r})^{-m}} \right]$$

$$= \frac{\omega_r}{\lambda_A^{-1} e^{\varepsilon_r/kT} - 1} \left[1 - \frac{d+1}{\sum\limits_{m=0}^{d} (\lambda_A^{-1} e^{\varepsilon_r/kT})^m} \right] \tag{41}$$

$$N_A = \sum_r \left[\frac{\omega_r}{\lambda_A^{-1} e^{\varepsilon_r/kT} - 1} \left\{ 1 - \frac{d+1}{\sum\limits_{m=0}^{d} (\lambda_A^{-1} e^{\varepsilon_r/kT})^m} \right\} \right] \tag{42}$$

and

$$\bar{E}_A = \theta \frac{\partial}{\partial \theta} \sum_r \omega_r \ln \left[\frac{1 - (\lambda_A \theta^{\varepsilon_r})^{d+1}}{1 - \lambda_A \theta^{\varepsilon_r}} \right]$$

$$= \sum_r \frac{\omega_r \varepsilon_r}{(\lambda_A \theta^{\varepsilon_r})^{-1} - 1} \left[1 - \frac{d+1}{\sum\limits_{m=0}^{d} (\lambda_A \theta^{\varepsilon_r})^{-m}} \right]$$

$$= \sum_r \frac{\omega_r \varepsilon_r}{\lambda_A^{-1} e^{\varepsilon_r/kT} - 1} \left[1 - \frac{d+1}{\sum\limits_{m=0}^{d} (\lambda_A^{-1} e^{\varepsilon_r/kT})^m} \right] \tag{43}$$

It can be easily shown that, for $d = 1$, Eqs. (41), (42), and (43) reduce to the Fermi–Dirac equations, and, if d is allowed to increase without limit, they become the Bose–Einstein equations.

The mathematical proof of the general results, Eqs. (29), (30), and (31), is given by Fowler.[1] The proof is given for three selector variables, but in general form so that it can be extended to include a greater number. In principle, it is similar to that for one selector variable given in the preceding section. First, it is shown that the triple series, ϕ, of the form of those in the integrands of the expressions for C, etc., exhibits a unique minimum in the domain of real positive values of x, y, z. The contour of integration is then chosen to pass through this point, designated by λ_A, λ_B, θ. Finally, it is shown that the main contribution to the integrals comes from the neighborhood of this point and the point itself. Thus, the application of the method of steepest descents is proved valid.

8. The Thermodynamic Significance of θ, C, λ_A, and λ_B

'One of the fascinating features of statistical thermodynamics is that quantities and functions, introduced primarily as mathematical devices, almost invariably acquire a fundamental physical meaning'.[1] How do the quantities θ, C, λ_A, and λ_B of the Darwin–Fowler method of developing statistical mechanics relate to the results of the preceding chapters?

The parameter θ which is given by Eq. (4.5) was found to have a common value for the systems A and B in equilibrium when the total energy of the assembly is constant. In thermodynamics (see Sect. 3.2), temperature is the characteristic common parameter of systems in equilibrium. Thus, θ, which arose from the mathematical method, is a temperature. By Eq. (4.10) θ has been related to the absolute temperature.

Next we rewrite Eq. (4.2) as

$$\frac{\bar{E}_A}{N_A} = \theta \frac{\partial}{\partial \theta} \ln \sum_r \theta^{r\varepsilon} \tag{1}$$

and compare it with Eq. (1.2.2) [or Eq. (4.6.4)]

$$E = kT^2 \frac{\partial}{\partial T} \sum_i e^{-\varepsilon_i/kT} \tag{1.1.2}$$

These must be equivalent; hence, we have

$$\sum_r \theta^{r\varepsilon} = \sum_r e^{-r\varepsilon/kT} = f_A \tag{2}$$

where

$$\theta = e^{-1/kT} \tag{3}$$

f_A is the partition function for a system A.

1 R. H. Fowler, *op. cit.*, pp. 47–53.
1 E. Schrödinger, *op. cit.*, pp. 36–37.

The total number of complexions for the assembly, C, is given by Eq. (5.20). The logarithm of C is thus

$$\ln C = -E \ln \theta + \ln \left[\left(\sum_r \theta^{re} \right)^{N_A} \left(\sum_s \theta^n \right)^{N_B} \right] - \tfrac{1}{2} \ln \left(2\pi\theta \frac{dE}{d\theta} \right)$$

$$= \frac{E}{kT} + \ln f_A^{N_A} f_B^{N_B} - \tfrac{1}{2} \ln \left(2\pi\theta \frac{dE}{d\theta} \right) \qquad (4)$$

The last quantity of the rightmost side of Eq. (4) is very small with respect to the others and can be neglected. From Eqs. (1.2.13) and (4.6.3) we have

$$\ln f_A^{N_A} f_B^{N_B} = -A/kT \qquad (5)$$

where A is the Helmholtz free energy of the assembly. Hence, using Eq. (3.15.16), we have

$$\ln C = \frac{E}{kT} - \frac{A}{kT} = \frac{S}{k} \qquad (6)$$

and the entropy of the assembly is equal to Boltzmann's constant times the logarithm of the total number of complexions. The same result was obtained in Sect. 4.5 by a completely different approach.

We give the significance of the parameters λ_A and λ_B by analogy only. Comparing Eqs. (7.33) and (7.37) with Eqs. (5.8.14) and (5.8.7), respectively, we must have for consistency

$$\lambda_A = e^{\mu_A/kT}; \qquad \lambda_B = e^{\mu_B/kT} \qquad (7)$$

From Eq. (1.10.1) we see that these parameters are the absolute activities of the systems A and B, respectively.

THE THERMODYNAMIC PROPERTIES OF CRYSTALS AND OF BLACK BODY RADIATION

1. Introduction

In 1819, Dulong and Petit reported the specific heats at room temperature and constant pressure of thirteen elements in the solid state.[1] Their results led to the following law: C_p at room temperature for a gram-atom of any solid element is about 6.2 cal/mole deg. Since each of the atomic nuclei in a crystal has three vibrational degrees of freedom about its equilibrium position and since $\frac{1}{2}kT$ of kinetic energy and $\frac{1}{2}kT$ of potential energy is present in each such degree of freedom at sufficiently high temperatures, the energy of such a crystal containing N atoms should be $3NkT$ and the corresponding specific heat would be $3R$ per gram-atom or 5.96 cal/°K. The disagreement between this result and the law of Dulong and Petit is accounted for by Eq. (3.5.42) relating C_p to C_V; at room temperature and constant pressure roughly 7 per cent more work must be done against the cohesive forces between the atoms in a typical crystal to raise the temperature by the same amount as under conditions of constant volume. The reason the law of Dulong and Petit works so well at room temperature for most crystals is that at high temperatures all the normal modes are fully excited to the limiting energy value kT. An exception is the diamond lattice for which the elastic force constants are abnormally large and C_p at room temperature is only about 1.3 cal/mole deg. Since the law of Dulong and Petit is a poor approximation at low temperatures for all crystals, a quantum statistical mechanical treatment of monatomic crystals is necessary.

2. Einstein's Model

An oversimplified picture of a crystal at temperature T can be obtained by imagining all but one of the atoms frozen in their equilibrium positions in the lattice. Assuming the field of the stationary atoms to be isotropic, the moving atom will be restored to its equilibrium position by a force that is proportional to the displacement of the moving atom. The motion in three dimensions of this vibrating atom can be described in terms of the

[1] P. L. Dulong and A. T. Petit, *Ann. Chim.*, **10**, 395 (1819).

cube of the partition function for a simple harmonic oscillator. The lowest state of an oscillator was taken as the zero of energy in deriving Eq. (1.6.4). Now the volume of a crystal will vary with temperature and as a result the zero of energy will also shift.[1] To account for this factor we use the following expression for the partition function of a harmonic oscillator in place of Eq. (1.6.4):

$$f = \frac{e^{-hv/2kT}}{1 - e^{-hv/kT}} \tag{1}$$

where the factor $e^{-hv/2kT}$ stems from the zero-point energy. For a crystal of N atoms we have the partition function

$$f_N = \prod_{i=1}^{3N} \frac{e^{-hv_i/2kT}}{1 - e^{-hv_i/kT}} \tag{2}$$

where since N is very large we have neglected the deduction of six translational and rotational degrees of freedom in the expression $3N - 6$. In Einstein's approximation[2] all the vibration frequencies in three dimensions are the same for all the atoms, i.e. the frequency distribution is a Dirac δ-function, and Eq. (2) becomes

$$f_N = \left(\frac{e^{-hv/2kT}}{1 - e^{-hv/kT}} \right)^{3N} \tag{3}$$

The reader should note that if this approximation is not made, the thermodynamic properties of a crystal can be derived from Eq. (2) as summations over $\sim 3N$ unspecified vibrational frequencies.[3] Considering the number of frequencies in a crystal, some such simplification as the Einstein approximation is essential in a practicable calculation of crystalline thermodynamic properties. From Eqs. (3) and (1.2.25) we see that the internal energy of the crystal is

$$E = 3NkT \left[\frac{1}{2} \frac{\theta_E}{T} + \frac{\theta_E/T}{e^{\theta_E/T} - 1} \right] \tag{4}$$

where $\theta_E = hv/k$ is called the *Einstein characteristic temperature* of the particular crystal. Using Eq. (1.2.32), we obtain for the heat capacity of a crystal of N atoms

$$C_V = 3Nk \left(\frac{\theta_E}{T} \right)^2 e^{\theta_E/T} (e^{\theta_E/T} - 1)^{-2} \tag{5}$$

This expression closely approximates observed specific heats except at very low temperatures. At higher temperatures (though not so high that

[1] R. H. Fowler and E. A. Guggenheim, *Statistical Thermodynamics*, Cambridge University Press, 1939, p. 138.
[2] A. Einstein, *Ann. Physik*, **22**, 180 (1907).
[3] J. E. Mayer and M. G. Mayer, *Statistical Mechanics*, Wiley, New York, 1940, p. 244.

the harmonic oscillator approximation is invalidated or crystal imperfections and melting become a factor), Eq. (5) can be rewritten as

$$C_V = 3Nk \left(\frac{\theta_E}{T}\right)^2 (e^{\theta_E/T} + e^{-\theta_E/T} - 2)^{-1} \tag{6}$$

Using the expansion $e^x = 1 + x + x^2/2! + \ldots$, this expression becomes

$$C_V = 3Nk \left(1 + \frac{1}{12}\left(\frac{\theta_E}{T}\right)^2 + \frac{1}{360}\left(\frac{\theta_E}{T}\right)^4 + \ldots\right)^{-1} \tag{7}$$

Hence, Dulong and Petit deduced a value of the heat capacity that is just the limiting value of the Einstein specific heat when $T \gg \theta_E$. For $\theta_E \gg T$ Eq. (5) reduces to

$$C_V = 3Nk \left(\frac{\theta_E}{T}\right)^2 e^{-\theta_E/T} \tag{8}$$

As we see in Figure 1, this equation predicts that the specific heat will drop precipitously to zero at low temperatures whereas C_V is observed to vary as T^3 when T approaches zero (Figure 1). This error was introduced by the assumption that the atoms vibrate about fixed equilibrium positions in the crystal lattice and may be corrected by treating the crystal as a system of coupled rather than independent, vibrating atoms.

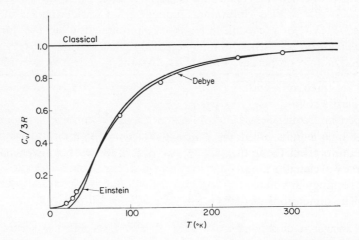

Figure 1. Classical, Einstein and Debye specific heat curves compared with experimental specific heats (circles) of copper. A constant value $\theta_D = 313°$K was used, but a single value of θ_D for copper cannot give a good fit over the entire temperature range. For example, $\theta_D = 319°$K would have given a better fit at $T \approx 30°$K. The value of $\theta_E = 0.72\theta_D = 225°$K is also arbitrary.

3. Vibrations in Continuous Media

Elastic vibrations travel through a simple cubic, monatomic crystal roughly ten times as fast as the velocity of sound in air because of the shorter distances between atoms in the lattice than between molecules in the atmosphere. Thus sound travels from the center of one atom to the center of the next during the time the atom moves through the empty distance separating it from its neighbors, which in the crystal is about one-tenth the total distance. For the case of a nearest neighbor distance $d = 2.5\,\text{Å}$ in the lattice, the velocity of sound is $v = 5 \times 10^5$ cm/sec and the maximum vibration frequency is $v_m = v/2d \approx 10^{13}$ sec^{-1}. A system of N particles will, in general, have $3N-6$ vibrational degrees of freedom. The question naturally arises: how many of these vibration frequencies lie in the range between v and $v + dv$? An answer is found in a consideration of the normal modes of vibration of a generalized continuous medium, which we shall treat in the manner of Jeans.[1]

An idealized gas, the hypothetical 'aether', and an elastic solid may all be treated as continuous media capable of transmitting longitudinal, transverse, and longitudinal plus transverse waves respectively. In every case these waves must satisfy the general wave equation

$$\frac{\partial^2 \phi}{\partial t^2} = a^2 \nabla^2 \phi \tag{1}$$

where a is the wave velocity, $\nabla^2 \equiv \partial^2/\partial x^2 + \partial^2/\partial y^2 + \partial^2/\partial z^2$ in cartesian coordinates, and t is the time. The wave function ϕ will have a different meaning in each of the three cases. For the case of sound waves in a gas there is only one independent solution of Eq. (1). There are two independent solutions for the transverse electromagnetic waves in the 'aether', and there are three independent solutions for the case of vibrations in continuous, elastic solids.

Since the frequencies of vibrations emitted by organ pipes vary inversely as the pipe lengths, we might expect the size and shape of a continuous medium to affect the frequencies of its normal modes. However, only the longest wavelengths are strongly dependent on these characteristics, and a finite rectangular volume can be discussed without a serious loss in generality.[2] The dimensions of the continuous medium will be taken as

$$
\begin{aligned}
x &= 0 \quad \text{to} \quad x = \alpha \\
y &= 0 \quad \text{to} \quad y = \beta \\
z &= 0 \quad \text{to} \quad z = \gamma
\end{aligned}
\tag{2}
$$

---

[1] J. H. Jeans, *The Dynamical Theory of Gases*, 4th Ed., Dover, New York, 1954, Chap. 16.
[2] H. Weyl, *Math. Ann.*, **71**, 441 (1911); R. Courant, *Math. Z.*, **7**, 14 (1920).

If the appropriate general solution of Eq. (1) is ϕ and this solution is ϕ_0 at $t = 0$, we may write for the value of ϕ_0 at every point within the volume $\alpha\beta\gamma$ the Fourier series expansion

$$\phi_0 = \sum_{l=0}^{\infty} \sum_{m=0}^{\infty} \sum_{n=0}^{\infty} A_{lmn} \cos\frac{l\pi x}{\alpha} \cos\frac{m\pi y}{\beta} \cos\frac{n\pi z}{\gamma}$$

$$+ \sum_{l=0}^{\infty} \sum_{m=0}^{\infty} \sum_{n=0}^{\infty} B_{lmn} \sin\frac{l\pi x}{\alpha} \cos\frac{m\pi y}{\beta} \cos\frac{n\pi z}{\gamma} + \dots \quad (3)$$

There are eight summation terms in this standing wave corresponding to the eight possible permutations of the product

$$f\left(\frac{l\pi x}{\alpha}\right) f\left(\frac{m\pi y}{\beta}\right) f\left(\frac{n\pi z}{\gamma}\right)$$

where each f may be either a sine or a cosine. The corresponding eight coefficients $A_{lmn}, B_{lmn}, \dots H_{lmn}$ are defined by eight relations of the type

$$A_{lmn} = \frac{8}{\alpha\beta\gamma} \int_0^\alpha \int_0^\beta \int_0^\gamma \phi_0 \cos\frac{l\pi x}{\alpha} \cos\frac{m\pi y}{\beta} \cos\frac{n\pi z}{\gamma} \, dx\, dy\, dz$$

$$B_{lmn} = \frac{8}{\alpha\beta\gamma} \int_0^\alpha \int_0^\beta \int_0^\gamma \phi_0 \sin\frac{l\pi x}{\alpha} \cos\frac{m\pi y}{\beta} \cos\frac{n\pi z}{\gamma} \, dx\, dy\, dz \quad (4)$$

It should be pointed out that Eq. (3) is a perfectly general expression with which we could fit the figure of an elephant in a cartesian coordinate system should the need arise. If we let $\dot{\phi}_0$ represent $\partial\phi/\partial t$ at $t = 0$, we may write

$$\dot{\phi}_0 = \sum_{l=0}^{\infty} \sum_{m=0}^{\infty} \sum_{n=0}^{\infty} A'_{lmn} \cos\frac{l\pi x}{\alpha} \cos\frac{m\pi y}{\beta} \cos\frac{n\pi z}{\gamma}$$

$$+ \sum_{l=0}^{\infty} \sum_{m=0}^{\infty} \sum_{n=0}^{\infty} B'_{lmn} \sin\frac{l\pi x}{\alpha} \cos\frac{m\pi y}{\beta} \cos\frac{n\pi z}{\gamma} + \dots \quad (5)$$

where the primed coefficients $A'_{lmn}, B'_{lmn}, \dots H'_{lmn}$ are necessarily different from the unprimed coefficients of Eqs. (3) and (4). To fit Eq. (1) we write the solution

$$\phi = \sum_{l=0}^{\infty} \sum_{m=0}^{\infty} \sum_{n=0}^{\infty} \left(A_{lmn}\cos pt + A'_{lmn}\frac{\sin pt}{p}\right) \cos\frac{l\pi x}{\alpha} \cos\frac{m\pi y}{\beta} \cos\frac{n\pi z}{\gamma}$$

$$+ \sum_{l=0}^{\infty} \sum_{m=0}^{\infty} \sum_{n=0}^{\infty} \left(B_{lmn}\cos pt + B'_{lmn}\frac{\sin pt}{p}\right) \sin\frac{l\pi x}{\alpha} \cos\frac{m\pi y}{\beta} \cos\frac{n\pi z}{\gamma} + \dots$$

$$(6)$$

ϕ of Eq. (6) reduces to Eq. (3) when $t = 0$, and $\partial\phi/\partial t$ reduces to Eq. (5) for $t = 0$. If Eq. (6) is to satisfy Eq. (1), p must be given by the relation

$$p^2 = a^2\pi^2\left(\frac{l^2}{\alpha^2} + \frac{m^2}{\beta^2} + \frac{n^2}{\gamma^2}\right) \quad (7)$$

This must be the case since from Eq. (6)

$$\partial^2 \phi / \partial t^2 = -p^2 \phi \tag{8}$$

and again from Eq. (6)

$$\nabla^2 \phi = -\left[\left(\frac{l\pi x}{\alpha} \right)^2 + \left(\frac{m\pi y}{\beta} \right)^2 + \left(\frac{n\pi z}{\gamma} \right)^2 \right] \phi \tag{9}$$

Since we are dealing with simple harmonic vibrations, p in Eq. (6) has the value $2\pi\nu$, where ν is a vibration frequency, and Eq. (7) may, therefore, be rewritten as

$$\left(\frac{l}{2\nu\alpha/a} \right)^2 + \left(\frac{m}{2\nu\beta/a} \right)^2 + \left(\frac{n}{2\nu\gamma/a} \right)^2 = 1 \tag{10}$$

Eq. (6) is a general solution to the wave equation; it represents sets of plane waves progressing through the medium. The boundary conditions for a specific type of wave motion in a given medium eliminate many of the terms included in Eq. (6). In the case of a gas the longitudinal sound waves constitute ϕ, and $\partial\phi/\partial x = 0$ at both $x = 0$ and α with similar relations applying in the y and z directions.[3] All terms but the first multiple summation in Eq. (6) give non-zero values for the first derivatives of ϕ with respect to at least one of the coordinate directions. Hence

$$\phi = \sum_{l=0}^{\infty} \sum_{m=0}^{\infty} \sum_{n=0}^{\infty} \left(A_{lmn} \cos pt + A'_{lmn} \frac{\sin pt}{p} \right) \cos \frac{l\pi x}{\alpha} \cos \frac{m\pi y}{\beta} \cos \frac{n\pi z}{\gamma} \tag{11}$$

is the complete solution to Eq. (1) for sound waves in a gas. Each set of integers (l, m, n) corresponds to one possible vibration frequency of a sound wave in the gas.

An electromagnetic wave in the hypothetical 'luminiferous aether' is resolvable into an electric and a magnetic component at right angles to one another and to the direction of wave propagation. In fact, when $\mathbf{E}$ is fixed $\mathbf{H}$ is completely determined. If E_x, E_y, and E_z represent the components of the electric vector and H_x, H_y, and H_z represent the components of the magnetic vector, all six must satisfy Eq. (1), i.e. $\phi = E_x$, and in addition the following relations must also hold:

$$\frac{\partial E_x}{\partial x} + \frac{\partial E_y}{\partial y} + \frac{\partial E_z}{\partial z} = 0 \tag{12}$$

$$\frac{\partial H_x}{\partial x} + \frac{\partial H_y}{\partial y} + \frac{\partial H_z}{\partial z} = 0 \tag{13}$$

Evidently, only two independent solutions of Eq. (1) can exist under these conditions. In order to conserve the energy of the 'aether' the walls of the volume $\alpha\beta\gamma$ must be perfectly reflecting and hence perfect conductors,

---

[3] Lord Rayleigh, *The Theory of Sound*, Dover, New York, 1945, p. 69.

whence we have $E_x = 0$ at $y = 0$ and β, and at $z = 0$ and γ. Two of the eight summation terms in Eq. (6) satisfy this boundary condition. Thus

$$E_x = \sum_{l=0}^{\infty} \sum_{m=0}^{\infty} \sum_{n=0}^{\infty} \left(G_{lmn} \cos pt + G'_{lmn} \frac{\sin pt}{p} \right) \cos \frac{l\pi x}{\alpha} \sin \frac{m\pi y}{\beta} \sin \frac{n\pi z}{\gamma}$$

$$+ \sum_{l=0}^{\infty} \sum_{m=0}^{\infty} \sum_{n=0}^{\infty} \left(H_{lmn} \cos pt + H'_{lmn} \frac{\sin pt}{p} \right) \sin \frac{l\pi x}{\alpha} \sin \frac{m\pi y}{\beta} \sin \frac{n\pi z}{\gamma} \quad (14)$$

E_y and E_z are like Eq. (14) except that the single cosine term is for the arguments $m\pi y/\beta$ and $n\pi z/\gamma$ respectively instead of for $l\pi x/\alpha$. However, Eq. (12) cannot be satisfied by these values of E_x, E_y, and E_z unless the terms involving the products of three sines are dropped. Thus, the solutions to the wave equation for electromagnetic radiation contain only two arbitrary constants for each value of l, m, and n rather than the sixteen constants of the general solution, Eq. (6). Consequently for each choice of the integers l, m, and n there are two normal modes of vibration of the 'aether'.

We next consider the case of an elastic solid. Longitudinal or compressional waves in an elastic solid are called the dilatation and must be of zero amplitude at the surfaces of the crystal. This being true we have the same solution as Eq. (11) given previously for the sound waves in a gas. Transverse vibrations of a different velocity of propagation can simultaneously exist in the continuous, elastic solid. There are three components of such torsional vibrations

$$\omega_x = \frac{1}{2} \left(\frac{\partial w}{\partial y} - \frac{\partial v}{\partial z} \right)$$

$$\omega_y = \frac{1}{2} \left(\frac{\partial u}{\partial z} - \frac{\partial w}{\partial x} \right)$$

$$\omega_z = \frac{1}{2} \left(\frac{\partial v}{\partial x} - \frac{\partial u}{\partial y} \right) \quad (15)$$

where u, v, and w are the velocity components of the medium. These torsional transverse waves are related by an equation analogous to Eq. (12)

$$\frac{\partial \omega_x}{\partial x} + \frac{\partial \omega_y}{\partial y} + \frac{\partial \omega_z}{\partial z} = 0 \quad (16)$$

Hence, the components of rotational distortion, ω_x, ω_y, and ω_z, provide only two independent solutions of the wave equation. As in the case of the transverse waves in the 'aether', the boundary conditions are that $\omega_x = 0$ at $y = 0$ and β and that ω_x is also zero at $z = 0$ and γ. Taking into consideration Eq. (16), we obtain as one of the two independent solutions

$$\omega_x = \sum_{l=0}^{\infty} \sum_{m=0}^{\infty} \sum_{n=0}^{\infty} \left(G_{lmn} \cos pt + G'_{lmn} \frac{\sin pt}{p} \right) \cos \frac{l\pi x}{\alpha} \sin \frac{m\pi y}{\beta} \sin \frac{n\pi z}{\gamma} \quad (17)$$

For every choice of l, m, and n there will thus be three normal modes of vibration of the continuous, elastic solid. The longitudinal wave will travel at a different velocity from the two transverse waves, i.e. a in Eq. (10) is not the same for all three vibrations.

Since the limits of summation in any of the above solutions extend to infinity, it is impractical to attempt the determination of the frequency distribution in any of the above cases by permuting the l's, m's, and n's and solving Eq. (10) for v. It is not difficult to obtain, however, an expression for the number of frequencies lying in the range between v and $v + dv$. Equation (10) is the equation of an ellipsoid in a space in which l, m, and n are the coordinates. Each lattice point corresponds to a set of positive integral values of l, m, and n, which, when substituted in Eq. (10), yield a frequency corresponding to an allowed normal mode of the medium of volume $\alpha\beta\gamma$. Since each lattice point adds one unit of volume in l, m, n or quantum space, the number N of normal modes with frequencies between zero and v is the volume of one octant of the ellipsoid corresponding to Eq. (10), i.e.

$$N' = \frac{1}{8}\left[\tfrac{4}{3}\pi\alpha\beta\gamma\left(\frac{2v}{a}\right)^3\right] \tag{18}$$

As we noted earlier, this is also the number of normal modes of vibration of a gas with frequencies between $v = 0$ and v, and is half the number of normal modes of the 'aether' with frequencies in this same range. It is then apparent that the number of normal modes of the 'aether' with frequencies in the range v to $v + dv$ is

$$dN = 2dN' = 2(\tfrac{1}{8})(\tfrac{4}{3}\pi\alpha\beta\gamma)\left(\frac{2}{a}\right)^3 3v^2\,dv$$

$$= 8\pi V \frac{v^2}{c^3}\,dv \tag{19}$$

where $V = \alpha\beta\gamma$ and $c = a$ is the velocity of light.

The corresponding expression for a continuous, elastic solid is similarly

$$dN = \tfrac{1}{8}(\tfrac{4}{3}\pi\alpha\beta\gamma)\left[\left(\frac{2}{a_1}\right)^3 + 2\left(\frac{2}{a_t}\right)^3\right] 3v^2\,dv$$

$$= 4\pi V\left(\frac{1}{a_1^3} + \frac{2}{a_t^3}\right) v^2\,dv \tag{20}$$

where a_1 is the velocity of the longitudinal waves and a_t is the velocity of the two transverse waves.

4. Radiation in a Box

If a box of volume V is heated to a temperature T, the number of normal modes of the electromagnetic radiation within the box having frequencies in the range v to $v+dv$ is given by Eq. (3.19). Regarding each such mode as a harmonic oscillator of the same frequency, we note that the product of the individual harmonic oscillator partition functions,

$$(1-e^{-hv/kT})^{-1} \tag{1.6.4}$$

gives the partition function f_N of the whole system of normal modes:

$$f_N = \prod_i (1-e^{-hv_i/kT})^{-8\pi V v_i^2 dv_i/c^3} \tag{1}$$

For sufficiently small frequency increments this becomes

$$\ln f_N = -\frac{8\pi V}{c^3} \int_0^\infty v^2 \ln(1-e^{-hv/kT})\,dv \tag{2}$$

Taking $x = e^{-hv/kT}$, we use Maclaurin's series

$$g(x) = g(0)+g'(0)x+g''(0)\frac{x^2}{2!}+g'''(0)\frac{x^3}{3!}+\cdots$$

to expand $\ln(1-e^{-hv/kT})$. The integral in Eq. (2) then becomes

$$-\int_0^\infty v^2\left(e^{-hv/kT}+\frac{e^{-2hv/kT}}{2}+\frac{e^{-3hv/kT}}{3}+\cdots\right)dv$$

$$= -\int_0^\infty v^2\left(\sum_{n=1}^\infty \frac{e^{-nhv/kT}}{n}\right)dv \tag{3}$$

On multiplication and division by $(nh/kT)^3$, the integral of Eq. (3), because it involves convergent sums, reduces to

$$-\sum_{n=1}^\infty \frac{1}{n}\left(\frac{kT}{nh}\right)^3 \int_0^\infty e^{-nhv/kT}\left(\frac{nhv}{kT}\right)^2\left(\frac{nh}{kT}\right)dv \tag{4}$$

This integral is simplified by letting $x = nhv/kT$. The result

$$-\sum_{n=1}^\infty \frac{1}{n}\left(\frac{kT}{nh}\right)^3 \int_0^\infty e^{-x}x^2\,dx \tag{5}$$

can be integrated by parts, $\int u\,dv = uv - \int v\,du$, if we set $e^{-x}dx = dv$ and $x^2 = u$. The integration yields

$$\int_0^\infty e^{-x}x^2\,dx = -2e^{-x}\big|_0^\infty = 2 \tag{6}$$

and Eq. (5) becomes

$$-2\left(\frac{kT}{h}\right)^3 \sum_{n=1}^\infty \frac{1}{n^4} = -2\left(\frac{kT}{h}\right)^3 \frac{\pi^4}{90} \tag{7}$$

where we have referred to Appendix 3 for the value of the summation. Substituting this result in Eq. (2), we have for the partition function

$$\ln f_N = \frac{8\pi^5 V}{45} \left(\frac{kT}{hc}\right)^3 \tag{8}$$

Using Eqs. (1.2.26) and (8), we have for the Helmholtz free energy of the radiation field

$$A = -\frac{8\pi^5 V}{45} \frac{(kT)^4}{(hc)^3} \tag{9}$$

From Eqs. (1.2.28) and (9) it is evident that the radiation pressure is

$$p = -\left(\frac{\partial A}{\partial V}\right)_T = \frac{8\pi^5}{45} \frac{(kT)^4}{(hc)^3} \tag{10}$$

and from Eqs. (1.2.29) and (9) we see that the entropy of radiation is

$$S = -\left(\frac{\partial A}{\partial T}\right)_V = \frac{32\pi^5 V}{45} \frac{k^4 T^3}{(hc)^3} \tag{11}$$

The equilibrium energy density of the radiation in the isothermal container from Eqs. (1.2.25) and (8) is

$$\frac{E}{V} = \frac{8\pi^5}{15} \frac{(kT)^4}{(hc)^3} \tag{12}$$

Since the emissive power of a black body is proportional to the energy density within an enclosure at the same temperature, Eq. (12) differs by only a factor $c/4$ from the Stefan–Boltzmann law, $W = \sigma T^4$, for the total radiant power emitted by a black body. $\sigma = 8\pi^5 k^4/60h^3c^2$ is Stefan's constant. A comparison of Eqs. (10) and (12) reveals that the radiation pressure is just a third of the energy density, whereas in a monatomic ideal gas the pressure equals two-thirds of the energy density.

Still another important result can be derived from Eq. (1). From Eq. (1.2.25) we see that the energy in the frequency range v to $v+dv$ is simply

$$dE_v = kT^2 \frac{\partial \ln f}{\partial T} = \frac{kT^2 8\pi V}{c^3} v^2 \left(\frac{hv}{kT^2}\right)(e^{hv/kT} - 1)^{-1} dv$$

$$= \frac{8\pi h V}{c^3} \frac{v^3 \, dv}{(e^{hv/kT} - 1)} \tag{13}$$

This is Planck's radiation law which laid the basis for quantum mechanics. For the limiting case where $hv \ll kT$, Eq. (13) reduces to the earlier Rayleigh–Jeans formula

$$dE_v = \frac{8\pi V v^2 kT \, dv}{c^3} \tag{14}$$

which was derived on the assumption that the classical equipartition energy kT could be assigned to each normal mode of the radiation field. This relation fits the experimental energy distribution curve at low frequencies and/or high temperatures but suggests that the energy increases rapidly to infinity as the frequency increases, a discrepancy sometimes called 'the ultraviolet catastrophe'. By taking the limiting case where $hv \gg kT$ in Eq. (13) we can obtain Wien's empirical spectral distribution formula for high frequencies

$$dE_v = \frac{8\pi h V v^3 \, e^{-hv/kT} \, dv}{c^3} \tag{15}$$

By equating the derivative of Eq. (13) to zero, it can be shown that the maximum of the spectral distribution moves to higher frequencies with rising temperature in agreement with Wien's displacement law.

Let us illustrate the preceding ideas by applying Eq. (10) in an approximate calculation of the force exerted on the surface of the earth by radiation from the sun. Taking the temperature of the surface of the sun to be 6000°C, the radiation pressure at this surface is

$$p_1 = \frac{8\pi^5 (1.38 \times 10^{-16} \times 6273)^4}{45(6.62 \times 10^{-27} \times 3 \times 10^{10})^3} = 39.2 \text{ dyne cm}^{-2}$$

Assuming an inverse square dependence for the attenuation of radiation with distance, the radiation pressure at the surface of the earth is

$$p_2 = p_1 \left(\frac{4.32 \times 10^5}{9.29 \times 10^7} \right) = 8.52 \times 10^{-4} \text{ dyne cm}^{-2}$$

where 4.32×10^5 miles is the radius of the sun and 9.29×10^7 miles is the radius of the earth's orbit about the sun. Since the earth has a radius of 3963 miles, the force exerted on the surface of the earth by the sun's radiation is

$$F = p_2 \pi (3963 \times 1.61 \times 10^5)^2 = 1.09 \times 10^{15} \text{ dynes}$$

Here we have assumed that the earth is a perfect reflector. Were the earth assumed to absorb all the radiation, the total force would be just half as large. In either case the force is negligibly small compared to forces commonly encountered in problems of terrestrial mechanics (a pressure p_2 of 8.52×10^{-4} dyne cm^{-2} equals 8.41×10^{-10} atm). The subject of black body radiation is also discussed in Chapter 5.

5. Debye's Model of Monatomic Crystals

If dN/dv is taken as the ordinate and v as the abscissa, the v^2 law of Eq. (3.20) for the distribution of frequencies in an isotropic elastic continuum yields a parabola that is zero at the origin and rises steeply with increasing v. Debye's approximation[1] consists in the use of only the first $3N$ allowed vibration frequencies starting with $v = 0$ in calculating the specific heat of a crystalline solid, where N is the number of atoms per mole of crystal. If we call v_m the cut-off frequency, Eq. (3.20) gives

$$\int_0^{v_m} 4\pi V \left(\frac{1}{a_l^3} + \frac{2}{a_t^3} \right) v^2 \, dv = 3N \tag{1}$$

and

$$v_m = \left[\frac{9N}{4\pi V \left(\dfrac{1}{a_l^3} + \dfrac{2}{a_t^3} \right)} \right]^{\frac{1}{3}} \tag{2}$$

Using Eq. (2) to eliminate the velocity dependence from Eq. (3.20), we have for the Debye vibrational distribution function in the range $v = 0$ to v_m

$$g(v) = \frac{9Nv^2}{v_m^3} \tag{3}$$

and zero elsewhere. The energy of a harmonic oscillator is readily derived from Eqs. (2.1) and (1.2.25). If the resulting expression is multiplied by (3) and the product is integrated over the allowed range of frequencies, we have the Debye expression for the internal energy of the lattice

$$E = \frac{9N}{v_m^3} \int_0^{v_m} \left[\frac{hv}{2} + \frac{hv}{e^{hv/kT} - 1} \right] v^2 \, dv \tag{4}$$

The first readily integrated term is, of course, the zero-point energy of the oscillators. While the integration of the second term cannot be performed analytically, it is possible to obtain two series approximations, the one valid at low temperatures and the other valid at high temperatures. There is an intermediate range of temperatures for which both series converge and hence the approximate solutions overlap. To simplify our notation we shall make the substitutions $u = \theta_D/T$, where $\theta_D = hv_m/k$ is called the characteristic or Debye temperature of the solid, and $x = hv/kT$. Let us call

$$D(u) = \frac{3}{u^3} \int_0^u \frac{x^3 \, dx}{(e^x - 1)} \tag{5}$$

the Debye function, so that Eq. (4) becomes

$$E = \tfrac{9}{8} N h v_m + 3NkT \cdot D(u) \tag{6}$$

[1] P. Debye, *Ann. Physik*, **39**, 789 (1912).

At low temperatures $\theta_D \gg T$, u is therefore large, and a suitable form of the Debye function is

$$D(u) = \frac{3}{u^3}\left[\int_0^\infty \frac{x^3}{e^x-1}dx - \int_u^\infty \frac{x^3}{e^x-1}dx\right] \qquad (7)$$

Now since

$$x^3(e^x-1)^{-1} = x^3 e^{-x} + x^3 e^{-2x} + x^3 e^{-3x} + \dots \qquad (8)$$

the substitution $nx = y$ reduces the problem of evaluating the first integral in Eq. (7) to one of performing the following integration by parts:

$$\sum_{n=1}^\infty \frac{1}{n^4}\int_0^\infty y^3 e^{-y}dy = \sum_{n=1}^\infty \frac{1}{n^4}\left[6\int_0^\infty e^{-y}dy\right] = 6\sum_{n=1}^\infty \frac{1}{n^4} \qquad (9)$$

From Appendix 3 we take the result

$$\sum_{n=1}^\infty \frac{1}{n^4} = \frac{\pi^4}{90}$$

hence the first integral in Eq. (7) is equal to $\pi^4/15$. In evaluating the second integral in Eq. (7) we settle for an integration by parts of only the first two terms of the series of Eq. (8). Combining results, we have for the Debye function at low temperatures

$$D(u) = \frac{\pi^4}{5u^3} - \left(3 + \frac{9}{u} + \frac{18}{u^2} + \frac{18}{u^3}\right)e^{-u} - \left(\frac{3}{2} + \frac{9}{4u} + \frac{9}{4u^2} + \frac{9}{8u^3}\right)e^{-2u} \qquad (10)$$

Now let us evaluate the Debye function at high temperatures. Since in this case $u = \theta_D/T$ is necessarily small, we may use the series expansion $e^x = 1 + x + x^2/2! + x^3/3! + \dots$ which yields

$$\begin{aligned}
D(u) &= \frac{3}{u^3}\int_0^u \frac{x^3}{(x+x^2/2+x^3/6+x^4/24+x^5/120+\dots)}dx \\
&= \frac{1}{u^3}\int_0^u \left(3x^2 - \frac{3}{2}x^3 + \frac{x^4}{4} - \frac{x^6}{240}\dots\right)dx \\
&= 1 - \tfrac{3}{8}u + \tfrac{1}{20}u^2 - \tfrac{1}{1680}u^4 \qquad (11)
\end{aligned}$$

Hence, from Eq. (6) the energy of the crystal at low temperatures is

$$E = \frac{9Nh\nu_m}{8} + 3NkT\left[\frac{\pi^4}{5}\left(\frac{T}{\theta_D}\right)^3 - \dots\right] \qquad (12)$$

and at high temperatures it is

$$E = \frac{9Nh\nu_m}{8} + 3NkT\left[1 - \frac{3}{8}\left(\frac{\theta_D}{T}\right) + \frac{1}{20}\left(\frac{\theta_D}{T}\right)^2 - \frac{1}{1680}\left(\frac{\theta_D}{T}\right)^4 + \dots\right] \qquad (13)$$

As is predicted by classical theory the energy above the zero-point energy approaches $3NkT$ as $T \to \infty$. Differentiating Eq. (6) with respect to T, we obtain for the specific heat of a crystal at constant volume

$$C_V = 3NkD(u) + 3NkT \frac{dD(u)}{dT} \tag{14}$$

Since $\dfrac{df(y)}{dz} = \dfrac{df(y)}{dy}\dfrac{dy}{dz}$, we may write for Eq. (14)

$$C_V = 3NkD(u) + 3NkT \left[\frac{dD(u)}{du}\right]\left[-\frac{u}{T}\right] \tag{15}$$

and since $\dfrac{d}{db}\displaystyle\int_a^b f(z)\,dz = f(b)$, Eq. (15) reduces to

$$C_V = 3Nk\left\{D(u) - u\left[-\frac{3}{u}D(u) + \frac{3}{e^u - 1}\right]\right\}$$

$$= 3Nk\left\{4D\left(\frac{\theta_D}{T}\right) - \frac{3(\theta_D/T)}{e^{\theta_D/T} - 1}\right\} \tag{16}$$

At low temperatures we may substitute Eq. (10) for $D(\theta_D/T)$ obtaining

$$C_V = 3Nk\left[\frac{4\pi^4}{5}\left(\frac{T}{\theta_D}\right)^3 + \dots\right] \tag{17}$$

Unlike the Einstein specific heat, this relation has the experimental T^3 dependence of C_V near the absolute zero of temperature. At high temperatures Eq. (11) may be substituted for $D(u)$ in Eq. (16) with the result that

$$C_V = 3Nk\left\{4[1 - \tfrac{3}{8}u + \tfrac{1}{20}u^2 - \tfrac{1}{1680}u^4] - \frac{3u}{1 + u + \tfrac{1}{2}u^2 + \dots - 1}\right\}$$

$$= 3Nk\left\{1 - \frac{1}{20}\left(\frac{\theta_D}{T}\right)^2 + \dots\right\} \tag{18}$$

Equation (18) reduces to the law of Dulong and Petit as $T \to \infty$. Equations (17) and (18) both indicate that the specific heat should be the same for all elemental crystals at temperatures which are the same fraction of the respective Debye temperatures of the crystal. This fact is borne out by the superimposed experimental heat capacity curves of Figure 2.1.

The semi-quantitative success of the Debye treatment of a crystal as a continuum hinges on the fact that at low temperatures most of the normal modes of vibration in a crystal have long wavelengths compared to interatomic distances. That the relation $g(v) = \alpha v^2$ is only approximately correct can be seen from several considerations.[2] According to the Debye approximation the T^3 law of Eq. (15) should hold for temperatures satisfying the relation $T < \theta_D/12$, yet for zinc and zinc blende (ZnS) a minimum occurs in the θ_D vs. T curve at still lower temperatures and a true T^3 dependence apparently does not start until $T \approx \theta_D/50$. A plot of θ_D vs. T

---

[2] M. Blackman, *Handbuch der Physik*, Springer, Berlin, 1955, **7.1**, p. 325.

over a wide range of temperatures provides another test of the αv^2 distribution. For silver the values of θ_D calculated from Eq. (14) using experimental molar heat capacities at various points in the range $T = 0$ to $100°$K differ from one another by as much as 6 per cent. If the Debye distribution of frequencies in the crystal were exact, θ_D would be independent of temperature (providing variations in θ_D arising from thermal changes in the elastic constants of the crystal[3] are neglected). (θ_D for silver is about $220°$K for temperatures near $100°$K.) Plots of θ_D vs. T for other monatomic crystals show similar deviations from linearity though seldom by more than 20 per cent.

Had the discrepancies between experimental heat capacities and those calculated by the Debye approximation not been so slight, attention might have been directed earlier to intensive calculations of heat capacities based on frequency distributions obtained by considering the discrete particles in the crystal lattice. We shall give only an introduction to this approach; the interested reader should turn to Blackman's review article[2] for an extended discussion.

6. More Exact Calculations of Frequency Distributions in Crystals

To illustrate the difficulties inherent in a calculation of $g(v)dv$, the number of normal modes with frequencies between v and $v+dv$, let us consider the simplest case: a chain of $N+1$ equidistant particles along the x axis (with the first particle at the origin) each of mass M, bound by elastic forces acting only between nearest neighbors, and restricted in motion to displacements along the x axis. As long as the wavelength λ is long compared to the lattice spacing a (the distance between equilibrium positions of consecutive particles), it makes no difference whether the waves are treated as occurring in an elastic, continuous string or in a chain of N discrete particles joined by N springs.

In the continuous case we let x represent the equilibrium location of an element of the string while u represents the displacement at a particular time of the same element as the longitudinal wave is carried by the string. The strain $e = \partial u/\partial x$ and the force F producing the strain are related by $F = ce$ where c is called the elastic stiffness.[1] Taking the linear density of the string to be ρ and considering an element of length Δx, the strain on one end is $e(x)$ while that on the other end is

$$e(x+\Delta x) = e(x)+\frac{\partial e}{\partial x}\,\Delta x = e(x)+\frac{\partial^2 u}{\partial x^2}\,\Delta x$$

[3] M. Born and T. von Karman, *Phys. Z.*, **13**, 297 (1912).
[1] C. Kittel, *Introduction to Solid State Physics*, Wiley, New York, 1956, Chap. 4.

The resultant force acting on Δx is the product of the difference of the strains and the elastic stiffness constant

$$F = c \left(\frac{\partial^2 u}{\partial x^2} \right) \Delta x \tag{1}$$

Since the mass of the string element is $\rho \Delta x$ and its acceleration is $\partial^2 u / \partial t^2$, Newton's second law gives the wave equation

$$\frac{\partial^2 u}{\partial x^2} = \left(\frac{\rho}{c} \right) \frac{\partial^2 u}{\partial t^2} \tag{2}$$

where the velocity

$$v = (c/\rho)^{\frac{1}{2}} \tag{3}$$

is independent of frequency. The solutions to Eq. (2) are the travelling waves

$$u = A \, e^{i(\omega t \pm kx)} \tag{4}$$

where $v = v\lambda$, $2\pi v = \omega = kv$ and the 'wave vector' $k = 2\pi/\lambda$. The normal modes of vibration of the crystal are standing waves given by linear combinations of the sine and cosine parts of Eq. (4)

$$\sin \omega t \sin kx \tag{5}$$

$$\cos \omega t \sin kx \tag{6}$$

$$\sin \omega t \cos kx \tag{7}$$

$$\cos \omega t \cos kx \tag{8}$$

with the proper coefficients. Provided the one dimensional crystal is sufficiently long, we can assume the two ends of the string to be either joined or held fixed without prejudicial effect on the calculated frequency distribution. Let us suppose the two ends of the string to be held rigidly so that nodes occur at these two points, i.e. $u = 0$ at $x = 0$ and at $x = Na = L$. Since $\sin n\pi = 0$ for all integral values of n, standing waves Eqs. (5) and (6) satisfy these boundary conditions whenever $kL = n\pi$. This last equality indicates that the allowed wavelengths and frequencies are

$$\lambda = 2L/n \tag{9}$$

and

$$v = vn/2L \tag{10}$$

respectively. Reintroducing the particles of the crystal into our continuum model, we note that the shortest allowed wavelength in the crystal is $\lambda = 2a$. If n is evaluated by substituting this value of λ in Eq. (9), we see from Eq. (10) that the maximum vibration frequency is

$$v_m = v/2a \tag{11}$$

According to Eq. (10), the normal modes of vibration are uniformly distributed over the entire range $v = 0$ to $v = v_m$, i.e. $g(v) = g$, a constant. The analogue of the Debye approximation for three-dimensional crystals, Eq. (5.1), is

$$\int_0^{v_m} g \, dv = N \tag{12}$$

whence from Eq. (11)

$$g = 2L/v \tag{13}$$

Now let us obtain the exact distribution of frequencies in the one-dimensional crystal which must be identical to Eq. (13) in the limit as $\lambda \gg a$. We shall consider only nearest neighbor interactions and shall denote the displacement of the nth atom from its equilibrium position by u_n. The energy of the lattice at temperatures for which the harmonic oscillator approximation applies is

$$E = \tfrac{1}{2} \sum_n M \dot{u}_n^2 = \frac{f}{2} \sum_n (u_{n+1} - u_n)^2 \tag{14}$$

where f is the elastic force constant of the crystal. The equation of motion of the nth particle is

$$M \ddot{u}_n = -f[(u_n - u_{n-1}) + (u_n - u_{n+1})] \tag{15}$$

As λ increases, the discontinuous lattice can be assumed to go over into the continuous string and the density

$$\rho = M/a \tag{16}$$

while the elastic stiffness is

$$c = fa \tag{17}$$

The second equality can be justified by considering the force required to produce a strain e in a single bond,

$$F = f(u_n - u_{n-1}) = fae \tag{18}$$

and noting that, as we said earlier, $F = ce$ so necessarily $c = fa$. The solution of Eq. (15) is the traveling wave

$$u_n = A \, e^{i(\omega t + kna)} \tag{19}$$

where the running index n occurs both as a subscript and as a factor in the exponential. Substituting Eq. (19) in Eq. (15) and dividing through by $Ae^{i(\omega t + kna)}$ which appears in every term, we obtain

$$-M\omega^2 = f(e^{ika} + e^{-ika} - 2) \tag{20}$$

Substitution of the identity $\cos \theta = (e^{i\theta} + e^{-i\theta})/2$ in Eq. (20) yields

$$\omega^2 = \frac{2f}{M}(1 - \cos ka) \tag{21}$$

and since $\sin \frac{1}{2}\theta = \sqrt{\frac{1}{2}(1 - \cos\theta)}$, Eq. (21) reduces to the dispersion relation

$$\omega = \pm (4f/M)^{\frac{1}{2}} \sin(ka/2) \tag{22}$$

In Figure 1, ω is plotted as a function of k using Eq. (22).

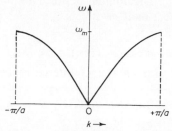

Figure 1. A plot of frequency ω as a function of wave number k for a linear monatomic crystal.

According to Eq. (22), the maximum frequency that the lattice can carry is

$$v_m = \frac{1}{\pi}\left(\frac{f}{M}\right)^{\frac{1}{2}} \tag{23}$$

when $k = \pm\pi/a$. We need not plot larger values of k since this would only duplicate motions described by the range $k = -\pi/a$ to $+\pi/a$. This range is known as the *first Brillouin zone*. When $k = 2\pi/\lambda$ is small and $\sin(ka/2) \approx ka/2$, Eq. (22) becomes

$$\omega = (f/M)^{\frac{1}{2}}ka \tag{24}$$

and from Eqs. (16), (17), and (3) we see that

$$\omega = vk \tag{25}$$

Since $k = 2\pi/\lambda$ and $\omega = 2\pi v$, it is apparent that the lattice treatment gives the same $v = v\lambda$ relation obtained from the continuous string model as long as $k \ll k_m$.

In order to calculate the heat capacity of the monatomic, one-dimensional crystal we must obtain the appropriate expression for $g(v)$. If the first and last particles of the $N+1$ particle chain are held fixed, the normal modes of vibration are linear combinations of the traveling wave solutions of Eq. (19). The normal modes will have the form

$$u_{k,n} = A_k \, e^{i\omega_k t} \sin kna \tag{26}$$

where A_k is a complex number determining the amplitude and phase of the wave and $\pi/L, 2\pi/L, 3\pi/L, \ldots N\pi/L$ are the only allowed values of k. That these values of k do satisfy the boundary conditions can be seen from the fact that when $k = \pi/L$, u is proportional to $\sin(\pi/L)na$, which in turn is zero for $n = 0$ and N. When $n = N/2$, u will have a maximum value since the sine function is then unity. For $k = N\pi/L = \pi/a = k_{max}$, u is zero for all values of n and the lattice is motionless. The $N-1$ allowed values of k, each corresponding to a particular solution of Eq. (26), are equal to the number of particles allowed to move simultaneously in the one-dimensional crystal. The number of normal modes per unit range of k, $g(k)$, for the one-dimensional crystal is L/π since there is one mode of vibration per $\Delta k = \pi/L$, i.e.

$$g(k)\Delta k = (L/\pi)(\pi/L) = 1 \tag{27}$$

To convert this result to the $g(v)$ encountered earlier, we use the relation

$$g(v)\,dv = g(k)\frac{dk}{dv}\,dv \tag{28}$$

and a rearranged form of Eq. (22)

$$k = (2/a)\sin^{-1}(v/v_m) \tag{29}$$

where from Eq. (23) $v_m = \pi^{-1}(f/M)^{\frac{1}{2}}$. From Eq. (29) we see that

$$\frac{dk}{dv} = \frac{2}{a(v_m^2 - v^2)^{\frac{1}{2}}} \tag{30}$$

Using Eq. (28) and the fact that $L = Na$, we obtain

$$g(v) = \frac{2N}{\pi}\frac{1}{(v_m^2 - v^2)^{\frac{1}{2}}} \tag{31}$$

In the limit as $v \to 0$, Eq. (31) becomes

$$g(v) = 2N/\pi v_m \tag{32}$$

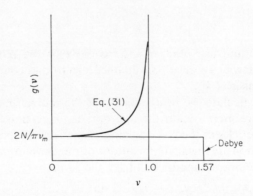

Figure 2. The frequency distribution in a one-dimensional crystal with only nearest neighbor interactions considered. (After T. L. Hill, *Introduction to Statistical Thermodynamics*, Addison-Wesley, Reading, Mass., 1960.)

The curve of Figure 2 is a plot of Eq. (31). We mentioned earlier in connection with Eqs. (10) and (11) that in the Debye approximation $g(v)$

is a constant out to a cut-off frequency $v_m^D = v/2a$. According to Eqs. (3), (16), and (17), the velocity $v = (c/p)^{\frac{1}{2}} = a(f/M)^{\frac{1}{2}}$ whence

$$v_m^D = \frac{1}{2}\sqrt{\frac{f}{M}} \tag{33}$$

This is just 1.57 times as large as the exact v_m of Eq. (23). The derivation we have just completed not only illustrates the principal considerations in an exact treatment of crystal lattice vibrations but also clarifies the reason for the remarkable success of the Debye approximation when applied to multi-dimensional crystals.

Let us turn our attention to an only slightly more complicated case: a one-dimensional crystal identical to the one just considered except that successive atoms alternate between a mass M and a mass m. The atoms of mass M are situated at the odd-numbered lattice points $2n+1, 2n+3, \ldots$. Again we neglect all but nearest neighbor interactions so that the equations of motion are

$$m\ddot{u}_{2n} = f(u_{2n+1} + u_{2n-1} - 2u_{2n})$$
$$M\ddot{u}_{2n+1} = f(u_{2n+2} + u_{2n} - 2u_{2n+1}) \tag{34}$$

The solutions are traveling waves of the form

$$u_{2n} = A\, e^{i(\omega t + 2nka)}$$
$$u_{2n+1} = B\, e^{i[\omega t + (2n+1)ka]} \tag{35}$$

Substitution in Eq. (34) yields

$$-\omega^2 mA = fB(e^{ika} + e^{-ika}) - 2fA$$
$$-\omega^2 MB = fA(e^{ika} + e^{-ika}) - 2fB \tag{36}$$

These two simultaneous homogeneous equations for the amplitudes A and B have a non-trivial solution only if the determinant of the coefficients of A and B vanishes:

$$\begin{vmatrix} -\omega^2 m + 2f & -2f\cos ka \\ -2f\cos ka & -\omega^2 M + 2f \end{vmatrix} = 0 \tag{37}$$

or

$$\omega^2 = f\left(\frac{1}{m} + \frac{1}{M}\right) \pm f\left[\left(\frac{1}{m} + \frac{1}{M}\right)^2 - \frac{4\sin^2 ka}{Mm}\right]^{\frac{1}{2}} \tag{38}$$

When k is small the roots are

$$\omega^2 = 2f\left(\frac{1}{m} + \frac{1}{M}\right) \tag{39}$$

and

$$\omega^2 = \frac{2f}{M+m}(ka)^2 \tag{40}$$

When $k = \pi/2a$ the two roots are

$$\omega^2 = 2f/m \tag{41}$$

and

$$\omega^2 = 2f/M \tag{42}$$

The two solutions of Eq. (38) are completely separate in the ω vs. k plot of Figure 3 where m has been assumed greater than M. The upper or high frequency branch of the dispersion curve is called the optical branch while the lower is called the acoustical branch. From Eqs. (36) and (39) we see

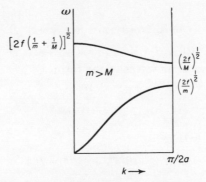

Figure 3. The angular frequency ω in a diatomic one-dimensional crystal as a function of the wave vector k.

that the ratio of the amplitudes A/B in the optical branch for small k is

$$A/B = -M/m \tag{43}$$

and therefore the two kinds of atoms vibrate in opposition to one another so that the center of mass of a unit cell consisting of adjacent atoms M and m is fixed. If the particles are ions of opposite charge, dipole radiation in the infrared part of the spectrum can excite such motions,[1] hence the name optical branch. The terms acoustical and optical are deceptive since it might be inferred from them that the gap in frequencies at the boundary of the first Brillouin zone (where $k = \pi/2a$) is a wide one. However, in the not atypical three-dimensional case of NaCl we see that $(m/M)^{\frac{1}{2}} = 1.24$.

[1] C. Kittel, *op. cit.*, pp. 112–116.

We can calculate the vibrational spectrum from Eq. (38) and the relation

$$g(v) = 2 \frac{dk}{dv} \qquad (44)$$

The result is shown in Figure 4 for $m/M = 3$. The points at which the density of frequencies becomes infinite correspond to the ends of the branches in Figure 3. The discontinuity in $g(v)$ is not a universal characteristic of crystals containing particles of different masses.[2]

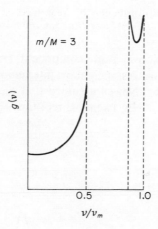

Figure 4. Distribution of normal vibrations in a diatomic one-dimensional crystal. (After T. L. Hill, *Introduction to Statistical Thermodynamics*, Addison-Wesley, Reading, Mass., 1960.)

Early approximate calculations of $g(v)$ for three-dimensional crystals yielded only a vague rounded outline of the frequency spectrum.[3] Recently, topological considerations have shown the spectra to be far more irregular than was once supposed.[4] Van Hove has shown that for three-dimensional crystals, $g(v)$ is continuous everywhere but has a minimum number of singularities. The simplest possible frequency distribution function of a solid is shown in Figure 5.[5]

[2] E. V. Sayre and J. J. Beaver, *J. Chem. Phys.*, **18**, 584 (1950).

[3] M. Blackman, *Proc. Roy. Soc. (London)*, **A159**, 416 (1937). (See Fowler and Guggenheim, *op. cit.*, p. 132.)

[4] L. van Hove, *Phys. Rev.*, **89**, 1189 (1953); H. B. Rosenstock, *Phys. Rev.*, **97**, 290 (1955).

[5] G. H. Wannier, *Elements of Solid State Theory*, Cambridge University Press, 1959, Chap. 3.

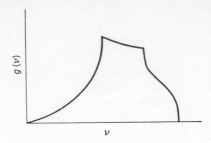

Figure 5. Simplest possible distribution of frequencies in a solid. (After Wannier, *Elements of Solid State Theory*, Cambridge, 1959.)

The frequency distribution in a one-component, simple cubic crystal with only first and second nearest neighbor interactions considered has the form shown in Figure 6.[6] Newell assumed that the force between nearest neighbors is approximately twenty-three times that between second nearest neighbors.

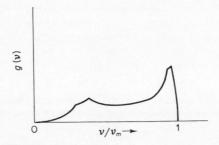

Figure 6. Approximate frequency distribution in a one-component, simple cubic crystal (After Newell, *J. Chem. Phys.*, **21**, 1877 (1953).)

The low frequency values of $g(v)$ are proportional to v^2 as predicted by the Debye approximation.

[6] G. F. Newell, *J. Chem. Phys.*, **21**, 1877 (1953).

THE DIELECTRIC, DIAMAGNETIC AND PARA-MAGNETIC PROPERTIES OF MATTER

1. Introduction

In 1785, Coulomb observed that the force between two point charges, q_1 and q_2, is given by

$$\mathbf{F} = \frac{q_1 q_2}{r^3} \mathbf{r} \tag{1}$$

where $\mathbf{r}$ is the separation between the charges. To describe the effect of an electric charge on its surroundings it is convenient to introduce the concept of an *electric field*. The electric field, $\mathbf{E}$, at a point is defined as the force that would be exerted on a unit point charge if it were placed at that point. In view of Eq. (1) the electric field for a single point charge q is

$$\mathbf{E} = \frac{q}{r^3} \mathbf{r} \tag{2}$$

Consider a surface dS in a field $\mathbf{E}$ (*vide* Figure 1)

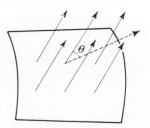

Figure 1. A surface dS in an electric field $\mathbf{E}$. The normal to the surface is shown dotted.

The *flux of* $\mathbf{E}$ across dS is defined as

$$N = E \cos \theta \, dS = \mathbf{E} \cdot d\mathbf{S} \tag{3}$$

where $d\mathbf{S} = \mathbf{n} \, dS$, $\mathbf{n}$ being a unit vector in the direction of the normal to dS. Consider a single point charge inside a surface S as is illustrated in Figure 2.

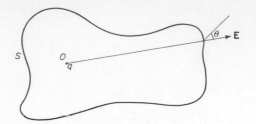

Figure 2. A single point charge q within a surface S.

The flux across the surface S is then given by

$$N = q \int_S \frac{\cos \theta \, dS}{r^2} \tag{4}$$

but $d\omega = \cos \theta \, dS/r^2$ is the solid angle subtended at O by the surface. Integrating $d\omega$ over the complete solid angle 4π gives

$$N = 4\pi q \tag{5}$$

For a volume distribution of charge ρ we have by superimposing their fields

$$N = \int_S \mathbf{E} \cdot d\mathbf{S} = 4\pi \int_V \rho \, dV \tag{6}$$

where V is the volume enclosed by the surface S. This result is known as *Gauss' law*.

At this point it is convenient to introduce the concept of the *divergence* of a vector,

$$\operatorname{div} \mathbf{A} = \lim_{\Delta V \to 0} \frac{\int \mathbf{A} \cdot d\mathbf{S}}{\Delta V} \tag{7}$$

where the integral is evaluated over the surface of the volume ΔV. Let us evaluate this function for the case of rectangular coordinates. Consider a small rectangular box whose dimensions are Δx, Δy, and Δz (*vide* Figure 3).

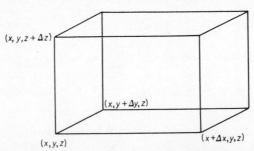

Figure 3. Diagram of the volume ΔV in rectangular coordinates.

If A_x is increasing as x increases at the rate $\partial A_x/\partial x$ then the increase in distance Δx is $(\partial A_x/\partial x)\,\Delta x$. Thus

$$\int_{\Delta V} \mathbf{A}\cdot d\mathbf{S} = \left[A_x + \frac{\partial A_x}{\partial x}\Delta x - A_x\right]\Delta y\Delta z$$

$$+ \left[A_y + \frac{\partial A_y}{\partial y}\Delta y - A_y\right]\Delta x\Delta z + \left[A_z + \frac{\partial A_z}{\partial z}\Delta z - A_z\right]\Delta x\Delta y$$

$$= \left[\frac{\partial A_x}{\partial x} + \frac{\partial A_y}{\partial y} + \frac{\partial A_z}{\partial z}\right]\Delta x\Delta y\Delta z \tag{8}$$

Thus

$$\operatorname{div} \mathbf{A} = \frac{\partial A_x}{\partial x} + \frac{\partial A_y}{\partial y} + \frac{\partial A_z}{\partial z} \equiv \nabla \cdot \mathbf{A} \tag{9}$$

From Eq. (7) we see that

$$\int_S \mathbf{A}\cdot d\mathbf{S} = \int_V \operatorname{div}\mathbf{A}\,dV \tag{10}$$

where V is the volume enclosed by the surface S. This result is known as *Green's theorem*.

Applying Green's theorem to Eq. (6) we have

$$\int_S \mathbf{E}\cdot d\mathbf{S} = \int_V \operatorname{div}\mathbf{E}\,dV = 4\pi\int_V \rho\,dV \tag{11}$$

Since this result is true for any surface we have *Poisson's equation*

$$\operatorname{div}\mathbf{E} = 4\pi\rho \tag{12}$$

Instead of dealing with the vector $\mathbf{E}$ it is more convenient to introduce the scalar quantity ϕ, called the *electric potential*, such that

$$E_x = -\frac{\partial\phi}{\partial x}, \qquad E_y = -\frac{\partial\phi}{\partial y}, \qquad E_z = -\frac{\partial\phi}{\partial z} \tag{13}$$

or

$$\mathbf{E} = -\nabla\phi = -\operatorname{grad}\phi \tag{14}$$

Substituting this into Poisson's equation we obtain

$$\nabla^2\phi = \frac{\partial^2\phi}{\partial x^2} + \frac{\partial^2\phi}{\partial y^2} + \frac{\partial^2\phi}{\partial z^2} = 4\pi\rho \tag{15}$$

In the special case $\rho = 0$ this is called *Laplace's equation*. Referring to Eq. (2) we see that the potential of a single point charge is

$$\phi = \frac{q}{r} \tag{16}$$

For a distribution of charge the potential is

$$\phi = \int_V \frac{\rho \, dV}{r} + \int_S \frac{\sigma \, dS}{r} \tag{17}$$

where ρ is the volume density of charge and σ the surface density of charge.

A pair of equal charges of opposite sign, $\pm q$, is called an *electric dipole*. Such an electric dipole is illustrated in Figure 4.

Figure 4. An electric dipole.

The potential at a large distance ($r \gg a$) from the dipole is

$$\phi = \frac{q}{\left(r^2 + \dfrac{a^2}{4} - ar\cos\theta\right)^{\frac{1}{2}}} - \frac{q}{\left(r^2 + \dfrac{a^2}{4} + ar\cos\theta\right)^{\frac{1}{2}}}$$

$$= \frac{q}{r}\left(1 + \frac{a^2}{4r^2} - \frac{a}{r}\cos\theta\right)^{-\frac{1}{2}} - \frac{q}{r}\left(1 + \frac{a^2}{4r^2} + \frac{a}{r}\cos\theta\right)^{-\frac{1}{2}}$$

$$= \frac{qa}{r^2}\cos\theta$$

$$\phi = \frac{\mathbf{m}\cdot\mathbf{r}}{r^3} \tag{18}$$

where $\mathbf{m} = q\mathbf{a}$. The electric field of a dipole is

$$\mathbf{E} = -\operatorname{grad}\phi = -\operatorname{grad}\frac{\mathbf{m}\cdot\mathbf{r}}{r^3} = -\mathbf{m}\cdot\operatorname{grad}\left(\frac{\mathbf{r}}{r^3}\right)$$

$$= -\left(\frac{\mathbf{m}}{r^3}\cdot\operatorname{grad}\right)\mathbf{r} - (\mathbf{m}\cdot\mathbf{r})\operatorname{grad}\left(\frac{1}{r^3}\right)$$

$$\mathbf{E} = -\frac{\mathbf{m}}{r^3} + \frac{3(\mathbf{m}\cdot\mathbf{r})}{r^5}\mathbf{r} \tag{19}$$

Consider an electric dipole in an electric field $\mathbf{E}$ (*vide* Figure 5).

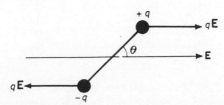

Figure 5. An electric dipole in an electric field $\mathbf{E}$.

If W is the potential energy of the dipole in the field, then

$$-\frac{dW}{d\theta} = qEa\sin\theta = \text{couple tending to increase }\theta \tag{20}$$

Choose the zero of the potential energy at $\theta = \pi/2$. Therefore

$$W = -mE\cos\theta = -\mathbf{m}\cdot\mathbf{E} \tag{21}$$

2. Static Dielectric Constant

Consider an *isotropic* insulator in a constant electric field. Each ion or atom of the substance is composed of a positively charged nucleus and negatively charged electrons. Under the influence of the electric field the nucleus will be displaced in the direction of the field and the electrons in the opposite direction inducing a dipole moment. This situation is illustrated in Figure 1 for a single electron atom.

Figure 1. A polarized atom in an electric field $\mathbf{E}$.

If the field is not too large the resulting dipole moment is proportional to **E**. Thus

$$\mathbf{m}_{ind} = \alpha_e \mathbf{E} \tag{1}$$

α_e is called the *electronic polarizability* of the atom. Typical values of the electronic polarizabilities of alkali and halide ions are given in Table 1.

TABLE 1. Electronic polarizability of alkali and halide ions in 10^{-24} cm³ [1]

Ion	α_e	Ion	α_e
Li⁺	0.02	F⁻	0.85
Na⁺	0.22	Cl⁻	3.00
K⁺	0.97	Br⁻	4.13
Rb⁺	1.50	I⁻	6.16
Cs⁺	2.42		

Furthermore, the ions of the substance or the atoms within the molecules of the substance may themselves be displaced resulting in an induced dipole moment which, for not too large fields, can be represented by a relation similar to Eq. (1) with α_e replaced by α_a, the *atomic polarizability*.

Let $\mathbf{P} = \chi_e \mathbf{E}$ be the dipole moment per unit volume, where **P** is called the *polarization* and χ_e the *electric susceptibility*, then

$$\phi = \int_V \frac{\mathbf{P} \cdot \mathbf{r}}{r^3} \, dV = \int_V \mathbf{P} \cdot \mathrm{grad} \left(\frac{1}{r} \right) dV \tag{2}$$

where the differentiation is with respect to the coordinates of the volume element and *not* with respect to the coordinates of the observer. Now,

$$\mathbf{\nabla} \cdot \frac{\mathbf{P}}{r} = \frac{1}{r} \mathbf{\nabla} \cdot \mathbf{P} + \mathbf{P} \cdot \mathbf{\nabla} \left(\frac{1}{r} \right) \tag{3}$$

Replacing the last term in Eq. (3) by the difference of the other two and substituting into Eq. (2), we have

$$\phi = \int_V \mathrm{div} \left(\frac{\mathbf{P}}{r} \right) dV - \int_V \frac{\mathrm{div}\,\mathbf{P}}{r} \, dV \tag{4}$$

and using Green's theorem,

$$\phi = \int_S \frac{\mathbf{P}}{r} \cdot d\mathbf{S} - \int_V \frac{\mathrm{div}\,\mathbf{P}}{r} \, dV \tag{5}$$

The potential is thus exactly the same as would have been obtained if there were within the insulator a volume density of charge $-\mathrm{div}\,\mathbf{P}$ and on the surface of the insulator a surface charge density P_n, where P_n is the

[1] C. Bottcher, *Rec. Trav. Chim.*, **62**, 325, 503 (1943).

normal component of **P**. Thus, within the insulator, since the surface charge does not enter Poisson's equation, we have

$$\text{div } \mathbf{E} = 4\pi(\rho - \text{div } \mathbf{P})$$

$$\text{div } (\mathbf{E} + 4\pi\mathbf{P}) = 4\pi\rho \tag{6}$$

We define the *electric displacement*, **D**, as

$$\mathbf{D} = \mathbf{E} + 4\pi\mathbf{P} = (1 + 4\pi\chi_e)\mathbf{E} \tag{7}$$

The static *dielectric constant* ε_s is defined as,

$$\varepsilon_s = 1 + 4\pi\chi_e \tag{8}$$

so that

$$\mathbf{D} = \varepsilon_s \mathbf{E} \tag{9}$$

Poisson's equation becomes

$$\text{div } \mathbf{D} = 4\pi\rho \tag{10}$$

If $\varepsilon_s \neq 1$ the substance is often called a *dielectric*.

3. Local Electric Field; the Lorentz Solution

The local electric field which acts on the molecules of a dielectric arises not only from the applied field but also from the electric fields due to the induced dipoles in the other molecules. To calculate this local field we shall use a method due to Lorentz.[1] In Figure 1 we have considered a dielectric between the plates of a *parallel plate capacitor* and within the dielectric we have considered a sphere about the point of reference whose radius is small enough so that the region outside the sphere may be regarded as a continuous medium. For the region inside, however, the structure of the substance must be taken into account. We shall assume the substance to have a cubic structure.

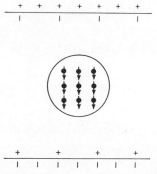

Figure 1. Dielectric material between the plates of a parallel plate capacitor.

[1] H. Lorentz, *The Theory of Electrons*, Dover, New York, 1952, p. 117.

In calculating the local field we must consider the following contributions: (i) the applied field $\mathbf{E}$, (ii) the field $\mathbf{E}_1$ due to the volume charge density, i.e. $-\operatorname{div}\mathbf{P}$, in the region of the dielectric outside the sphere, (iii) the field $\mathbf{E}_2$ due to the surface charge density P_n at the surface of the sphere, and finally (iv) the field $\mathbf{E}_3$ due to the dipoles within the sphere.

Since $\mathbf{P}$ is constant $\operatorname{div}\mathbf{P} = 0$ so that $\mathbf{E}_1 = 0$. Referring to Figure 2, $\mathbf{E}_2$ can be calculated as follows:

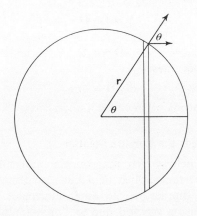

Figure 2. Small sphere within the dielectric on which the surface charge density is P_n.

$$E_2 = \int_0^\pi \frac{(P\cos\theta)(2\pi r^2 \sin\theta\, d\theta)\cos\theta}{r^2}$$

$$= 2\pi P \int_0^\pi \cos^2\theta \sin\theta\, d\theta \tag{1}$$

If the axis of the dipoles is taken as the x-axis then from Eq. (1.19),

$$E_3 = m \sum_i \frac{3x_i^2 - r_i^2}{r_i^5} \tag{2}$$

But because of the cubic structure of the dielectric

$$\sum_i x_i^2 = \sum_i y_i^2 = \sum_i z_i^2 = \tfrac{1}{3}\sum_i r_i^2 \tag{3}$$

so that $E_3 = 0$. Thus

$$E_{loc} = E + \tfrac{4}{3}\pi P \tag{4}$$

4. The Clausius–Mossotti Formula

From Eq. (2.1) the polarization is given by

$$P = \sum_i n_i \alpha_i E^i_{\text{loc}} \tag{1}$$

where n_i is the number of atoms of type i in a unit volume and α_i includes both the atomic and the electronic polarizability. If the local field is a Lorentz field then

$$P = \sum_i n_i \alpha_i (E + \tfrac{4}{3}\pi P)$$

$$P = \frac{\sum_i n_i \alpha_i}{1 - \tfrac{4}{3}\pi \sum_i n_i \alpha_i} E \tag{2}$$

Thus

$$\frac{\varepsilon_s - 1}{4\pi} = \frac{\sum_i n_i \alpha_i}{1 - \tfrac{4}{3}\pi \sum_i n_i \alpha_i}$$

$$\frac{\varepsilon_s - 1}{\varepsilon_s + 2} = \tfrac{4}{3}\pi \sum_i n_i \alpha_i \tag{3}$$

This equation is usually known as the *Clausius–Mossotti formula*.[1] If an alternating field is applied, then for sufficiently high frequencies, the heavy atoms will not be able to move fast enough to keep up with the field and only the electronic polarizability will be left. Hence,

$$\frac{\varepsilon_\infty - 1}{\varepsilon_\infty + 2} = \tfrac{4}{3}\pi \sum_i n_i \alpha_i^e \tag{4}$$

where ε_∞ is the high frequency dielectric constant. Now the magnetic permeability μ is very nearly unity for a dielectric and thus the optical index of refraction n_0 is given by $n_0^2 = \varepsilon_\infty$. Substitution of this result in Eq. (4) yields the *Lorentz–Lorenz formula*[2]

$$\frac{n_0^2 - 1}{n_0^2 + 2} = \tfrac{4}{3}\pi \sum_i n_i \alpha_i^e \tag{5}$$

Table 1 gives values for ε_s and ε_∞ for the alkali halides.

[1] R. Clausius, *Die Mechanische Wärmelehre*, Vieweg-Verlag, Brunswick, Germany, 1879, Vol. II, p. 94; O. Mossotti, *Mem. di math. e fisica di Modena*, **24**, II, 49 (1850).
[2] H. Lorentz, *Ann. Physik*, **9**, 641 (1880); L. Lorenz, *ibid.*, **11**, 70 (1880).

TABLE 1. Static and high frequency dielectric constants for alkali halides.
(After Cusack.[3])

Substance	F		Cl		Br		I	
	ε_s	ε_∞	ε_s	ε_∞	ε_s	ε_∞	ε_s	ε_∞
Li	9.2	1.91	11.05	2.68	12.1	3.04	11.03	3.55
Na	4.9	1.74	5.77	2.32	5.99	2.60	6.60	2.96
K	6.05	1.83	4.76	2.7	4.78	2.35	4.94	2.64
Rb	5.91	1.93	5.20	2.18	4.70	2.34	4.81	2.58

5. Orientational Polarization

The molecules of some substances have permanent dipole moments. Such substances are called *dipolar* or *polar*. If the molecules of a polar substance are free to rotate, then in the absence of an electric field thermal agitation will cause the dipole moments of the molecule to be randomly oriented resulting in no net moment. However, the application of an electric field will tend to compensate for this thermal agitation and a temperature-dependent electric moment will result. In the case of some solids and liquids the orienting effect of the field will be opposed by the strength of the molecular interactions.

Consider, as did Debye,[1] a gas containing a large number of identical molecules each having a permanent dipole moment $\boldsymbol{\mu}$. The potential energy of an individual molecule is then given by Eq. (1.21):

$$W = -\mu E \cos \theta \tag{1}$$

Hence the average component of the dipole moment in the field direction is

$$\bar{\mu} = \frac{\displaystyle\int \mu \cos \theta \; e^{-\varepsilon/kT} \, d\omega}{\displaystyle\int e^{-\varepsilon/kT} \, d\omega} \tag{2}$$

The integrations over all the variables except θ will divide out. Thus

$$\frac{\bar{\mu}}{\mu} = \frac{\displaystyle\int_0^\pi \cos \theta \; e^{(\mu E/kT)\cos\theta} \sin \theta \, d\theta}{\displaystyle\int_0^\pi e^{(\mu E/kT)\cos\theta} \sin \theta \, d\theta} \tag{3}$$

3 N. Cusack, *The Electric and Magnetic Properties of Solids*, Longmans, Green, London, 1958, p. 384.
1 P. Debye, *Z. Physik*, **13**, 97 (1912).

The factor sin θ appears because the orientational part of $d\omega$ is identical to the angular part of the spherical polar coordinate element of volume, $\sin\theta\,d\theta\,d\phi$. Introducing the notation $a = \mu E/kT$ and $x = \cos\theta$

$$\frac{\bar{\mu}}{\mu} = \frac{\int_{-1}^{1} x\,e^{ax}\,dx}{\int_{-1}^{1} e^{ax}\,dx} = \frac{\partial}{\partial a}\left(\ln\int_{-1}^{1} e^{ax}\,dx\right)$$

$$= \frac{\partial}{\partial a}\ln\frac{e^a - e^{-a}}{a} = \frac{e^a + e^{-a}}{e^a - e^{-a}} - \frac{1}{a}$$

$$\frac{\bar{\mu}}{\mu} = \coth a - \frac{1}{a} \tag{4}$$

If we define the *Langevin function*[2] $\mathscr{L}(x)$ by

$$\mathscr{L}(x) = \coth x - \frac{1}{x} \tag{5}$$

then

$$\frac{\bar{\mu}}{\mu} = \mathscr{L}\left(\frac{\mu E}{kT}\right) \tag{6}$$

For $x \ll 1$, $\coth x = 1/x + \frac{1}{3}x$ so that $\mathscr{L}(x) = \frac{1}{3}x$ for $x \ll 1$. On the other hand for $x \gg 1$, $\mathscr{L}(x) = \coth x = e^x/e^x = 1$. $\mathscr{L}(x)$ is shown in Figure 1.

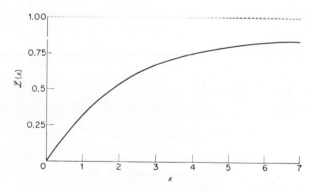

Figure 1. The Langevin function.

For the case of large fields or low temperatures $\bar{\mu} = \mu$. This situation corresponds to the complete alignment of the dipoles in the field direction.

[2] P. Langevin, *J. Physique*, **4**, 678 (1905).

On the other hand, as long as the temperature is high or the field small enough (which is the usual case), then

$$\bar{\mu} = \frac{\mu^2 E}{3kT} \tag{7}$$

so that the dipolar polarizability is[3]

$$\alpha_d = \frac{\mu^2}{3kT} \tag{8}$$

Hence, including the electronic and atomic polarizabilities, the polarization is given by

$$P = n\left(\alpha_e + \alpha_a + \frac{\mu^2}{3kT}\right) E \tag{9}$$

where n is the number of dipoles per unit volume. The static dielectric constant is then given by the *Debye formula*

$$\varepsilon_s - 1 = \frac{4\pi P}{E} = 4\pi n\left(\alpha_e + \alpha_a + \frac{\mu^2}{3kT}\right)$$

since for a gas the local field and the internal field are identical.

The characteristic temperature dependence of the static dielectric constants of some vapors is given in Figure 2.[4]

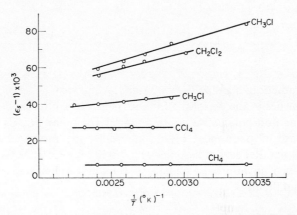

Figure 2. $\varepsilon_s - 1$ as a function of $1/T$ for some vapors (after Sanger[4]).

[3] For a quantum mechanical derivation of this result, see *Q.C.*, pp. 337–340.
[4] R. Sanger, *Physik. Z.*, **27**, 556 (1926).

From Figure 2 it is observed that CH_4 and CCl_4 have no permanent dipole moments. This is to be expected because of the symmetry of these molecules. The other vapors, having asymmetrical molecules, are polar. For further experimental results the reader is referred to Symth's useful book.[5]

6. The Polarization Catastrophe

Consider the case of a polar liquid or solid. Assume that the local field is given by the Lorentz expression or, in other words, assume the validity of the Clausius–Mossotti formula. Substitution of Eq. (5.8) into the Clausius–Mossotti formula gives

$$\frac{\varepsilon_s - 1}{\varepsilon_s + 2} = \frac{4\pi}{3} n \frac{\mu^2}{3kT} \tag{1}$$

where the atomic and electronic polarizabilities have been neglected. Solving for ε_s gives

$$\varepsilon_s = \frac{1 + 2\dfrac{4\pi}{3} n \dfrac{\mu^2}{3kT}}{1 - \dfrac{4\pi}{3} n \dfrac{\mu^2}{3kT}} \tag{2}$$

In other words we could choose $T_0 = \frac{4}{3}\pi n m^2 / 3k$ such that $\varepsilon_s(T_0) = \infty$ and $\varepsilon_s < 0$ for $T < T_0$. To gain an order of magnitude for T_0:

$$\mu \simeq 1 \text{ esu} \times 10^{-8} = 10^{-18} \text{ cgs and } n \simeq 10^{23}$$

so that
$$T_0 \simeq \frac{10^{23} \times 10^{-36}}{10^{-16}} \simeq 10^{3\,\circ}\text{K}$$

Thus for $T < 10^{3\,\circ}$K we would expect $\varepsilon < 0$, but this is not observed. This contradiction is called the polarization catastrophe.

The error lies in the use of the Lorentz field as the internal field, which is accurate for non-polar substances but fails for polar liquids and solids. For the case of permanent dipole moments, the moments are not, in general, all parallel as was assumed in deriving the Lorentz field. Onsager has developed an approximate theory for polar substances which overcomes this difficulty.

7. Onsager's Formula for a Polar Liquid

Before embarking on this problem, a few remarks about solving potential problems will be of value. The problems with which we shall

---

[5] C. P. Symth, *Dielectric Behavior and Structure*, McGraw-Hill, New York, 1955.

be concerned will be such that the volume charge density is zero. We must therefore solve Laplace's equation:

$$\nabla^2\phi = \frac{\partial^2\phi}{\partial x^2} + \frac{\partial^2\phi}{\partial y^2} + \frac{\partial^2\phi}{\partial z^2} = 0 \tag{1}$$

There are an unlimited number of solutions to this equation. The solution of interest is obtained by requiring that it satisfy the boundary conditions of the problem. For electrostatics two important boundary conditions will now be considered. First, ϕ is a single-valued function (otherwise work could be continuously produced by a charge moving cyclically in a closed path with no resulting change in the environment of the charge—in contradiction to the law of conservation of energy). Secondly, if we consider a dielectric interface and draw a cylinder of constant cross section, dS, across the interface (*vide* Figure 1) then since there is no charge enclosed

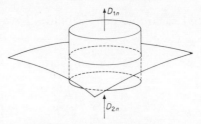

Figure 1. A dielectric interface.

within the cylinder

$$\int \mathbf{D} \cdot d\mathbf{S} = 0 \tag{2}$$

The length of the walls of the cylinder can be made arbitrarily small so that the contribution of the walls to Eq. (2) vanishes. Thus,

$$(D_{1n} - D_{2n})\,dS = 0$$
$$D_{1n} = D_{2n} \tag{3}$$

Thus we have that D_n is continuous across a dielectric interface. In terms of the electric potential this means that $\varepsilon_s\,\partial\phi/\partial n$ is continuous across the interface.

Generally, it is most convenient to work in the coordinates determined by the boundaries. In deriving Onsager's formula we shall be concerned with spherical boundaries, so let us express Eq. (1) in spherical polar coordinates (*vide* Figure 2)

$$x = r\sin\theta\cos\varphi$$
$$y = r\sin\theta\sin\varphi$$
$$z = r\cos\theta \tag{4}$$

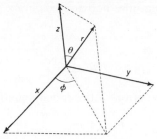

Figure 2. Geometric relationship between the spherical polar and rectangular coordinates.

By means of Eqs. (4) a change of variables in Laplace's equation can be undertaken. The process is tedious so the mechanics of the process are omitted.[1] The result is

$$\nabla^2\phi = \frac{1}{r^2}\frac{\partial}{\partial r}\left(r^2\frac{\partial\phi}{\partial r}\right) + \frac{1}{r^2\sin^2\theta}\frac{\partial}{\partial\theta}\left(\sin\theta\frac{\partial\phi}{\partial\theta}\right) + \frac{1}{r^2\sin^2\theta}\frac{\partial^2\phi}{\partial\varphi^2} = 0 \quad (5)$$

We shall be concerned with problems involving symmetry about the z-axis so we can neglect the φ-dependence. Let us attempt a solution to Eq. (5) in the form,

$$R(r)\Theta(\theta) \quad (6)$$

Thus,

$$\frac{\Theta}{r^2}\frac{d}{dr}\left(r^2\frac{dR}{dr}\right) + \frac{R}{r^2\sin^2\theta}\frac{d}{d\theta}\left(\sin\theta\frac{d\Theta}{d\theta}\right) = 0 \quad (7)$$

Dividing through by $R\Theta/r^2$ yields

$$\frac{1}{R}\frac{d}{dr}\left(r^2\frac{dR}{dr}\right) + \frac{1}{\Theta\sin^2\theta}\frac{d}{d\theta}\left(\sin\theta\frac{d\Theta}{d\theta}\right) = 0 \quad (8)$$

The two parts each involve different variables. This can only be the case if each is equal to a constant

$$\frac{d}{dr}\left(r^2\frac{dR}{dr}\right) - \lambda R = 0$$

$$\frac{1}{\sin^2\theta}\frac{d}{d\theta}\left(\sin\theta\frac{d\Theta}{d\theta}\right) + \lambda\Theta = 0 \quad (9)$$

It can be shown that the θ equation has a finite solution only if $\lambda = n(n+1)$ where n is some integer. The solutions to this equation are then $P_n(\cos\theta)$ and $Q_n(\cos\theta)$. However, $Q_n(\cos\theta)$ is infinite for $\theta = 0$, π and, hence, need not be considered further. The functions $P_n(\cos\theta)$ are called *Legendre polynomials*. A few of these polynomials are given below.

---

[1] For a general method of obtaining ∇^2 in any coordinate system, see *Q.C.*, Appendix III.

TABLE 1. Legendre polynomials, for $n = 0, 1, 2, 3$

$$P_0 = 1 \qquad P_2 = \frac{3\cos^2\theta - 1}{2}$$

$$P_1 = \cos\theta \qquad P_3 = \frac{5\cos^3\theta - 3\cos\theta}{2}$$

With $\lambda = n(n+1)$ the solution of the radial equation is

$$R = A_n r^n + \frac{B_n}{r^{n+1}} \tag{10}$$

Thus, for the case of axial symmetry about the z-axis, the solution to Laplace's equation in spherical polar coordinates is

$$\sum_n \left(A_n r^n + \frac{B_n}{r^{n+1}} \right) P_n(\cos\theta) \tag{11}$$

With this background we can now obtain Onsager's formula. Following Onsager[2] we assume:

1. A molecule occupies a sphere of radius a and its polarizability is isotropic.
2. Short range forces are negligible—only long range dipolar interactions are considered.

The second assumption means that the surroundings of a molecule can be treated as a continuum with dielectric constant ε_s.

In calculating the local field we must consider two parts:

1. the external field and the polarization due to it;
2. the 'reaction' field to the dipole.

To calculate the first contribution we must solve for the potential inside a cavity of radius a in a dielectric under the influence of an electric field. Choose the coordinate axis so that the z-axis is in the direction of **E** giving Figure 3.

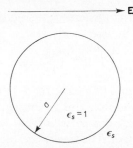

Figure 3. A cavity of radius a within a polar liquid in an electric field **E** which is in the direction of the z-axis.

[2] L. Onsager, *J. Am. Chem. Soc.*, **58**, 1486 (1936).

The following conditions must be satisfied by the potential

(i) $\nabla^2 \phi_1 = \nabla^2 \phi_2 = 0$

(ii) $\phi_1 = \phi_2$ and $\dfrac{\partial \phi_1}{\partial r} = \varepsilon_s \dfrac{\partial \phi_2}{\partial r}$ at $r = a$

(iii) $\phi_2 \rightarrow -Er \cos \theta$ as $r \rightarrow \infty$

(iv) ϕ_1 is finite at $r = 0$

Thus since the boundary conditions only involve $\cos \theta$ we would expect only $P_1(\cos \theta) = \cos \theta$ to appear in the solution. Hence,

$$\phi_1 = \left(Ar + \frac{B}{r^2} \right) \cos \theta$$

$$\phi_2 = \left(Cr + \frac{D}{r^2} \right) \cos \theta \tag{12}$$

$B = 0$ for finiteness at the origin. Condition (iii) implies $C = -E$. Conditions (ii) give

$$Aa = -Ea + \frac{D}{a^2}$$

$$A = \varepsilon_s \left[-E - \frac{2D}{a^3} \right] \tag{13}$$

Solving for A gives

$$A = -\frac{3\varepsilon_s}{2\varepsilon_s + 1} E \tag{14}$$

Thus

$$\phi_1 = -\frac{3\varepsilon_s}{2\varepsilon_s + 1} Er \cos \theta \tag{15}$$

The electric field at the origin is

$$E_{(1)} = -\frac{\partial \phi_1}{\partial z} \bigg|_{r=a} = \frac{3\varepsilon_s}{2\varepsilon_s + 1} E \tag{16}$$

To calculate the second contribution we must solve for the potential in the problem illustrated by Figure 4.

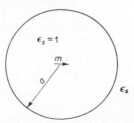

Figure 4. Spherical molecule of radius a and dipole moment **m** in a continuum with dielectric constant ϵ_s.

(i) $\nabla^2 \phi_1 = \nabla^2 \phi_2 = 0$

(ii) $\phi_1 = \phi_2$ and $\dfrac{\partial \phi_1}{\partial r} = \varepsilon_s \dfrac{\partial \phi_2}{\partial r}$ at $r = a$

(iii) $\phi_2 \to 0$ as $r \to \infty$

(iv) $\phi_1 \to \dfrac{m \cos \theta}{r^2}$ as $r \to 0$

Hence, taking into account conditions (iii) and (iv) we expect solutions of the form

$$\phi_1 = \frac{m \cos \theta}{r^2} + Ar \cos \theta$$

$$\phi_2 = \frac{B \cos \theta}{r^2} \tag{17}$$

Conditions (ii) give

$$\frac{m}{a^2} + Aa = \frac{B}{a^2}$$

$$-\frac{2m}{a^3} + A = -\frac{2\varepsilon_s B}{a^3} \tag{18}$$

Solving for A gives

$$A = \frac{2}{a^3} \frac{\varepsilon_s - 1}{2\varepsilon_s + 1} m = gm \tag{19}$$

Hence the local field is

$$\mathbf{E}_{\text{loc}} = \frac{3\varepsilon_s}{2\varepsilon_s + 1} \mathbf{E} + g\mathbf{m} \tag{20}$$

The dipole moment consists of both a permanent moment $\boldsymbol{\mu}$ and an induced moment, i.e.

$$\mathbf{m} = \boldsymbol{\mu} + \alpha \mathbf{E}_{\text{loc}} \tag{21}$$

where α is the polarizability of the molecule. Thus

$$\mathbf{m} = \boldsymbol{\mu} + \alpha \left[\frac{3\varepsilon_s}{2\varepsilon_s + 1} \mathbf{E} + g\mathbf{m} \right] \tag{22}$$

Solving for $\mathbf{m}$ gives

$$\mathbf{m} = \frac{\boldsymbol{\mu}}{1 - \alpha g} + \frac{3\varepsilon_s}{2\varepsilon_s + 1} \frac{\alpha \mathbf{E}}{1 - \alpha g} \tag{23}$$

Putting this expression into Eq. (20) gives

$$\mathbf{E}_{loc} = \frac{3\varepsilon_s}{2\varepsilon_s + 1} \mathbf{E} + \frac{g}{1 - \alpha g} \boldsymbol{\mu} + \frac{3\varepsilon_s}{2\varepsilon_s + 1} \frac{\alpha g}{1 - \alpha g} \mathbf{E}$$

$$= \frac{3\varepsilon_s}{2\varepsilon_s + 1} \frac{\mathbf{E}}{1 - \alpha g} + \frac{g\boldsymbol{\mu}}{1 - \alpha g} \tag{24}$$

Now let us calculate the mean dipole moment. Since the induced moment is always in the direction of the applied field we have from Eq. (23)

$$\overline{m} = \frac{\overline{\mu}}{1 - \alpha g} + \frac{3\varepsilon_s}{2\varepsilon_s + 1} \frac{\alpha E}{1 - \alpha g} \tag{25}$$

$\overline{\mu}$ is given by

$$\frac{\overline{\mu}}{\mu} = \frac{\int_0^\pi \cos\theta \, e^{-\boldsymbol{\mu}\cdot\mathbf{E}_{loc}/kT} \sin\theta \, d\theta}{\int_0^\pi e^{-\boldsymbol{\mu}\cdot\mathbf{E}_{loc}/kT} \sin\theta \, d\theta} \tag{26}$$

where

$$\boldsymbol{\mu}\cdot\mathbf{E}_{loc} = \frac{3\varepsilon_s}{2\varepsilon_s + 1} \frac{\mu E \cos\theta}{1 - \alpha g} + \frac{\mu^2 g}{1 - \alpha g} \tag{27}$$

The second term is independent of θ and so will divide out of Eq. (26). Thus

$$\frac{\overline{\mu}}{\mu} = \mathscr{L} \left[\frac{3\varepsilon_s \mu E}{(2\varepsilon_s + 1)(1 - \alpha g)kT} \right] \tag{28}$$

As we have seen in Sect. 6, $\mu \simeq 10^{-18}$ cgs. Thus for a field of the order of 10^3 volts/cm $= 10$ statvolts/cm the argument is

$$\frac{10^{-18} \times 10}{10^{-16} T} \simeq \frac{1}{10T}$$

so that for $T \gg \frac{1}{10}$ °K we have $\mathscr{L}(x) = \frac{1}{3}x$ and, therefore,

$$\overline{\mu} = \frac{3\varepsilon_s \mu^2 E}{(2\varepsilon_s + 1)(1 - \alpha g)3kT} \tag{29}$$

Hence

$$\overline{m} = \frac{3\varepsilon_s}{2\varepsilon_s + 1} \left\{ \frac{\mu^2}{(1 - \alpha g)^2 3kT} + \frac{\alpha}{1 - \alpha g} \right\} E \tag{30}$$

Since P is the dipole moment per unit volume we have

$$P = \frac{m}{\frac{4}{3}\pi a^3} = \frac{\varepsilon_s - 1}{4\pi} E \tag{31}$$

For the moment consider the case of a non-polar liquid, i.e. $\mu = 0$. From Eqs. (30) and (31) we have

$$\varepsilon_s - 1 = \frac{3\varepsilon_s}{2\varepsilon_s + 1} \frac{\alpha}{1 - \alpha g} \frac{3}{a^3} \tag{32}$$

But substituting in the value of g from Eq. (19) we obtain

$$\varepsilon_s - 1 = \frac{3\varepsilon_s}{2\varepsilon_s + 1} \frac{\alpha}{1 - \dfrac{2\alpha}{a^3} \dfrac{\varepsilon_s - 1}{2\varepsilon_s + 1}} \frac{3}{a^3}$$

$$= 9\varepsilon_s \frac{\alpha/a^3}{(2\varepsilon_s + 1) - \dfrac{2\alpha}{a^3}(\varepsilon_s - 1)} \tag{33}$$

Multiplying both sides of Eq. (33) by $(2\varepsilon_s + 1) - \dfrac{2\alpha}{a^3}(\varepsilon_s - 1)$ and solving for α/a^3 gives

$$(\varepsilon_s - 1)\left[2\varepsilon_s + 1 - \frac{2\alpha}{a^3}(\varepsilon_s - 1)\right] = \frac{3\alpha}{a^3}$$

$$(\varepsilon_s - 1)(2\varepsilon_s + 1) = [9\varepsilon_s + 2(\varepsilon_s - 1)^2]\,\frac{\alpha}{a^3}$$

$$= (2\varepsilon_s + 1)(\varepsilon_s + 2)\,\frac{\alpha}{a^3}$$

$$\frac{\varepsilon_s - 1}{\varepsilon_s + 2} = \frac{\alpha}{a^3} \tag{34}$$

which is the Clausius–Mossotti formula since $n = 1/\tfrac{4}{3}\pi a^3$ is the number of dipoles per unit volume. Hence our result has the correct limiting form.

We now return to the case of a polar liquid. In a high frequency alternating field the permanent dipole will not be able to follow the field and $\bar{\mu} = 0$. Hence,

$$\frac{\varepsilon_\infty - 1}{\varepsilon_\infty + 2} = \frac{n_0^2 - 1}{n_0^2 + 2} = \frac{\alpha}{a^3} \tag{35}$$

Using this result to eliminate α from Eq. (30) gives

$$\bar{m} = \frac{3\varepsilon_s}{2\varepsilon_s + 1} \left\{ \frac{\mu^2}{\left(1 - 2\dfrac{n_0^2 - 1}{n_0^2 + 2}\dfrac{\varepsilon_s - 1}{2\varepsilon_s + 1}\right)^2 3kT} + \frac{a^3 \dfrac{n_0^2 - 1}{n_0^2 + 2}}{\left(1 - 2\dfrac{n_0^2 - 1}{n_0^2 + 2}\dfrac{\varepsilon_s - 1}{2\varepsilon_s + 1}\right)} \right\} E$$

$$= \frac{3\varepsilon_s}{2\varepsilon_s + 1} \left\{ \frac{\mu^2}{3kT} \frac{(2\varepsilon_s + 1)^2(n_0^2 + 2)}{(6\varepsilon_s + 3n_0^2)^2} + \frac{(n_0^2 - 1)(2\varepsilon_s + 1)}{6\varepsilon_s + 3n_0^2} a^3 \right\} E$$

$$\bar{m} = \frac{3\varepsilon_s}{2\varepsilon_s + n_0^2} \left\{ \frac{\mu^2}{3kT} \frac{2\varepsilon_s + 1}{2\varepsilon_s + n_0^2} \left(\frac{n_0^2 + 2}{3}\right)^2 + \frac{n_0^2 - 1}{3} a^2 \right\} E \tag{36}$$

Eliminating $\bar{m}$ from Eq. (36) by means of Eq. (31) gives

$$\frac{a^3}{3}(\varepsilon_s-1) = \frac{3\varepsilon_s}{2\varepsilon_s+n_0^2}\left\{\frac{\mu^2}{3kT}\frac{2\varepsilon_s+1}{2\varepsilon_s+n_0^2}\left(\frac{n_0^2+2}{3}\right)^2 + \frac{n_0^2-1}{3}a^3\right\}$$

$$\frac{a^3}{3}\left[\varepsilon_s-1-\frac{3\varepsilon_s}{2\varepsilon_s+n_0^2}(n_0^2-1)\right] = \frac{3\varepsilon_s}{2\varepsilon_s+n_0^2}\frac{2\varepsilon_s+1}{2\varepsilon_s+n_0^2}\left(\frac{n_0^2+2}{3}\right)^2\frac{\mu^2}{3kT}$$

$$\frac{a^3}{3}(2\varepsilon_s+1)(\varepsilon_s-n_0^2) = \frac{3\varepsilon_s}{2\varepsilon_s+n_0^2}(2\varepsilon_s+1)\left(\frac{n_0^2+2}{3}\right)^2\frac{\mu}{3kT} \tag{37}$$

But $n = 1/\frac{4}{3}\pi a^3$ and thus we have *Onsager's formula*

$$\varepsilon_s-n_0^2 = \frac{3\varepsilon_s}{2\varepsilon_s+n_0^2}\left(\frac{n_0^2+2}{3}\right)^2\frac{4\pi n\mu^2}{3kT} \tag{38}$$

8. Polar Solids

In a liquid, because of the absence of any preferred directions, the average energy of a dipole is independent of its orientation. However, in a crystal this will no longer be the case and the average energy of a dipole will, in general, depend on its orientation relative to the crystal axis.

To gain a qualitative picture of the processes involved consider a two-dimensional face centered square lattice. Assume that the particles have only a permanent dipole moment, i.e. $\alpha = 0$. At absolute zero the least energy is assumed by the configuration shown in Figure 1 or equivalently

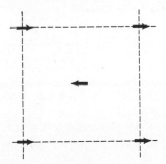

Figure 1. Two-dimensional face centered square lattice in a configuration of least energy.

by a configuration in which the orientations of the corner and center dipoles are exchanged since it is purely arbitrary which dipoles are chosen as corner dipoles. In a three-dimensional structure the situation will be more complicated, for example there will in general be more than two equilibrium positions, but the above model has many of the qualitative features of more complicated structures.

For convenience, we shall call → the right direction and ← the wrong direction for the corner dipoles and ← the right direction and → the wrong direction for center dipoles. As the temperature goes up some of the dipoles acquire enough thermal energy to flip over. If enough dipoles flip over the environment of a dipole will become ambiguous and the energy $V(T)$ required for the dipole to flip will decrease. The temperature variation of $V(T)$ is shown in Figure 2.

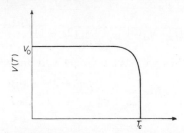

Figure 2. $V(T)$ as a function of T.

Above the critical temperature, T_c, the crystal is completely disordered and there is no distinction between right and wrong directions.

Let ω be the probability of finding a dipole in the wrong direction. Then $1-\omega$ is the probability of finding a dipole in the right direction. Hence,

$$\frac{\omega}{1-\omega} = e^{-V(T)/kT} \tag{1}$$

Solving Eq. (1) for ω and $1-\omega$ gives

$$\omega = \frac{e^{-V(T)/kT}}{1+e^{-V(T)/kT}} \tag{2}$$

$$1-\omega = \frac{1}{1+e^{-V(T)/kT}} \tag{3}$$

For small temperatures $V(T)/kT \simeq V_0/kT \gg 1$ so that $\omega \ll 1$ and for $T > T_c$, $V(T) = 0$ so $\omega = \frac{1}{2}$.

Now apply an electric field. For definiteness let the field be applied in the $\rightarrow$ direction, for which case we have Figure 3. E_{loc} is the local field (Onsager type),

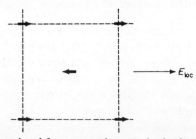

Figure 3. Two-dimensional face centered square lattice in an electric field.

$$\mathbf{E}_{\mathrm{loc}} = \frac{3\varepsilon_s}{2\varepsilon_s + 1}\mathbf{E} + g\boldsymbol{\mu} = \mathbf{E}_{(1)} + g\boldsymbol{\mu} \tag{4}$$

α is zero by assumption. The corner dipoles have an additional energy $-\mu E_{(1)} - g\mu^2$ for the right direction and $\mu E_{(1)} - g\mu^2$ for the wrong direction. The center dipoles have an additional energy $\mu E_{(1)} - g\mu^2$ or $-\mu E_{(1)} - g\mu^2$ for the right or wrong directions. Hence for the corner dipoles $\mathscr{E}_{\mathrm{wrong}} - \mathscr{E}_{\mathrm{right}} = V + 2\mu E_{(1)}$ and for a center dipole $\mathscr{E}_{\mathrm{wrong}} - \mathscr{E}_{\mathrm{right}} = V - 2\mu E_{(1)}$. Thus if ω_1 and ω_2 are respectively the probabilities of a corner dipole and a center dipole being in the wrong direction,

$$\omega_1 = \frac{e^{-(V + 2\mu E_{(1)})/kT}}{1 + e^{-(V + 2\mu E_{(1)})/kT}} \tag{5}$$

$$\omega_2 = \frac{e^{-(V - 2\mu E_{(1)})/kT}}{1 + e^{-(V - 2\mu E_{(1)})/kT}} \tag{6}$$

There are four cases to consider:

Configuration	Probability	Dipole moment/unit cell in the direction of E
$\rightarrow$ $\rightarrow$	$(1 - \omega_1)\omega_2$	2μ
$\rightarrow$ $\leftarrow$	$(1 - \omega_1)(1 - \omega_2)$	0
$\leftarrow$ $\leftarrow$	$\omega_1(1 - \omega_2)$	-2μ
$\leftarrow$ $\rightarrow$	$\omega_1 \omega_2$	0

The mean dipole moment per unit cell is then the weighted average of these four cases,

$$\bar{m} = 2\mu(1 - \omega_1)\omega_2 - 2\mu\omega_1(1 - \omega_2) = 2\mu(\omega_2 - \omega_1) \tag{7}$$

Substituting the values of ω_1 and ω_2 from Eqs. (5) and (6) we have

$$\bar{m} = 2\mu\left\{\frac{e^{-(V - 2\mu E_{(1)})/kT}}{1 + e^{-(V - 2\mu E_{(1)})/kT}} - \frac{e^{-(V + 2\mu E_{(1)})/kT}}{1 + e^{-(V + 2\mu E_{(1)})/kT}}\right\}$$

$$= 2\mu\left\{\frac{e^{-(V - 2\mu E_{(1)})/kT} - e^{-(V + 2\mu E_{(1)})/kT}}{1 + e^{-V/kT}(e^{2\mu E_{(1)}/kT} + e^{-2\mu E_{(1)}/kT}) + e^{-2V/kT}}\right\}$$

$$= 2\mu\frac{e^{2\mu E_{(1)}/kT} - e^{-2\mu E_{(1)}/kT}}{e^{V/kT} + e^{-V/kT} + e^{2\mu E_{(1)}/kT} + e^{-2\mu E_{(1)}/kT}}$$

$$\bar{m} = \frac{2\mu \sinh\dfrac{2\mu E_{(1)}}{kT}}{\cosh\dfrac{V(T)}{kT} + \cosh\dfrac{2\mu E_{(1)}}{kT}} \tag{8}$$

There are two interesting limiting cases.

(i) For low temperatures, since $\cosh x = \sinh x = e^x/2$ for $x \gg 1$, we have

$$\overline{m} = \frac{2\mu\, e^{2\mu E_{(1)}/kT}}{e^{V/kT} + e^{2\mu E_{(1)}/kT}} = \frac{2\mu}{e^{(V - 2\mu E_{(1)})/kT} + 1} \tag{9}$$

Thus so long as $V > 2\mu E_{(1)}$, $\overline{m} \simeq 0$, which is logical because the crystal is in an ordered state.

(ii) For ordinary temperatures $2\mu E_{(1)}/kT$ is small and

$$\overline{m} = 2\mu \frac{2\mu E_{(1)}/kT}{\cosh \dfrac{V(T)}{kT} + 1} \tag{10}$$

Hence

$$P = \frac{\varepsilon_s - 1}{4\pi} E = n\overline{m} = n\, \frac{3\varepsilon_s}{2\varepsilon_s + 1} \frac{4\mu^2/kT}{\cosh \dfrac{V(T)}{kT} + 1} E$$

$$\varepsilon_s - 1 = \frac{3\varepsilon_s}{2\varepsilon_s + 1} \frac{4\pi n(4\mu^2/kT)}{\cosh \dfrac{V(T)}{kT} + 1} \tag{11}$$

If T_c is not too low and V_0 is not too small then for temperatures below T_c, $V(T)/kT \gg 1$ and hence

$$\varepsilon_s - 1 = \frac{3\varepsilon_s}{2\varepsilon_s + 1} 4\pi n \left(\frac{4\mu^2}{kT}\right) 2e^{-V(T)/kT} \tag{12}$$

The exponential and thus ε_s increases as T increases. For temperatures above T_c, $V(T) = 0$ and

$$\varepsilon_s - 1 = \frac{3\varepsilon_s}{2\varepsilon_s + 1} 4\pi n \left(\frac{4\mu^2}{kT}\right) \frac{1}{2} \tag{13}$$

so that ε_s decreases with increasing temperature. The temperature dependence of ε_s is then of the form shown in Figure 4.

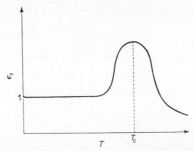

Figure 4. ε_s as a function of T for a typical polar solid.

More complicated solids have analogous properties.

9. Dipole Relaxation Time

If we consider the case of a dielectric under the influence of the alternating field

$$E = E_0 \cos \omega t \tag{1}$$

then both P and D will also vary periodically with the time but P and D may lag in phase relative to E. Thus,

$$D = D_0 \cos(\omega t - \delta) = D_0(\cos \omega t \cos \delta + \sin \omega t \sin \delta) \tag{2}$$

We introduce the two quantities

$$\varepsilon_1 = \frac{D_0 \cos \delta}{E_0}, \qquad \varepsilon_2 = \frac{D_0 \sin \delta}{E_0} \tag{3}$$

and obtain

$$D = E_0(\varepsilon_1 \cos \omega t + \varepsilon_2 \sin \omega t) \tag{4}$$

It is often convenient to introduce complex quantities. Thus,

$$E = E_0 \, e^{-i\omega t}$$

remembering at all times that we are only interested in the real part of these quantities. Thus if we lump ε_1 and ε_2 into the single complex quantity

$$\varepsilon = \varepsilon_1 + i\varepsilon_2 \tag{5}$$

we have the convenient result

$$D = \varepsilon E_0 \, e^{-i\omega t} \tag{6}$$

Again it is to be emphasized that only real parts are of interest. The reason for using complex quantities is the greater ease of using Eq. (6) than Eq. (4).

However, if the relationship between E and D is linear, ε_1 and ε_2 are not entirely independent. Consider the case of turning the field $E(u)$ on at time u and off at time $u + du$ as is illustrated in Figure 1.

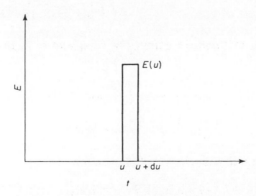

Figure 1. Electric field $E(u)$ applied during the time interval $u < t < u + du$.

A displacement D will result for $t > u + du$ as a result of the tendency of D to lag in phase behind E. Thus for $t > u + du$

$$D(t-u) = E(u)\alpha(t-u)\,du \tag{7}$$

where $\alpha(t-u)$ is some decay function which depends on the material. The displacement D also contains a part which is in phase with E. Thus for $u < t < u + du$

$$D(t-u) = \varepsilon_\infty E(u) + E(u)\alpha(0)\,du \tag{8}$$

If a time-varying field is applied, then the field can be divided into a number of parts each of the form of Figure 1. Hence, if we assume that future events have no effect and that the composition of the material does not change, i.e. the decay constant is the same for each element, then

$$D(t) = \varepsilon_\infty E(t) + \int_{-\infty}^{t} E(u)\alpha(t-u)\,du \tag{9}$$

Now consider

$$E = E_0 \cos \omega t \tag{10}$$

then

$$D(t) = \varepsilon_\infty E_0 \cos \omega t + E_0 \int_{-\infty}^{t} \cos \omega u\, \alpha(t-u)\,du$$

$$= \varepsilon_\infty E_0 \cos \omega t + E_0 \int_{0}^{\infty} \cos \omega(t-x)\,\alpha(x)\,dx$$

$$= \varepsilon_\infty E_0 \cos \omega t + E_0 \int_{0}^{\infty} (\cos \omega t \cos \omega x + \sin \omega t \sin \omega x)\,\alpha(x)\,dx$$

$$D(t) = \left(\varepsilon_\infty + \int_{0}^{\infty} \cos \omega x\, \alpha(x)\,dx \right) E_0 \cos \omega t$$

$$+ \left(\int_{0}^{\infty} \sin \omega x\, \alpha(x)\,dx \right) E_0 \sin \omega t \tag{11}$$

Comparing Eqs. (11) and the definitions of ε_1 and ε_2 as given by Eq. (3), we have

$$\varepsilon_1(\omega) = \varepsilon_\infty + \int_{0}^{\infty} \cos \omega x\, \alpha(x)\,dx$$

$$\varepsilon_2(\omega) = \int_{0}^{\infty} \sin \omega x\, \alpha(x)\,dx \tag{12}$$

This can be put into a single complex equation

$$\varepsilon(\omega) = \varepsilon_\infty + \int_{0}^{\infty} e^{i\omega x}\, \alpha(x)\,dx \tag{13}$$

Following Debye[1] assume that $\alpha(t)$ has the form

$$\alpha(t) = \alpha(0)\, e^{-t/\tau} \tag{14}$$

where τ is the relaxation time. To calculate $\alpha(0)$ consider a constant field; then Eq. (9) becomes

$$D(t) = \varepsilon_\infty E + E \int_{-\infty}^{t} \alpha(0)\, e^{-(t-u)/\tau}\, du$$

$$= \{\varepsilon_\infty + \alpha(0)\tau\}E = \varepsilon_0 E$$

$$\alpha(0) = \frac{\varepsilon_0 - \varepsilon_\infty}{\tau} \tag{15}$$

Thus with this form of $\alpha(0)$ if Eq. (14) is substituted into Eq. (13) we obtain

$$\varepsilon(\omega) = \varepsilon_\infty + \frac{\varepsilon_0 - \varepsilon_\infty}{\tau} \int_{0}^{\infty} e^{(i\omega - 1/\tau)x}\, dx$$

$$= \varepsilon_\infty + \frac{\varepsilon_0 - \varepsilon_\infty}{\tau}\, \frac{-1}{i\omega - 1/\tau}$$

$$\varepsilon(\omega) = \varepsilon_\infty + \frac{\varepsilon_0 - \varepsilon_\infty}{1 + \omega^2 \tau^2}(1 + i\omega\tau) \tag{16}$$

Equating real and imaginary parts, we have the *Debye equations*

$$\varepsilon_1(\omega) - \varepsilon_\infty = \frac{\varepsilon_0 - \varepsilon_\infty}{1 + \omega^2 \tau^2}$$

$$\varepsilon_2(\omega) = (\varepsilon_0 - \varepsilon_\infty)\frac{\omega\tau}{1 + \omega^2 \tau^2} \tag{17}$$

10. Model for the Debye Equations

We consider the dielectric material as an assembly of molecules, each with a permanent dipole moment $\mathbf{m}$, whose interactions can be neglected. Each molecule has two equilibrium positions separated by a potential barrier. From the theory of absolute reaction rates the number of times a molecule passes over the barrier is

$$v = \frac{kT}{h}\, e^{-\Delta G^{\ddagger}/kT} \tag{1}$$

where $\Delta G^{\ddagger}$ is the Gibbs' free energy of activation and the transmission coefficient κ has been taken equal to unity.

Now apply an electric field $\mathbf{E}$, yielding the situation illustrated in Figure 1.

[1] P. Debye, *Polar Molecules*, Dover, New York, 1945, p. 20.

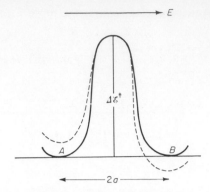

Figure 1. Energy barrier of height $\Delta\mathscr{E}^{\ddagger}$. The solid line represents the case $\mathbf{E} = 0$, and the broken line, the case $\mathbf{E} > 0$.

The number of molecules per unit time passing from position A to position B is thus

$$\frac{kT}{h} e^{-(\Delta G^{\ddagger} - \frac{1}{2}eEa)/kT} \qquad (2)$$

and the number of molecules per unit time passing from position B to position A is thus

$$\frac{kT}{h} e^{-(\Delta G^{\ddagger} + \frac{1}{2}eEa)/kT} \qquad (3)$$

where the symbol e in the exponent denotes the electronic charge. Thus if n_A and n_B are the number of particles per unit volume in positions A and B

$$\frac{dn_A}{dt} = -\frac{dn_B}{dt} = \frac{kT}{h} e^{-\Delta G^{\ddagger}/kT} \left[n_B e^{-eEa/2kT} - n_A e^{eEa/2kT} \right] \qquad (4)$$

Provided $eaE \ll kT$ we can expand the exponentials

$$\frac{dn_A}{dt} = -\frac{dn_B}{d} = \frac{kT}{h} e^{-\Delta G^{\ddagger}/kT} \left[n_B \left(1 - \frac{eEa}{2kT} \right) - n_A \left(1 + \frac{eEa}{2kT} \right) \right] \qquad (5)$$

We are interested in the change in dipole moment with time. This will be proportional to $dn_B/dt - dn_A/dt$

$$\frac{d(n_B - n_A)}{dt} = 2\frac{kT}{h} e^{-\Delta G^{\ddagger}/kT} \left[n_A \left(1 + \frac{eEa}{2kT} \right) - n_B \left(1 - \frac{eEa}{2kT} \right) \right]$$

$$= 2\frac{kT}{h} e^{-\Delta G^{\ddagger}/kT} \left[-(n_B - n_A) + n\frac{eEa}{2kT} \right] \qquad (6)$$

where $n = n_A + n_B$. Solving this equation

$$n_B - n_A = C \exp\left(-\frac{2kT}{h}e^{-\Delta G^{\ddagger}/kT}\right)t + n\frac{eEa}{2kT} \qquad (7)$$

Thus with the initial condition $n_A = n_B = n/2$ we have

$$n_B - n_A = n\frac{eEa}{2kT}(1 - e^{-t/\tau}) \qquad (8)$$

where

$$\tau = \frac{h}{2kT}e^{\Delta G^{\ddagger}/kT} \qquad (9)$$

Equation (8) implies an exponential decay, which was the basic assumption used in obtaining the Debye equations. For a fuller discussion of various models leading to the Debye equations the reader is referred to Frölich's book.[1]

11. Density Fluctuations and Light Scattering

From the theory of light scattering it can be shown that the intensity of light, ΔI_θ, scattered by a small dielectric particle at an angle θ from the direction of the incident plane wave, whose intensity is I, and a distance r from the particle is given by[1]

$$\frac{\Delta I_\theta}{I} = \frac{\pi^2}{2\lambda_0^4}(\Delta\varepsilon_\infty)^2 V^2 \frac{1 + \cos^2\theta}{r^2} \qquad (1)$$

where λ_0 is the wavelength of the incident wave in a vacuum, $\Delta\varepsilon_\infty$ is the difference between the high frequency dielectric constants of the particle and the surrounding medium, and V is the volume of the particle.

From the Lorentz–Lorenz formula we have

$$\frac{\varepsilon_\infty - 1}{\varepsilon_\infty + 2} = \frac{4\pi}{3}n\alpha = \frac{4\pi}{3}\frac{\rho N}{M}\alpha \qquad (2)$$

where N is Avogadro's number, ρ the density of the substance and M the molecular weight. Hence

$$\left(\frac{\varepsilon_\infty - 1}{\varepsilon_\infty + 2}\right)\frac{1}{\rho} = \text{constant} \qquad (3)$$

[1] H. Frölich, *Theory of Dielectrics*, 2nd Ed., Oxford University Press, 1958, p. 11.
[1] K. Stacey, *Light Scattering in Physical Chemistry*, Academic Press, New York, 1956, pp. 1–15.

Since $\Delta\rho$ and $\Delta\varepsilon_\infty$ are small quantities, we obtain

$$\frac{1}{\rho}\left[\frac{1}{\varepsilon_\infty+2} - \frac{\varepsilon_\infty-1}{(\varepsilon_\infty+2)^2}\right]\Delta\varepsilon_\infty - \frac{\varepsilon_\infty-1}{\varepsilon_\infty+2}\frac{\Delta\rho}{\rho^2} = 0$$

$$\Delta\varepsilon_\infty = \frac{\Delta\rho}{\rho}\frac{(\varepsilon_\infty-1)(\varepsilon_\infty+2)}{3} \tag{4}$$

If we now consider light scattering by density fluctuations in a gas,[2, 3] then by substituting Eq. (4) into Eq. (1) we have

$$\frac{\Delta I_\theta}{I} = \frac{\pi^2}{2\lambda_0^4}\frac{(\varepsilon_\infty-1)^2(\varepsilon_\infty+2)^2}{9}\left(\frac{\Delta\rho}{\rho}\right)^2 V^2\frac{1+\cos^2\theta}{r^2} \tag{5}$$

In our discussion of particle fluctuations in Sect. 4.17 we found that

$$(\Delta N)^2 = \overline{(\bar{N}-N)^2} = \left(\frac{\partial^2\ln\Xi}{\partial(\mu/kT)^2}\right)_{V,T} \tag{6}$$

But from Eq. (4.15.15) we have

$$\bar{N} = \left(\frac{\partial\ln\Xi}{\partial\mu/kT}\right)_{V,T} \tag{7}$$

Thus,

$$\left(\frac{\Delta N}{\bar{N}}\right)^2 = \left(\frac{\Delta\rho}{\rho}\right)^2 = \frac{kT}{\bar{N}^2}\left(\frac{\partial\bar{N}}{\partial\mu}\right)_{V,T} \tag{8}$$

the second equality being true because $\rho = Nm/V$ and V is constant. From Eqs. (4.15.10) and (4.15.12) we have

$$V\,dp = S\,dT + \bar{N}\,d\mu \tag{9}$$

Hence since T is constant

$$d\mu = \frac{V}{\bar{N}}dp \tag{10}$$

Thus,

$$\left(\frac{\partial\mu}{\partial\bar{N}/V}\right)_T = \frac{V}{\bar{N}}\left(\frac{\partial p}{\partial\bar{N}/V}\right)_T$$

$$V\left(\frac{\partial\mu}{\partial\bar{N}}\right)_{T,V} = -\frac{V^3}{\bar{N}^2}\left(\frac{\partial p}{\partial V}\right)_{N,T} \tag{11}$$

Substituting Eq. (11) into Eq. (8) and noting that the compressibility, κ, is given by

$$\kappa = -\frac{1}{V}\left(\frac{\partial V}{\partial p}\right)_{N,T} \tag{12}$$

2 M. von Smoluchowski, *Ann. Physik*, **21**, 756 (1906); **25**, 205 (1908).
3 A. Einstein, *Ann. Physik*, **17**, 549 (1905); **19**, 373 (1906); **33**, 1275 (1910).

we obtain

$$\left(\frac{\Delta\rho}{\rho}\right)^2 = \frac{kT}{V}\kappa \tag{13}$$

Hence

$$\frac{\Delta I_\theta}{I} = -\frac{3c}{16\pi}V\frac{1+\cos^2\theta}{r^2} \tag{14}$$

where

$$c = \frac{8\pi^3}{27\lambda_0^4}kT\,\kappa(\varepsilon_\infty - 1)^2(\varepsilon_\infty + 2)^2 \tag{15}$$

The scattering in a spherical shell of thickness Δr is then

$$\frac{\Delta I}{I} = -\frac{3c}{16\pi}2\pi\int_0^\pi (1+\cos^2\theta)\sin\theta\,d\theta\frac{r^2\Delta r}{r^2}$$

$$\frac{\Delta I}{I} = -C\Delta r \tag{16}$$

so that C is an attenuation factor for scattering. Equation (16) was first obtained by Lord Rayleigh[4] in his theory of atmospheric scattering. He explained the blue color of the sky by means of the factor $1/\lambda_0^4$ in Eq. (15). Blue light having a short wavelength is scattered most strongly and hence the light which reaches our eyes after having been scattered in the upper atmosphere is largely composed of blue light.

For more information about light scattering by non-crystalline materials the reader is referred to a recent article by Debye.[5]

12. Magnetic Materials

We treat the case of magnetism by analogy to electricity. Ampere investigated the magnetic interactions of current-carrying coils and observed that if the wires carrying the currents to and from the coils were very close together they contributed nothing to the forces between the coils and that the force between two small coils was precisely of the same type as the force between two electric dipoles. Thus we define the *magnetic moment* of a coil of area dS carrying a current i as

$$\mathbf{m} = \frac{i}{c}d\mathbf{S} \tag{1}$$

The magnetic field $\mathbf{H}$ is defined in analogy to Eq. (1.20)

$$\text{couple} = \mathbf{m}\times\mathbf{H} \tag{2}$$

[4] Lord Rayleigh, *Phil. Mag.*, **41**, 107, 274, 447 (1871); **12**, 81 (1881); **44**, 28 (1897).
[5] P. Debye, 'Scattering of Radiation by Non-crystalline Media', in *Non-crystalline Solids*, V. Frechette, Ed., Wiley, New York, 1960.

Matter is composed of charged particles. The motion of these charged particles produces tiny electric currents which in the presence of a magnetic field H will experience couples tending to orient them in the direction of H. The only exceptions will be atoms in which the several tiny currents cancel. In this way a medium will become magnetized by an imposed field. We can define a vector B, called the *magnetic induction*,

$$B = H + 4\pi M \tag{3}$$

where M, the magnetic moment per unit volume, is called the *intensity of magnetization* or simply the magnetization. The intensity of magnetization varies with H and if H is not too large we have

$$M = \chi_m H \tag{4}$$

where χ_m is the *magnetic susceptibility* of the substance. If $\chi_m < 0$ the substance is said to be *diamagnetic* and if $\chi_m > 0$ the substance is said to be *paramagnetic*. Thus, considering only isotropic substances,

$$B = \mu H = (1 + 4\pi\chi_m)H \tag{5}$$

where μ is called the *permeability* of the substance. For a diamagnetic substance $\mu < 1$ and for a paramagnetic substance $\mu > 1$.

Some substances have a magnetic moment even when there is no applied magnetic field and are said to be *ferromagnetic*. We shall consider this case in Chapter 10.

Since there are no 'magnetic charges', we cannot argue that no work is done in taking a 'charge' around a closed path so as to insure the single-valued nature of a magnetic scalar potential. For this reason it is more useful to use a magnetic vector potential A such that

$$B = \text{curl} A = \nabla \times A \tag{6}$$

To determine A uniquely one more condition is needed. Usually we require that

$$\text{div} A = 0 \tag{7}$$

Further since there are no 'magnetic charges' the analogy to Poisson's equation is,

$$\text{div} B = 0 \tag{8}$$

13. Thermodynamics and Statistical Mechanics of Magnetization

The potential energy of a magnetic dipole μ in a magnetic field is given by

$$W = -\mu \cdot H \tag{1}$$

Obviously the work required to increase the magnetization of a material by an amount dM is

$$-H\,dM \tag{2}$$

The first law of thermodynamics is then[1]

$$T\,dS = dE - \mathbf{H}\cdot d\mathbf{M} \tag{3}$$

Any of our previous thermodynamic relations can then be obtained by replacing P by $-H$ and V by M. Thus the enthalpy is given by

$$H = E - \mathbf{H}\cdot\mathbf{M} + pV \tag{4}$$

the Helmholtz function by

$$A = E - TS \tag{5}$$

and Gibbs' function by

$$G = E - TS - \mathbf{H}\cdot\mathbf{M} + pV \tag{6}$$

For a system of independent permanent dipoles, if m_i is the component of the magnetic moment of a dipole in the direction of $\mathbf{H}$ then the magnetization M is given by

$$M = n\overline{m} = n\frac{\sum_i m_i\, e^{m_i H/kT}}{\sum_i e^{m_i H/kT}}$$

$$= nkT\frac{\partial}{\partial H}\left(\ln\sum_i e^{m_i H/kT}\right)$$

$$M = nkT\left(\frac{\partial \ln f_m}{\partial H}\right)_T \tag{7}$$

where n is the number of dipoles per unit volume and f_m is the magnetic partition function.

14. Diamagnetism and the Larmor Precession

We recall from Sect. 2.6 that for any vector $\mathbf{G}$

$$\frac{d\mathbf{G}}{dt} = \frac{\partial\mathbf{G}}{\partial t} + \boldsymbol{\omega}\times\mathbf{G} \tag{1}$$

where $d\mathbf{G}/dt$ and $\partial\mathbf{G}/\partial t$ are respectively the time rates of change of $\mathbf{G}$ as measured in a stationary coordinate system and a system rotating with angular velocity $\boldsymbol{\omega}$. The force on an electric charge q is found to be given by what is called the Lorentz force[1]

$$\mathbf{F} = q\mathbf{E} + q\frac{\mathbf{v}\times\mathbf{H}}{c} \tag{2}$$

---

[1] Some authors prefer to use $T\,dS = dE + M\,dH$. This is also correct but in this case dE is defined so that it does not include the energy of the field. For a full discussion of this point see E. A. Guggenheim, *Proc. Roy. Soc. (London)*, **A155**, 49, 70 (1946).

[1] C. Coulson, *Electricity*, Oliver and Boyd, Edinburgh, 1948, p. 62.

Now applying Eq. (1) we have

$$\dot{\mathbf{r}} = \frac{d\mathbf{r}}{dt} = \frac{\partial \mathbf{r}}{\partial t} + \boldsymbol{\omega} \times \mathbf{r} \tag{3}$$

$$\ddot{\mathbf{r}} = \frac{d\dot{\mathbf{r}}}{dt} = \frac{\partial \dot{\mathbf{r}}}{\partial t} + \boldsymbol{\omega} \times \dot{\mathbf{r}}$$

$$= \frac{\partial^2 \mathbf{r}}{\partial t^2} + 2\boldsymbol{\omega} \times \frac{\partial \mathbf{r}}{\partial t} + \boldsymbol{\omega} \times (\boldsymbol{\omega} \times \mathbf{r}) \tag{4}$$

The second term is called the *coriolis acceleration* and the third term the *centrifugal acceleration*. Thus, for an atomic electron of charge $-e$ and mass m

$$m\left[\frac{\partial^2 \mathbf{r}}{\partial t^2} + 2\boldsymbol{\omega} \times \frac{\partial \mathbf{r}}{\partial t} + \boldsymbol{\omega} \times (\boldsymbol{\omega} \times \mathbf{r})\right] = -e\left[\mathbf{E} + \frac{\partial \mathbf{r}}{\partial t} \times \frac{\mathbf{H}}{c} + (\boldsymbol{\omega} \times \mathbf{r}) \times \frac{\mathbf{H}}{c}\right] \tag{5}$$

Choose $\boldsymbol{\omega}$ such that

$$2m\boldsymbol{\omega} \times \frac{\partial \mathbf{r}}{\partial t} = -e\frac{\partial \mathbf{r}}{\partial t} \times \frac{\mathbf{H}}{c}$$

$$\omega_L = \frac{e\mathbf{H}}{2mc} \tag{6}$$

This is called the *Larmor frequency*. Hence,

$$m\frac{\partial^2 \mathbf{r}}{\partial t^2} = -e\mathbf{E} - e(\boldsymbol{\omega} \times \mathbf{r}) \times \frac{\mathbf{H}}{c} - m\boldsymbol{\omega} \times (\boldsymbol{\omega} \times \mathbf{r})$$

$$= -e\mathbf{E} - e\left(\frac{e\mathbf{H}}{2mc} \times \mathbf{r}\right) \times \frac{\mathbf{H}}{c} - m\mathbf{H} \times (\mathbf{H} \times \mathbf{r})\frac{e^2}{4m^2c^2}$$

$$m\frac{\partial^2 \mathbf{r}}{\partial t^2} = -e\mathbf{E} + \frac{e^2}{2mc^2}\mathbf{H} \times (\mathbf{H} \times \mathbf{r}) \tag{7}$$

The field $\mathbf{E}$ due to the nucleus will be of the order

$$\frac{Ze}{r^2} \simeq \frac{Z \times 10^{-10}}{10^{-16}} \simeq Z(10^6) \text{ cgs} \tag{8}$$

But

$$\frac{e}{2mc^2}\mathbf{H} \times (\mathbf{H} \times \mathbf{r}) \simeq \frac{10^{-10} \times 10^{-8}}{10^{-27} \times 10^{21}}H^2 \simeq 10^{-12}H^2 \text{ cgs}$$

But $H < 10^4$ oersted so the second term in Eq. (7) can be neglected. Hence

$$m\frac{\partial^2 \mathbf{r}}{\partial t^2} = -e\mathbf{E} \tag{9}$$

This result is referred to as *Larmor's theorem*.[1] Thus a rotation simulates the effect of a magnetic field. This result is not true if there is no electric field since then we cannot neglect the second term in Eq. (7). For $E = 0$ we get

$$\frac{mv^2}{r} = -\frac{evH}{c}$$

$$\omega = -\frac{eH}{mc} \qquad (10)$$

This frequency of precession of a free electron is called the *cyclotron frequency*. We see that as a result of the applied magnetic field the electron precesses about **H** (*vide* Figure 1).

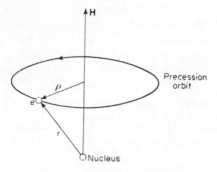

Figure 1. A precessing electron.

This precessing electron is equivalent to a current $i = -e/(2\pi/\omega_L)$ in a loop of area $\pi\langle\rho^2\rangle$ where $\langle\rho^2\rangle = \langle x^2\rangle + \langle y^2\rangle$ is the average square distance of an electron from the precession axis. Hence the magnetic moment of the precessing electron is

$$\mathbf{m} = -\pi\langle\rho^2\rangle\frac{e\omega_L}{2\pi c} = -\frac{e\langle\rho^2\rangle}{2c}\left(\frac{eH}{2mc}\right)$$

$$= -\frac{e^2\langle\rho^2\rangle}{4mc^2}\mathbf{H} \qquad (11)$$

For a spherical atom the average square distance of an electron from the nucleus is given by

$$\langle r^2\rangle = \langle x^2\rangle + \langle y^2\rangle + \langle z^2\rangle = \tfrac{3}{2}\langle\rho^2\rangle \qquad (12)$$

This result is also true for a non-spherical atom. This is the principle

[1] J. Larmor, *Aether and Matter*, Cambridge University Press, 1900, p. 341.

of spectroscopic stability.[2] Hence for a substance with z electrons per atom and n atoms per unit volume the *diamagnetic susceptibility* is given by

$$\chi_d = -\frac{nZe^2\langle r^2\rangle}{6mc^2} \tag{13}$$

a result due to Langevin[3] and Pauli.[4] It should be noted that χ_d is temperature-independent.

To calculate χ_d we must know $\langle r^2\rangle$, which is usually calculated from the wave functions obtained by Hartree's method of the self consistent field[5] or some other approximate method such as that of Slater.[6] The quality of these approximate wave functions decreases as z increases. The diamagnetic susceptibilities of various alkali and halide ions' are listed in Table 1.

TABLE 1. Molar diamagnetic susceptibilities of ions in crystals[7]

Ion	Experimental values ($\times 10^{-6}$ cm³/mole)	Calculated values ($\times 10^{-6}$ cm³/mole)
F⁻	9.1	8.1
Cl⁻	24.8	25.2
Br⁻	36.4	39.2
Li⁺	0.6	0.7
Na⁺	4.3	4.1
K⁺	14.0	14.1

15. Langevin Theory of Paramagnetism

In addition to the diamagnetism described in the preceding section an atom may have a permanent magnetic dipole μ. Reasoning as in Sect. 5, we have, assuming the dipoles to be independent,

$$M = n\mu\mathscr{L}\left(\frac{\mu H}{kT}\right) \tag{1}$$

where $\mathscr{L}(x) = \coth x - 1/x$. As we shall see in the next section $\mu \simeq 10^{-20}$ cgs so since $H < 10^4$ oersted we have

$$\frac{\mu H}{kT} \simeq \frac{10^{-20} \times 10^4}{10^{-16}T} = \frac{1}{T}$$

[2] J. H. van Vleck, *The Theory of Electric and Magnetic Susceptibilities*, Oxford University Press, 1932, p. 35.

[3] P. Langevin, *J. Physique*, **4**, 678 (1905).

[4] W. Pauli, *Z. Physik*, **2**, 201 (1920).

[5] *Q.C.*, pp. 163–167.

[6] *Q.C.*, pp. 162–163.

[7] W. Myers, *Rev. Mod. Phys.*, **24**, 15 (1952).

Hence except at very low temperatures $\mu H/kT \ll 1$ and thus,

$$M = \frac{n\mu^2}{3kT} H \tag{2}$$

The *paramagnetic susceptibility* is then

$$\chi_p = \frac{n\mu^2}{3kT} \tag{3}$$

where n is the number of atoms per unit volume. Equation (3) is known as *Curie's Law*[8] and was first discovered experimentally.

From Eq. (3) we see that

$$\chi_p \simeq \frac{10^{23} \times 10^{-40}}{10^{-16}T} = \frac{10^{-1}}{T} \text{ cgs/mole}$$

whereas we have seen that diamagnetic susceptibilities are typically of the order of 10^{-6} cgs/mole and, therefore, although diamagnetism is present in an atom with a permanent dipole moment it is completely masked by paramagnetism at reasonable temperatures.

Because electric dipole moments are of the order of 10^{-18} cgs whereas magnetic dipole moments are of the order of 10^{-20} cgs we can neglect dipole–dipole interactions and therefore it is not necessary to calculate local fields for the magnetic case.

16. Origin of Permanent Magnetic Dipoles

The motion of an electron in its orbit is equivalent to a current flowing in a loop:

$$i = -\frac{e\omega}{2\pi} = -\frac{ev}{2\pi a} \tag{1}$$

The magnetic moment is then

$$\mu = -\frac{i\pi a^2}{c} = \frac{e}{2c} av = -\frac{e}{2mc} p \tag{2}$$

where p is the angular momentum of the electron. It can be shown from quantum mechanics that[1] the angular momentum is restricted to the values

$$\sqrt{l(l+1)}\hbar \tag{3}$$

where $l = 0, 1, 2, 3, \ldots$ Electrons in states with $l = 0, 1, 2, 3, \ldots$ are called, respectively, $s, p, d, f, g, \ldots$ electrons. An s state electron has then zero angular momentum and thus no magnetic moment arising from its orbital motion. Furthermore, the only possible values of the component of the angular momentum along any specified direction (such as the direction

[8] P. Curie, *Ann. Chim. Phys.*, **5**, 289 (1895).
[1] *Q.C.*, pp. 39–44.

of an applied field **H**) of an electron in state l is restricted to the values

$$m_l \hbar \tag{4}$$

where $m_l = l, l-1, \ldots, 0, \ldots, -(l-1), -l$. In accord with this,

$$|\mathbf{\mu}| = \frac{e\hbar}{2mc} \sqrt{l(l+1)} \tag{5}$$

and the component of $\mathbf{\mu}$ in any specified direction is

$$\mu_z = \frac{e\hbar}{2mc} m_l \tag{6}$$

The quantity $\mu_B = e\hbar/2mc = 0.927 \times 10^{-20}$ erg oersted^{-1} is called the *Bohr magneton*.

Besides orbital angular momentum an electron also has angular momentum arising from its spin. The spin angular momentum has only two values $s = \pm \frac{1}{2}$. Thus

$$|\mathbf{s}| = \sqrt{s(s+1)}\hbar = \frac{\sqrt{3}}{2}\hbar$$

$$s_z = \pm \frac{1}{2}\hbar \tag{7}$$

For spin, Eq. (2) is not valid. Instead it is found that

$$\mu_z = g \frac{e}{2mc} s\hbar \tag{8}$$

with g, called the *spectroscopic splitting factor* or often the *gyromagnetic ratio*, having the value 2.0023. Hence the magnetic moment arising from spin is

$$\mu_z = \pm \frac{e\hbar}{2mc} \tag{9}$$

For the case of an atom of not too high Z $(Z \leqslant 70)$ the orbital angular momentum vectors may be added to form a vector **L** for which

$$|\mathbf{L}| = \sqrt{L(L+1)}\hbar \tag{10}$$

The spin angular momentum vectors may also be added to form a vector **S** for which

$$|\mathbf{S}| = \sqrt{S(S+1)}\hbar \tag{11}$$

The vectors **L** and **S** are then added to give the resultant angular momentum **J**. Also,

$$|\mathbf{J}| = \sqrt{J(J+1)}\hbar \tag{12}$$

$$J_z = M_J \hbar \tag{13}$$

where M_J can go, in steps of 1, from J to $-J$. This scheme of summing the orbital and spin angular momenta separately and then combining the resultants to form the total angular momentum is known as *Russell–Saunders coupling* or *L–S coupling*.[2] For this case

$$\boldsymbol{\mu}_L = \mu_B \mathbf{L} \qquad \boldsymbol{\mu}_S = 2\mu_S \mathbf{S} \tag{14}$$

where $\mathbf{L}$ is in units of $\hbar$ since $\hbar$ has been absorbed into μ_B. Thus,

$$\boldsymbol{\mu}_J = \mu_B(\mathbf{L}+2\mathbf{S}) = \mu_B(\mathbf{J}+\mathbf{S}) \tag{15}$$

We note that $\boldsymbol{\mu}_J$ is not parallel to $\mathbf{J}$. The component of $\boldsymbol{\mu}_J$ parallel to $\mathbf{J}$, which will be the effective magnetic moment, is given by

$$\boldsymbol{\mu} = \mu_B(\mathbf{J}+\mathbf{S}) \cdot \frac{\mathbf{J}}{|\mathbf{J}|}\frac{\mathbf{J}}{|\mathbf{J}|}$$

$$\boldsymbol{\mu} = \mu_B \left[\frac{|\mathbf{J}|^2+\mathbf{S}\cdot\mathbf{J}}{|\mathbf{J}|^2}\right]\mathbf{J} \tag{16}$$

But

$$\mathbf{L} = \mathbf{J}-\mathbf{S} \tag{17}$$

so

$$|\mathbf{L}|^2 = |\mathbf{J}|^2+|\mathbf{S}|^2-2\mathbf{S}\cdot\mathbf{J}$$

$$\mathbf{S}\cdot\mathbf{J} = \frac{|\mathbf{J}|^2+|\mathbf{S}|^2-|\mathbf{L}|^2}{2} \tag{18}$$

Thus,

$$\boldsymbol{\mu} = \mu_B\left[1+\frac{|\mathbf{J}|^2+|\mathbf{S}|^2-|\mathbf{L}|^2}{2|\mathbf{J}|^2}\right]\mathbf{J} \tag{19}$$

Hence, the gyromagnetic ratio is

$$g = 1+\frac{|\mathbf{J}|^2+|\mathbf{S}|^2-|\mathbf{L}|^2}{2|\mathbf{J}|^2} \tag{20}$$

But $|\mathbf{J}|^2 = J(J+1)$, etc., so

$$g = 1+\frac{J(J+1)+S(S+1)-L(L+1)}{2J(J+1)} \tag{21}$$

an expression first obtained by Landé.[3] In order to calculate g and hence μ we must know L, S, and J. These can be predicted most conveniently by means of an experimentally derived set of rules known as Hund's rules which state:

1. S has the largest possible value consistent with the Pauli principle.
2. L has the largest value consistent with rule 1.
3. For an incompletely filled shell:

    $J = L-S$ for a less than half filled shell;
    $J = L+S$ for a more than half filled shell.

[2] H. Russell and F. Saunders, *Astrophys. J.*, **61**, 38 (1925).
[3] A. Landé, *Z. Physik*, **15**, 189 (1923).

For a completely filled shell because of the Pauli principle each electron is paired with an electron with opposite spin so $J = 0$.

The nuclear magnetic moment which arises from nuclear spin also contributes to the magnetic moment of an atom. Nuclear magnetic moments are expressed in a unit analogous to the Bohr magneton called a *nuclear magneton*

$$\mu_n = \frac{e\hbar}{2m_p c} = 5.05 \times 10^{-24} \text{ erg oersted}^{-1}$$

where m_p is the mass of a proton. Nuclear magnetic moments are thus smaller than electronic magnetic moments by a factor 10^3 and can often be neglected.

17. Quantum Theory of Paramagnetism

From our discussion of the preceding section we see that the energy of an atom in a magnetic field is given by

$$\mathscr{E} = -\boldsymbol{\mu} \cdot \mathbf{H} = -\mu_B g \mathbf{J} \cdot \mathbf{H}$$
$$= \mu_B g H M_J \tag{1}$$

where M_J is restricted to the $2J+1$ values $-J, -J+1, \ldots, 0, \ldots J-1, J$, and g is given by Eq. (16.21). The magnetic partition function for an atom is

$$f_m = \sum_{M_J=-J}^{J} \exp\left(\frac{\mu_B g H}{kT} M_J\right) \tag{2}$$

If we let $x = \mu_B g J H / kT$ then

$$f_m = \sum_{M_J=-J}^{J} (e^{-x})^{M_J/J} = e^x \left[\sum_{n=0}^{2J} (e^{-x/J})^n\right] \tag{3}$$

But this last sum is a geometric progression[1] and thus

$$f_m = e^x \left[\frac{1-(e^{-x/J})^{2J+1}}{1-e^{x/J}}\right] = e^x \frac{e^{x/2J} - e^{-2x} e^{-x/2J}}{e^{x/2J} - e^{-x/2J}}$$

$$= \frac{\sinh \dfrac{2J+1}{2J} x}{\sinh \dfrac{x}{2J}} \tag{4}$$

---

[1] A geometric progression is a sum of the form
$$S_n = 1 + a + a^2 + \ldots + a^{n-1}$$

To sum this series we note that $1 + aS_n = S_{n+1} = S_n + a^n$ and hence solving for S_n we obtain

$$S_n = \frac{1 - a^n}{1 - a}$$

Thus by Eq. (13.7) we have

$$M = NkT \left(\frac{\partial \ln f_m}{\partial H} \right)_T$$

$$M = Ng\mu_B J B_J(x) \tag{5}$$

where

$$B_J(x) = \frac{2J+1}{2J} \coth \frac{2J+1}{2J} x - \frac{1}{2J} \coth \frac{x}{2J} \tag{6}$$

$B_J(x)$ is called the *Brillouin function*.[2] Let us consider two limiting cases:

1. $x \gg 1$, low temperature, high fields. As $y \to \infty$, coth $y = 1$, thus,

$$M = Ng\mu_B J \tag{7}$$

The dipoles are completely aligned.

2. $x \ll 1$, high temperatures, low fields (usual case). For $y \ll 1$, coth y = $1/y + \frac{1}{3}y$ and thus,

$$\begin{aligned}
B_J(x) &= \frac{2J+1}{2J} \left(\frac{2J}{2J+1} \frac{1}{x} + \frac{1}{3}x \frac{2J+1}{2J} \right) - \frac{1}{2J} \left(\frac{2J}{x} + \frac{1}{3} \frac{x}{2J} \right) \\
&= \frac{4J^2 + 4J}{4J^2} \frac{x}{3} = \frac{J+1}{J} \frac{x}{3}
\end{aligned} \tag{8}$$

Hence

$$M = N \frac{[g\mu_B \sqrt{J(J+1)}]^2}{3kT} H \tag{9}$$

and the magnetic susceptibility is then given by Curie's law,

$$\chi_m = N \frac{[g\mu_B \sqrt{J(J+1)}]^2}{3kT} H \tag{10}$$

The semi-classical theory of Langevin gave the same result since

$$\mu = g\mu_B \sqrt{J(J+1)} \tag{11}$$

This theory applies particularly well to the ions of the rare earth elements. The rare earth elements are distinguished by their partially filled $4f$ shells. Thus the electron configuration of the rare earth ions is,

$$(1s)^2 |(2s)^2 (2p)^6 |(3s)^2 (3p)^6 |(3d)^{10} (4s)^2 (4p)^6 (4f)^n |(5s)^2 (5p)^6$$

For f electrons, $l = 3$ and thus the $4f$ shell can accept

$$2(2l+1) = 2(2 \times 3 + 1) = 14 \text{ electrons.}$$

If the values of L, S, and J are assigned by Hund's rules, then for the 14 rare earth elements and lanthanum we obtain the values for μ/μ_B given in Table 1.

---

[2] L. Brillouin, *J. Physique*, **8**, 74 (1927).

TABLE 1. μ/μ_B for rare earth ions

No. of electrons in 4f shell	Ion	S	L	J	g	calc.	exp.
0	La^{3+}	0	0	0	—	0	0
1	Ce^{3+}	$\frac{1}{2}$	3	$\frac{5}{2}$	$\frac{6}{7}$	2.54	2.4
2	Pr^{3+}	1	5	4	$\frac{4}{5}$	3.58	3.5
3	Nd^{3+}	$\frac{3}{2}$	6	$\frac{9}{2}$	$\frac{8}{11}$	3.62	3.5
4	Pm^{3+}	2	6	4	$\frac{3}{5}$	2.68	—
5	Sm^{3+}	$\frac{5}{2}$	5	$\frac{5}{2}$	$\frac{2}{7}$	0.84	1.5
6	Eu^{3+}	3	3	0	—	0	3.4
7	Gd^{3+}	$\frac{7}{2}$	0	$\frac{7}{2}$	2	7.94	8.0
8	Tb^{3+}	3	3	6	$\frac{3}{2}$	9.72	9.5
9	Dy^{3+}	$\frac{5}{2}$	5	$\frac{15}{2}$	$\frac{4}{3}$	10.63	10.6
10	Ho^{3+}	2	6	8	$\frac{5}{4}$	10.60	10.4
11	Er^{3+}	$\frac{3}{2}$	6	$\frac{15}{2}$	$\frac{6}{5}$	9.59	9.5
12	Tm^{3+}	1	5	6	$\frac{7}{6}$	7.57	7.3
13	Yb^{3+}	$\frac{1}{2}$	3	$\frac{7}{2}$	$\frac{8}{7}$	4.54	4.5
14	Lu^{3+}	0	0	0	—	0	0

A graphical comparison of these results is given in Figure 1.

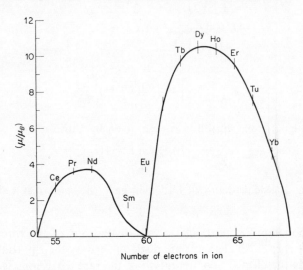

Figure 1. Theoretical and experimental values of μ/μ_B for lanthanum and the rare earths (after van Vleck[3]). The curve represents theoretical values.

The agreement is excellent except for Sm^{3+} and Eu^{3+}. Van Vleck[3] and Frank[4] have successfully calculated μ for these ions by considering higher order energy levels.

[3] J. H. van Vleck, *op. cit.*, p. 244.
[4] A. Frank, *Phys. Rev.*, **39**, 119 (1932).

For the case of the ions of the iron group the paramagnetism is due to the $3d$ shell. The $4f$ shell which is responsible for the paramagnetism of the rare earth ions lies well inside the atom and so is screened by the $5s$ and $5p$ shells. However, for the iron group ions the $3d$ shell is the outermost shell and is exposed to strong electric fields due to neighboring ions. The effect of this inhomogeneous electric field is to break up the L–S coupling and further to perturb the electronic motion so that the components of L are no longer constants of the motion and so that the time average of any given component of L is zero. Under these circumstances the orbital angular momentum is said to be *quenched*. The magnetic moment instead of being given by Eq. (11) is then given by

$$\mu = 2\sqrt{S(S+1)}\mu_B \tag{12}$$

since the gyromagnetic ratio for a spinning electron is 2. Table 2 lists μ/μ_B for the iron group elements.

TABLE 2. μ/μ_B for iron group ions

No. of electrons in $3d$ shell	Ion	S	calc.	exp.
0	K^+, Ca^{2+}, Sc^{3+} Ti^{4+}, V^{5+}	0	0	0
1	Ti^{3+}, V^{4+}	$\frac{1}{2}$	1.73	1.8
2	V^{3+}	1	2.83	2.8
3	Cr^{3+}, V^{2+}	$\frac{3}{2}$	3.87	3.8
4	Mn^{3+}, Cr^{2+}	2	4.90	4.9
5	Fe^{3+}, Mn^{2+}	$\frac{5}{2}$	5.92	5.9
6	Fe^{2+}	2	4.90	5.4
7	Co^{2+}	$\frac{3}{2}$	3.87	4.8
8	Ni^{2+}	1	2.83	3.2
9	Cu^{2+}	$\frac{1}{2}$	1.73	1.9
10	Cu^+, Zn^{2+}	0	0	0

18. Magnetic Cooling

Let us calculate the entropy of a paramagnetic salt at low temperatures. The entropy is composed of two parts: one part due to the lattice and another part due to angular momentum of the ions:

$$S = S_L + S_M \tag{1}$$

Now for low temperatures we have from Eq. (7.5.17) that

$$C_V = \frac{12\pi^4}{5} Nk \left(\frac{T}{\Theta}\right)^3 \tag{2}$$

Thus

$$S_L = \int_0^T \frac{C_V \, dT}{T} = \frac{4\pi^4}{5} Nk \left(\frac{T}{\Theta}\right)^3 \tag{3}$$

At the temperatures of interest, S_L is negligible compared to S_M. S_M can be calculated from the magnetic partition function

$$S_M = Nk \left(\frac{\partial}{\partial T} T \ln f_m\right)_{M,V} = Nk \frac{\partial}{\partial T} \left(T \ln \frac{\sinh \frac{2J+1}{2J} x}{\sinh \frac{x}{2J}} \right)$$

$$= \ln \frac{\sinh \frac{2J+1}{2J} x}{\sinh \frac{x}{2J}} - x B_J(x) \tag{4}$$

It is to be noted that

$$S_M = S_M \left(\frac{H}{T}\right) \tag{5}$$

In the Curie region we have

$$\ln \frac{\sinh \frac{2J+1}{2J} x}{\sinh \frac{x}{2J}} = \ln \left(\frac{\frac{2J+1}{2J} x + \frac{1}{6} \left(\frac{2J+1}{2J}\right)^3 x^3 + \ldots}{\frac{x}{2J} + \frac{1}{6} \left(\frac{x}{2J}\right)^3 + \ldots} \right)$$

$$= \ln (2J+1) \left(\frac{1 + \frac{x^2}{6} \left(\frac{2J+1}{2J}\right)^2}{1 + \frac{x^2}{6} \left(\frac{1}{2J}\right)^2} \right)$$

$$= \ln (2J+1) + \ln \left(1 + \frac{x^2}{3} \frac{J+1}{J}\right) \tag{6}$$

and

$$B_J(x) = \frac{1}{3} \frac{J+1}{J} x \tag{7}$$

Thus,[1]

$$\frac{S_M}{Nk} = \ln (2J+1) - \frac{[g\sqrt{J(J+1)}\mu_B]^2}{6k^2} \left(\frac{H}{T}\right)^2 \tag{8}$$

---

[1] According to Eq. (8) S_M does not go to zero as T goes to zero but this is of no concern as Eq. (8) is not valid for extremely low temperatures. In Eq. (4) $S_M \to 0$ as $T \to 0$ as required.

Because of Eq. (4) we see that one of the effects of an external magnetic field is to align the magnetic moments and thereby introduce more order into the system causing a reduction in entropy. Because of this fact it is possible to attain extremely low temperatures by a method called *adiabatic demagnetization*.[2] Temperatures down to 10^{-3}°K have been reached by this method. This method consists of two steps:

1. the isothermal magnetization of the specimen which is in thermal contact with liquid helium,
2. the specimen is then insulated and adiabatically demagnetized causing a decrease in temperature.

The results of these two steps are schematically illustrated in Figure 1.

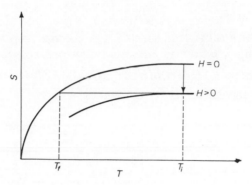

Figure 1. Entropy of a paramagnetic salt in the absence and in the presence of a magnetic field.

The internal electric fields due to other ions in the crystal will give rise to small Stark effects which become important as kT becomes small. This results in the entropy curve for $H = 0$ falling off faster and sets a lower limit on the temperatures that can be achieved by this method.

19. Nuclear Magnetic Resonance[1]

In analogy to our discussion of Sect. 16 the spin angular momentum **p** of a nucleus is given by

$$|\mathbf{p}| = \sqrt{I(I+1)}\hbar \tag{1}$$

where I is an integer. The components of the nuclear spin along a specified direction are

$$p_Z = M_I \hbar \tag{2}$$

[2] P. Debye, *Ann. Physik*, **81**, 1154 (1926); W. Giauque, *J. Am. Chem. Soc.*, **49**, 1864 (1927).

[1] This and the following sections closely follow G. Pake, *Am. J. Phys.*, **18**, 438, 473 (1950).

where M_I is restricted to the values $I, I-1, \ldots, -(I-1), -I$. The nuclear magnetic moment is then,

$$|\mathbf{\mu}| = g\mu_n\sqrt{I(I+1)} \tag{3}$$

where $\mu_n = e\hbar/2m_pc$ ($= 5.05 \times 10^{-24}$ erg oersted^{-1}) is the nuclear magneton. The components of $\mathbf{\mu}$ along a specified direction are then given by

$$\mu_Z = g\mu_n M_I \tag{4}$$

It is convenient to introduce a parameter γ by

$$\mathbf{\mu} = \gamma\mathbf{p} \tag{5}$$

In other words,

$$\gamma = \frac{g\mu_n}{\hbar} \tag{6}$$

Thus, a magnetic field $\mathbf{H}_0$, applied in the z direction, separates the energy levels of the various spin states into the following so called *Zeeman levels*,

$$-I\gamma\hbar H_0, \quad -(I-1)\gamma\hbar H_0, \quad \ldots, \quad (I-1)\gamma\hbar H_0, \quad I\gamma\hbar H_0 \tag{7}$$

This is illustrated in Figure 1 for the case $I = \frac{1}{2}$

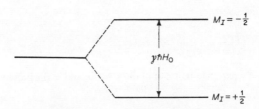

Figure 1. Zeeman splitting of nuclear energy levels in a magnetic field.

The aim of nuclear magnetic resonance experiments is to induce transitions between these Zeeman levels by emission or absorption of radiation. The frequency of the required radiation is then

$$\omega = \gamma H_0 \tag{8}$$

The selection rule for these transitions is [2]

$$\Delta M_I = \pm 1 \tag{9}$$

These transitions were first observed by Purcell et al.[3] and independently by Bloch et al.[4]

[2] *Q.C.*, pp. 116, 159–162.

[3] E. M. Purcell, H. C. Torrey, and R. V. Pound, *Phys. Rev.*, **69**, 37 (1946); N. Bloembergen, E. M. Purcell, and R. V. Pound, *Phys. Rev.*, **73**, 679 (1948).

[4] F. Bloch, W. W. Hansen, and M. E. Packard, *Phys. Rev.*, **69**, 127 (1946); **70**, 474 (1946); F. Bloch, *Phys. Rev.*, **70**, 460 (1946).

We can gain an insight into the resonance absorption using the following classical picture. Consider the nucleus in a magnetic field H_0. Referring to Eq. (12.2), the torque, L, acting on the nucleus is

$$L = \mu \times H_0 \tag{10}$$

The rotational analogue to Newton's second law of motion is

$$\frac{d\mathbf{p}}{dt} = L \tag{11}$$

where $\mathbf{p}$ is the angular momentum of the nucleus. Thus from Eq. (2.9.10)

$$\frac{d\mathbf{p}}{dt} = \frac{\partial \mathbf{p}}{\partial t} + \omega \times \mathbf{p} = \mu \times H_0 \tag{12}$$

and since $\mu = \gamma \mathbf{p}$ we have

$$\frac{\partial \mathbf{p}}{\partial t} = \mu \times \left(H_0 + \frac{\omega}{\gamma} \right) \tag{13}$$

Thus, $\partial \mathbf{p}/\partial t = 0$ if

$$\omega = -\gamma H_0 \tag{14}$$

[cf. Eq. (8)]. The effect of a magnetic field H_0 is simulated by a rotation ω given by Eq. (14), or in other words the magnetic moment μ would remain stationary in a reference frame rotating with angular frequency ω. Now suppose that a much smaller field H_1 is applied in a direction perpendicular to the direction of H_0 (*vide* Figure 2).

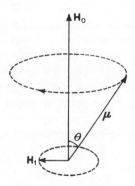

Figure 2. Rotation of the magnetic moment μ.

If the direction of H_1 itself rotates with angular frequency ω then μ always experiences a torque tending to increase θ. Thus if we vary the rate of rotation of $\mathbf{H}_1$ we get a resonance curve of the form of Figure 3. The order of magnitude of $v = \omega/2\pi$ is

$$v \simeq \frac{\gamma H}{2\pi} = \frac{g\mu_n H}{h} = \frac{10^{-24} \times 10^4}{10^{-27}} = 10^7 \text{ cycles}$$

$$= 10 \text{ Mcycles}$$

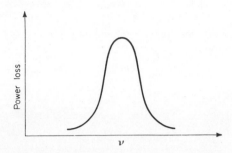

Figure 3. Power loss as a function of frequency.

In an experimental arrangement $\mathbf{H}_1$ does not rotate, but is a sinusoidally varying field with fixed direction. Such a field can be considered as being the superposition of two equal fields one following μ and the other affecting μ only twice in a cycle.

20. Spin–Lattice Relaxation Time

Consider an assembly of nuclei, each of spin $\mathbf{I}$, in a small magnetic field such as that of the earth. Since the energies of the different Zeeman levels are almost exactly the same, the nuclear spins will be essentially equally distributed among the $2I+1$ spin states. If the assembly is placed in a large magnetic field, $\mathbf{H}_0$, then the spin states will have different energies and spins in higher spin states will 'cool down' by giving up some of their energy to the lattice and going to lower states. We are interested in the rate at which equilibrium is approached.

Let $N(p)$ and $N(q)$ be the equilibrium populations of two Zeeman levels p and q which differ in energy by U_p-U_q. Then by the *principle of detailed balancing* (Sect. 1.9) we have

$$N(p)W(p{\rightarrow}q) = N(q)W(q{\rightarrow}p) \tag{1}$$

where $W(p{\rightarrow}q)$ is the probability of a transition from p to q. Thus

$$\frac{W(p{\rightarrow}q)}{W(q{\rightarrow}p)} = \frac{N(q)}{N(p)} = e^{(U_p - U_q)/kT} \tag{2}$$

If we consider, for example, the case $I = \frac{1}{2}$ then, since $\mu H_0/kT \ll 1$ except at very low temperatures, we have to a sufficient degree of accuracy

$$\frac{W(- \rightarrow +)}{W(+ \rightarrow -)} = 1 + \frac{2\mu H_0}{kT} \tag{3}$$

The excess number $n = N(+) - N(-)$ changes by two for each transition and thus,

$$\frac{dn}{dt} = 2N(-)W(- \rightarrow +) - 2N(+)W(+ \rightarrow -) \tag{4}$$

If P is the mean value of $W(- \rightarrow +)$ and $W(+ \rightarrow -)$, then Eq. (4) becomes

$$\frac{dn}{dt} = 2P(n_0 - n) \tag{5}$$

where $n_0 = \mu H_0[N(+) - N(-)]/kT$ is the equilibrium value of n. We define a time T_1 by

$$T_1 = \frac{1}{2P} \tag{6}$$

T_1 is called the *spin–lattice relaxation time*. Thus,

$$n = n_0[1 - e^{-t/T_1}] \tag{7}$$

T_1 is then the time required for all but $1/e$ of the equilibrium excess to reach the lower energy state. Measured values of T_1 vary from 10^{-4} seconds to several hours.

Waller[1] examined the interaction of the nuclear spins with the thermal vibrations of the lattice and obtained relaxation times which were several orders of magnitude too large. However, this is probably due to the presence of small quantities of paramagnetic impurities. Bloembergen, Purcell and Pound[2] have found that Brownian motion provides the relaxation mechanism in fluids.

We can discuss the distribution of spins among the various spin states by means of the concept of the *spin temperature*. For the case $I = \frac{1}{2}$ we define the spin temperature, T_s, by

$$\frac{N_+}{N_-} = e^{2\mu H_0/kT_s} \simeq 1 + \frac{2\mu H_0}{kT_s} \tag{8}$$

T_s is equal to T at thermal equilibrium. Spin–lattice relaxation is then the tendency of the spin and the lattice systems to come to the same temperature.

[1] I. Waller, *Z. Physik*, **79**, 370 (1932).
[2] See footnote 3 of Sect. 19.

21. Spin–Spin Interaction

In addition to the interactions between the spin and lattice systems each nuclear spin interacts with the neighboring spins through their magnetic fields. Each nuclear spin is in a fluctuating local field due to neighboring dipoles. The magnitude of this local field is about $\mu/a^3 \simeq 5$ oersted. This fluctuation of the local field over several oersted causes a spread of values of the precession frequencies (see Figure 19.3.)

A second process can also occur. If nuclei A and nuclei B are nearly antiparallel, the precessing component of A's magnetic moment produces at B a precessing magnetic field nearly at the proper frequency to produce a transition, and vice versa. Thus it is possible for A and B to flip each other over. Although this effect does not change the energy of the spin system it does limit the lifetime of a state and, through the Heisenberg relations, causes an energy spread.

22. The Bloch Equations

Consider the magnetic moment **M** of the *whole sample* under investigation. Then if **P** is the total angular momentum

$$\mathbf{M} = \gamma \mathbf{P} \tag{1}$$

The rotational analogue to Newton's law of motion is

$$\frac{d\mathbf{P}}{dt} = \mathbf{L} = \mathbf{M} \times \mathbf{H} \tag{2}$$

where **L** is the torque. Substituting Eq. (2) into Eq. (1) we have

$$\frac{dM}{dt} = \gamma(\mathbf{M} \times \mathbf{H}) \tag{3}$$

Now we want to include relaxation effects. T_1 only affects the component of **M** in the direction of $\mathbf{H}_0$, which we shall take to be the z direction. The fluctuating local magnetic fields at the nuclei cause the precessing spins to get out of phase and cause M_x and M_y to average out to zero. M_x and M_y are found to decay exponentially. We therefore speak of a *spin–spin relaxation time* T_2. T_2 is typically of the order of 10^{-4} to 10^{-5} sec. Including T_1 and T_2 in Eq. (3) we have

$$\frac{dM_{x,y}}{dt} = \gamma(\mathbf{M} \times \mathbf{H})_{x,y} - \frac{M_{x,y}}{T_2}$$

$$\frac{dM_z}{dt} = \gamma(\mathbf{M} \times \mathbf{H})_z - \frac{M_z - M_0}{T_1} \tag{4}$$

where M_0 is the equilibrium value of M_z. **H** is given by

$$\mathbf{H} = 2H_1 \cos \omega t \, \mathbf{i} + H_0 \mathbf{k} \tag{5}$$

As we mentioned in Sect. 19, we divide the oscillating field into two parts: one that rotates in the same direction as the precession due to $\mathbf{H}_0$ and one that rotates in the opposite direction. We need consider only the part that rotates in the same direction as the precession.
Thus

$$\mathbf{H} = H_1 \cos \omega t \, \mathbf{i} - H_1 \sin \omega t \, \mathbf{j} + H_0 \, \mathbf{k} \tag{6}$$

Substituting Eq. (6) into Eqs. (4) we obtain the *Bloch equations*[1]

$$\frac{dM_x}{dt} = \gamma[M_y H_0 - M_z H_1 \sin \omega t] - \frac{M_x}{T_2} \tag{7}$$

$$\frac{dM_y}{dt} = \gamma[M_z H_1 \cos \omega t - M_x H_0] - \frac{M_y}{T_2} \tag{8}$$

$$\frac{dM_z}{dt} = -\gamma[M_x H_1 \sin \omega t + M_y H_1 \cos \omega t] - \frac{M_z - M_0}{T_1} \tag{9}$$

23. Steady State Solution of the Bloch Equations

Let us solve the Bloch equations for oscillating M_x and M_y in terms of M_z. Set

$$M_+ = M_x + iM_y$$

$$M_- = M_x - iM_y \tag{1}$$

Thus, adding and subtracting Eqs. (22.7) and (22.8), we have

$$\frac{dM_+}{dt} = \gamma[-iM_+ H_0 + iM_z H_1 \, e^{-i\omega t}] - \frac{M_+}{T_2}$$

$$\frac{dM_-}{dt} = \gamma[iM_- H_0 - iM_z H_1 \, e^{i\omega t}] - \frac{M_-}{T_2} \tag{2}$$

We can remove the time dependence by setting

$$M_+ = \overline{M}_+ \, e^{-i\omega t}$$

$$M_- = \overline{M}_- \, e^{i\omega t} \tag{3}$$

Thus

$$-i\omega \overline{M}_+ = \gamma[-i\overline{M}_+ H_0 + iM_z H_1] - \frac{\overline{M}_+}{T_2}$$

$$\overline{M}_+ = \frac{\omega_0 \left(\dfrac{H_1}{H_0}\right) M_z}{\omega_0 - \omega - \dfrac{i}{T_2}} \tag{4}$$

[1] F. Bloch, *Phys. Rev.*, **70**, 460 (1946).

Also

$$i\omega\overline{M}_- = \gamma[i\overline{M}_- H_0 - iM_z H_1] - \frac{\overline{M}_-}{T_2}$$

$$\overline{M}_- = \frac{\omega_0 \left(\dfrac{H_1}{H_0}\right) M_z}{\omega_0 - \omega + \dfrac{i}{T_2}} \tag{5}$$

Thus substituting Eqs. (4) and (5) into Eq. (3), we obtain

$$M_+ = M_x + iM_y = \frac{\omega_0 \left(\dfrac{H_1}{H_0}\right) M_z}{\omega_0 - \omega - \dfrac{i}{T_2}} e^{-i\omega t}$$

$$= \frac{\omega_0 \left(\dfrac{H_1}{H_0}\right) M_z}{(\omega_0 - \omega)^2 + \dfrac{1}{T_2^2}} \left(\omega_0 - \omega + \frac{i}{T_2}\right)(\cos\omega t - i\sin\omega t) \tag{6}$$

Equating real and imaginary parts in Eq. (6) gives

$$M_x = \frac{\omega_0 \left(\dfrac{H_1}{H_0}\right) M_z}{(\omega_0 - \omega)^2 + \dfrac{1}{T_2^2}} \left\{(\omega_0 - \omega)\cos\omega t + \frac{1}{T_2}\sin\omega t\right\} \tag{7}$$

$$M_y = \frac{\omega_0 \left(\dfrac{H_1}{H_0}\right) M_z}{(\omega_0 - \omega)^2 + \dfrac{1}{T_2^2}} \left\{\frac{1}{T_2}\cos\omega t - (\omega_0 - \omega)\sin\omega t\right\} \tag{8}$$

We can obtain a steady state solution of the Bloch equations for M_z by setting $dM_z/dt = 0$ in Eq. (22.9) and substituting for M_x and M_y by means of Eqs. (7) and (8):

$$\frac{M_z - M_0}{T_1} = -\gamma \frac{H_1 \omega_0 \left(\dfrac{H_1}{H_0}\right) M_z}{(\omega_0 - \omega)^2 + \dfrac{1}{T_2^2}} \left[\frac{1}{T_2}\sin^2\omega t + \frac{1}{T_2}\cos^2\omega t\right]$$

$$= -\gamma^2 \frac{H_1^2}{T_2} \frac{M_z}{(\omega_0 - \omega)^2 + \dfrac{1}{T_2^2}} \tag{9}$$

In obtaining the last equality we have used the fact that $\omega_0 = \gamma H_0$. Solving for M_z gives for the steady state solution to Eq. (22.9)

$$M_z = M_0 \frac{(\omega_0 - \omega)^2 T_2^2 + 1}{T_2^2(\omega_0 - \omega)^2 + 1 + \gamma H_1^2 T_1 T_2} \tag{10}$$

The steady state solutions to Eqs. (22.7) and (22.8) are obtained by substituting Eq. (10) into Eqs. (7) and (8). Hence,

$$M_x = \frac{\gamma H_1 T_2^2 M_0}{T_2^2(\omega_0 - \omega)^2 + 1 + \gamma^2 H_1^2 T_1 T_2} \left\{ (\omega_0 - \omega)\cos \omega t + \frac{1}{T_2}\sin \omega t \right\} \tag{11}$$

$$M_y = \frac{\gamma H_1 T_2^2 M_0}{T_2^2(\omega_0 - \omega)^2 + 1 + \gamma^2 H_1^2 T_1 T_2} \left\{ \frac{1}{T_2}\cos \omega t + (\omega_0 - \omega)\sin \omega t \right\} \tag{12}$$

Since $M_0 = \chi_0 H_0$ we have for Eq. (11)

$$M_x = \chi' 2H_1 \cos \omega t + \chi'' 2H_1 \sin \omega t \tag{13}$$

As seen from Eq. (22.5), the first term represents the in-phase magnetic intensity and the second term the out-of-phase intensity. χ' and χ'' are often called the *Bloch susceptibilities* and are given by

$$\chi' = \tfrac{1}{2}\chi_0 \omega_0 T_2 \frac{T_2(\omega_0 - \omega)}{1 + T_2^2(\omega_0 - \omega)^2 + \gamma H_1^2 T_1 T_2} \tag{14}$$

$$\chi'' = \tfrac{1}{2}\chi_0 \omega_0 T_2 \frac{1}{1 + T_2^2(\omega_0 - \omega)^2 + \gamma H_1^2 T_1 T_2} \tag{15}$$

If we define $\chi = \chi' + i\chi''$, then M_x and M_y are respectively the real and imaginary parts of

$$\chi 2H_1\, e^{-i\omega t} \tag{16}$$

The energy absorbed per second by a unit volume of the sample is seen from Eq. (13.2) to be

$$A(\omega) = \frac{\omega}{2\pi} \int_{t=0}^{t=2\pi/\omega} \mathbf{H} \cdot d\mathbf{M} \tag{17}$$

Since H_0 does not oscillate it does not contribute to A. Evaluating Eq. (17) gives

$$A(\omega) = \frac{\omega^2}{2\pi} 2H_1^2 \int_0^{2\pi/\omega} \{(-\chi' \sin \omega t \cos \omega t + \chi'' \cos^2 \omega t)$$
$$+ (\chi'' \sin^2 \omega t + \chi' \sin \omega t \cos \omega t)\}\, dt$$

$$A(\omega) = 2\omega H_1^2 \chi'' \tag{18}$$

$$A(\omega) = \omega H_1^2 \chi_0 \frac{\omega_0 T_2}{1 + T_2^2(\omega_0 - \omega)^2 + \gamma H_1^2 T_1 T_2} \tag{19}$$

There are two cases to be considered

(1) *Low power case* $\gamma^2 H_1^2 T_1 T_2 \ll 1$

$$A(\omega) = \omega H_1^2 \chi_0 \frac{\omega_0 T_2}{1 + T_2^2(\omega_0 - \omega)^2} \tag{20}$$

If $dA/d\omega = 0$ then

$$1 + T_2^2(\omega_0^2 - \omega^2) = 0$$

$$\omega^2 = \frac{1}{T_2^2} + \omega_0^2 \simeq \omega_0^2 \tag{21}$$

since $T_2 \sim 10^{-5}$ sec and $\omega_0 \sim 10^7$ sec^{-1}. The power loss as a function of the frequency is depicted in Figure 1.

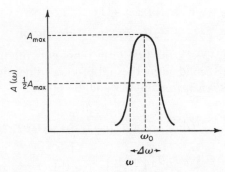

Figure 1. Power loss as a function of angular frequency in low power case.

Let us calculate $\Delta\omega$, the width at half of the maximum absorption.

$$\tfrac{1}{2}A_{max} = \tfrac{1}{2}H_1^2 \chi_0 \omega_0^2 T_2 = H_1^2 \chi_0 \omega_0 T_2 \frac{\omega}{1 + T_2^2(\omega_0 - \omega)^2}$$

$$\frac{\omega}{\omega_0} = 1 + \frac{1}{T_2^2 \omega_0^2} \pm \frac{1}{T_2 \omega_0} \sqrt{1 + \frac{1}{T_2^2 \omega_0^2}} \tag{22}$$

Since $T_2 \sim 10^{-5}$ sec and $\omega_0 \sim 10^7$ sec^{-1}, we have $T_2\omega_0 \simeq 10^2 \gg 1$. Thus,

$$\frac{\omega}{\omega_0} = 1 \pm \frac{1}{T_2 \omega_0}$$

$$\omega = \omega_0 \pm \frac{1}{T_2}$$

$$\Delta\omega = \frac{2}{T_2} \tag{23}$$

Equation (23) provides a method of measuring T_2.

(2) *High power case,* $10^4 \gg \gamma^2 H_1^2 T_1 T_2 \gg 1$

$$A(\omega) = \omega H_1^2 \chi_0 \frac{\omega_0 T_2}{T_2^2(\omega - \omega_0)^2 + \gamma H_1^2 T_1 T_2} = \frac{\chi_0 \omega_0}{\gamma T_1} \frac{\omega}{1 + \frac{T_2}{\gamma H_1^2 T_1}(\omega - \omega_0)^2} \quad (24)$$

Comparing Eq. (24) with Eq. (20), we see that for A_{max}

$$\omega^2 = \frac{T_2 T_1 \gamma^2 H_1^2}{T_2^2} + \omega_0^2 \simeq \omega_0^2 \quad (25)$$

Continuing the analogy $\dfrac{T_2}{T_1 \gamma^2 H_1^2} \sim T_2^2$, we have

$$\Delta\omega = \gamma H_1 \sqrt{\frac{T_1}{T_2}} \gg \frac{1}{T_2}$$

Thus, we have Figure 2.

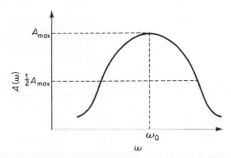

Figure 2. Power loss as a function of angular frequency in high power case.

Nuclear magnetic resonance can be used to determine such nuclear properties as the angular momentum and in addition has found increasing use in chemistry,[1] in analysis and in the study of molecular structure,[2] kinetics, solutions, and hindered internal rotation.

[1] J. A. Pople, W. G. Schneider, and H. J. Bernstein, *High-resolution Nuclear Magnetic Resonance,* McGraw-Hill, New York, 1959.
[2] H. Hecht, D. Grant, and H. Eyring, *Mol. Phys.,* **3,** 577 (1960).

9

ELECTRONS IN SOLIDS

1. Classical Drude Theory

In 1853 Wiedemann and Franz[1] discovered that for all metals the ratio of the thermal conductivity to the electrical conductivity was a universal function of the temperature. This fact is known as the Wiedemann–Franz law. This suggests that the same mechanism is responsible for electrical and thermal conduction in metals.

Soon after the discovery of electrons Drude[2] and Lorentz[3] were able to explain the thermal and electrical conduction in metals on the assumption that a metal contains a number of free electrons which have become detached from the metal atoms and acting as a perfect gas can move through the whole metal colliding only with the atoms. If an electric field E is applied, then the electrons will receive an acceleration

$$a = -\frac{eE}{m} \tag{1}$$

If λ is the mean distance between collisions and $\bar{v}$ the random thermal velocity, then $\lambda/\bar{v}$ is the average time between collisions and hence a drift velocity, u, given by

$$u = -\frac{1}{2}\frac{eE}{m}\frac{\lambda}{\bar{v}} \tag{2}$$

will be superimposed on the much greater random thermal velocity $\bar{v}$. In obtaining Eq. (2) we have assumed that on the average during a collision an electron loses all the drift velocity acquired during acceleration. The electric current density is then

$$\mathbf{j} = -ne\mathbf{u} = \tfrac{1}{2}n\frac{e^2\mathbf{E}}{m}\frac{\lambda}{\bar{v}} \tag{3}$$

where n is the number of electrons per unit volume. The *electrical conductivity* σ is defined by

$$\mathbf{j} = \sigma\mathbf{E} \tag{4}$$

[1] G. Wiedemann and R. Franz, *Ann. Physik*, **89**, 497 (1853).
[2] P. Drude, *Ann. Physik*, **1**, 566 (1900).
[3] H. Lorentz, *Proc. Acad. Sci. Amsterdam*, **7**, 438, 585 (1905).

Thus

$$\sigma = \frac{ne^2\lambda}{2m\bar{v}} \tag{5}$$

It is noted that σ is independent of **E**; this is *Ohm's law*. The principle of equipartition of energy (Sect. 4.8) yields

$$\tfrac{1}{2}m\overline{v^2} = \tfrac{3}{2}kT \tag{6}$$

To a sufficient degree of accuracy, $\overline{v^2} \sim \bar{v}^2$, and so Eqs. (5) and (6) yield

$$\sigma = \frac{ne^2\lambda\bar{v}}{6kT} \tag{7}$$

Let us now calculate the thermal conductivity. Let there be a thermal gradient, dT/dz, in the z direction. Then if AB is a plane perpendicular to

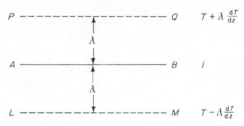

Figure 1. Diagram of thermal gradient in the z direction perpendicular to the plane AB.

the z direction and PQ and LM are parallel planes at a distance λ above and below AB there will be, due to thermal motions, a continual transfer of more energetic molecules downwards through AB and of less energetic molecules upwards through AB resulting in a net transfer of energy downwards through AB (*vide* Figure 1). Since the thermal motion is random there is no preferred direction and hence there will be $n/6$ electrons per unit volume travelling in the $\pm x$, $\pm y$, $\pm z$ directions. Since $T+\lambda\, dT/dz$ and $T-\lambda\, dT/dz$ are virtually equal, the rates at which these two groups of electrons cross AB will be equal. Hence in one second

$$\frac{n}{6}\bar{v} \tag{8}$$

molecules, at a temperature of $T+\lambda\, dT/dz$, will cross a unit area of AB from above and an equal number, at a temperature of $T-\lambda\, dT/dz$, will cross a unit area of AB from below. Hence, if C_V is the specific heat of an electron then the rate of energy transfer per unit area through the temperature difference $2\lambda\, dT/dz$ is

$$W = -\frac{n}{6}\bar{v}\cdot C_V \cdot 2\lambda\frac{dT}{dz} \tag{9}$$

Thus the thermal conductivity is

$$\kappa = \frac{n\bar{v}\lambda}{3} C_V \tag{10}$$

Since we are treating the electrons as a perfect gas, $C_V = \frac{3}{2}k$, and thus

$$\kappa = \frac{1}{2}n\bar{v}\lambda k \tag{11}$$

Combining Eqs. (7) and (11) we have the Wiedemann–Franz law

$$L = \frac{\kappa}{\sigma T} = 3\left(\frac{k}{e}\right)^2 = 2.2 \times 10^{-8} \text{ watt ohm deg}^{-2} \tag{12}$$

L is called the *Lorenz number*. In Table 1 experimental values of L are given for various metals. Equation (12) is seen to be in fair agreement with these values.

TABLE 1. Experimental Lorenz numbers ($\times 10^8$ watt ohm deg^{-2}) at 0°c.

Ag	2.31	Pb	2.47
Cd	2.42	Na	2.19
Mo	2.61		

Despite the success of this classical theory in explaining the Wiedemann–Franz law the theory must be regarded as unsatisfactory because it is not consistent. Since the electrical conductivity of a metal is typically of the order of 10^{17} esu and $\lambda \sim 10^{-8}$ cm, we have from Eq. (7)

$$n = \frac{6kT\sigma}{e^2\lambda\bar{v}} = \frac{6\sigma}{e^2\lambda}\sqrt{\frac{mkT}{3}}$$

$$\simeq \frac{10^{17}}{10^{-20} \times 10^{-8}}\sqrt{10^{-27} \times 10^{-12}}$$

$$\simeq 10^{24} \text{ electrons/cm}^3$$

so that there is about *one free* electron per atom. Hence since each free electron contributes $\frac{3}{2}k$ to the specific heat, we would expect the specific heat of a metal to be of the order of

$$C_V = 3R + \frac{3}{2}R$$

$$\simeq 9 \text{ cal mole}^{-1} \text{ deg}^{-1}$$

where the first term is the lattice specific heat. However, experimentally the contribution of the conduction electrons is found to be only about 1/100 of the second term.

Furthermore, since each electron has a magnetic moment μ_B, we would expect the conduction electrons to make a paramagnetic contribution

$$\chi = \frac{N\mu_B^2}{kT} \tag{13}$$

to the magnetic susceptibility of the metal. However, experimentally the susceptibility of non-ferromagnetic metals is independent of temperature and only $1/100$ of the expected value.

The deficiencies of the above theory are removed by the application of Fermi–Dirac statistics.

2. Sommerfeld's Theory

In 1928 Sommerfeld[1] obtained more satisfactory results by using Fermi–Dirac instead of classical statistics. If we set $s = \frac{1}{2}$ and use the customary notation $\mu = \varepsilon_F$, the Fermi energy, Eq. (5.11.20) becomes

$$\varepsilon_F(0) = \frac{h^2}{2m}\left(\frac{3}{8\pi}n\right)^{\frac{2}{3}} \tag{1}$$

If we assume one free electron per atom then

$$\varepsilon_F(0) \simeq \frac{10^{-54}}{10^{-27}}(10^{24})^{\frac{2}{3}} = 10^{-11} \text{ erg}$$

Even for $T = 4000°\text{K}$, $kT \simeq 10^{-13}$ erg and hence, since $\varepsilon_F \sim \varepsilon_F(0)$, $kT \ll \varepsilon_F$ for all temperatures at which metals exist. Therefore, the electrons are degenerate. Hence, referring to Eqs. (5.11.19, 21, 23, 24, 25) we have

$$n = \frac{8\pi}{3}\left(\frac{2m}{h^2}\right)^{\frac{3}{2}}\varepsilon_F(0)^{\frac{3}{2}}\left[1 + \frac{\pi^2}{8}\left(\frac{kT}{\varepsilon_F(0)}\right)^2 + \ldots\right] \tag{2}$$

$$\varepsilon_F = \varepsilon_F(0)\left[1 - \frac{\pi^2}{12}\left(\frac{kT}{\varepsilon_F(0)}\right)^2 + \ldots\right] \tag{3}$$

$$E = \tfrac{3}{5}N\varepsilon_F(0)\left[1 + \frac{5\pi^2}{12}\left(\frac{kT}{\varepsilon_F(0)}\right)^2 + \ldots\right] \tag{4}$$

$$C_V = \frac{\pi^2}{2}Nk\left(\frac{kT}{\varepsilon_F(0)}\right) \tag{5}$$

$$S = \frac{\pi^2}{2}Nk\left(\frac{kT}{\varepsilon_F(0)}\right) \tag{6}$$

Since $kT \ll \varepsilon_F(0)$, we see from Eq. (5) that the conduction electrons make a negligible contribution to the specific heat. Let us now consider the problem of the magnetic susceptibility.

[1] A. Sommerfeld, *Z. Physik*, **47**, 1 (1928).

3. The Magnetic Susceptibility of Free Electrons

Owing to its spin, each conduction electron in a metal has a magnetic moment whose component in the direction of a magnetic field is $\pm\mu_B$, the Bohr magneton. Hence, in the presence of the magnetic field each conduction electron has an extra energy $\pm\mu_B H$. If there are n conduction electrons per unit volume then the magnetic moment per unit volume due to these electrons is

$$M = \mu_B(n_+ - n_-) \tag{1}$$

where n_+ and n_- are, respectively, the number of conduction electrons per unit volume with orientation parallel or antiparallel to the magnetic field. Hence

$$M = \frac{\mu_B}{V} \int \{\tfrac{1}{2}g(\varepsilon + \mu_B H) - \tfrac{1}{2}g(\varepsilon - \mu_B H)\} f(\varepsilon)\, d\varepsilon \tag{2}$$

where ε is the total energy, kinetic plus magnetic, and $g(\varepsilon)$ is given by Eq. (5.9.4). The factor of $\tfrac{1}{2}$ is included because the spin degeneracy has been removed by the application of the magnetic field.

$$g(\varepsilon \pm \mu_B H) = 4\pi \left(\frac{2m}{h^2}\right)^{\frac{3}{2}} V\sqrt{\varepsilon}\left(1 \pm \frac{\mu_B H}{\varepsilon}\right)^{\frac{1}{2}} \tag{3}$$

Since $\mu_B H \ll \varepsilon_F(0)$, we have

$$g(\varepsilon \pm \mu_B H) = 4\pi \left(\frac{2m}{h^2}\right)^{\frac{3}{2}} V\sqrt{\varepsilon}\left(1 \pm \frac{\mu_B H}{2\varepsilon}\right) \tag{4}$$

Substituting Eq. (4) into Eq. (2) gives

$$M = 4\pi \left(\frac{2m}{h^2}\right)^{\frac{3}{2}} \frac{\mu_B^2 H}{2} \int_0^\infty \frac{f(\varepsilon)\, d\varepsilon}{\sqrt{\varepsilon}} \tag{5}$$

Applying Sommerfeld's theorem, Eq. (5.11.18) yields

$$M = 4\pi \left(\frac{2m}{h^2}\right)^{\frac{3}{2}} \mu_B^2 H \left\{\varepsilon_F^{\frac{1}{2}} - \frac{\pi^2}{24}\varepsilon_F^{-\frac{3}{2}} + \ldots\right\} \tag{6}$$

which combined with Eq. (2.1) gives

$$M = \frac{3n\mu_B^2 H}{2} \varepsilon_F(0)^{-\frac{3}{2}}\varepsilon_F \left\{1 - \frac{\pi^2}{24}\left(\frac{kT}{\varepsilon_F(0)}\right)^2 + \ldots\right\} \tag{7}$$

Because $\mu_B H \ll \varepsilon_F(0)$, the dependence of ε_F on H can be neglected. Hence using Eq. (2.3) we obtain

$$\begin{aligned}
M &= \frac{3n\mu_B^2 H}{2\varepsilon_F(0)} \left\{1 - \frac{\pi^2}{24}\left(\frac{kT}{\varepsilon_F(0)}\right)^2 + \ldots\right\}^2 \\
&= \frac{3n\mu_B^2 H}{2\varepsilon_F(0)} \left\{1 - \frac{\pi^2}{12}\left(\frac{kT}{\varepsilon_F(0)}\right)^2 + \ldots\right\}
\end{aligned} \tag{8}$$

Thus the paramagnetic susceptibility is

$$\chi_p = \frac{3}{2}\frac{n\mu_B^2}{\varepsilon_F(0)}\left[1 - \frac{\pi^2}{12}\left(\frac{kT}{\varepsilon_F(0)}\right)^2 + \cdots\right] \tag{9}$$

The first term in the above expression was calculated by Pauli[1] and the second term was calculated by Stoner.[2]

In addition to the paramagnetic contribution of the electron spins there is a diamagnetic contribution due to the translational motion of the electrons. Landau[2, 3] has calculated this contribution and found it to be $-\chi_p/3$. The resultant susceptibility when spin and translational motions are superposed is not obviously the sum of the two contributions calculated independently. Stoner,[2] however, has shown that to the second order in T the two contributions are additive. Thus, since the translational contribution is negative,

$$\chi = \frac{n\mu_B^2}{\varepsilon_F(0)}\left[1 - \frac{\pi^2}{12}\left(\frac{kT}{\varepsilon_F(0)}\right)^2 + \cdots\right] \tag{10}$$

The second term is small compared with the first, so the magnetic susceptibility of an electron gas is temperature-independent and the free electron model is at least qualitatively correct. Quantitatively the agreement is poor because of the perturbing effect of the potential of the lattice, which we have not taken into account.

4. The Richardson Effect

Let ε_0 be the energy required to remove a free electron with no kinetic energy from the metal to infinity. We define the *work function* ϕ of the metal by

$$\phi = \varepsilon_0 - \varepsilon_F \tag{1}$$

Thus, we have Figure 1 as our model for a metal.

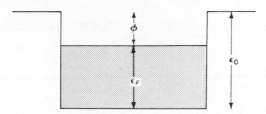

Figure 1. Potential model of a metal where ε_F is the Fermi energy, ϕ the work function, and ε_0 the energy to remove an electron of zero kinetic energy.

[1] W. Pauli, *Z. Physik*, **41**, 81 (1927).
[2] E. Stoner, *Proc. Roy. Soc. (London)*, **A152**, 672 (1935).
[3] L. Landau, *Z. Physik*, **64**, 629 (1930).

For $T > 0$ the distribution function for the electrons has the form shown in Figure 2.

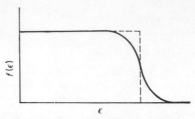

Figure 2. Distribution function for electrons in a metal, $T > 0$.

Thus, some of the electrons will have sufficient energy to leave the metal. This is the so-called *Richardson effect* or *thermionic emission*.[1]

Since we can associate a volume of h^3 in phase space with each energy level, the number of allowed states per unit volume corresponding to an element $dp_x dp_y dp_z$ is

$$N(\mathbf{p})\,dp_x\,dp_y\,dp_z = \frac{2}{h^3}\frac{dp_x\,dp_y\,dp_z}{\exp\left\{\dfrac{p_x^2+p_y^2+p_z^2}{2mkT}-\dfrac{\varepsilon_F}{kT}\right\}+1} \qquad (2)$$

Hence the number of electrons striking a unit area of the surface with momenta in the interval $dp_x dp_y dp_z$ is

$$v_x N(\mathbf{p})\,dp_x\,dp_y\,dp_z = \frac{2}{h^3}\frac{p_x}{m}\frac{dp_x\,dp_y\,dp_z}{\exp\left\{\dfrac{p_x^2+p_y^2+p_z^2}{2mkT}-\dfrac{\varepsilon_F}{kT}\right\}+1} \qquad (3)$$

If we assume that every electron for which $p_x \geq \sqrt{2m\varepsilon_0}$ leaves the metal, then the current density is

$$j = e\int_{-\infty}^{\infty}dp_y\int_{-\infty}^{\infty}dp_z\int_{\sqrt{2m\varepsilon_0}}^{\infty}\frac{p_x}{m}N(\mathbf{p})\,dp_x \qquad (4)$$

Using p_y, p_z and ε as variables of integration, Eq. (4) becomes

$$j = \frac{2e}{h^3}\int_{-\infty}^{\infty}dp_y\int_{-\infty}^{\infty}dp_z\int_{(p_y^2+p_z^2)/2m+\phi+\varepsilon_F}^{\infty}\frac{d\varepsilon}{e^{(\varepsilon-\varepsilon_F)/kT}+1} \qquad (5)$$

At ordinary temperatures $e^{(\varepsilon-\varepsilon_F)/kT} \gg 1$ and hence

$$j = \frac{2e(kT)}{h^3}e^{-\phi/kT}\int_{-\infty}^{\infty}e^{-p_y^2/2mkT}\,dp_y\int_{-\infty}^{\infty}e^{-p_z^2/2mkT}\,dp_z$$

$$= \frac{4\pi me(kT)^2}{h^3}e^{-\phi/kT}$$

$$j = AT^2\,e^{-\phi/kT} \qquad (6)$$

[1] O. W. Richardson, *Phil. Mag.*, **23**, 594 (1912).

where $A = 4\pi mek^2/h^3 = 120$ amp cm^{-2} deg^{-2}. In obtaining Eq. (6) we have used Integral (2) in Appendix 2.

This simple theory is not quite accurate for an actual metal since some of the electrons for which $p_x \geq \sqrt{2m\varepsilon_0}$ will be reflected by the potential barrier. If r is the reflection coefficient, then Eq. (6) becomes

$$j = A(1-r)T^2 e^{-\phi/kT} \tag{7}$$

Also the existence of a negative space charge in the activity will cause ϕ to appear larger. Consideration must also be given to the fact that the macroscopic area of a metal is not in general equal to the actual surface area because of roughness and to the fact that small amounts of adsorbed molecules can change ϕ appreciably.

5. The Boltzmann Transport Equation

Let $f(\mathbf{r}, \mathbf{v}, t)$ be the number of electrons with coordinates in the interval $(x, x+dx; y, y+dy; z, z+dz)$ and velocities in the interval $(v_x, v_x+dv_x; v_y, v_y+dv_y; v_z, v_z+dv_z)$. The value of $f(\mathbf{r}, \mathbf{v}, t)$ will, in general, change with time because of collisions and because of the drift of the electrons in and out of the volume $d\mathbf{r}\, d\mathbf{v}$. Hence,

$$\frac{\partial f}{\partial t} = \left(\frac{\partial f}{\partial t}\right)_{\text{drift}} + \left(\frac{\partial f}{\partial t}\right)_{\text{collisions}} \tag{1}$$

If $\mathbf{F}$ is the external force per unit mass then

$$-\left(\frac{\partial f}{\partial t}\right)_{\text{drift}} = \frac{\partial f}{\partial x}v_x + \frac{\partial f}{\partial y}v_y + \frac{\partial f}{\partial z}v_z + \frac{\partial f}{\partial v_x}\frac{\partial v_x}{\partial t} + \frac{\partial f}{\partial v_y}\frac{\partial v_y}{\partial t} + \frac{\partial f}{\partial v_z}\frac{\partial v_z}{\partial t}$$

$$= \frac{\partial f}{\partial x}v_x + \frac{\partial f}{\partial y}v_y + \frac{\partial f}{\partial z}v_z + \frac{\partial f}{\partial v_x}F_x + \frac{\partial f}{\partial v_y}F_y + \frac{\partial f}{\partial v_z}F_z$$

$$-\left(\frac{\partial f}{\partial t}\right)_{\text{drift}} = (\mathbf{v}\cdot\nabla)f + (\mathbf{F}\cdot\nabla_v)f \tag{2}$$

where $\nabla_v = (\partial/\partial v_x, \partial/\partial v_y, \partial/\partial v_z)$. Substituting Eq. (2) into Eq. (1) we have the *Boltzmann transport equation*[1]

$$\frac{\partial f}{\partial t} + (\mathbf{v}\cdot\nabla)f + (\mathbf{F}\cdot\nabla_v)f = \left(\frac{\partial f}{\partial t}\right)_{\text{collisions}} \tag{3}$$

The equilibrium distribution is defined by

$$\frac{\partial f}{\partial t} = 0 \tag{4}$$

[1] L. Boltzmann, *Wien. Ber.*, **72**, 427 (1875).

If f never varies greatly from the equilibrium distribution function, f_0, then we may introduce a relaxation time, τ, by means of the equation

$$\left(\frac{\partial f}{\partial t}\right)_{\text{collisions}} = -\frac{f-f_0}{\tau} \tag{5}$$

It is noted that τ may be a function of $\mathbf{r}$ and $\mathbf{v}$. For this case the Boltzmann transport equation becomes

$$\frac{\partial f}{\partial t} + (\mathbf{v} \cdot \nabla)f + (\mathbf{F} \cdot \nabla_v)f = -\frac{f-f_0}{\tau} \tag{6}$$

6. Electrical and Thermal Conductivity

We consider a metal under the influence of an electric field E_x in the x direction and a temperature gradient dT/dx. Provided the electric field is small, a relaxation time, τ, can be introduced. Since the charge on an electron is negative, Eq. (5.6) becomes in the steady state

$$v_x \frac{\partial f}{\partial x} - \frac{eE_x}{m}\frac{\partial f}{\partial v_x} = -\frac{f-f_0}{\tau} \tag{1}$$

Thus

$$f = f_0 - \tau\left(v_x \frac{\partial f}{\partial x} - \frac{eE_x}{m}\frac{\partial f}{\partial v_x}\right) \tag{2}$$

We solve this equation by putting

$$f = f_0 + v_x \chi \tag{3}$$

and since E_x is small we neglect the products of χ with E_x and v_x. Under these conditions we have

$$f = f_0 - \tau\left(v_x \frac{\partial f_0}{\partial x} - \frac{eE_x}{m}\frac{\partial f_0}{\partial v_x}\right) \tag{4}$$

Hence

$$\chi = -\frac{\tau}{v_x}\left(v_x \frac{\partial f_0}{\partial x} - \frac{eE_x}{m}\frac{\partial f_0}{\partial v_x}\right) \tag{5}$$

Now

$$\frac{\partial f_0}{\partial v_x} = \frac{\partial f_0}{\partial \varepsilon}\frac{\partial \varepsilon}{\partial v_x} = mv_x \frac{\partial f_0}{\partial \varepsilon} \tag{6}$$

Thus Eq. (5) becomes

$$\chi = -\tau\left(\frac{\partial f_0}{\partial x} - eE_x \frac{\partial f_0}{\partial \varepsilon}\right) \tag{7}$$

The electric current density is

$$j_x = -e \int_{-\infty}^{\infty} v_x f \, dv_x \, dv_y \, dv_z \tag{8}$$

The minus sign appears because the electron charge is negative. Each electron has kinetic energy $\frac{1}{2}mv^2$. Since in unit time all the electrons within a distance v_x from a unit area will flow across the unit area, the heat flow per unit area is

$$w_x = \frac{1}{2}m \int_{-\infty}^{\infty} v_x v^2 f \, dv_x \, dv_y \, dv_z \tag{9}$$

Since terms in f_0 cannot give rise to a net flow in any direction, Eqs. (8) and (9) become

$$j_x = -e \int_{-\infty}^{\infty} \tau v_x^2 \left[eE_x \frac{\partial f_0}{\partial \varepsilon} - \frac{\partial f_0}{\partial x} \right] dv_x \, dv_y \, dv_z \tag{10}$$

$$w_x = \frac{1}{2}m \int_{-\infty}^{\infty} \tau v_x^2 v^2 \left[eE_x \frac{\partial f_0}{\partial \varepsilon} - \frac{\partial f_0}{\partial x} \right] dv_x \, dv_y \, dv_z \tag{11}$$

Equations (10) and (11) would be the same if v_x were replaced by v_y or v_z. Therefore we can replace v_x^2 by $v^2/3$ and $dv_x \, dv_y \, dv_z$ by $4\pi v^2 dv$ and get

$$j_x = -\frac{4\pi e}{3} \int_0^{\infty} \tau v^4 \left[eE_x \frac{\partial f_0}{\partial \varepsilon} - \frac{\partial f_0}{\partial x} \right] dv \tag{12}$$

$$w_x = \frac{2\pi m}{3} \int_0^{\infty} \tau v^6 \left[eE_x \frac{\partial f_0}{\partial \varepsilon} - \frac{\partial f_0}{\partial x} \right] dv \tag{13}$$

But if $y = (\varepsilon - \varepsilon_F)/kT$ then

$$\frac{\partial f_0}{\partial x} = \frac{\partial f_0}{\partial \varepsilon} \frac{d\varepsilon}{dy} \frac{dy}{dT} \frac{dT}{dx} \tag{14}$$

$$= \frac{\partial f_0}{\partial \varepsilon} \left[\frac{\varepsilon_F}{T} - \frac{\varepsilon}{T} - \frac{d\varepsilon_F}{dT} \right] \frac{dT}{dx} \tag{15}$$

Substituting Eq. (15) into Eqs. (12) and (13) and changing the variable of integration from v to $\varepsilon = \frac{1}{2}mv^2$ gives

$$j_x = -\frac{16\pi me}{3h^3} \left[K_1 \left\{ eE_x + \left(\frac{d\varepsilon_F}{dT} - \frac{\varepsilon_F}{T} \right) \frac{dT}{dx} \right\} + \frac{K_2}{T} \frac{dT}{dx} \right] \tag{16}$$

$$w_x = \frac{16\pi me}{3h^3} \left[K_2 \left\{ eE_x + \left(\frac{d\varepsilon_F}{dT} - \frac{\varepsilon_F}{T} \right) \frac{dT}{dx} \right\} + \frac{K_3}{T} \frac{dT}{dx} \right] \tag{17}$$

where

$$K_n = \frac{h^3}{2m^3} \int_0^{\infty} \lambda \varepsilon^n \left(\frac{\partial f_0}{\partial \varepsilon} \right) d\varepsilon \tag{18}$$

and where $\lambda = v\tau$ takes the part of the mean free path.

The electrical conductivity is usually measured under the condition $dT/dx = 0$. For this case

$$j_x = -\frac{16\pi me^2}{3h^3} K_1 E_x \tag{19}$$

and therefore

$$\sigma = -\frac{16\pi me^2}{3h^3} K_1 \tag{20}$$

The thermal conductivity is usually measured under the condition $j_x = 0$. Since there will be a non-uniform electron density, $E_x \neq 0$, eliminating E_x from Eqs. (16) and (17) under the condition $j_x = 0$ gives

$$w_x = \frac{16\pi m}{3h^3} \frac{K_1 K_3 - K_2^2}{TK_1} \frac{dT}{dx} \tag{21}$$

Hence the thermal conductivity is

$$\kappa = \frac{16\pi m}{3h^3} \frac{K_2^2 - K_1 K_3}{TK_1} \tag{22}$$

Thus far, our discussion is true for any distribution function. However, in a metal the electrons obey Fermi–Dirac statistics. Thus,

$$f_0 = \frac{2m^3}{h^3} \frac{1}{e^{(\varepsilon - \varepsilon_F)/kT} + 1} = \frac{2m^3}{h^3} f(\varepsilon) \tag{23}$$

It is to be remembered that f_0 is a velocity distribution function. Hence the factor h^3 appears to convert from energy to the momenta, the factor m^3 to convert from the momenta to the velocities and the factor 2 is required by the spin degeneracy. Equations (20) and (22) can be evaluated by means of Sommerfeld's theorem, Eqs. (5.11.13, 18). Hence

$$K_n = -\lambda_F \varepsilon_F^n - \frac{\pi^2}{6} (kT)^2 \left(\frac{d^2 \lambda \varepsilon^n}{d\varepsilon^2}\right)_{\varepsilon_F} \tag{24}$$

where $\lambda_F = \lambda(\varepsilon_F)$ is the mean free path of an electron at the Fermi level. In calculating σ only the first term of Eq. (24) is important, hence

$$\sigma = \frac{16\pi me^2}{3h^3} \lambda_F \varepsilon_F$$

$$= \frac{ne^2 \lambda_F}{mv_F} \tag{25}$$

where $v_F = (2\varepsilon_F/m)^{\frac{1}{2}}$. Equation (2.1) has been used in obtaining Eq. (25).

In calculating κ the terms independent of T in the K_n cancel and the major contribution will come from the $(kT)^2$ terms

$$\kappa = \frac{16\pi m}{3h^3 T}\left[\left\{\lambda_F \varepsilon_F^3 + \frac{\pi^2}{6}(kT)^2\left(\frac{d^2\lambda\varepsilon^3}{d\varepsilon^2}\right)_{\varepsilon_F}\right\}\right.$$
$$\left. - \frac{\{\lambda_F \varepsilon_F^2 + \frac{1}{6}\pi^2(kT)^2(d^2\lambda\varepsilon^2/d\varepsilon^2)_{\varepsilon_F}\}^2}{\lambda_F \varepsilon_F + \frac{1}{6}\pi^2(kT)^2(d^2\lambda\varepsilon/d\varepsilon^2)_{\varepsilon_F}}\right]$$

$$= \frac{16\pi m}{3h^3 T}\left[\frac{\pi^2}{6}(kT)^2\left\{\varepsilon_F^3\left(\frac{d^2\lambda\varepsilon}{d\varepsilon^2}\right)_{\varepsilon_F} + \left(\frac{d^2\lambda\varepsilon^3}{d\varepsilon^2}\right)_{\varepsilon_F} - 2\varepsilon_F\left(\frac{d^2\lambda\varepsilon^2}{d\varepsilon^2}\right)_{\varepsilon_F}\right\}\right]$$

$$= \frac{16\pi m}{3h^3 T}\left[\frac{\pi^2}{3}\lambda_F \varepsilon_F(kT)^2\right]$$

$$\kappa = \frac{\pi^2}{3}\frac{k^2 n\lambda_F}{mv_F}T \tag{26}$$

From Eqs. (25) and (26) we obtain the Sommerfeld expression for the Lorenz number

$$L = \frac{\kappa}{\sigma T} = \frac{\pi^2}{3}\left(\frac{k}{e}\right) = 2.45 \times 10^{-8} \text{ watt ohm deg}^{-2} \tag{28}$$

which value is in better accord with Table 1.1.

7. Thermoelectric Effects

Before discussing thermoelectricity in metals on the basis of the free electron model it is necessary to distinguish between three effects: the Seebeck, Peltier, and Thomson effects.

If two dissimilar metals A and B are connected and the two junctions are maintained at different temperatures there is a potential difference between the two junctions. Such an arrangement is called a *thermocouple*. For a given pair of metals this thermal potential difference depends only on the junction temperatures. If the circuit is broken and some third metal is inserted, forming two new junctions, and these junctions are maintained at the same temperature, the potential difference is unaffected. This is referred to as the *Seebeck effect*.

If, by means of a battery, a current is produced in a thermocouple with its junctions at the same temperature, it is found that, allowing for the Joule heat produced because of the resistance of the metals, heat must be either supplied or extracted to keep the junction at its initial temperature. This is called the *Peltier effect* and this heat is called the *Peltier heat*. The Peltier heat is reversible. If the direction of the current is reversed, its magnitude remaining the same, absorption can be changed to liberation. The Peltier heat is produced at a rate proportional to the current, i.e.,

$$\text{Peltier heat per second} = \pi_{AB}\,I \tag{1}$$

where π_{AB} is called the *Peltier coefficient*, and depends on the temperature and the metals of the junction. The Joule heat on the other hand is always liberated and is proportional to the square of the current.

If a current exists in a wire in which there is a temperature gradient, the temperature distribution is found to vary by an amount not entirely due to the Joule heat. This is called the *Thomson effect* and heat that must be supplied or extracted to maintain the initial temperature distribution is called the *Thomson heat*. The Thomson heat, like the Peltier heat, is reversible. The rate at which Thomson heat is absorbed by a region supporting a temperature difference dT and carrying a current I is

$$\text{Thomson heat per second} = \sigma_T I \, dT \qquad (2)$$

where σ_T is called the *Thomson coefficient* and is a function of the temperature and of the material of the wire but not of the current.

We can investigate these effects by means of Eqs. (6.16) and (6.17). Solving Eq. (6.16) for E_x gives

$$E_x = -\frac{3h^3}{16\pi me^2}\frac{j_x}{K_1} - \frac{K_2}{K_1}\frac{1}{eT}\frac{dT}{dx} - \frac{1}{e}\left(\frac{d\varepsilon_F}{dT} - \frac{\varepsilon_F}{T}\right)\frac{dT}{dx} \qquad (3)$$

Eliminating E_x from Eq. (6.17) we have

$$w_x = -\frac{K_2}{eK_1}j_x + \frac{16\pi m}{3h^3}\frac{K_1 K_3 - K_2^2}{TK_1}\frac{dT}{dx} \qquad (4)$$

We found in Sect. 8.1 that qE_x is the force acting on a charge and therefore $qE_x\Delta x$ is the work done in moving the charge through a distance Δx. Thus the rate at which heat is generated in a section of wire of unit cross-section and length Δx is

$$\frac{dQ}{dt}\Delta x = j_x E_x \Delta x - \frac{\partial w_x}{\partial x}\Delta x \qquad (5)$$

The first term is the rate at which electrical work is done (Joule heat) and the second term is the excess heat conduction out of the element. Substituting Eqs. (3) and (4) into Eq. (5) we have

$$\frac{dQ}{dt} = \frac{j_x^2}{\sigma} + \frac{j_x}{e}T\frac{d}{dT}\left(\frac{K_2}{TK_1} - \frac{\varepsilon_F}{T}\right)\frac{dT}{dx} + \frac{d}{dx}\left(\kappa\frac{dT}{dx}\right) \qquad (6)$$

The definitions of σ and κ, Eqs. (6.20) and (6.22), have been used in obtaining Eq. (6). The first term represents the Joule heat and the last term the heat flux due to the thermal gradient. The second term represents the Thomson heat. Hence from Eq. (2)

$$\sigma_T = -\frac{T}{e}\frac{d}{dT}\left(\frac{K_2}{TK_1} - \frac{\varepsilon_F}{T}\right) \qquad (7)$$

The minus sign appears because σ_T is defined in terms of the heat absorbed and Eq. (6) gives the heat liberated.

We can also obtain an expression for the Peltier heat from Eq. (6). We focus our attention on the second term since the Peltier effect is reversible. The Peltier coefficient is given by

$$\pi_{AB} = -\frac{T}{e} \int_A^B \frac{d}{dT}\left(\frac{K_2}{TK_1} - \frac{\varepsilon_F}{T}\right)\frac{dT}{dx}\,dx$$

$$= -\frac{T}{e}\left[\left(\frac{K_2}{TK_1} - \frac{\varepsilon_F}{T}\right)_B - \left(\frac{K_2}{TK_1} - \frac{\varepsilon_F}{T}\right)_A\right] \tag{8}$$

It is convenient to introduce the parameter S^*, called the *thermoelectric power*, by means of

$$S^* = \int_0^T \frac{\sigma_T}{T}\,dT \tag{9}$$

$$= -\frac{1}{eT}\left[\frac{K_2}{K_1} - \varepsilon_F\right] \tag{10}$$

Equation (8) becomes

$$\pi_{AB} = -T(S_A^* - S_B^*) \tag{11}$$

The electromotive force (emf) of a circuit is found by integrating $-E_x$ around the circuit for the case $j_x = 0$. In other words, the open circuit electrostatic voltage is equal to the total emf of the circuit. Hence if the two junctions are located at x_1 and x_2 and are maintained at temperatures T_1 and T_2 then the Seebeck emf is

$$\mathscr{E}_{AB} = -\left(\int_{x_1}^{x_2} E_x\,dx\right)_A + \left(\int_{x_1}^{x_2} E_x\,dx\right)_B$$

$$= \left(\int_{T_1}^{T_2} E_x\frac{dx}{dT}\,dT\right)_B - \left(\int_{T_1}^{T_2} E_x\frac{dx}{dT}\,dT\right)_A \tag{12}$$

Substituting the value of E_x given by Eq. (3) for the case $j_x = 0$ we obtain, since $d\varepsilon_F/dT$ is small,

$$\mathscr{E}_{AB} = -\frac{1}{e}\int_{T_1}^{T_2}\left[\left(\frac{K_2}{K_1 T} - \frac{\varepsilon_F}{T}\right)_B - \left(\frac{K_2}{K_1 T} - \frac{\varepsilon_F}{T}\right)_A\right]dT$$

$$= \int_{T_1}^{T_2}(S_B^* - S_A^*)\,dT \tag{13}$$

We can now obtain the famous *Kelvin equations*.[1] Differentiating Eq. (13) and comparing it with Eq. (11) we have

$$\frac{\pi_{AB}}{T} = \frac{d\mathscr{E}_{AB}}{dT} \tag{14}$$

[1] W. Thomson, *Proc. Roy. Soc. (Edinburgh)*, 3, 255 (1854).

Differentiating Eq. (13) twice and comparing with Eq. (9) we have the second of these equations

$$\sigma_A - \sigma_B = - T \frac{d^2 \mathscr{E}_{AB}}{dT^2} \tag{15}$$

Thus far the theory has been true for any distribution function. For the case of a degenerate free electron gas Eq. (7) becomes, in view of Eq. (6.24),

$$\sigma_T = - \frac{T}{e} \frac{d}{dT} \left[\frac{\lambda_F \varepsilon_F^2 + \frac{1}{6} \pi^2 (kT)^2 (d^2 \lambda \varepsilon^2 / d\varepsilon^2)_{\varepsilon_F}}{T \{ \lambda_F \varepsilon_F + \frac{1}{6} \pi^2 (kT)^2 (d^2 \lambda \varepsilon / d\varepsilon^2)_{\varepsilon_F} \}} - \frac{\varepsilon_F}{T} \right] \tag{16}$$

Expanding the denominator yields

$$\sigma_T = - \frac{T}{e} \frac{d}{dT} \left[\frac{\pi^2}{6} \frac{k^2 T}{\lambda_F \varepsilon_F} \left\{ \left(\frac{d^2 \lambda \varepsilon^2}{d\varepsilon^2} \right)_{\varepsilon_F} - \varepsilon_F \left(\frac{d^2 \lambda \varepsilon}{d\varepsilon^2} \right)_{\varepsilon_F} \right\} \right]$$

$$\sigma_T = - \frac{\pi^2 k^2 T}{3e} \left[\frac{1}{\varepsilon_F} + \frac{1}{\lambda_F} \left(\frac{d\lambda}{d\varepsilon} \right)_{\varepsilon_F} \right] \tag{17}$$

Hence in the free electron model the thermoelectric power is

$$S^* = - \frac{\pi^2 k^2 T}{3e} \left[\frac{1}{\varepsilon_F} + \frac{1}{\lambda_F} \left(\frac{d\lambda}{d\varepsilon} \right)_{\varepsilon_F} \right] \tag{18}$$

The free electron model suffers from the weakness that it does not predict how λ depends on ε. By taking the lattice structure of the metal into account it can be shown[2] that $\lambda \propto \varepsilon^2$ for nearly free electrons. Hence for nearly free electrons we have

$$\sigma_T = - \frac{\pi^2 kT}{e \varepsilon_F} \tag{19}$$

which is of the right order of magnitude. Despite the many successes of the free electron model it is unable to account for the positive Thomson coefficients observed in such metals as lithium and copper. Because of this we can conclude that the free electron model of a metal gives only a partially correct picture of the origin of metallic properties. We shall discuss the more complete band theory of solids in Sect. 9.

8. Isothermal Hall Effect

Consider a conducting plate placed in a magnetic field in the z direction. Further let the conductor be subjected to an external electric field in the x direction so that a current j_x flows in the x direction. The effect of the magnetic field will be to deflect the electrons such that electrons accumulate on the lower face of the plate until a so-called *Hall voltage* is set up in the

[2] A. H. Wilson, *The Theory of Metals*, Cambridge University Press, 1936, p. 208.

y direction sufficient to neutralize the force exerted by the magnetic field, as is shown in Figure 1.

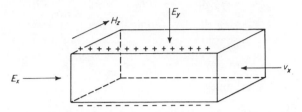

Figure 1. Schematic illustration of production of Hall voltage.

Consider the Drude theory. As a result of the field E_x the electrons acquire a drift velocity v_x and hence experience a force

$$F_y = 0 = -e\left(E_y - \frac{1}{c}v_x H_z\right)$$

$$E_y = \frac{v_x H_z}{c} \tag{1}$$

But

$$j_x = -nev_x \tag{2}$$

Thus

$$R_H = \frac{E_y}{j_x H_z} = -\frac{1}{nec} \tag{3}$$

R_H is called the *Hall coefficient*. We shall now show rigorously that Eq. (3) is true for a Fermi–Dirac distribution of electrons.

For the case of a metal under the influence of electric fields in the x and y directions and a magnetic field in the z direction, Eq. (5.6) becomes in the steady state

$$v_x \frac{\partial f}{\partial x} + v_y \frac{\partial f}{\partial y} - \frac{e}{m}\left(E_x + \frac{v_y H_z}{c}\right)\frac{\partial f}{\partial v_x} - \frac{e}{m}\left(E_y - \frac{v_x H_z}{c}\right)\frac{\partial f}{\partial v_y} = -\frac{f - f_0}{\tau} \tag{4}$$

In analogy to Eq. (6.3) we seek a solution of the form

$$f = f_0 + v_x \chi_1 + v_y \chi_2 \tag{5}$$

where χ_1 and χ_2 are assumed functions of $v^2 = v_x^2 + v_y^2 + v_z^2$. Further we assume that E_x and E_y are small enough so that products of χ_1 and χ_2 with E_x, E_y, v_x and v_y can be neglected. Hence

$$v_x \frac{\partial f_0}{\partial x} + v_y \frac{\partial f_0}{\partial y} - \frac{e}{m}\left(E_x \frac{\partial f_0}{\partial v_x} + E_y \frac{\partial f_0}{\partial v_y}\right)$$

$$- \frac{e}{mc}\left(v_y H_z \frac{\partial f}{\partial v_x} - v_x H_z \frac{\partial f}{\partial v_y}\right) + \frac{v_x}{\tau}\chi_1 + \frac{v_y}{\tau}\chi_2 = 0 \tag{6}$$

Since $\varepsilon = \frac{1}{2}m(v_x^2 + v_y^2 + v_z^2)$ and χ_1, χ_2 are functions of $v^2 = v_x^2 + v_y^2 + v_z^2$ we have

$$\frac{\partial f_0}{\partial v_x} = \frac{\partial f_0}{\partial \varepsilon}\frac{d\varepsilon}{dv_x} = mv_x\frac{\partial f_0}{\partial \varepsilon}, \qquad \frac{\partial f_0}{\partial v_y} = mv_y\frac{\partial f_0}{\partial \varepsilon} \qquad (7)$$

$$\frac{\partial \chi_i}{\partial v_x} = mv_x\frac{\partial \chi_i}{\partial \varepsilon}, \qquad \frac{\partial \chi_i}{\partial v_y} = mv_y\frac{\partial \chi_i}{\partial \varepsilon} \qquad (8)$$

Equation (6) now becomes

$$v_x\frac{\partial f_0}{\partial x} + v_y\frac{\partial f_0}{\partial y} - e(E_xv_x + E_yv_y)\frac{\partial f_0}{\partial \varepsilon} - \frac{e}{mc}(v_yH_z\chi_1 - v_xH_z\chi_2)$$

$$+ \frac{v_x}{\tau}\chi_1 + \frac{v_y}{\tau}\chi_2 = 0 \quad (9)$$

Since this result is identically true for any value of v_x and v_y we can separately equate the coefficients of v_x and v_y to zero and obtain

$$\frac{\partial f_0}{\partial x} - eE_x\frac{\partial f_0}{\partial \varepsilon} + \frac{e`}{mc}H_z\chi_2 + \frac{\chi_1}{\tau} = 0 \qquad (10)$$

$$\frac{\partial f_0}{\partial y} - eE_y\frac{\partial f_0}{\partial \varepsilon} - \frac{e}{mc}H_z\chi_1 + \frac{\chi_2}{\tau} = 0 \qquad (11)$$

Solving for χ_1 and χ_2 gives

$$\chi_1 = -\tau \frac{\left(\dfrac{\partial f_0}{\partial x} - eE_x\dfrac{\partial f_0}{\partial \varepsilon}\right) - \tau\dfrac{eH_z}{mc}\left(\dfrac{\partial f_0}{\partial y} - eE_y\dfrac{\partial f_0}{\partial \varepsilon}\right)}{1 + \left(\tau\dfrac{eH_z}{mc}\right)^2} \qquad (12)$$

$$\chi_2 = -\tau \frac{\tau\dfrac{eH_z}{mc}\left(\dfrac{\partial f_0}{\partial x} - eE_x\dfrac{\partial f_0}{\partial \varepsilon}\right) + \left(\dfrac{\partial f_0}{\partial y} - eE_y\dfrac{\partial f_0}{\partial \varepsilon}\right)}{1 + \left(\tau\dfrac{eH_z}{mc}\right)^2} \qquad (13)$$

The current densities in the x and y directions are given by equations analogous to Eq. (6.10)

$$j_x = -e\int_{-\infty}^{\infty} v_x f\,dv_x\,dv_y\,dv_z = -e\int_{-\infty}^{\infty} v_x^2\chi_1\,dv_x\,dv_y\,dv_z \qquad (14)$$

$$j_y = -e\int_{-\infty}^{\infty} v_y f\,dv_x\,dv_y\,dv_z = -e\int_{-\infty}^{\infty} v_y^2\chi_2\,dv_x\,dv_y\,dv_z \qquad (15)$$

The integrals in Eq. (14) containing f_0 and χ_2 are zero since the integrands are odd functions of v_x, and similarly in Eq. (15).

Equations (4) through (15) are general. We now restrict ourselves to the isothermal Hall effect, i.e.,

$$j_y = 0 \tag{16}$$

Since the metal is at a constant temperature throughout there is no thermal gradient in the x or y direction. In other words,

$$\frac{\partial f_0}{\partial x} = \frac{\partial f_0}{\partial y} = 0 \tag{17}$$

Substituting Eqs. (16) and (17) and Eqs. (12) and (13) into Eqs. (14) and (15) we have on replacing v_x^2 by $v^2/3$ and $dv_x dv_y dv_z$ by $4\pi v^2 dv$,

$$j_x = -\frac{4\pi e^2}{3} \left[E_x \int_0^\infty \tau \frac{v^4}{1+\alpha^2} \frac{\partial f_0}{\partial \varepsilon} dv - E_y \int_0^\infty \tau \frac{\alpha v^4}{1+\alpha^2} \frac{\partial f_0}{\partial \varepsilon} dv \right] \tag{18}$$

$$j_y = 0 = -\frac{4\pi e^2}{3} \left[E_x \int_0^\infty \tau \frac{\alpha v^4}{1+\alpha^2} \frac{\partial f_0}{\partial \varepsilon} dv + E_y \int_0^\infty \tau \frac{v^4}{1+\alpha^2} \frac{\partial f_0}{\partial \varepsilon} dv \right] \tag{19}$$

where $\alpha = \tau e H_z/mc$. Changing the variable of integration in Eqs. (18) and (19) to $\varepsilon = \frac{1}{2}mv^2$ we have

$$j_x = -\frac{8\pi e^2}{3m^2} \left[E_x \int_0^\infty \lambda \frac{\varepsilon}{1+\alpha^2} \frac{\partial f_0}{\partial \varepsilon} d\varepsilon - E_y \int_0^\infty \lambda \frac{\alpha\varepsilon}{1+\alpha^2} \frac{\partial f_0}{\partial \varepsilon} d\varepsilon \right] \tag{20}$$

$$0 = -\frac{8\pi e^2}{3m^2} \left[E_x \int_0^\infty \lambda \frac{\alpha e}{1+\alpha^2} \frac{\partial f_0}{\partial \varepsilon} d\varepsilon + E_y \int_0^\infty \lambda \frac{\varepsilon}{1+\alpha^2} \frac{\partial f_0}{\partial \varepsilon} d\varepsilon \right] \tag{21}$$

where $\lambda = v\tau$. Thus far our results have been true for any distribution function. For the case of a degenerate electron gas we have seen, Eq. (6.23), that

$$f_0 = \frac{2m^3}{h^3} \frac{1}{e^{(\varepsilon-\varepsilon_F)/kT}+1} = \frac{2m^3}{h^3} f(\varepsilon) \tag{22}$$

Keeping only the first term in Sommerfeld's theorem, we have from Eqs. (5.11.13, 18)

$$\int_0^\infty F(\varepsilon) \frac{df}{d\varepsilon} d\varepsilon = -F(\varepsilon_F) \tag{23}$$

Hence

$$j_x = \frac{16\pi me^2}{3h^3} \left[E_x \frac{\lambda_F \varepsilon_F}{1+\alpha_F^2} - E_y \alpha_F \frac{\lambda_F \varepsilon_F}{1+\alpha_F^2} \right] \tag{24}$$

$$0 = \frac{16\pi me^2}{3h^3} \left[E_x \alpha_F \frac{\lambda_F \varepsilon_F}{1+\alpha_F^2} + E_y \frac{\lambda_F \varepsilon_F}{1+\alpha_F^2} \right] \tag{25}$$

where $\lambda_F = \lambda(\varepsilon_F)$ and $\alpha_F = (\lambda_F/v_F)(eH_z/mc)$. Solving for E_x and E_y we have

$$E_x = \frac{3h^3}{16\pi me^2} \frac{1}{\lambda_F \varepsilon_F} j_x \qquad (26)$$

$$E_y = -\frac{3h^3}{16\pi me^2} \frac{\alpha_F}{\lambda_F \varepsilon_F} j_x$$

$$= -\frac{3h^3}{16\pi me^2 c} \frac{H_z}{v_F \varepsilon_F} j_x \qquad (27)$$

Comparing Eqs. (26) and (6.25) we see that to second order in H_z the electrical conductivity is independent of H_z. From Eq. (27) we have

$$R_H = \frac{E_y}{J_x H_z} = -\frac{3h^3}{16\pi m^2 ec} \frac{1}{v_F \varepsilon_F}$$

$$= -\frac{1}{nec} \qquad (28)$$

where Eq. (2.1) and the fact that $v_F = \sqrt{2\varepsilon_F/m}$ have been used in obtaining Eq. (28). Hence, for the case of a degenerate electron gas the Drude theory is seen to give the correct result for the Hall coefficient.

Calculated and experimental values of R_H are given in Table 1.

TABLE 1. Hall coefficients of a number of metals at rocm temperature, in 10^{11} volt cm amp^{-1} oersted^{-1} (after C. Kittel, *Introduction to Solid State Physics*, 2nd Ed., Wiley, New York, 1956, p. 298)

Metal	Observed R_H	Calculated R_H
Li	−17.0	−13.1
Na	−25.0	−24.4
K	−42.0	−47
Cs	−78.0	−73
Cu	−5.5	−7.4
Ag	−8.4	−10.4
Au	−7.2	−10.5
Be	+24.4	−2.5
Zn	+3.3	−4.6
Cd	+6.0	−6.5
Al	−4	—
Bi	∼−1000	−4.1

The agreement is seen to be satisfactory for the monovalent metals. However for beryllium, zinc, and cadmium the above theory predicts the wrong sign. This problem was not overcome until the advent of band theory, which we shall now discuss briefly.

9. Band Theory of Solids

So far we have treated the electrons in a solid as being free and have not considered the potential due to the lattice of the substance. If this periodic potential is taken into account it is found[1] that on solving Schrödinger's equation the energy spectrum consists of '*allowed bands*' and '*forbidden gaps*' such that the electrons can only have energies whose values lie within the allowed bands. This situation is illustrated schematically in Figure 1 for the case of a metal, i.e., a substance for which the last energy band is only partially occupied at absolute zero so that at any temperature electrons can be removed from an occupied level and give rise to conduction.

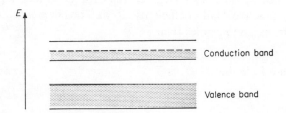

Figure 1. Schematic illustration of allowed energy bands of a metal.

The shaded levels are those occupied at absolute zero.

On this basis we can distinguish between a metal, a semiconductor, and an insulator. An insulator is a substance for which the lowest bands are completely filled and the next allowed band is completely empty. In the case of an *intrinsic semiconductor* the gap between the highest occupied band, called the *valence band*, and the lowest empty band, called the *conduction band*, is small enough ($\sim$ 1 ev) so that an electron in the valence band can receive enough thermal energy to cross the energy gap, leaving behind a *hole* (the absence of an electron) which will act as a positive charge (*vide* Figure 2).

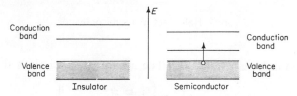

Figure 2. Schematic illustration of allowed energy bands of an insulator and a semi-conductor.

[1] A. J. Dekker, *Solid State Physics*, Prentice-Hall, Englewood Cliffs, N.J., 1957, Chapter 10.

For an intrinsic semiconductor conduction arises both from electrons in the conduction band and holes in the valence band. In other words

$$j = e(n_h v_h - n_e v_e) \tag{1}$$

where n_h and n_e are the number of holes and the number of electrons in a unit volume of the solid and v_e and v_h are the velocities of the electrons and of the holes. Thus,

$$\sigma = e(n_h \mu_h + n_e \mu_e) \tag{2}$$

where μ_e and μ_h are called the *mobilities* of the conduction electrons and of the holes and are defined as the velocities in the direction of the field for unit electric field.

The existence of holes as charge carriers for conduction gives an explanation of positive Hall coefficients. If we consider a solid, Figure 3, with n_e electrons and n_h holes then

$$j_x = (n_h \mu_h + n_e \mu_e) e E_x \tag{3}$$

The force on a hole due to H_z is

$$F_h = -\frac{e}{c} \mu_h E_x H_z \tag{4}$$

and the force on an electron due to H_z is

$$F_e = -\frac{e}{c} \mu_e E_x H_z \tag{5}$$

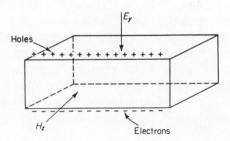

Figure 3. Hall effect in a semiconductor.

At equilibrium there is a field E_y. The net force on a hole is then

$$eE_y - \frac{e}{c} \mu_h E_x H_z \tag{6}$$

and the net force on an electron is

$$-eE_y - \frac{e}{c} \mu_e E_x H_z \tag{7}$$

At equilibrium $j_y = 0$. Thus we have

$$n_h \mu_h \left(eE_y - \frac{e}{c} \mu_h E_x H_z \right) = n_e \mu_e \left(-eE_y - \frac{e}{c} \mu_e E_x H_z \right) \qquad (8)$$

Hence

$$\frac{e}{c}(n_e \mu_e^2 - n_h \mu_h^2) E_x H_z = -e(n_e \mu_e + n_h \mu_h) E_y$$

$$\frac{1}{c}(n_e \mu_e^2 - n_h \mu_h^2) \frac{j_x H_z}{n_e \mu_e + n_h \mu_h} = -e(n_e \mu_e + n_h \mu_h) E_y \qquad (9)$$

Solving for $E_y / j_x H_z$, we have

$$R_H = \frac{E_y}{j_x H_z} = -\frac{1}{ec} \frac{n_e \mu_e^2 - n_h \mu_h^2}{n_e \mu_e + n_h \mu_h} \qquad (10)$$

On the basis of Sect. 8 we can conclude that Eq. (10) is correct if Fermi–Dirac statistics are applicable. If Boltzmann statistics apply then, as we shall see in Sect. 12, the right-hand side of Eq. (10) should be multiplied by $3\pi/8$. If the contribution of the holes exceeds that of the electrons, we see from Eq. (10) that R_H can be positive.

One other modification of the above theory is introduced by band theory. We have seen in the free electron model that, to within an additive constant,

$$\varepsilon = \frac{p^2}{2m} \qquad (11)$$

If we introduce the wave vector, $\mathbf{k}$, by

$$\mathbf{p} = \hbar \mathbf{k} \qquad (12)$$

then we have, to within an additive constant

$$\varepsilon = \frac{\hbar^2 k^2}{2m} \qquad (13)$$

On the basis of band theory it can be shown[1] that it is possible to introduce a quantity m^*, called the *effective mass*, such that,

$$\frac{1}{m^*} = \frac{1}{\hbar^2} \frac{\partial^2 \varepsilon}{\partial k^2} \qquad (14)$$

and hence if m is replaced with m^* Eq. (13) is still true. It is to be noted that m^* will, in general, no longer be a constant.

10. Intrinsic Semiconductors

Assume that the energy surfaces of the semiconductor are parabolic with the valence band having a maximum and the conduction band having a minimum at $k = 0$, as illustrated in Figure 1.

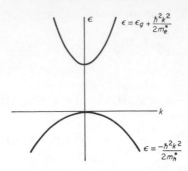

Figure 1. Valence and conduction bands of a semiconductor when the energy surfaces are parabolic.

Since the energy surfaces are parabolic, m_e^* and m_h^* are constants and hence the density of states $g(\varepsilon)$ is given by (see Sect. 5.9)

$$g(\varepsilon) = 4\pi \left(\frac{2m_e^*}{h^2}\right)^{\frac{3}{2}} V(\varepsilon - \varepsilon_g)^{\frac{1}{2}} \qquad \varepsilon > \varepsilon_g$$

$$g(\varepsilon) = 0 \qquad 0 < \varepsilon < \varepsilon_g$$

$$g(\varepsilon) = 4\pi \left(\frac{2m_h^*}{h^2}\right)^{\frac{3}{2}} V(-\varepsilon)^{\frac{1}{2}} \qquad \varepsilon < 0 \qquad (1)$$

The number of electrons in the conduction band is then

$$N_e = \int \frac{g(\varepsilon)\,d\varepsilon}{e^{(\varepsilon - \varepsilon_F)/kT} + 1} \qquad (2)$$

where the integration extends from ε_g to the top of the conduction band. We can replace the upper limit by ∞ since the band width $\gg kT$. Thus,

$$N_e = 4\pi \left(\frac{2m_e^*}{h^2}\right)^{\frac{3}{2}} V \int_{\varepsilon_g}^{\infty} \frac{(\varepsilon - \varepsilon_g)^{\frac{1}{2}}\,d\varepsilon}{e^{(\varepsilon - \varepsilon_F)/kT} + 1} \qquad (3)$$

Since the conduction band is unoccupied at absolute zero ε_F must lie below ε_g. If ε_F does not lie too close to ε_g, i.e. $\varepsilon_g - \varepsilon_F \gg kT$, then we need only consider the exponential in the denominator of the integrand since we are only concerned with the classical tail of $f(\varepsilon)$. In other words the *density of electrons in the conduction band is small.* Hence,

$$n = \frac{N_e}{V} = 4\pi \left(\frac{2m_e^*}{h^2}\right)^{\frac{3}{2}} e^{\varepsilon_F/kT} \int_{\varepsilon_g}^{\infty} (\varepsilon - \varepsilon_g)^{\frac{1}{2}} e^{-\varepsilon/kT}\,d\varepsilon$$

$$= 2 \left(\frac{2\pi m_e^* kT}{h^2}\right)^{\frac{3}{2}} e^{(\varepsilon_F - \varepsilon_g)/kT} \qquad (4)$$

where we have used integral (3) in Appendix 2.

The number of holes in the valence band is

$$N_h = \int g(\varepsilon) \left[1 - \frac{1}{e^{(\varepsilon - \varepsilon_F)/kT} + 1} \right] d\varepsilon = \int \frac{g(\varepsilon)\, d\varepsilon}{e^{(\varepsilon_F - \varepsilon)/kT} + 1} \tag{5}$$

The integration extends from the bottom of the valence band to zero. Because the width of the band is large we replace the lower limit by $-\infty$ and obtain on integrating

$$p = \frac{N_h}{V} = 2 \left(\frac{2\pi m_h^* kT}{h^2} \right)^{\frac{3}{2}} e^{-\varepsilon_F/kT} \tag{6}$$

In obtaining Eq. (6) we have assumed that ε_F is not too close to the top of the conduction band and therefore we have ignored the one in the denominator of the integrand of Eq. (5).

It is to be noted that

$$np = 4 \left(\frac{2\pi kT}{h^2} \right)^3 (m_e^* m_h^*)^{\frac{3}{2}} e^{-\varepsilon_g/kT} \tag{7}$$

np is constant for a given temperature. This is the law of mass action for the 'reaction'

$$\text{electron} + \text{hole} \rightleftharpoons 0$$

Conservation of charge requires that $n = p$. Hence from Eq. (7) we have

$$n = p = 2 \left(\frac{2\pi kT}{h^2} \right)^{\frac{3}{2}} (m_e^* m_h^*)^{\frac{3}{4}} e^{-\varepsilon_g/2kT} \tag{8}$$

Equating the right-hand sides of Eqs. (4) and (6) gives

$$m_e^{*\frac{3}{2}} e^{-(\varepsilon_g - \varepsilon_F)/kT} = m_h^{*\frac{3}{2}} e^{-\varepsilon_F/kT}$$

$$e^{2\varepsilon_F/kT} = \left(\frac{m_h^*}{m_e^*} \right)^{\frac{3}{2}} e^{\varepsilon_g/kT}$$

$$\varepsilon_F = \tfrac{1}{2}\varepsilon_g + \tfrac{3}{4} kT \ln \left(\frac{m_h^*}{m_e^*} \right) \tag{9}$$

The second term is quite small so

$$\varepsilon_F \simeq \tfrac{1}{2}\varepsilon_g \tag{10}$$

The Fermi level lies slightly above the middle of the energy gap. If $m_h^* = m_e^*$, $\varepsilon_F = \tfrac{1}{2}\varepsilon_g$.

From Eq. (9.2) and Eq. (8) we have

$$\sigma = e\{\mu_e + \mu_h\} 2 \left(\frac{2\pi kT}{h^2} \right)^{\frac{3}{2}} (m_e^* m_h^*)^{\frac{3}{4}} e^{-\varepsilon_g/2kT} \tag{11}$$

Although the mobilities are themselves temperature-dependent the real temperature dependence of σ is through the exponential. For an intrinsic semiconductor

$$\sigma \propto e^{-\varepsilon_g/2kT}$$

$$\ln \sigma = -\frac{\varepsilon_g}{2kT} + \text{constant} \tag{12}$$

11. Impurity Semiconductors

Consider silicon or germanium, which are members of the fourth group of the periodic table, with arsenic or some other member of the fifth group as an impurity. The impurity atoms go into the lattice substitutionally as in Figure 1.

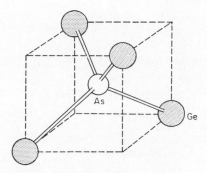

Figure 1. As impurity in Ge lattice.

The four covalent bonds with the neighboring Ge or Si atoms require four As electrons leaving one extra electron which will orbit about the As$^+$ ion. Treating the extra electron and the As$^+$ ion as a hydrogen-like atom,[1] we obtain for the ionization energy required to send the electron into the conduction band

$$\mathscr{E}_{\text{ionization}} = \frac{m^* e^4}{2\varepsilon_s^2 \hbar^2} \tag{1}$$

where ε_s is the dielectric constant of Ge or Si. To gain an estimate of the ionization energy put $\varepsilon_s = 16$ (Ge) and $m^* = m$. Since the ionization energy of H is 13.6 ev we have

$$\mathscr{E}_{\text{ionization}} = \frac{13.6}{256} \text{ ev} = 0.05 \text{ ev}$$

---

[1] See *Q.C.*, pp. 3–4, 80–83 for a discussion of the hydrogen atom.

Thus the energy level of the extra electron is just below the conduction band (*vide* Figure 2).

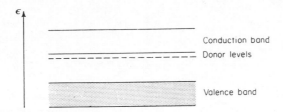

Figure 2. Schematic illustration of allowed energy bands of an *n*-type impurity semiconductor.

The energy level of the extra electron is called a *donor level* and the impurity a *donor* since thermal energy will send these extra electrons into the conduction band. For this case the material is called an *n-type impurity semiconductor* since there are more holes than electrons.

If gallium or boron or some other third group member is put into the lattice as an impurity then the Ga atom will have one too few electrons to form the four covalent bonds with the neighboring Ge or Si atoms. As a result an electron in the valence band may receive enough thermal energy to fill this lack of an electron, leaving behind a hole in the valence band. In this case the impurity atom is called an *acceptor* and the energy level of the accepted electron is called an *acceptor level* (*vide* Figure 3). For this case there are more holes than electrons and the material is called a *p-type impurity semiconductor*.

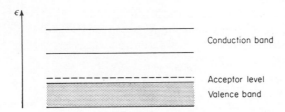

Figure 3. Schematic illustration of allowed energy bands of a *p*-type semiconductor.

We shall now calculate the electron and hole concentrations in an impurity semiconductor. Consider the energy surfaces as parabolic with minima or maxima at $k = 0$ as is shown in Figure 4.

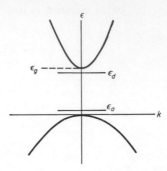

Figure 4. Parabolic energy surfaces for impurity semiconductors.

The donor and acceptor levels differ from the energy levels of a particle since Coulomb repulsion makes it unlikely that one acceptor atom will have two electrons on it even though the Pauli principle allows two. We can most easily see the result of this consideration by using the method of the most probable distribution (Sect. 4.4). If n_i is the number of electrons in the valence band with energy ε_i whose degeneracy is g_i and n_a is the number of electrons in the N_a acceptor levels with energy ε_a, then we have the constraining equations

$$n_a \varepsilon_a + \sum_i n_i \varepsilon_i = E$$

$$n_a + \sum_i n_i = N \tag{2}$$

The number of arrangements over the ith valence band level will be

$$\frac{g_i!}{n_i!(g_i - n_i)!} \tag{3}$$

since there are $g_i!$ ways of putting the n_i electrons into the ith level and both the electrons and holes are indistinguishable. The number of arrangements of the n_a electrons over the N_a acceptor levels is

$$\frac{N_a!}{n_a!(N_a - n_a)!} \tag{4}$$

Hence the number of ways n_a electrons can go to N_a acceptors is

$$W = 2^{n_a} \frac{N_a!}{n_a!(N_a - n_a)!} \prod_i \frac{g_i!}{n_i!(g_i - n_i)!} \tag{5}$$

The factor 2^{n_a} appears because an electron can go to an acceptor in two ways, spin up or spin down. The most probable distribution is found by maximizing Eq. (5) subject to Eqs. (2). In order that we may apply Stirling's approximation we maximize ln W. Taking the logarithm of Eq. (5) and applying Stirling's approximation

$$\ln W = n_a \ln 2 + N_a \ln N_a - n_a \ln n_a - (N_a - n_a) \ln (N_a - n_a)$$
$$+ \sum_i \{g_i \ln g_i - n_i \ln n_i - (g_i - n_i) \ln (g_i - n_i)\} \quad (6)$$

The variation of Eqs. (2) and (6) is

$$\varepsilon_a \delta n_a + \sum_i \varepsilon_i \delta n_i = 0 \quad (7)$$

$$\delta n_a + \sum_i \delta n_i = 0 \quad (8)$$

$$\{\ln 2 + \ln (N_a - n_a) - \ln n_a\}\delta n_a + \sum_i \{\ln (g_i - n_i) - \ln n_i\}\delta n_i = 0 \quad (9)$$

Multiplying Eq. (7) by β and Eq. (8) by $-\alpha$ and adding the resulting equations to Eq. (9) gives

$$\left\{\ln 2 \frac{N_a - n_a}{n_a} + \beta\varepsilon_i - \alpha\right\} \delta n_a + \sum_i \left\{\ln \frac{g_i - n_i}{n_i} + \beta\varepsilon_i - \alpha\right\} \delta n_i = 0 \quad (10)$$

Since there are only two constraining equations, all but two of the variables are independent and, therefore, there exist values for α and β such that each coefficient in Eq. (10) can be independently set equal to zero. Thus

$$n_a = \frac{N_a}{\frac{1}{2}e^{(\varepsilon_a - \varepsilon_F)/kT} + 1}, \qquad n_i = \frac{g_i}{e^{(\varepsilon_i - \varepsilon_F)/kT} + 1} \quad (11)$$

where the usual identifications, $\beta = 1/kT$, $\alpha = \varepsilon_F/kT$ have been made. For the electrons in the valence band Fermi–Dirac statistics apply, but for the electrons in the acceptor levels the factor $\frac{1}{2}$ arises because of our correlation considerations, i.e. Coulomb repulsion excludes two electrons being on the same acceptor atom.

If n is the concentration of electrons in the conduction band, p the concentration of holes in the valence band, N_d^+ the concentration of ionized donors, and N_a^- the concentration of ionized acceptors, then electrical neutrality requires

$$n + N_a^- = p + N_d^+ \quad (12)$$

N_a^- is given by Eq. (11),

$$N_a^- = \frac{N_a}{\frac{1}{2}e^{(\varepsilon_a - \varepsilon_F)/kT} + 1} \quad (13)$$

N_d^+ is given by

$$N_d^+ = N_d - n_d = N_d \left[1 - \frac{1}{\frac{1}{2}e^{(\varepsilon_d - \varepsilon_F)/kT} + 1}\right]$$

$$= \frac{N_d}{2e^{(\varepsilon_F - \varepsilon_d/kT)} + 1} \quad (14)$$

n and p are given by Eqs. (10.4, 6). Hence Eq. (12) requires

$$n_e^0 \, e^{(\varepsilon_F - \varepsilon_g)/kT} + \frac{N_a}{\frac{1}{2}e^{(\varepsilon_a - \varepsilon_F)/kT} + 1} = n_h^0 \, e^{-\varepsilon_F/kT} + \frac{N_d}{2e^{(\varepsilon_F - \varepsilon_d)/kT} + 1} \quad (15)$$

where

$$n_e^0 = 2\left(\frac{2\pi m_e^* kT}{h^2}\right)^{\frac{3}{2}} \quad (16)$$

$$n_h^0 = 2\left(\frac{2\pi m_h^* kT}{h^2}\right)^{\frac{3}{2}} \quad (17)$$

Let us restrict ourselves to the case $N_a = 0$. Further we assume that there are a sufficiently large number of donors so that a lot of electrons are put into the conduction band decreasing p according to the reaction $n + p \rightleftharpoons 0$. Thus $p \ll n$ and Eq. (15) becomes

$$n_e^0 \, e^{(\varepsilon_F - \varepsilon_g)/kT} = \frac{N_d}{2e^{(\varepsilon_F - \varepsilon_d)/kT} + 1} \quad (18)$$

$$2n_e^0 \, e^{-(\varepsilon_d + \varepsilon_g)/kT}(e^{\varepsilon_F/kT})^2 + n_e^0 \, e^{-\varepsilon_g/kT}(e^{\varepsilon_F/kT}) - N_d = 0 \quad (19)$$

Taking the positive root

$$e^{\varepsilon_F/kT} = \frac{e^{\varepsilon_d/kT}}{4}\left[-1 + \left\{1 + \frac{8N_d}{n_e^0}e^{(\varepsilon_g - \varepsilon_d)/kT}\right\}^{\frac{1}{2}}\right] \quad (20)$$

There are two limiting cases.

Case 1

$$\frac{8N_d}{n_e^0}e^{(\varepsilon_g - \varepsilon_d)/kT} \ll 1, \text{ i.e. either } N_d \text{ is small or } T \text{ is large}$$

$$e^{\varepsilon_F/kT} = \frac{N_d}{n_e^0}e^{\varepsilon_g/kT}$$

$$\varepsilon_F = \varepsilon_g + kT\ln\frac{N_d}{n_e^0} \quad (21)$$

Hence $\varepsilon_F \ll \varepsilon_g$. Substituting the above result into Eq. (18) gives

$$n = n_e^0 \, e^{-(\varepsilon_F - \varepsilon_g)/kT} = n_e^0\frac{N_d}{n_e^0} = N_d \quad (22)$$

For this case all the donors are ionized. This is the usual situation.

Case 2

$\dfrac{8N_d}{n_e^0} e^{(\varepsilon_g - \varepsilon_d)/kT} \gg 1$, i.e., either N_d is large or T is small

$$e^{\varepsilon_F/kT} = \frac{1}{\sqrt{2}} \left(\frac{N_d}{n_e^0}\right)^{\frac{1}{2}} e^{(\varepsilon_g - \varepsilon_d)/2kT}$$

$$\varepsilon_F = \frac{\varepsilon_g + \varepsilon_d}{2} + \frac{kT}{2} \ln\left(\frac{N_d}{2n_e^0}\right) \tag{23}$$

And hence,

$$n = \sqrt{\frac{n_e^0 N_d}{2}} \, e^{-(\varepsilon_g - \varepsilon_d)/2kT} \tag{24}$$

Thus at low temperatures n varies as $\sqrt{N_d}$.

Identical results hold for the case $N_a = 0$. If N_a and N_d are of the same order of magnitude, Eq. (15) must be solved graphically.

12. Conductivity and Isothermal Hall Effect in a Semiconductor

We restrict ourselves to a single type of charge carrier—say electrons in the conduction band. As we have seen, the density of electrons in the conduction band is small and hence we are concerned with the classical tail of the Fermi–Dirac distribution. Thus from Eqs. (6.18, 20, 23) we have

$$\sigma = -\frac{16\pi m_e^* e^2}{3h^3} \int_0^\infty \lambda \varepsilon \left(\frac{\partial f}{\partial \varepsilon}\right) d\varepsilon \tag{1}$$

where

$$f(\varepsilon) = \frac{1}{e^{(\varepsilon - \varepsilon_F)/kT} + 1} \simeq e^{(\varepsilon_F - \varepsilon)/kT} \tag{2}$$

Assuming λ is constant we have

$$\sigma = \frac{16\pi m_e^* e^2 \lambda}{3h^3 kT} e^{\varepsilon_F/kT} \int_0^\infty \varepsilon \, e^{-\varepsilon/kT} \, d\varepsilon$$

$$= \frac{16\pi m_e^* e^2 \lambda}{3h^3} kT \, e^{\varepsilon_F/kT} \tag{3}$$

We have used Integral (1) in Appendix 2 in obtaining Eq. (3). Let us introduce n_c, the density of carriers,

$$n_c V = \int_0^\infty g(\varepsilon) f(\varepsilon) \, d\varepsilon$$

$$= 4\pi \left(\frac{2m_e^*}{h^2}\right)^{\frac{3}{2}} V \, e^{\varepsilon_F/kT} \int_0^\infty \varepsilon^{\frac{1}{2}} \, e^{-\varepsilon/kT} \, d\varepsilon$$

$$n_c = 2\left(\frac{2\pi m_e^* kT}{h^2}\right)^{\frac{3}{2}} e^{\varepsilon_F/kT} \tag{4}$$

where Integral (3) in Appendix 2 has been used. The average velocity of the conduction electrons is

$$
\bar{v} = \frac{\displaystyle\int_0^\infty v\, e^{-m_e^* v^2/2kT}\, v^2\, dv}{\displaystyle\int_0^\infty e^{-m_e^* v^2/2kT}\, v^2\, dv} = \sqrt{\frac{2kT}{m_e^*}}\, \frac{\displaystyle\int_0^\infty x^3 e^{-x^2}\, dx}{\displaystyle\int_0^\infty x^2 e^{-x^2}\, dx}
$$

$$
= \sqrt{\frac{8kT}{\pi m_e^*}} \tag{5}
$$

Integral (2) in Appendix 2 has been used in obtaining Eq. (5). From Eqs. (3), (4), and (5) we have

$$
\sigma = \frac{8}{3\pi}\, \frac{n_c e^2 \lambda}{m_e^* \bar{v}} \tag{6}
$$

We now consider the isothermal Hall effect. Equations (8.20) and (8.21) become if α is small compared to one

$$
j_x = \frac{16\pi m_e^* e^2}{3h^3 kT}\, \lambda\, e^{\varepsilon_F/kT} \left[E_x \int_0^\infty \varepsilon\, e^{-\varepsilon/kT} d\varepsilon - \frac{\lambda e}{c}\, \frac{E_y H_z}{\sqrt{2m_e^*}} \int_0^\infty \sqrt{\varepsilon}\, e^{-\varepsilon/kT} d\varepsilon \right] \tag{7}
$$

$$
0 = \frac{16\pi m_e^* e^2}{3h^3 kT}\, \lambda\, e^{\varepsilon_F/kT} \left[\frac{\lambda e}{c}\, \frac{E_x H_z}{\sqrt{2m_e^*}} \int_0^\infty \sqrt{\varepsilon}\, e^{-\varepsilon/kT} d\varepsilon + E_y \int_0^\infty \varepsilon\, e^{-\varepsilon/kT} d\varepsilon \right] \tag{8}
$$

Solving for E_y in Eqs. (7) and (8) and referring to Eq. (3) gives, if second order terms in H_z are neglected,

$$
E_y = \frac{-16\pi m_e^* e^3 \lambda^2}{3\sqrt{2m_e^*}\, ch^3 kT\sigma^2}\, e^{\varepsilon_F/kT} j_x H_z \int_0^\infty \sqrt{\varepsilon}\, e^{-\varepsilon/kT} d\varepsilon
$$

$$
R_H = \frac{E_y}{j_x H_z} = \frac{-16\pi m_e^* e^3 \lambda^2}{3\sqrt{2m_e^*}\, ch^3 kT\sigma^2}\, e^{\varepsilon_F/kT}\, \frac{kT}{2}\, \sqrt{\pi kT} \tag{9}
$$

where Integral (3) in Appendix 2 has been used. Using Eq. (4) we have

$$
R_H = -\frac{1}{\sigma^2}\, \frac{n_c e^3 \lambda^2}{3m_e^* ckT}
$$

$$
= -\frac{3\pi}{8}\, \frac{1}{n_c ec} \tag{10}
$$

The last equality has been obtained by means of Eq. (5).

13. Recombination and Lifetime of Minority Carriers

Consider an n-type semiconductor and let n_0 and p_0 be the equilibrium concentrations of conduction electrons and holes. If the semiconductor is exposed to light, an electron may absorb a photon and receive enough energy to go into the conduction band forming an electron–hole pair as shown in Figure 1.

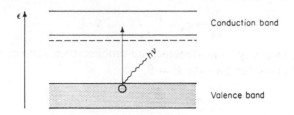

Figure 1. Photoelectric promotion of an electron from the valence band to the conduction band.

This excess of electron–hole pairs does not remain and the system returns to equilibrium by recombination of the excess electrons and holes. If there are not too many excess carriers, then the decay is usually exponential and a lifetime can be assigned to them. Thus,

$$\frac{dn}{dt} = -\frac{n-n_0}{\tau_e}, \qquad \frac{dp}{dt} = -\frac{p-p_0}{\tau_h} \tag{1}$$

where τ_e and τ_h are respectively the lifetimes of the electrons and the holes. The holes will diffuse whether or not a field is applied. Thus the current density of the holes will be made up of two parts: one due to the field and one due to the concentration gradient,

$$\mathbf{j}_h = pe\mu_h\mathbf{E} - eD_h\nabla p \tag{2}$$

where D_h is the *diffusion coefficient* of the holes and μ_h is the hole mobility.

D_h and μ_h are related. If we consider a thermal equilibrium situation for which $j = 0$, then

$$p = Ce^{-e\phi/kT} \tag{3}$$

where C is a constant and ϕ is the electrostatic potential. Since $E = -\nabla\phi$, Eq. (2) becomes

$$\mathbf{j}_h = 0 = eCe^{-e\phi/kT}\left[\mu_h(-\nabla\phi) - D_h\left(-\frac{\nabla\phi}{kT}\right)e\right]$$

$$\mu_h kT = eD_h \tag{4}$$

This is the so-called *Einstein relation* and applies whenever conduction and diffusion take place by the same mechanism.

We can obtain another relation involving D_h. The hole current flowing out of any volume V is

$$\int \mathbf{j}_h \cdot d\mathbf{S} \tag{5}$$

which must equal the decrease in the number of holes within V after the change due to the generation and recombination of holes has been considered. Thus considering the limit $V \to 0$ we have because of Eq. (8.1)

$$\frac{\partial p}{\partial t} = g_h - \frac{p - p_0}{\tau_h} - \frac{1}{e}\nabla \cdot \mathbf{j}_h \tag{6}$$

If we consider only a one-dimensional problem then substituting Eq. (2) into Eq. (6) gives, for the case $E = 0$,

$$\frac{\partial p}{\partial t} = g_h - \frac{p - p_0}{\tau_h} + D_h \frac{\partial^2 p}{\partial x^2} \tag{7}$$

As the holes flow away from the region in which they are generated, Eq. (7) becomes in the steady state

$$D_h \frac{d^2 p}{dx^2} = \frac{p - p_0}{\tau_h} \tag{8}$$

Equation (8) has the solution

$$p - p_0 = p_0\, e^{-x/L_h} \tag{9}$$

where

$$L_h = \sqrt{D_h \tau_h} \tag{10}$$

The length L_h is known as the *diffusion length* for holes and is a measure of the length a hole diffuses during a lifetime.

14. p–n Junctions[1]

Whenever a p-type and an n-type semiconductor are in contact with a very thin interface between them the two materials are said to form a p–n junction. A p–n junction is usually made by pulling the crystal out of a melt of say molten germanium with an excess of donors. The crystal will then be n-type. Later an excess of acceptor impurities is added to the melt and the new crystal becomes p-type. For convenience we shall assume that the junction has been formed by sticking p-type germanium to n-type germanium. Thus, before the p- and n-type germanium are joined we have the situation illustrated in Figure 1.

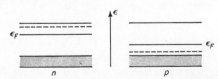

Figure 1. Energy bands of p- and n-type Ge.

1 W. Shockley, *Bell System Tech. J.*, **28**, 435 (1949); *Proc. I.R.E.*, **40**, 1289 (1952).

On joining the *p*- and *n*-type germanium the Fermi levels become equal since at equilibrium the chemical potential is the same for the two materials (*vide* Figure 2).

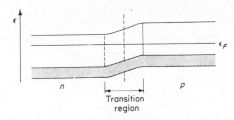

Figure 2. Energy bands of *p*- and *n*-type Ge in contact.

We shall assume that the transition region is small compared with the diffusion lengths of the electrons or the holes. Let us now discuss the rectification properties of a *p–n* junction. There are two situations to be considered: forward and reverse bias. These two situations are illustrated in Figure 3.

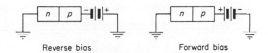

Figure 3. Forward and reverse bias in a *p–n* junction.

The effect of these two cases is shown in Figure 4.

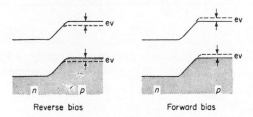

Figure 4. Effect of bias on energy bands of a *p–n* junction.

Let n_0 and p_0 be the equilibrium concentrations of electrons and holes in the *n* and *p* regions, respectively, and let V be the applied voltage. Since the potential drop takes place in the transition region where $E = 0$, we may use Eq. (13.7) with appropriate steady state conditions $g_e = 0$, $\partial n / \partial t = 0$,

$$\frac{n - n_0}{\tau_e} = D_e \frac{d^2 n}{dx^2} \tag{1}$$

If we let $n = n_0 + \Delta n$ then Eq. (1) becomes

$$D_e \frac{d^2 \Delta n}{dx^2} = \frac{\Delta n}{\tau_e} \tag{2}$$

The solution to Eq. (2) is

$$\Delta n = A e^{-x/L_e} + B e^{x/L_e} \tag{3}$$

where $L_e^2 = D_e \tau_e$. The second term in Eq. (3) becomes infinite as $x \to \infty$ and therefore $B = 0$. At $x = 0$ we have according to Boltzmann statistics

$$n = n_0 + \Delta n = n_0 e^{eV/kT}$$

$$\Delta n = n_0 (e^{eV/kT} - 1) \tag{4}$$

Hence $A = n_0 (e^{eV/kT} - 1)$ and Eq. (3) yields

$$n = n_0 + n_0 (e^{eV/kT} - 1) e^{-x/L_e} \tag{5}$$

From Eq. (13.2) we obtain for the electron current at $x = 0$

$$j_e(0) = -eD_e \nabla n \big|_{x=0}$$

$$= e \frac{D_e}{L_e} n_0 (e^{eV/kT} - 1) \tag{6}$$

The analysis for the hole current is analogous and yields

$$j_h(0) = e \frac{D_h}{L_h} p_0 (e^{eV/kT} - 1) \tag{7}$$

Thus the total current is

$$j = j_e(0) + j_h(0)$$

$$= e \left(\frac{D_h p_0}{\tau_h} + \frac{D_e n_0}{\tau_e} \right) (e^{eV/kT} - 1) \tag{8}$$

The current is low for $V < 0$ and therefore the p–n junction can act as a rectifier as is illustrated in Figure 5.

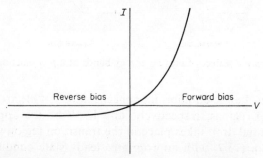

Figure 5. I as a function of *V* in a *p–n* junction.

Because of this and similar properties, semiconductors are used in transistors which perform the functions of vacuum tubes.

It is interesting that in biological systems one encounters analogies to the various electronic devices used in communications. Elsasser has discussed this situation.[2]

[2] W. M. Elsasser, *The Physical Foundation of Biology*, Pergamon Press, New York, 1958.

10

COOPERATIVE PHENOMENA; FERROMAGNETISM AND ANTIFERROMAGNETISM

1. Introduction

In Chapter 8 we successfully described the dielectric, diamagnetic, and paramagnetic properties of various substances by considering the atoms of the substance as non-interacting. However, not all of the properties of matter can be described in this manner. For example, in our simplified treatment of a polar solid (Sect. 8.8) we found that at low temperatures the atoms of the solid 'cooperated' to form an ordered structure and that with increasing temperature thermal agitation tended to overcome this 'cooperative' action so that at a critical temperature T_c an abrupt phase change to a disordered structure occurred. This order–disorder transformation is one of a large group of phenomena called *cooperative phenomena* in which certain subsystems, as for example atoms, cooperate to form units.

In this chapter we shall discuss ferromagnetism as a typical example of a cooperative phenomenon and then conclude with a short discussion of two other important examples of cooperative phenomena: superstructure in alloys and a lattice gas.

2. Ferromagnetism; Weiss' Theory

A substance is called *ferromagnetic* if it is capable of having a magnetic moment $\mathbf{M}$[1] in the absence of an applied field. If a ferromagnetic substance is heated above a temperature characteristic of the substance, called the *Curie temperature*, T_c, the spontaneous magnetization vanishes and the substance becomes paramagnetic. Above T_c the magnetic susceptibility obeys the *Curie–Weiss law*:

$$\chi_m = \frac{C}{T - \theta_c} \tag{1}$$

where θ_c is called the paramagnetic Curie temperature and may be slightly larger than T_c (ferromagnetic Curie temperature). Ferromagnetic materials

---

[1] Throughout this chapter we shall use the symbol $\mathbf{M}$ to denote the *total* magnetic moment.

also exhibit a phenomenon called *hysteresis*. As is seen from Figure 1 the magnetic moment is not a unique function of the applied field but depends on the past history of the substance.

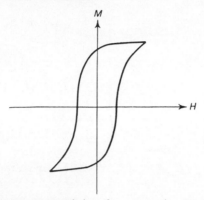

Figure 1. Hysteresis in a ferromagnetic material.

The first progress in understanding ferromagnetism was made by Pierre Weiss[2] who assumed:

1. A macroscopic ferromagnetic specimen contains a large number of spontaneously magnetized regions, called *domains*. A single domain is assumed to have a magnetization curve of the type of Figure 2. The magnetic moment of the specimen is the vector sum of the magnetic moments of the individual domains.
2. Within each domain there is an internal field proportional to the magnetization which causes an alignment of the atomic dipoles.

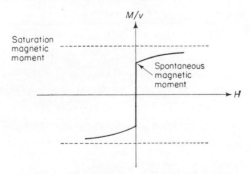

Figure 2. Magnetization curve of a domain.

Thus if we consider a unit volume the total field is given by

$$H_{\text{total}} = H + \lambda M \tag{2}$$

[2] P. Weiss, *J. Physique*, **6**, 667 (1907).

where λ is called the *Weiss constant*. Now we have seen that

$$M = ng\mu_B J B_J(x) \tag{3}$$

where

$$x = \frac{g\mu_B J H}{kT} \quad \text{and} \quad B_J(x) = \frac{2J+1}{2J} \coth\frac{2J+1}{2J}x - \frac{1}{2J}\coth\frac{x}{2J}$$

Hence

$$M = ng\mu_B J B_J\left(\frac{g\mu_B J}{kT}(H+\lambda M)\right) \tag{4}$$

For T sufficiently large, $B_J(x) = \frac{1}{3}\frac{J+1}{J}x$, so that we have

$$M = \frac{ng\mu_B J}{3}\left(\frac{J+1}{J}\right)\frac{g\mu_B J}{kT}(H+\lambda M)$$

$$= \frac{n\mu^2}{3kT}(H+\lambda M) \tag{5}$$

since $\mu = g\sqrt{J(J+1)}\,\mu_B$. Thus solving for M we obtain the Curie–Weiss law,

$$M = \frac{n\mu^2/3k}{T - \lambda n\mu^2/3k}H \tag{6}$$

Thus[3]

$$T_c = \frac{\lambda n\mu^2}{3k} \tag{7}$$

We can estimate the order of magnitude for λ by noting that for iron $\theta_c = 1043°$K, and thus

$$\lambda = \frac{3kT_c}{n\mu^2} = \frac{10^{-16}\times 10^3}{10^{23}\times 10^{-40}} = 10^4$$

The internal field cannot be due to dipole–dipole interactions since if it were $\lambda = 4\pi/3$.

Now let us investigate the spontaneous magnetic moment. Setting $H = 0$ in Eq. (4) gives for the spontaneous magnetic moment, M_s,

$$M_s = ng\mu_B J B_J(y) \tag{8}$$

where

$$y = \frac{g\mu_B J\lambda}{kT}M_s \tag{9}$$

---

[3] The Weiss theory does not distinguish between T_c and θ_c.

For $T < T_c$ we can solve for M_s graphically by plotting M_s as a function of y from the simultaneous Eqs. (8) and (9).

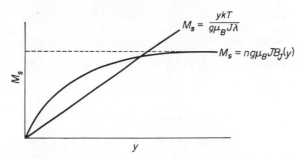

$$M_s = \frac{ykT}{g\mu_B J\lambda}$$

$$M_s = ng\mu_B J B_J(y)$$

Figure 3. Method for graphical determination of spontaneous magnetic moment as a function of temperature.

In this way a plot of M_s *vs.* T may be obtained for various values of J. In Figure 4 curves are given for $J = \frac{1}{2}$, 1 and ∞.

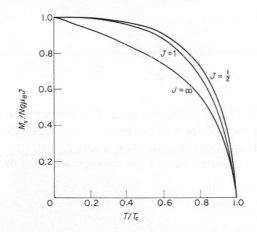

Figure 4. Spontaneous magnetic moment for various values of J.

The experimental results are found to agree with the curve for which $J = \frac{1}{2}$ indicating that ferromagnetism is associated with the electron spins rather than orbital angular momentum. This conclusion is further strengthened by so-called gyromagnetic experiments[4] by which one directly measures g (see Table 1).

[4] S. Barnett, *Proc. Am. Acad. Arts Sci.*, **75**, 109 (1944); S. Brown, A. Meyer, and G. Scott, *C. R. Acad. Sci., Paris*, **238**, 2502 (1954).

TABLE 1. The gyromagnetic ratio for some ferromagnetic substances

Fe	1.93
Co	1.87
Ni	1.92
Magnetic (Fe_3O_4)	1.93
Heusler alloy (Cu_2MnAl)	2.00
Permalloy (78% Ni, 22% Fe)	1.91

With $J = \frac{1}{2}$ and $g = 2$ we have from Eq. (4) that

$$M = N\mu_B[2 \coth 2y - \coth y]$$

$$= N\mu_B \left[\frac{\cosh^2 y + \sinh^2 y}{\sinh y \cosh y} - \frac{\cosh y}{\sinh y} \right]$$

$$= N\mu_B \tanh y$$

$$M = N\mu_B \tanh \frac{\mu_B(H + \lambda M)}{kT} \tag{10}$$

and from Eq. (7) we have that

$$T_c = \frac{\lambda n \mu_B^2}{k} \tag{11}$$

3. Source of Weiss Field

Heisenberg[1] has given an explanation of the Weiss field based on the Heitler–London method for bond orbitals.[2] As an example consider two atoms, A and B, each with one electron, 1 and 2.

Let ψ_a and ψ_b be the space part of the atomic wave functions for A and B.

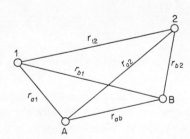

Figure 1. Spatial relationship of atoms A and B, each with one electron, 1 and 2.

1 W. Heisenberg, *Z. Physik*, **49**, 619 (1928).
2 W. Heitler and F. London, *Z. Physik*, **44**, 455 (1927).

The possible anti-symmetric wave functions for the complete system are then, in the Heitler–London approximation,

$$
\begin{vmatrix}
\psi_a(1)\alpha(1) & \psi_b(1)\alpha(1) \\
\psi_a(2)\alpha(2) & \psi_b(2)\alpha(2) \\
\psi_a(1)\beta(1) & \psi_b(1)\alpha(1) \\
\psi_a(2)\beta(2) & \psi_b(2)\alpha(2)
\end{vmatrix}
\quad
\begin{vmatrix}
\psi_a(1)\alpha(1) & \psi_b(1)\beta(1) \\
\psi_a(2)\alpha(2) & \psi_b(2)\beta(2) \\
\psi_a(1)\beta(1) & \psi_b(1)\beta(1) \\
\psi_a(2)\beta(2) & \psi_b(2)\beta(2)
\end{vmatrix}
\tag{1}
$$

where α denotes spin up and β spin down. Written out we have

$$
[\psi_a(1)\psi_b(2)-\psi_a(2)\psi_b(1)]\alpha(1)\alpha(2)
$$
$$
[\psi_a(1)\psi_b(2)\alpha(1)\beta(2)-\psi_a(2)\psi_b(1)\alpha(2)\beta(1)]
$$
$$
[\psi_a(1)\psi_b(2)\alpha(2)\beta(1)-\psi_a(2)\psi_b(1)\alpha(1)\beta(2)]
\tag{2}
$$
$$
[\psi_a(1)\psi_b(2)-\psi_a(2)\psi_b(1)]\beta(1)\beta(2)
$$

Instead of using the second and third wave functions it is more convenient to use a sum and a difference of these wave functions, thus

$$
[\psi_a(1)\psi_b(2)+\psi_a(2)\psi_b(1)][\alpha(1)\beta(2)-\alpha(2)\beta(1)]
\tag{3}
$$

$$
[\psi_a(1)\psi_b(2)-\psi_a(2)\psi_b(1)]
\begin{cases}
\alpha(1)\alpha(2) \\
[\alpha(1)\beta(2)+\alpha(2)\beta(1)] \\
\beta(1)\beta(2)
\end{cases}
\tag{4}
$$

Under these conditions the wave functions are eigenfunctions of the total spin; Eq. (3) represents the singlet state, $S = 0$, and Eqs. (4) represent the triplet state, $S = 1$.

The Hamiltonian of the system is

$$
\left\{ -\frac{\hbar^2}{2m}\nabla_1^2 - \frac{e^2}{r_{a1}} \right\} + \left\{ -\frac{\hbar^2}{2m}\nabla_2^2 - \frac{e^2}{r_{b2}} \right\} + \frac{e^2}{r_{12}} + \frac{e^2}{r_{ab}} - \frac{e^2}{r_{b1}} - \frac{e^2}{r_{a2}}
\tag{5}
$$

so that if we denote the interaction potential by V_{ab}, where

$$
V_{ab} = \frac{e^2}{r_{12}} + \frac{e^2}{r_{ab}} - \frac{e^2}{r_{b1}} - \frac{e^2}{r_{a2}}
\tag{6}
$$

the interaction energy is

$$
\mathscr{E}_{int} = \int \psi^* V_{ab} \psi \, d\tau_1 \, d\tau_2
\tag{7}
$$

In each case the spin eigenfunctions sum out to give one so that there are just two cases: the singlet and triplet,

$$
\mathscr{E}_S = \int [\psi_a(1)\psi_b(2)+\psi_a(2)\psi_b(1)]^* V_{ab}[\psi_a(1)\psi_b(2)+\psi_a(2)\psi_b(1)] \, d\tau_1 \, d\tau_2
$$
$$
\mathscr{E}_T = \int [\psi_a(1)\psi_b(2)-\psi_a(2)\psi_b(1)]^* V_{ab}[\psi_a(1)\psi_b(2)-\psi_a(2)\psi_b(1)] \, d\tau_1 \, d\tau_2
\tag{8}
$$

Assuming that ψ_a and ψ_b include appropriate numerical constants so that the ψ are normal and that the overlap between the two atoms is small enough so that ψ_a and ψ_b are essentially orthogonal, we have

$$\mathscr{E}_S = K + J$$
$$\mathscr{E}_T = K - J \tag{9}$$

where K and J are respectively called the Coulomb and exchange energies and are given by

$$K = \int \psi_a^*(1)\psi_a(1)V_{ab}\psi_b^*(2)\psi_b(2)\,d\tau_1\,d\tau_2$$

$$J = \int \psi_a^*(1)\psi_b(2)V_{ab}\psi_a^*(2)\psi_b(1)\,d\tau_1\,d\tau_2 \tag{10}$$

Equation (9) can be written in a convenient form due to Dirac:[3] by the law of cosines we have

$$S^2 = S_1^2 + S_2^2 + 2S_1 \cdot S_2 \tag{11}$$

where S is the total spin. In this discussion it is convenient to express spin in *units of* $\hbar/2$. Thus for the singlet case $S = 0$ and for the triplet case $S^2 = 8$. In each case S_1^2 and S_2^2 are equal to 3. Hence,

$$\mathbf{S}_1 \cdot \mathbf{S}_2 = \begin{cases} -3 \\ 1 \end{cases} \tag{12}$$

for the singlet and triplet cases respectively. Hence for both cases,

$$\mathscr{E} = K - \tfrac{1}{2}(\mathbf{S}_1 \cdot \mathbf{S}_2 + 1)J$$
$$= (K - \tfrac{1}{2}J) - \tfrac{1}{2}J\mathbf{S}_1 \cdot \mathbf{S}_2 \tag{13}$$

If $J > 0$, then lined-up spin will have a lower energy and ferromagnetism will result. This is, in general, the case; see Hund's rules. The first term in Eq. (13) is a constant and will henceforth be neglected as it is not important in ferromagnetism.

4. The Ising Model[1]

We replace $\mathbf{S}_1 \cdot \mathbf{S}_2 = S_{1x}S_{2x} + S_{1y}S_{2y} + S_{1z}S_{2z}$ by $S_{1z}S_{2z}$ where z is the direction of the applied field. This is justified[2] since, according to quantum mechanics, only one component of the spin can be specified. Further we assume that exchange interaction is appreciable only for nearest neighbors. We are thus led to the *Ising model*. Consider a lattice in which a spin capable of two orientations is located at each site. The two orientations of the spin are specified by the value of S_z which is either $+1$ or -1. Including the effect of the external field H, the energy of the system is

$$E = -\tfrac{1}{2}J \sum_{\langle i,j \rangle} S_i S_j - \mu_B H \sum_i S_i \tag{1}$$

[3] P. A. M. Dirac, *Proc. Roy. Soc.* (*London*), **A123**, 174 (1929).
[1] E. Ising, *Z. Physik*, **31**, 253 (1925).
[2] This assumption is not correct at low temperatures. At low temperatures one must use the spin wave method; see F. Bloch, *Z. Physik*, **61**, 206 (1930).

where we have for convenience dropped the subscript z. The notation $\sum\limits_{\langle i, j\rangle}$ means the summation is only over pairs of nearest neighbors. In obtaining Eq. (1) we have assumed that the coupling factor J is the same for all nearest neighbors.

In order to calculate the thermodynamic properties of a ferromagnetic substance we must evaluate the partition function

$$f_N = \sum_{\langle S_i\rangle} \exp\left[\frac{J}{2kT}\sum_{\langle i,j\rangle} S_i S_j + \frac{\mu_B H}{kT}\sum_i S_i\right] \tag{2}$$

where the sum $\sum\limits_{\langle S_i\rangle}$ goes over the 2^N possible combinations of the N spins. This is, in general, an extremely difficult problem and a number of methods of solving this problem have been formulated. The simplest method is the Bragg–Williams approximation.

5. The Bragg–Williams Approximation

Following Bragg and Williams,[1] we assume a random arrangement of the spins. If N_+ is the number of spins for which $S_i = +1$ and N_- the number of spins for which $S_i = -1$ then N_+/N and N_-/N are the probabilities of finding a $+$ or a $-$ spin on a given site. Because of the assumption of random arrangement of spins we have from Eq. (4.1) that

$$E = -\tfrac{1}{4}zNJ\left[\left(\frac{N_+}{N}\right)^2 + \left(\frac{N_-}{N}\right)^2 - \frac{2N_+ N_-}{N^2}\right] - \mu_B H(N_+ - N_-) \tag{1}$$

where z is the number of nearest neighbors of a lattice site and N the number of spins. The magnetic moment is

$$M = \mu_B[N_+ - N_-] \tag{2}$$

assuming that $N_+ > N_-$. N is given by

$$N = N_+ + N_- \tag{3}$$

Solving Eqs. (2) and (3) for N_+/N and N_-/N, we obtain

$$\frac{N_+}{N} = \frac{1}{2}\left[1 + \frac{M}{N\mu_B}\right]$$

$$\frac{N_-}{N} = \frac{1}{2}\left[1 - \frac{M}{N\mu_B}\right] \tag{4}$$

[1] W. Bragg and E. Williams, *Proc. Roy. Soc. (London)*, **A145**, 699 (1934); **A151**, 540 (1935); **A152**, 231 (1935).

Substituting Eqs. (4) into Eq. (1) gives

$$E = -\frac{zJM^2}{4N\mu_B^2} - MH \tag{5}$$

We can calculate the entropy by means of the Boltzmann relation

$$S = k \ln W_{BW} \tag{6}$$

where W_{BW} is the number of arrangements of the spins over the N lattice sites. Thus,

$$W_{BW} = \frac{N!}{N_+! N_-!} \tag{7}$$

Using Stirling's approximation

$$\ln N! = N \ln N - N \tag{8}$$

we obtain from Eqs. (6) and (7)

$$\begin{aligned}
S &= k[N \ln N - N_+ \ln N_+ - N_- \ln N_-] \\
&= k[(N_+ + N_-) \ln N - N_+ \ln N_+ - N_- \ln N_-] \\
&= -k\left[N_+ \ln \frac{N_+}{N} + N_- \ln \frac{N_-}{N}\right] \\
S &= -Nk\left[\frac{N_+}{N} \ln \frac{N_+}{N} + \frac{N_-}{N} \ln \frac{N_-}{N}\right]
\end{aligned} \tag{9}$$

Using Eqs. (4), we obtain

$$S = Nk\left[\ln 2 - \frac{1}{2}\left(1 - \frac{M}{N\mu_B}\right)\ln\left(1 - \frac{M}{N\mu_B}\right) - \frac{1}{2}\left(1 + \frac{M}{N\mu_B}\right)\ln\left(1 + \frac{M}{N\mu_B}\right)\right] \tag{10}$$

Thus

$$A = E - TS = -\frac{zJM^2}{4N\mu_B^2} - MH$$

$$- NkT\left[-\ln 2 + \frac{1}{2}\left(1 - \frac{M}{N\mu_B}\right)\ln\left(1 - \frac{M}{N\mu_B}\right) + \frac{1}{2}\left(1 + \frac{M}{N\mu_B}\right)\ln\left(1 + \frac{M}{N\mu_B}\right)\right] \tag{11}$$

We obtain the equilibrium value of M by requiring that

$$\frac{\partial A}{\partial M} = 0 \tag{12}$$

Differentiating Eq. (11) gives

$$-\frac{zJM}{2N\mu_B^2} - H + NkT\left[-\frac{1}{2N\mu_B}\ln\left(1 - \frac{M}{N\mu_B}\right)\right.$$

$$\left.+ \frac{1}{2N\mu_B}\ln\left(1 + \frac{M}{N\mu_B}\right) - \frac{1}{2N\mu_B} + \frac{1}{2N\mu_B}\right] = 0$$

$$\frac{2\mu_B}{kT}\left(\frac{zJM}{2N\mu_B^2} + H\right) = \ln\frac{1 + M/N\mu_B}{1 - M/N\mu_B}$$

$$\frac{1 + M/N\mu_B}{1 - M/N\mu_B} = e^{2x} \tag{13}$$

where $x = \dfrac{\mu_B}{kT}\left(\dfrac{zJM}{2N\mu_B^2} + H\right)$. Hence

$$M = N\mu_B\frac{e^{2x} - 1}{e^{2x} + 1} = N\mu_B\frac{e^x - e^{-x}}{e^x + e^{-x}} = N\mu_B\tanh x$$

$$= N\mu_B\tanh\frac{\mu_B}{kT}\left(\frac{zJM}{2N\mu_B^2} + H\right) \tag{14}$$

This is the familiar result, Eq. (2.10), from the Weiss theory. Thus we have

$$\lambda = \frac{zJ}{2N\mu_B^2} \tag{15}$$

Let us see if this λ is of the right order of magnitude. We estimate J as

$$J = \int \psi^*\left(\frac{e^2}{r_{12}} + \ldots\right)\psi \, d\tau_1 \, d\tau_2$$

$$\simeq \frac{e^2}{r_{12}} \simeq \frac{10^{-20}}{10^{-8}} \simeq 10^{-12} \text{ ergs}$$

$$\lambda = \frac{10^{-12}}{10^{24} \times 10^{-40}} \simeq 10^4$$

which is of the correct order of magnitude.

Substituting Eq. (15) into Eq. (2.11), we obtain an expression for the Curie temperature

$$T_c = \frac{zJ}{2k} \tag{16}$$

Setting $H = 0$ in Eq. (14) gives the spontaneous magnetic moment, M_s:

$$M_s = N\mu_B\tanh\frac{zJM_s}{2N\mu_B kT} \tag{17}$$

This equation can be solved graphically to give M_s as a function of temperature, giving Figure 1.

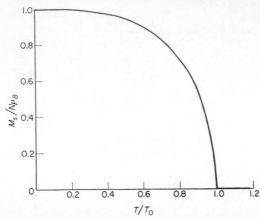

Figure 1. Spontaneous magnetic moment in the Bragg–Williams approximation.

The magnetic specific heat for zero field, C_m, can be obtained by setting $H = 0$ in Eq. (5) and differentiating with respect to T,

$$C_m = \frac{dE}{dT} = -\frac{zJM_s}{2N\mu_B^2}\frac{dM_s}{dT} \tag{18}$$

From Eq. (17) we have

$$\frac{dM_s}{dT} = N\mu_B \left[\operatorname{sech}^2 \frac{zJM_s}{2N\mu_B kT} \right] \left[\frac{zJ}{2N\mu_B kT}\frac{dM_s}{dT} - \frac{zJM_s}{2N\mu_B kT^2} \right]$$

$$= -\frac{zJM_s}{2kT^2} \frac{\operatorname{sech}^2 \dfrac{zJM_s}{2N\mu_B kT}}{1 - \dfrac{zJ}{2kT}\operatorname{sech}^2 \dfrac{zJM_s}{2N\mu_B kT}} \tag{19}$$

Multiplying by $\cosh^2 \dfrac{zJM_s}{2N\mu_B kT}$ and taking note of Eq. (16), we obtain

$$\frac{dM_s}{dT} = -\frac{M_s T_c/T^2}{\cosh^2 \dfrac{M_s T_c}{N\mu_B T} - \dfrac{T_c}{T}} \tag{20}$$

Thus substituting Eq. (20) into Eq. (18) gives

$$\frac{C_m}{Nk} = \frac{(M_s/N\mu_B)^2(T_c/T)^2}{\cosh^2\left\{ \left(\dfrac{M_s}{N\mu_B}\right)\left(\dfrac{T_c}{T}\right) \right\} - \dfrac{T_c}{T}} \tag{21}$$

Reading values of $M_s/N\mu_B$ from Figure 1, we obtain the form of C_m vs. T which is plotted in Figure 2.

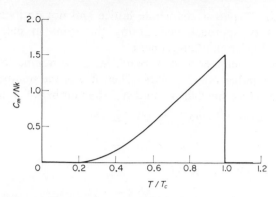

Figure 2. Magnetic specific heat for zero field in the Bragg–Williams approximation.

To see that $C_m = \frac{3}{2}Nk$ at T_c we expand Eq. (17)

$$M_s = N\mu_B \left[\frac{zJM_s}{2N\mu_B kT} - \frac{1}{3}\left(\frac{zJM_s}{2N\mu_B kT}\right)^3 + \ldots \right] \qquad (22)$$

Dividing through by M_s and differentiating, we have

$$0 = \left[-\frac{zJ}{2kT^2} + \left(\frac{zJ}{2k}\right)^3\left(\frac{M_s}{N\mu_B}\right)^2\frac{1}{T^4} \right]dT - \frac{2}{3}\left(\frac{zJ}{2kT}\right)^3\frac{M_s\,dM_s}{(N\mu_B)^2}$$

Rearranging terms gives

$$\left[\left(\frac{zJ}{2kT}\right)^2\left(\frac{M_s}{N\mu_B}\right)^2 - 1 \right] = \frac{2}{3}\left(\frac{zJ}{2kT}\right)^2 T \frac{M_s}{N^2\mu_B^2}\frac{dM_s}{dT} \qquad (23)$$

Noting from Figure 1 that $T/T_c \to 1$ faster than $M_s \to 0$, we have in the region $T \simeq T_c$ since $zJ/2kT_c = 1$, Eq. (16),

$$\frac{dM_s}{dT} = -\frac{N\mu_B^2}{M_s}\frac{3}{2T_c}\left[1 - \left(\frac{M_s}{N\mu_B}\right)^2 + \ldots \right] \qquad (24)$$

which combined with Eq. (18) gives in the limit as $M_s \to 0$

$$C_m = \frac{3}{2}Nk \qquad (25)$$

In the next section we shall find that a one-dimensional linear lattice ($z = 2$) cannot be ferromagnetic. In the Bragg–Williams approximation, however, this result is not obtained and therefore the method must be regarded as unsatisfactory.

6. The Quasi-chemical Approximation

The Bragg–Williams approximation is not entirely satisfactory. One weakness of the approach is its macroscopic character. In obtaining Eq. (5.1) it was assumed that the energy of a spin depended upon the distribution of $+$ and $-$ spins in the whole lattice and not on its neighbors. A more satisfactory approach considering the spins in detail has been developed by Fowler and Guggenheim.[1]

Let N_{++} be the number of $++$ pairs, N_{--} the number of $--$ pairs, and N_{+-} the number of $+-$ pairs. Then if z is the number of nearest neighbors of a lattice site and N_+ and N_- the number of $+$ and $-$ spins,

$$2N_{++} + N_{+-} = zN_+$$

$$2N_{--} + N_{+-} = zN_- \tag{1}$$

Solving for N_{++} and N_{--} gives

$$N_{++} = \frac{zN_+ - N_{+-}}{2}$$

$$N_{--} = \frac{zN_- - N_{+-}}{2} \tag{2}$$

The total number of pairs, P, is given by

$$P = N_{++} + N_{--} + N_{+-} = \tfrac{1}{2}zN \tag{3}$$

where N is the total number of spins. We want N_{++}, N_{--}, and N_{+-} in terms of N_+ and N_- and hence in terms of N and M. To do this one more expression is needed. The approximation consists in assuming that all the spin pairs are independent even though we can see from Eqs. (1) that they are not. This approximation is called quasi-chemical since it treats the pairs as independent chemical bonds. On this assumption a $++$ pair and a $--$ pair combine to form two $+-$ pairs according to the 'reaction':

$$[++] + [--] \to 2[+-]$$

We have by analogy with chemical equilibrium (Sect. 1.7)[2]

$$\frac{N_{++}N_{--}}{(N_{+-})^2} = \tfrac{1}{4}e^{2J/kT} = \frac{x^2}{4} \tag{4}$$

since $2J$ is the energy change in the reaction and a factor of 2^2 is needed

[1] R. H. Fowler and E. A. Guggenheim, *Proc. Roy. Soc.* (*London*), **A174**, 189 (1940).
[2] The equivalent expression in the Bragg–Williams approximation is

$$\frac{N_{++}\,N_{--}}{(N_{+-})^2} = \frac{\left(\dfrac{N_+}{N}\right)^2 \left(\dfrac{N_-}{N}\right)^2}{\left(2\dfrac{N_+\,N_-}{N^2}\right)^2} = \frac{1}{4}$$

since N_+/N and N_-/N are, in the Bragg–Williams approximation, the probabilities of finding a $+$ or a $-$ spin on a given site.

because of the unsymmetric $+-$ 'bond'. Thus substituting Eqs. (2) into Eq. (4) gives

$$\frac{(zN_+ - N_{+-})(zN_- - N_{+-})}{(N_{+-})^2} = x^2$$

$$\frac{z^2 N_+ N_- - zN_{+-} N + (N_{+-})^2}{(N_{+-})^2} = x^2 \tag{5}$$

Substituting Eqs. (5.4) into Eq. (5) gives

$$(x^2 - 1)N_{+-}^2 + (zN)N_{+-} - \tfrac{1}{4}z^2 N^2(1 - m^2) = 0 \tag{6}$$

where $m = M/N\mu_B$. Solving for N_{+-} yields

$$N_{+-} = zN \frac{-1 + \sqrt{1 + (1 - m^2)(x^2 - 1)}}{2(x^2 - 1)}$$

$$= zN \frac{\alpha - 1}{2(x^2 - 1)} = \frac{zN}{2} \frac{1 - m^2}{\alpha + 1} \tag{7}$$

where the abbreviation

$$\alpha = \sqrt{1 + (1 - m^2)(x^2 - 1)} \tag{8}$$

has been introduced. Thus if Eqs. (2) and Eqs. (5.4) are coupled with Eq. (7) we have

$$N_{++} = \frac{zN}{4}\left[(1 + m) - \frac{1 - m^2}{\alpha + 1}\right]$$

$$N_{--} = \frac{zN}{4}\left[(1 - m) - \frac{1 - m^2}{\alpha + 1}\right] \tag{9}$$

If we concern ourselves only with the spontaneous magnetic moment then the energy of the system is

$$E = -\tfrac{1}{2}J \sum_{\langle i, j \rangle} S_i S_j = -\tfrac{1}{2}J[N_{++} + N_{--} - N_{+-}]$$

$$= -J \frac{zN}{4}\left[1 - 2\frac{1 - m^2}{\alpha + 1}\right] \tag{10}$$

The last equality was obtained by substituting the values of N_{++}, N_{--}, and N_{+-} from Eqs. (7) and (9). The Helmholtz function is given by

$$A = E - TS = -kT \ln f_N$$

But unfortunately the calculation of S is algebraically involved and so we shall use a less direct but easier method. We define E' by

$$A = E' - kT \ln W_{BW} = -kT \ln f_N \tag{11}$$

where W_{BW} is given by Eq. (5.7). Now

$$E = -k \frac{\partial \ln f}{\partial (1/T)} = \frac{\partial (E'/T)}{\partial (1/T)}$$

$$E' = T \int_0^{1/T} E \, d\left(\frac{1}{T}\right) \tag{12}$$

since $E' = 0$ when $1/T = 0$.

Referring to the definition of α, Eq. (8), solving for x^2, and using the definition of x, Eq. (4), we obtain

$$\frac{2J}{kT} = \ln\left(1 + \frac{\alpha^2 - 1}{1 - m^2}\right) = \ln \frac{\alpha^2 - m^2}{1 - m^2} \tag{13}$$

Differentiating gives

$$d\left(\frac{1}{T}\right) = \frac{k}{J} \frac{\alpha \, d\alpha}{\alpha^2 - m^2} \tag{14}$$

Thus, Eq. (12) becomes

$$E' = -\frac{zNkT}{4} \int_1^\alpha \left(1 - 2\frac{1 - m^2}{\alpha + 1}\right) \frac{\alpha \, d\alpha}{\alpha^2 - m^2}$$

$$= -\frac{zNkT}{4} \int_1^\alpha \left(\frac{2}{\alpha + 1} + \frac{m - \frac{1}{2}}{\alpha - m} - \frac{m + \frac{1}{2}}{\alpha + m}\right) d\alpha$$

$$= -\frac{zNkT}{4} \left[2\ln\frac{\alpha + 1}{2} + (m - \tfrac{1}{2})\ln\frac{\alpha - m}{1 - m} - (m + \tfrac{1}{2})\ln\frac{\alpha + m}{1 + m}\right] \tag{15}$$

$$= -\frac{zNkT}{4} \left[2\ln\frac{\alpha + 1}{2} + (m - 1)\ln\frac{\alpha - m}{1 - m}\right.$$

$$\left. - (m + 1)\ln\frac{\alpha + m}{1 + m} + \tfrac{1}{2}\ln\frac{\alpha^2 - m^2}{1 - m^2}\right]$$

Referring to Eq. (13) we have

$$E' = -\frac{zNkT}{4} \left[2\ln\frac{\alpha + 1}{2} + (m - 1)\ln\frac{m - \alpha}{m - 1} - (m + 1)\ln\frac{m + \alpha}{m + 1} + \frac{J}{kT}\right] \tag{16}$$

Substituting $kT \ln W_{BW}$ as given by Eq. (5.10) and E' as given by Eq. (16) into Eq. (11) we obtain

$$A = \tfrac{1}{2}NkT \left[(1 + m)\ln(1 + m) + (1 - m)\ln(1 - m) - 2\ln 2\right.$$

$$\left. + \frac{z}{2}\left\{(1 + m)\ln\frac{\alpha + m}{1 + m} + (1 - m)\ln\frac{\alpha - m}{1 - m} - 2\ln\frac{\alpha + 1}{2} - \frac{J}{kT}\right\}\right] \tag{17}$$

At equilibrium $\partial A/\partial m = 0$ and so

$$
\ln \frac{1+m}{1-m} + \frac{z}{2}\left\{ \ln \frac{\alpha+m}{\alpha-m} - \ln \frac{1+m}{1-m} + \frac{1+m}{\alpha+m}\left(1 + \frac{d\alpha}{dm}\right) \right.
$$
$$
\left. - \frac{1-m}{\alpha-m}\left(1 - \frac{d\alpha}{dm}\right) - \frac{2}{\alpha+1}\frac{d\alpha}{dm} \right\} = 0 \quad (18)
$$

But

$$
\alpha = \sqrt{1+(1-m^2)(x^2-1)}
$$
$$
\frac{d\alpha}{dm} = \frac{1-x^2}{\alpha}\, m = \frac{m}{\alpha}\left(\frac{1-\alpha^2}{1-m^2}\right) \quad (19)
$$

Substituting Eq. (19) into Eq. (18) gives

$$
\left(1 - \frac{z}{2}\right)\ln \frac{1+m}{1-m} + \frac{z}{2}\ln \frac{\alpha+m}{\alpha-m} = 0 \quad (20)
$$

This equation always has the one root $m = 0$. At sufficiently low temperatures there is also a non-zero root. At the Curie temperature the two roots merge into the single root $m = 0$. Thus the Curie temperature is determined by the conditions,

$$
m = 0, \qquad \frac{\partial A}{\partial m} = 0, \qquad \frac{\partial^2 A}{\partial m^2} = 0 \quad (21)
$$

Differentiating Eq. (20) gives

$$
\left(1 - \frac{z}{2}\right)\left(\frac{1}{1+m} + \frac{1}{1-m}\right) + \frac{z}{2}\left(\frac{1}{\alpha+m} + \frac{1}{\alpha-m}\right) = 0 \quad (22)
$$

Since α is seen to equal x for $m = 0$ (see Eq. (8)), we have for $m = 0$

$$
\frac{z}{z-2} = \alpha = x = e^{J/kT_c}
$$
$$
\frac{J}{kT_c} = \ln \frac{z}{z-2} \quad (23)
$$

For a one-dimensional linear lattice ($z = 2$) the assumption that the spin pairs are independent is rigorously correct and therefore the quasi-chemical approximation is exact for this case. In particular we see from Eq. (23) that for $z = 2$, $T_c = 0$ and hence a one-dimensional linear lattice cannot be ferromagnetic. This result was first obtained by Ising.[3]

Earlier Bethe[4] using a different approach obtained these same results. The equivalence of his method and the quasi-chemical approach has been demonstrated by Chang.[5] The methods of Fowler and Guggenheim how-

[3] E. Ising, *Z. Physik*, **31**, 253 (1925).
[4] H. Bethe, *Proc. Roy. Soc. (London)*, **A150**, 552 (1935).
[5] T. Chang, *Proc. Cambridge Phil. Soc.*, **35**, 265 (1939).

ever have the advantage of being more easily applicable to complicated problems in alloys. For this reason we shall not consider Bethe's method further.

7. Kirkwood's Method[1]

In the absence of an applied field the partition function is

$$f_N = \sum_{\langle S_i \rangle} \exp\left(\frac{J}{2kT} \sum_{\langle i, j \rangle} S_i S_j\right) \tag{1}$$

which coupled with Eq. (6.11) gives

$$\frac{E'}{kT} = -\ln\left[\frac{1}{W_{BW}} \sum_{\langle S_i \rangle} e^y\right] \tag{2}$$

where $y = \dfrac{J}{2kT} \sum_{\langle i, j \rangle} S_i S_j$. Expanding the exponential gives

$$\frac{E'}{kT} = -\ln\left[1 + \langle y \rangle + \frac{\langle y^2 \rangle}{2!} + \frac{\langle y^3 \rangle}{3!} + \ldots\right] \tag{3}$$

where

$$\langle y^n \rangle = \frac{1}{W_{BW}} \sum_{\langle S_i \rangle} y^n \tag{4}$$

Expanding the logarithm yields

$$-\frac{E'}{kT} = \langle y \rangle + \frac{1}{2!}\{\langle y^2 \rangle - \langle y \rangle^2\} + \frac{1}{3!}\{\langle y^3 \rangle - 3\langle y^2 \rangle\langle y \rangle + 2\langle y \rangle^3\} \tag{5}$$

The problem has thus been reduced to calculating the $\langle y^n \rangle$. Although in principle this can be done for any n and for any lattice, the process is laborious, but it has been done for $n \leq 4$ for a simple cubic or square lattice.[2] The result of these calculations is

$$-\frac{E'}{NkT} = \frac{z}{2}\left\{\left(\frac{J}{2kT}\right)m^2 + \frac{1}{2}\left(\frac{J}{2kT}\right)^2(1-m^2)^2 + \frac{2}{3}\left(\frac{J}{2kT}\right)^3 m^2(1-m^2)\right.$$

$$\left. + \frac{1}{12}\left(\frac{J}{2kT}\right)^4(1-m^2)^2\{(3z-9)(1-m^2)^2 + 2(1-3m^2)^2\} + \ldots\right\} \tag{6}$$

---

[1] J. Kirkwood, *J. Chem. Phys.*, **6**, 70 (1938).

[2] D. ter Haar, *Elements of Statistical Mechanics*, Rinehart, New York, 1954, pp. 274–279. For higher order terms for more complex lattices see E. A. Guggenheim, *Mixtures*, Oxford University Press, 1952.

Hence Helmholtz's function is given by

$$A = \frac{NkT}{2}\left[(1+m)\ln(1+m)+(1-m)\ln(1-m)-2\ln 2\right.$$

$$-z\left\{\left(\frac{J}{2kT}\right)m^2+\frac{1}{2}\left(\frac{J}{2kT}\right)^2(1-m^2)^2+\frac{2}{3}\left(\frac{J}{2kT}\right)^3 m^2(1-m^2)\right.$$

$$\left.\left.+\frac{1}{12}\left(\frac{J}{2kT}\right)^4(1-m^2)^2\{(3z-9)(1-m^2)^2+2(1-3m^2)^2\}+\ldots\right\}\right] \quad (7)$$

The equilibrium value of m is given by $\partial A/\partial m = 0$,

$$\ln\frac{1+m}{1-m} = zm\left[\frac{J}{kT}-\frac{1}{2!}\left(\frac{J}{kT}\right)^2(1-m^2)+\frac{1}{3!}\left(\frac{J}{kT}\right)^3(1-m^2)(1-3m^2)\right.$$

$$\left.-\frac{1}{4!}\left(\frac{J}{kT}\right)^4(1-m^2)\{(3z-9)(1-m^2)^2+2(1-3m^2)(2-3m^2)\}+\ldots\right]$$

$$(8)$$

The Curie temperature is found from Eqs. (6.21). Differentiating Eq. (8) and setting $m = 0$ gives

$$\frac{2}{z} = \frac{J}{kT_c}-\frac{1}{2!}\left(\frac{J}{kT_c}\right)^2+\frac{1}{3!}\left(\frac{J}{kT_c}\right)^3-(3z-5)\frac{1}{4!}\left(\frac{J}{kT_c}\right)^4+\ldots \quad (9)$$

Despite the fact that we can solve the problem to any degree of accuracy by including a sufficient number of terms in the above series the usefulness of this method is limited by the fact that these series converge slowly for $T < T_c$.

Let us compare Eq. (9) with the corresponding equations in the Bragg–Williams and quasi-chemical approximations

$$\text{B.W.} \quad \frac{2}{z} = \frac{J}{kT_c} \quad (10)$$

$$\text{Q.C.} \quad \frac{2}{z} = 1-e^{-J/kT_c} = \frac{J}{kT_c}-\frac{1}{2!}\left(\frac{J}{kT_c}\right)^2+\frac{1}{3!}\left(\frac{J}{kT_c}\right)^3-\frac{1}{4!}\left(\frac{J}{kT_c}\right)^4+\ldots$$

$$(11)$$

The Bragg–Williams approximation agrees with Kirkwood's series only in the first term whereas the quasi-chemical approximation agrees with Kirkwood's result in the first three terms. A further comparison of the three approaches can be obtained from the results[3] for a simple cubic lattice shown in Figures 1 and 2.

[3] F. Nix and W. Shockley, *Rev. Mod. Phys.*, **10**, 1 (1938).

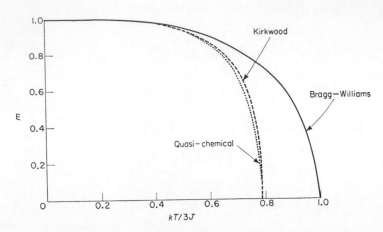

Figure 1. Spontaneous magnetic moment of a simple cubic lattice according to the various approximations.

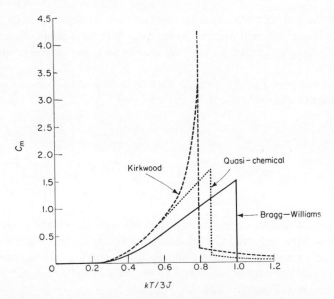

Figure 2. Magnetic specific heat of a simple cubic lattice for zero field according to the various approximations.

8. The Matrix Method[1, 2, 3]

Consider a one-dimensional cyclic chain composed of N spins. The partition function for the system is

$$f_N = \sum_{\langle s_i \rangle} \exp\{K(s_1 s_2 + s_2 s_3 + \ldots + s_N s_1) + I(s_1 + \ldots + s_N)\} \qquad (1)$$

where $K = J/2kT$, $I = \mu_B H/kT$, and the summation is over all possible values of the s_i. The terms which involve s_2 and its nearest neighbors are

$$\sum_{s_2 = \pm 1} \exp\{K(s_1 s_2) + \tfrac{1}{2}I(s_1 + s_2)\} \exp\{K(s_2 s_3) + \tfrac{1}{2}I(s_2 + s_3)\} \qquad (2)$$

This can be considered as the product of the row matrix

$$(\exp\{Ks_1 + \tfrac{1}{2}I(s_1 + 1)\}, \exp\{Ks_1 + \tfrac{1}{2}I(s_1 - 1)\}) \qquad (3)$$

and the column matrix

$$\begin{pmatrix} \exp\{Ks_3 + \tfrac{1}{2}I(1 + s_3)\} \\ \exp\{-Ks_3 + \tfrac{1}{2}I(-1 + s_3)\} \end{pmatrix} \qquad (4)$$

Since s_1 itself can be regarded as an operator which can take on two values, ± 1, we can consider Eq. (3) as a 2×2 matrix, $A(1, 2)$, whose rows are characterized by the value of s_1 and whose columns are characterized by the value of s_2, i.e.

$$A(1, 2) = \begin{pmatrix} e^{K+I} & e^{-K} \\ e^{-K} & e^{K-I} \end{pmatrix} \qquad (5)$$

Similarly s_3 can take on two values and so Eq. (4) can be regarded as a 2×2 matrix, $A(2, 3)$, whose rows are characterized by the value of s_2 and whose columns are characterized by the value of s_3. Since $A(1, 2) = A(2, 1) = \ldots = A(N, 1) = A$ we have

$$f_N = \sum_{\langle s_i \rangle} A(1, 2)A(2, 3)\ldots A(N, 1)$$

$$= \text{trace } A^N \qquad (6)$$

This expression can be evaluated by diagonalizing A^N. If λ_i are the eigenvalues of A then λ_i^N can easily be seen to be the eigenvalues of A^N. Solving for the eigenvalues of A, we have

$$\begin{vmatrix} e^{K+I} - \lambda & e^{-K} \\ e^{-K} & e^{K-I} - \lambda \end{vmatrix} = 0$$

$$\lambda^2 - 2\lambda e^K \cosh I + e^{2K} - e^{-2K} = 0$$

$$\lambda_{1, 2} = e^K \cosh I \pm \sqrt{e^{2K} \cosh^2 I - e^{2K} + e^{-2K}}$$

$$= e^K \cosh I \pm \sqrt{e^{2K} \sinh^2 I + e^{-2K}} \qquad (7)$$

[1] H. Kramers and G. Wannier, *Phys. Rev.*, **60**, 252, 263 (1941).
[2] E. Lassettre and J. Howe, *J. Chem. Phys.*, **9**, 747, 801 (1941).
[3] E. Montroll and J. Mayer, *J. Chem. Phys.*, **9**, 626 (1941).

Therefore,

$$f_N = \lambda_1^N + \lambda_2^N$$

$$f_N = \left\{ e^{J/2kT} \cosh \frac{\mu_B H}{kT} + \sqrt{e^{J/kT} \sinh^2 \frac{\mu_B H}{kT} + e^{-J/kT}} \right\}^N$$

$$+ \left\{ e^{J/2kT} \cosh \frac{\mu_B H}{kT} - \sqrt{e^{J/kT} \sinh^2 \frac{\mu_B H}{kT} + e^{-J/kT}} \right\}^N \quad (8)$$

an exact result which could have been obtained by a direct summation of Eq. (1). If N is large and if $|\lambda_2| < |\lambda_1|$ then we have

$$f_N = \lambda_1^N = \left\{ e^{J/2kT} \cosh \frac{\mu_B H}{kT} + \sqrt{e^{J/kT} \sinh^2 \frac{\mu_B H}{kT} + e^{-J/kT}} \right\}^N \quad (9)$$

and for $H = 0$ the partition function becomes

$$f_N = \left(2 \cosh \frac{J}{2kT} \right)^N \quad (10)$$

We can calculate the magnetic moment M by

$$M = kT \frac{\partial \ln f}{\partial H}$$

$$= N\mu_B \frac{e^{J/2kT} \sinh \frac{\mu_B H}{kT}}{\sqrt{e^{J/kT} \sinh^2 \frac{\mu_B H}{kT} + e^{-J/kT}}} \quad (11)$$

We note that $M = 0$ if $H = 0$, which means that the lattice is not ferromagnetic.

9. Exact Solution for a Two-Dimensional Square Lattice

Kramers and Wannier[1] extended the matrix method to include two-dimensional lattices in the limit of large N for the case of no magnetic field. They obtained the exact value of the Curie temperature and an approximate expression for the partition function by a variational method. A few years later Onsager[2] obtained an exact expression for the partition function by a long and sophisticated argument. Kaufman[3] by using spinors and the theory of Lie Algebras has considerably simplified Onsager's analysis. A second method due to Kac and Ward[4] has been developed

1 H. Kramers and G. Wannier, *Phys. Rev.*, **60**, 252, 263 (1941); see also G. Wannier, *Rev. Mod. Phys.*, **17**, 50 (1945).
2 L. Onsager, *Phys. Rev.*, **65**, 117 (1944).
3 B. Kaufman, *Phys. Rev.*, **76**, 1232 (1949).
4 M. Kac and J. Ward, *Phys. Rev.*, **88**, 1332 (1952).

which involves no specialized algebraic techniques of the type used in the matrix method but introduces some unsolved problems in topology.

Because of the difficulties of the two-dimensional problem we shall omit derivations and limit ourselves to a discussion of the results for a square lattice. As in the one-dimensional problem the partition function is given by

$$f_N = \lambda_1^N \tag{1}$$

where λ_1 is the largest eigenvalue of an appropriate matrix and N the number of spins. The partition function turns out to be given by

$$\ln f_N = N\left[\ln\left\{2\cosh\frac{J}{kT}\right\} + \frac{1}{2\pi}\int_0^\pi \ln\left\{\frac{1+(1-\kappa^2\sin^2\phi)^{\frac{1}{2}}}{2}\right\}d\phi\right] \tag{2}$$

where

$$\kappa = \frac{2\sinh J/kT}{\cosh^2 J/kT} \tag{3}$$

κ is zero for $T = 0$ and ∞ and has a maximum value of unity when $\sinh J/kT = 1$. Hence there is a real Curie temperature given by

$$\sinh\frac{J}{kT_c} = 1 \tag{4}$$

The specific heat is plotted against temperature in Figure 1 and is noted to be logarithmically infinite at T_c.

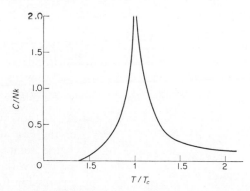

Figure 1. Specific heat of a two-dimensional square lattice.

Yang[5] has calculated the spontaneous magnetic moment of a square lattice and has obtained

$$M_s = N\mu_B\left[\frac{\cosh^2 J/kT}{\sinh^4 J/kT}\left\{\sinh^2\frac{J}{kT} - 1\right\}\right]^{\frac{1}{8}} \tag{5}$$

[5] C. N. Yang, *Phys. Rev.*, **85**, 809 (1952).

for $T < T_c$, and $M_s = 0$ for $T \geqslant T_c$. Equation (5) is plotted in Figure 2.

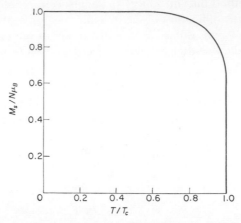

Figure 2. Spontaneous magnetic moment of a two-dimensional square lattice. (After C. N. Yang.[5])

For a summary of the properties of other two-dimensional lattices, such as rectangular and hexagonal lattices, the reader is referred to the comprehensive review of Newell and Montroll.[6]

As of yet no exact solution for a three-dimensional lattice has been obtained. However it has been possible to obtain series expansions for the partition function for high and low temperatures.[7]

The approach outlined in the preceding sections is based on the Heitler–London method, which supposes that the electrons responsible for ferromagnetism always remain on the same atom. Bloch,[8] Slater,[9] and especially Stoner[10] have had considerable success in explaining ferromagnetism by assuming the electrons responsible for ferromagnetism to be free. This approach is called the *collective electron theory of ferromagnetism.* In spite of the different bases of the two approaches they yield substantially the same information. This strengthens the belief that the truth lies somewhere between the two extreme views. For a review of the current status of the collective theory and other theories of ferromagnetism the reader is referred to the papers of Kittel, Zener, Heikes, Slater, Wohlfarth, and van Vleck at the Symposium on Exchange held at the Washington Conference on Magnetism.[11]

6 G. Newell and E. Montroll, *Rev. Mod. Phys.*, **25**, 353 (1953).

7 A. Wakefield, *Proc. Cambridge Phil. Soc.*, **47**, 419, 799 (1951).

8 F. Bloch, *Z. Physik*, **57**, 545 (1939).

9 J. C. Slater, *Phys. Rev.*, **49**, 537, 931 (1936); **52**, 198 (1937).

10 E. Stoner, *Proc. Roy. Soc. (London)*, **A165**, 372 (1938); **A169**, 339 (1939).

11 *Rev. Mod. Phys.*, **25** (1953).

10. Antiferromagnetism

Thus far we have discussed the case in which the exchange integral J is positive. If J is negative, then at low enough temperatures neighboring spins will tend to an antiparallel orientation. When this is the case, the substance is said to be *antiferromagnetic*. Antiferromagnetism was first investigated theoretically by Néel[1] and later discovered experimentally as a property of MnO.[2] The magnetic susceptibility of MnO is plotted in Figure 1.

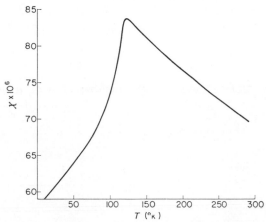

Figure 1. Magnetic susceptibility of MnO measured in a 5000 oersted field.[2]

The peak temperature is called the Néel temperature, T_N. Above T_N the substance is paramagnetic and below T_N the substance is antiferromagnetic.

The simplest case of antiferromagnetism arises in the so-called *two sublattice model* in which the entire lattice can be divided into two equivalent sublattices A and B such that all the nearest neighbors of an A lattice site are B lattice sites. This can be done for a simple cubic and a body centered cubic lattice, shown in Figure 2, but not for a face centered lattice.

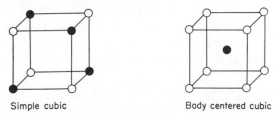

Simple cubic   Body centered cubic

Figure 2. A simple cubic lattice (left) and a body centered cubic lattice (right).

[1] L. Néel, *Ann. Phys.*, **18**, 5 (1932); **5**, 232 (1936).
[2] H. Bizette, C. Squire and B. Tsai, *C. R. Acad. Sci., Paris*, **207**, 449 (1938).

Consider a unit volume of the substance. If the only interactions are anti-ferromagnetic AB, AA, and BB interactions, then we have in the Weiss internal field approximation that the magnetic fields at an A and a B site are, respectively,

$$\mathbf{H}_A = \mathbf{H} - \alpha\mathbf{M}_A - \beta\mathbf{M}_B \tag{1}$$

$$\mathbf{H}_B = \mathbf{H} - \beta\mathbf{M}_A - \alpha\mathbf{M}_B$$

where α and β are positive Weiss constants and $\mathbf{M}_A$ and $\mathbf{M}_B$ are the magnetic moments of the A and B lattices.

For high enough temperatures, thermal agitation would overcome the antiparallel ordering and we would expect paramagnetism. Thus

$$\mathbf{M}_A = \frac{N\mu^2}{3kT}\mathbf{H}_A, \qquad \mathbf{M}_B = \frac{N\mu^2}{3kT}\mathbf{H}_B \tag{2}$$

where $\mu = \mu_B g\sqrt{J(J+1)}$ and N is the number of A or B sites per unit volume. Thus

$$\mathbf{M} = \mathbf{M}_A + \mathbf{M}_B = \frac{N\mu^2}{3kT}\{2\mathbf{H} - (\alpha+\beta)\mathbf{M}\} \tag{3}$$

$$\mathbf{M} = \frac{2N\mu^2/3k}{T + \dfrac{N\mu^2}{3k}(\alpha+\beta)}\mathbf{H} = \frac{c}{T+\theta}\mathbf{H} \tag{4}$$

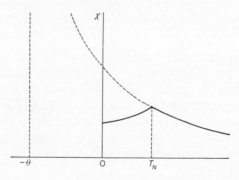

Figure 3. χ as a function of T for the two sublattice model.

For $T < T_N$, $\mathbf{M}_A$ and $\mathbf{M}_B$ are not zero even if $H = 0$ and if we are in the region of T_N we are still far away from saturation effects. Hence,

$$\mathbf{M}_A = -\frac{N\mu^2}{3kT_N}(\alpha\mathbf{M}_A + \beta\mathbf{M}_B)$$

$$\mathbf{M}_B = -\frac{N\mu^2}{3kT_N}(\beta\mathbf{M}_A + \alpha\mathbf{M}_B) \tag{5}$$

or

$$\mathbf{M}_A \left[1 + \alpha \frac{N\mu^2}{3kT_N} \right] + \mathbf{M}_B \left[\beta \frac{N\mu^2}{3kT_N} \right] = 0$$

$$\mathbf{M}_A \left[\beta \frac{N\mu^2}{3kT_N} \right] + \mathbf{M}_B \left[1 + \alpha \frac{N\mu^2}{3kT_N} \right] = 0$$

(6)

The necessary and sufficient condition that there exists a non-trival solution for $\mathbf{M}_A$ and $\mathbf{M}_B$ is that the determinant of the coefficients vanish. Thus,

$$1 + \alpha \frac{N\mu^2}{3kT_N} = \beta \frac{N\mu^2}{3kT_N}$$

$$T_N = (\beta - \alpha) \frac{N\mu^2}{3k}$$

(7)

The magnetic susceptibility is plotted in Figure 3 as a function of the temperature for the two sublattice model. We note that

$$\frac{T_N}{\theta} = \frac{\beta - \alpha}{\beta + \alpha}$$

(8)

If we considered only nearest neighbor interactions, i.e. set $\alpha = 0$, we would have $T_N = \theta$. However, as can be seen in Table 1, $T_N \neq \theta$ and therefore the AA and BB interactions must be included.

TABLE 1. T_N and θ for selected antiferromagnetics[3]

	T_N	θ
MnO	122	610
MnS	165	528
MnF$_2$	72	113
FeO	198	570

11. Order–Disorder Transformations in Alloys

Consider a binary alloy AB. The alloy is said to be *ordered* if A and B are in a regular periodic arrangement and *disordered* otherwise. A common ordered arrangement is one in which all the A atoms have B atoms as nearest neighbors. We shall consider such a case. Choose one arbitrary lattice site and call it an α-site. Call each of its nearest neighbors β-sites and continue the process until an α and a β sublattice have been formed. In a state of complete order all the A atoms will be on α-sites and all the B atoms will be on β-sites. Define s_i to be $+1$ for a site occupied by an

[3] A. Lidiard, *Rept. Progr. Phys.*, **17**, 201 (1954).

A atom and -1 for a site occupied by a B atom. Then if w_{AA}, w_{BB}, and w_{AB} are the energies associated with AA, BB, and AB pairs then

$$E = w_{AA}N_{AA} + w_{BB}N_{BB} + w_{AB}N_{AB} \tag{1}$$

Let us define J by

$$J = \tfrac{1}{2}(w_{AA} + w_{BB}) - w_{AB} \tag{2}$$

Hence

$$E = \tfrac{1}{2}P(w_{AA} + w_{BB}) - JN_{AB} + \text{constant} \tag{3}$$

where P is the total number of pairs. Also,

$$\sum_{\langle i,j \rangle} s_i s_j = N_{AA} + N_{BB} - N_{AB}$$

$$= P - 2N_{AB} \tag{4}$$

So,

$$E = \tfrac{1}{2}J \sum_{\langle i,j \rangle} s_i s_j + \text{constant} \tag{5}$$

which is of the same form as Eq. (4.1). Order–disorder transformations in binary alloys can thus be put within the framework of the Ising model.[1] The analogue of the spontaneous magnetization is called the *long range order parameter* $\mathscr{S}$ and so by replacing $M_s/N\mu_B$ by $\mathscr{S}$ in the preceding sections one gains a description of order–disorder transitions.

Recently Yang and Lee have formulated the process of sublimation of a solid so that it can be treated on the basis of the Ising model.[2]

[1] F. Nix and W. Shockley, *Rev. Mod. Phys.*, **10**, 1 (1938).
[2] C. N. Yang and T. D. Lee, *Phys. Rev.*, **87**, 404 (1952).

11

REAL GASES

1. Introduction; ortho- and para-Hydrogen

A fairly complete discussion of perfect gases has been given in preceding chapters. The translational partition function was discussed in Sect. 1.4, the rotational partition functions were derived in Sects. 1.5 and 2.6, the vibrational partition function was derived in Sect. 1.6, and gaseous equilibrium was discussed in Sect. 1.7. The determination of the normal modes of vibration of a polyatomic molecule was illustrated in Sect. 2.7. Some of these results were rederived from the point of view of ensemble theory in Chapter 4. Finally, gases of indistinguishable particles without interparticle interactions were considered in Chapter 5.

In the present chapter we shall first consider ortho- and para-hydrogen and then hindered internal rotation in ethane, subjects which might equally well be included in a discussion of perfect gases. Then we shall treat a monatomic, one-component, imperfect gas, i.e. one in which intermolecular forces cannot be neglected. This will require a discussion of virial coefficients and cluster integrals. We are indebted to works by J. E. Mayer and T. L. Hill for much of this portion of our discussion. Having derived equations of state for imperfect gases in terms of the activity and the gas density, we shall turn our attention briefly to semi-empirical equations of state that bridge the first-order transition between the gaseous and the liquid critical phenomena, and the law of corresponding states.

The specific heat of gaseous hydrogen was first measured by Eucken[1] in 1912. A straightforward quantum mechanical calculation of the rotational specific heat of the diatomic hydrogen molecules yields values which are considerably in excess of the experimental results. This error cannot be due to a neglect of other energy contributions since, if this were the case, the theoretical values of the specific heat would be less than the experimental values. In 1926, Heisenberg[2] and Hund[3] pointed out that, because of the Pauli principle, the hydrogen molecule must be antisym-

---

[1] A. Eucken, *Sitzber. Preuss. Akad. Wiss.*, **1912**, 41.
[2] W. Heisenberg, *Z. Physik*, **41**, 239 (1927).
[3] F. Hund, *Z. Physik*, **42**, 93 (1927).

metric in the two identical hydrogen atoms. The vibrational and electronic wave functions are symmetric in the ground state (which is the only state which need be considered). The spin wave function is symmetric or anti-symmetric when the total spin is one (parallel spins) or zero (antiparallel spins). The state with $S = 0$ is called the *para* state and the state with $S = 1$ is called the *ortho* state. The rotational wave function is symmetric or antisymmetric for even or odd rotational quantum numbers[4] and there-fore, since the total wave function must be antisymmetric, only the follow-ing combinations are possible:

$$S = 0, \qquad j = 0, 2, 4, \ldots$$
$$S = 1, \qquad j = 1, 3, 5, \ldots \tag{1}$$

If ρ is the nuclear spin degeneracy of one of the two identical nuclei, where ψ_i are the corresponding degenerate eigenfunctions, then it is possible to form $\frac{1}{2}\rho(\rho-1)$ antisymmetric combinations of the type $\psi_i(1)\,\psi_j(2) - \psi_i(2)\,\psi_j(1)$, $\frac{1}{2}\rho(\rho-1)$ symmetric combinations of the type $\psi_i(1)\,\psi_j(2) + \psi_i(2)\,\psi_j(1)$, and ρ symmetric combinations of the type $\psi_i(1)\,\psi_i(2)$. Hence, there are $\frac{1}{2}\rho(\rho-1)$ antisymmetric eigenfunctions and $\frac{1}{2}\rho(\rho+1)$ symmetric eigenfunctions for the nuclear spins of the molecule.

For hydrogen $\rho = 2(\frac{1}{2}) + 1 = 2$. Therefore, $\frac{1}{2}\rho(\rho-1) = 1$ and $\frac{1}{2}\rho(\rho+1) = 3$. If these nuclear spin weight factors are included in the rotational partition functions, then the rotational partition functions for ortho- and para-hydrogen are, respectively

$$f_r^o = 3 \sum_{j=1,3}^{\infty} (2j+1)\, e^{-j(j+1)\theta_r/T}$$
$$f_r^p = \sum_{j=0,2}^{\infty} (2j+1)\, e^{-j(j+1)\theta_r/T} \tag{2}$$

where

$$\theta_r = \frac{h^2}{8\pi^2 I k}$$

This division into ortho and para states successfully explains the alternating intensity in the molecular spectrum of hydrogen. However, the rotational specific heat of hydrogen was not explained until Dennison[5] postulated that interchanges between ortho and para states did not take place freely but that, even at low temperatures, the high temperature equilibrium proportions remain 'frozen' so that hydrogen behaves as a mixture of two substances. The rotational partition function of hydrogen is then

$$\ln f_r = \tfrac{3}{4}\ln f_r^o + \tfrac{1}{4}\ln f_r^p \tag{3}$$

4 *Q.C.*, pp. 59, 74.
5 D. M. Dennison, *Proc. Roy. Soc.* (*London*), **A115**, 483 (1927).

The rotational specific heat, which may be calculated from Eq. (3), is in excellent agreement with the experimental values.

Similar considerations apply to deuterium. For deuterium $\rho = 2(1) + 1 = 3$ and, therefore, $\frac{1}{2}\rho(\rho - 1) = 3$ and $\frac{1}{2}\rho(\rho + 1) = 6$. The rotational partition functions for ortho- and para-deuterium are, respectively

$$f_r^o = 6 \sum_{j=0,2}^{\infty} (2j+1) e^{-j(j+1)\theta_r/T}$$

$$f_r^p = 3 \sum_{j=1,3}^{\infty} (2j+1) e^{-j(j+1)\theta_r/T} \tag{4}$$

and

$$\ln f_r = \tfrac{2}{3} \ln f_r^o + \tfrac{1}{3} \ln f_r^p \tag{5}$$

The nuclei in hydrogen deuteride are distinguishable and as a result the symmetry properties which caused the distinction between ortho and para states are not applicable. A straightforward calculation of the rotational specific heat of hydrogen deuteride yields results which are in agreement with experiment.

The properties of hydrogen in its liquid state are discussed in Sect. 12.5.

2. Hindered Internal Rotation

Internal rotation in polyatomic molecules and the forces which give rise to torsional vibration or hindered rotation rather than free rotation in molecules such as ethane, acetaldehyde, and propylene have long been subjects of scientific investigation. At one time the absence of stereo-isomers of such molecules gave rise to the belief that the internal rotations were free. This supposition was discredited by quantum mechanical calculations[1] and by thermodynamic data collected during the 1930's. We shall describe the calculation of the heat capacity of ethane arising from hindered rotation and also mention several tentative explanations for the existence of a barrier to free rotation in ethane. An excellent review of the experimental methods of determining barrier heights and of the many explanations for such barriers to free rotation has been given by Wilson.[2] The whole field of internal rotation in molecules is discussed in a monograph by Mizushima.[3]

One of the $3N - 6 = 18$ normal modes of vibration in ethane corresponds to the rotation of one of the methyl groups with respect to the other methyl

[1] H. Eyring, *J. Am. Chem. Soc.*, **54**, 3191 (1932).

[2] E. B. Wilson, Jr., *Advances in Chemical Physics* (I. Prigogine, Ed.), Vol. II, Interscience Publishers, Inc., New York, 1959, p. 367.

[3] S. Mizushima, *Structure of Molecules and Internal Rotation*, Academic Press, New York, 1954.

group about the axis of the carbon–carbon bond. If an imaginary sighting is made along the carbon–carbon bond axis and the hydrogen atoms on the nearest carbon atom hide those of the other methyl group, the methyl groups are said to be in the eclipsed or opposed position. A potential energy of $V_0 = 2.7$ to 3.0 kcal per mole[4] exists for this configuration which is absent when the two methyl groups are in the staggered position, i.e. when the methyl groups are out of phase with one another by the maximum angle of $60°$. If the phase angle Φ is taken to be zero when the methyl groups are in the staggered position, the variation in potential energy V is given approximately by

$$V = \tfrac{1}{2}V_0(1 - \cos 3\Phi) \tag{1}$$

as shown in Figure 1. At high temperatures such that $kT \gg V_0$

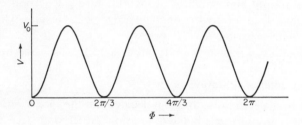

Figure 1. Potential energy barrier to internal rotation in ethane.

the methyl group may be treated as a free rotor. The partition function for such a rigid rotator having one degree of freedom is Eq. (1.5.4):

$$f_{1r} = \frac{(2\pi IkT)^{\tfrac{1}{2}}2\pi}{\sigma h} \tag{2}$$

where $\sigma = 3$ for a methyl group.[5] Hence, the specific heat for free rotation, i.e. high temperatures, is from Eq. (1.2.32)

$$C_V = \left(\frac{\partial E}{\partial T}\right)_V = k\frac{\partial}{\partial T}\left(T^2\frac{\partial \ln f_{1r}}{\partial T}\right)_V$$

$$= k/2 \text{ per ethane molecule} \tag{3}$$

[4] E. B. Wilson, Jr., *op. cit.*, p. 370.
[5] K. S. Pitzer and W. D. Gwinn, *J. Chem. Phys.*, **10**, 428 (1942).

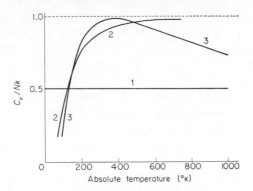

Figure 2. Contribution to C_V by hindered internal rotor. (After T. L. Hill, *Introduction to Statistical Thermodynamics*, Addison-Wesley, Reading, Mass., 1960.)

or $C_V = \frac{1}{2}Nk$ per mole. The horizontal line of Figure 2 is a plot of Eq. (3). In the opposite limiting case for which $kT \ll V_0$ the system is confined to the minima of the potential wells of Figure 1, and the system can be treated as a harmonic oscillator. The specific heat curve at low temperatures should therefore resemble the Einstein specific heat curve of Figure 7.2.1, except that the limiting value of C_V/Nk is 1.0 rather than 3.0. Curve 2 of Figure 2 is such a curve for which the characteristic frequency $h\nu/k = 350°K$. Curve 3 of Figure 2 is drawn through the experimental heat capacities[6] of that normal mode in ethane to which no experimental infrared or Raman frequency is assignable. We see that neither of the limiting C_V curves fits these results. This is not surprising since at room temperature kT is 0.025 ev or about two-tenths of the experimental barrier height $V_0 = 0.12$ to 0.13 ev. C_V for the intermediate case of hindered internal rotation is obtained by first substituting (1) for the potential $V(\phi)$ in the one-dimensional Schrödinger equation

$$\frac{d^2\psi}{d\phi^2} + \frac{8\pi^2 I}{h^2}[E - V(\phi)]\psi = 0 \tag{4}$$

where I is the reduced moment of inertia of the methyl group as in Eq. (2) above, and then solving (4) for the energy levels.[3, 5] The energy levels are substituted in the partition function $f_\phi = \sum_i e^{-\varepsilon_i/kT}$, and the heat capacity is calculated from Eq. (1.2.32). Curve 3 of Figure 2 is the resulting theoretical curve. The details of the energy level calculation are available elsewhere.[7, 8, 9]

[6] G. B. Kistiakowsky, J. R. Lacher and F. Stitt, *J. Chem. Phys.*, **7**, 289 (1939).

[7] E. B. Wilson, *Chem. Rev.*, **27**, 31 (1940).

[8] *Q.C.*, pp. 358–360.

[9] K. S. Pitzer, *Quantum Chemistry*, Prentice-Hall, Englewood Cliffs, N.J., 1953, p. 239.

Since experimental values of V_0 are available[2] and the cosine law of Eq. (1) is, in general, an adequate approximation, we have been able to ignore the problem of explaining the barrier to internal rotation in a statistical mechanical calculation of heat capacities. Conflicting theories regarding the origin of this barrier constitute the present frontier in the field of hindered internal rotation and warrant at least a cursory examination. From conclusions analogous to those of Sect. 1.8 it would seem reasonable that *trans* delocalization of electrons in a staggered ethane molecule would be energetically more favorable than delocalization of electrons between *cis* hydrogen atoms in the eclipsed or opposed structure. An interaction of this type qualitatively accounts for the barrier to free internal rotation in ethane and suggests that bond structures other than the principal one contribute to the stabilization of the staggered isomer.[10] While the potential barrier must arise from known electrostatic attractions and repulsions of the nuclei and electrons, mathematical difficulties make all but the most approximate quantum mechanical calculations of V_0 in ethane impossible. From a survey[2] of many such approximate treatments Wilson concludes that the most plausible explanation for the ethane barrier is a 'repulsion of C—H bond orbitals on the carbons, due to their being more concentrated than *sp* hybrids'. It should be remarked that for sp^3 hybridization the only interactions contributing to a barrier about the C—C bond axis are those between the hydrogen atoms in different methyl groups. This, of course, requires delocalization of electrons.

In addition to the interaction between the two sets of three C—H bonds arising because the bonds are not pure *sp* hybrids[2, 11, 12] there is also an interaction between the hydrogen atoms. This was calculated originally assuming constant bond orders.[1] A brief explanation of 'bond orders' should be helpful. In the singlet state where the electron spins are antiparallel the two hydrogen atoms attract by the exchange integral and so are said to have a bond order of unity. In the triplet state (spins parallel) they repel by an amount equal to the exchange integral and so are said to be antibonding with a bond order of minus one. If two hydrogen atoms have no bond between them, they have a bond order of $-\frac{1}{2}$ corresponding to the fact that there are three chances out of four that they are in the triplet state and so are antibonding and one chance out of four of being in a singlet state. Thus we have for the bond order $(\frac{3}{4})(-1)+(\frac{1}{4})(+1) = -\frac{1}{2}$. Everything from antibonding with a bond order of minus one to bonding with a bond order of unity may arise depending on the circumstances.

10 H. Eyring, G. H. Stewart and R. P. Smith, *Proc. Natl. Acad. Sci. U.S.*, **44**, 259 (1958).
11 E. Gorin, J. Walter and H. Eyring, *J. Am. Chem. Soc.*, **61**, 1876 (1939).
12 L. Pauling, *Proc. Natl. Acad. Sci. U.S.*, **44**, 211 (1958).

Nuclear magnetic resonance allows us to determine experimentally the bond order between hydrogens by measuring the nuclear magnetic line splitting. Since bond order times the exchange integral gives the interaction between hydrogen atoms, one can by using splitting of appropriate ethylenic molecules calculate the barrier height in ethane. The best estimates at present available[13] indicate a barrier height of 2.3 kcal as a result of the changing interaction of hydrogens with angle of rotation.

3. Intermolecular Forces

Short-range attractive forces between chemically saturated molecules become significant when two molecules are separated by only a few molecular diameters. The major portion of such van der Waals forces arises from mutual perturbations of the electron clouds of the two molecules. The instantaneous dipole moments give rise to a potential energy varying inversely as the sixth power of the distance between the molecules. This dispersion energy was first interpreted by London,[1] hence the name 'London forces'. If the distance r between the centers of two chemically saturated molecules is reduced to less than a single molecular diameter, a strong repulsive force predominates. These 'exchange forces' were at one time erroneously ascribed to the collision of hard impenetrable spheres representing the molecules. With the advent of quantum mechanics it became apparent[2] that interelectronic forces governed by the Pauli exclusion principle were, in fact, responsible for this repulsion.[3] The potential energy arising from these repulsive forces can be represented by the exponential

$$u = A\,e^{-r/\rho} \tag{1}$$

where r is the intermolecular distance, $\rho \approx 0.2$ Å is the distance over which the repulsion drops by a factor e, and A must be estimated from experimental data. However, the less correct form

$$u = Br^{-n} \tag{2}$$

is mathematically more convenient and hence more widely used. The value of the power n has been variously estimated as anywhere from 9 to 14.

For chemically saturated, roughly spherical molecules the potential

[13] H. G. Hecht, D. M. Grant and H. Eyring, *Mol. Phys.*, **3**, 577 (1960).

[1] F. London, *Z. Physik. Chem.*, **B11**, 222 (1930); *Trans. Faraday Soc.*, **33**, 8 (1937).

[2] W. Heitler and F. London, *Z. Physik*, **44**, 455 (1927).

[3] For a survey of intermolecular forces see J. A. Beattie and W. H. Stockmayer, *A Treatise on Physical Chemistry*, Van Nostrand, New York, 1951, edited by H. S. Taylor and S. Glasstone, pp. 291–311.

energy arising from the London and exchange forces is approximated by the 'Lennard-Jones 6–12 potential'

$$u(r) = -2\varepsilon \left(\frac{r_0}{r}\right)^6 + \varepsilon \left(\frac{r_0}{r}\right)^{12} \qquad (3)$$

where ε is the depth of the minimum of the potential well below the asymptote of the potential energy curve for large intermolecular separations r, r_0 is the separation of the molecular centers at the minimum, the sixth power term represents the intermolecular attraction, and the power 12 on the repulsive term is arbitrary. The potential well is necessarily shallow since the molecules do not unite to form a stable supermolecule. Refinements in Eq. (3) other than the use of Eq. (1) are possible. For instance, the dispersion effect would be more completely represented by the inclusion of an r^{-8} term representing dipole–quadrupole contributions. However, Eq. (3) already contains three parameters that to date have not been assigned unique values from experimental data. Later in this chapter we shall derive an expression for the pressure p in terms of $u(r)$ that can be used to evaluate the constants in expressions for the potential energy such as Eq. (3). We shall make no attempt, however, to survey the results of such investigations.[4, 5]

4. Imperfect Gases and the Virial Equation

The reader is doubtlessly already acquainted with semi-empirical equations of state for real gases such as van der Waals' equation, Berthelot's equation, and Dieterici's equation.[1] We shall have occasion to discuss these when we consider the first-order phase transition from the gaseous to the liquid state. The perfect gas law $pV/nRT = 1$ for very dilute gases is also very familiar. In the next few pages we shall derive an equation of state for gases of intermediate density for which the intermolecular forces of the preceding section are significant but for which condensation is not imminent.

Statistical mechanics gives a sound theoretical basis to the virial expansion

$$\frac{p}{kT} = \rho + B_2(T)\rho^2 + B_3(T)\rho^3 + \ldots \qquad (1)$$

where ρ is the density and $B_2(T)$ and $B_3(T)$ are called the second and third virial coefficients respectively. Expressions for the coefficients in the

[4] R. H. Fowler and E. A. Guggenheim, *Statistical Thermodynamics*, Cambridge University Press, 1939, Chapter 7.

[5] J. O. Hirschfelder, C. F. Curtiss and R. B. Bird, *Molecular Theory of Gases and Liquids*, Wiley, New York, 1954, Chapter 3.

[1] J. A. Beattie and W. H. Stockmayer, *op. cit.*, p. 198 *et seq.*

virial equation of state can be derived either from the virial theorem of Clausius[2, 3, 4] or from the partition function for a system of N identical molecules. We shall demonstrate the use of the virial theorem first since it will clarify the use of the expression 'second virial coefficient' to describe the temperature-dependent coefficient of ρ^2 in Eq. (1).

In Sect. 2.8 we saw that the average total kinetic energy of a system of particles is

$$\bar{T} = -\tfrac{1}{2} \sum_i \overline{(X_i x_i + Y_i y_i + Z_i z_i)} \tag{2.8.5}$$

where the right-hand side is called the virial, the summation is over all the particles of the system, X_i is the component of force in the x_i direction acting on the ith particle, and the long bar denotes a time average. In the case of an imperfect gas the virial is made up of intermolecular forces and forces exerted on the molecules by the container walls.

Denoting an element of the surface of the container by dS and the direction cosines of a line drawn normal to this surface element by l, m and n, we have for the components of the force exerted on the gas $-lpdS$, $-mpdS$, $-npdS$. Hence, the contribution to $\sum_i X_i x_i$ made by molecule wall collisions is $\iint -lpxdS$. Assuming the pressure p to be the same throughout the container, this contribution may be rewritten as $-p\iint lxdS$ and the total contribution of molecule–wall collisions to the virial is

$$\tfrac{1}{2}p \iint (lx + my + nz)\,dS \tag{2}$$

Now Green's theorem[5] states that

$$\iiint \left(\frac{\partial P}{\partial x} + \frac{\partial Q}{\partial y} + \frac{\partial R}{\partial z} \right) dx\,dy\,dz = \iint P\,dy\,dz + Q\,dx\,dz + R\,dx\,dy$$

$$= \iint (Pl + Qm + Rn)\,dS$$

and hence Eq. (2) is equal to

$$\tfrac{1}{2}p \iiint \left(\frac{\partial x}{\partial x} + \frac{\partial y}{\partial y} + \frac{\partial z}{\partial z} \right) dx\,dy\,dz = \tfrac{3}{2}pV \tag{3}$$

where V is the volume of the container.

Let us make the very general assumption that the force between two molecules is a function of the intermolecular distance r_{12} and may be

[2] J. H. Jeans, *The Dynamical Theory of Gases*, Dover, New York, 4th Ed., 1954, p. 130 *et seq.*

[3] R. H. Fowler, *Statistical Mechanics*, Cambridge University Press, 2nd Ed., 1929, pp. 286–288.

[4] J. O. Hirschfelder *et al.*, *op. cit.*, Chapter 3.

[5] See Sect. 8.1 for a proof of Green's theorem.

written as $-\partial u/\partial r_{12}$. If the centers of two interacting molecules are located at (x_1, y_1, z_1) and (x_2, y_2, z_2) respectively, and the components of the force on these molecules are X_1, Y_1, Z_1 and X_2, Y_2, Z_2, we have

$$X_1 = -\frac{\partial u}{\partial r_{12}}\frac{(x_1-x_2)}{r_{12}} \quad \text{and} \quad X_2 = -\frac{\partial u}{\partial r_{12}}\frac{(x_2-x_1)}{r_{12}} \tag{4}$$

and therefore

$$X_1 x_1 + X_2 x_2 = -\frac{\partial u}{\partial r_{12}}\frac{(x_1-x_2)^2}{r_{12}} \tag{5}$$

From the latter equation we deduce that the contribution made to the virial by this particular pair interaction is

$$-\frac{1}{r_{12}}\frac{\partial u}{\partial r_{12}}[(x_1-x_2)^2+(y_1-y_2)^2+(z_1-z_2)^2] \tag{6}$$

Since the term in brackets equals r_{12}^2, it is apparent that the contribution to the virial made by all the intermolecular interactions in the gas is

$$\frac{1}{2}\sum_{i>j} r_{ij}\frac{\overline{\partial u}}{\partial r_{ij}} \tag{7}$$

where the summation is over all *pairs* of molecules. Substituting Eq. (3) and Eq. (7) for the virial in Eq. (2.8.5) and noting that $\overline{T} = \frac{1}{2}\sum_i \overline{m_i v_i^2}$, we obtain the general form of the equation of state

$$pV = \frac{1}{3}\sum_i \overline{m_i v_i^2} - \frac{1}{3}\sum_{i>j} r_{ij}\frac{\overline{\partial u}}{\partial r_{ij}} \tag{8}$$

We begin the simplification of this expression by noting that the mean kinetic energy of translation of a perfect gas is

$$\frac{1}{3}\sum_i \overline{m_i v_i^2} = NkT \tag{9}$$

Next we must sum $r_{ij}\,\partial u/\partial r_{ij}$ over all pairs of molecules. There are $\frac{1}{2}N(N-1) \simeq \frac{1}{2}N^2$ such pairs. If the molecules exerted no force on one another and were randomly distributed throughout the volume, the total number of pairs of molecules separated by an intermolecular distance in the range r to $r+dr$ would be

$$(\tfrac{1}{2}N^2)\frac{d\omega}{V} = \tfrac{1}{2}N^2\frac{4\pi r^2\,dr}{V} \tag{10}$$

where $d\omega$ is a solid angle in polar coordinates. If short-range intermolecular forces are included and the gas is too dilute for trimolecular clusters to occur, the average number of pairs of molecules separated by an inter-molecular distance in the range r to $r+dr$ is

$$\tfrac{1}{2}N^2 e^{-u/kT} \frac{4\pi r^2 \, dr}{V} \tag{11}$$

We then have

$$-\tfrac{1}{3} \sum_{i>j} \overline{r_{ij} \frac{\partial u}{\partial r_{ij}}} \cong -\tfrac{1}{3} \int_0^\infty \frac{2\pi N^2 r^3}{V} \frac{\partial u}{\partial r} e^{-u/kT} \, dr \tag{12}$$

and hence from (8), (9) and (12) the equation of state is

$$pV = NkT - \tfrac{2}{3}\pi \frac{N^2}{V} \int_0^\infty r^3 \frac{\partial u}{\partial r} e^{-u/kT} \, dr \tag{13}$$

By making the very reasonable assumption that $u(r)$ goes to zero as r goes to infinity we can integrate Eq. (13) by parts:

$$\int_0^\infty (r^3) \frac{\partial u}{\partial r} e^{-u/kT} \, dr = -3kT \int_0^\infty r^2 \, dr + 3kT \int_0^\infty e^{-u/kT} r^2 \, dr \tag{14}$$

Thus Eq. (13) becomes

$$\frac{p}{kT} = \frac{N}{V} \left[1 - \tfrac{1}{2} \frac{N}{V} \int_0^\infty 4\pi r^2 (e^{-u/kT} - 1) \, dr \right] \tag{15}$$

The first virial coefficient in this equation of state is unity whereas the second coefficient is

$$B_2(T) = -\tfrac{1}{2} \int_0^\infty 4\pi r^2 (e^{-u/kT} - 1) \, dr \tag{16}$$

We shall later obtain precisely the same expression for $B_2(T)$ from ensemble theory.

5. Imperfect Gas Pressure as a Power Series in the Activity

In this section we give a derivation of the virial equation of state for an imperfect gas based upon the grand partition function. A review of several thermodynamic functions will be a useful preliminary to this undertaking.

The chemical potential μ of a perfect gas is given by

$$\frac{\mu}{kT} = \ln \left(\frac{h^2}{2\pi mkT} \right)^{\tfrac{3}{2}} + \ln \frac{\bar{N}}{V}, \qquad \frac{\bar{N}}{V} \to 0 \tag{4.16.5}$$

For the sake of brevity let us denote $h/(2\pi mkT)^{\tfrac{1}{2}}$ by the symbol λ. This quantity, which has the dimensions of length, is sometimes called the de

Broglie wavelength at temperature T. The activity a can then be defined by

$$\frac{\mu}{kT} = \ln \lambda^3 + \ln a \qquad \lim_{N/V \to 0} a = \frac{N}{V} \tag{1}$$

Now from Eq. (3.7.19) we see that for a perfect gas

$$\frac{\mu}{kT} = \ln \lambda^3 + \ln p \tag{2}$$

and according to Eq. (3.7.21) the fugacity f of an imperfect gas is defined by

$$\frac{\mu}{kT} = \ln \lambda^3 + \ln f/f^0 \qquad \lim_{p \to 0} f = p \tag{3}$$

Hence, the fugacity f and the activity a are related by

$$\frac{f}{kT} = a \tag{4}$$

Armed with these thermodynamic results let us proceed with the derivation of the equation of state first in powers of the activity a and later in powers of the density ρ. The starting point for this treatment is the grand partition function

$$\Xi(V, T, \mu) = e^{pV/kT} \tag{4.15.10}$$

$$= \sum_{N \geqslant 0} e^{N\mu/kT} f_N(V, T, N) \tag{5}$$

Now the canonical partition function f_N is given by

$$f_N(V, T, N) = \sum_n e^{-E_n/kT} \tag{6}$$

$$= \frac{1}{N! h^{3N}} \int \cdots \int e^{-H(p, q)/kT} \, dp_1 \ldots dp_N \, dq_1 \ldots dq_N \tag{7}$$

where Eq. (7) is valid only in the limit as (1) the density of molecules in μ space is low and (2) the energy states of the system are closely spaced. The first condition is not satisfied by such gases as hydrogen and helium at very low temperatures. At moderate temperatures the second condition is only satisfied by monatomic gases. We shall neglect the possibility of internal degrees of freedom in our imperfect gas molecules on this account, and for the sake of simplicity we shall also assume only one species of molecule is present. The Hamiltonian of Eq. (7) has the form

$$H = \sum_{i=1}^{N} \frac{1}{2m} (p_{x_i}^2 + p_{y_i}^2 + p_{z_i}^2) + U \tag{8}$$

and since the as yet unspecified intermolecular potential U is independent of the momentum coordinates, integration of Eq. (7) over the $3N$ different p_i yields

$$f_N = \left(\frac{2\pi m k T}{h^2}\right)^{3N/2} Q_N \tag{9}$$

where

$$Q_N = \frac{1}{N!} \int_V \cdots \int e^{-U/kT} \, d\mathbf{r}_1 \ldots d\mathbf{r}_N \tag{10}$$

The symbol $d\mathbf{r}_i$ denotes the volume element $dx_i \, dy_i \, dz_i$, where the coordinates are those of the molecular center of mass. If Q_N, the configurational partition function, is known as a function of volume and temperature, the pressure of the gas can be calculated from

$$p = -\left(\frac{\partial A}{\partial V}\right)_{T,N} = kT\left(\frac{\partial \ln f_N}{\partial V}\right)_{T,N} = kT\left(\frac{\partial \ln Q_N}{\partial V}\right)_{T,N} \tag{11}$$

For a perfect gas U is zero within the container and infinite without, whence we have

$$Q_N = \left(\frac{eV}{N}\right)^N \quad \text{and} \quad p = kTN/V \tag{12}$$

Returning now to the grand partition function, we see that we may rewrite Eq. (5) as

$$\Xi = \sum_{N \geqslant 0} a^N Q_N \tag{13}$$

where the activity $a = e^{\mu/kT}(2\pi m k T/h^2)^{\frac{3}{2}}$ in agreement with Eq. (1).

Let us consider a one-component, monatomic gas of N atoms for which the total intermolecular potential energy U can be expressed as a sum of $\frac{1}{2}N(N-1)$ molecular pair interactions

$$U = \frac{1}{2}\sum_{i \neq j} u(r_{ij}) \equiv \sum_{i > j} u(r_{ij}) \tag{14}$$

with

$$r_{ij} = |\mathbf{r}_i - \mathbf{r}_j| \tag{15}$$

In order that our later series expressions converge we must require that the pair interaction potential $u(r_{ij})$ decrease with increasing r_{ij} more rapidly than r_{ij}^{-3}. Except for this restriction $u(r_{ij})$ retains its completely general nature. It should also be said that the assumption of pair-wise additivity of forces overlooks no significant contributions to the intermolecular potential.[1]

---

[1] J. E. Mayer, *Handbuch der Physik*, Springer, Berlin, 1958, **12**, p. 123.

Now let us begin the Ursell–Mayer evaluation of the configuration integral of Eq. (10).[1, 2] First we define the function

$$f_{ij} = e^{-u(r_{ij})/kT} - 1 \tag{16}$$

From Eqs. (14) and (16) we see that the exponential of Eq. (10) may be rewritten as

$$e^{-U/kT} = e^{-\Sigma u(r_{ij})/kT} = \prod e^{-u(r_{ij})/kT} \tag{17}$$

$$= \prod_{1 \leqslant i \leqslant j \leqslant N} (1 + f_{ij})$$

The sum of terms resulting from the indicated multiplication can be arranged systematically as

$$e^{-U/kT} = 1 + \sum f_{ij} + \sum f_{ij} f_{kl} + \sum f_{ij} f_{kl} f_{mn} + \dots \tag{18}$$

For N large this expression, of course, disguises a fantastically large number of different terms. For instance, the second term contains all the $\frac{1}{2}N(N-1)$ possible pair terms.

In a perfect gas all the $u(r_{ij})$'s are zero; the exponential of Eq. (10) is therefore unity for all i's and j's, and the f_{ij}'s are all zero. Then the configurational partition function is

$$Q_N = \frac{1}{N!} \int_V \dots \int (1)\, dr_i \dots dr_N = \left(\frac{eV}{N}\right)^N \tag{19}$$

as in Eq. (12).

It should be emphasized that a new partition function f_N can be obtained from Eq. (7) for every configuration of the molecules of the imperfect gas, i.e. for every possible set of values $r_1, \dots, r_N$. The exponential of the configuration integral, Eq. (10), for each such set of r's can be obtained from Eq. (18) with an f present for every non-negligible intermolecular attraction.

It is evident from our discussion of intermolecular forces in Sect. 3 that f_{ij} is negligibly small for a pair of chemically saturated molecules unless r_{ij} is decreased to a distance of the order of a few Ångstrom units. Furthermore, any term in Eq. (18) involving a product of f's must vanish if anyone of the r_{ij}'s involved is large. Each possible combination of the f's from none to all $\frac{1}{2}N(N-1)$ gives rise to a term in Eq. (18) and each such product term can be represented by a two-dimensional drawing. In such a drawing the molecules are represented by numbered circles and small values of the distance r_{ij} with consequent non-negligible values of f_{ij}

2 T. L. Hill, *Statistical Mechanics*, McGraw-Hill, New York, 1956, Chapter 5.

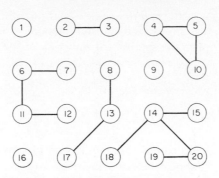

Figure 1. Schematic representation of the product term $f_{2,3}\, f_{4,10}\, f_{4,5}\, f_{5,10}\, f_{6,7}\, f_{6,11}$ $f_{11,12}\, f_{8,13}\, f_{13,17}\, f_{14,18}\, f_{14,15}\, f_{14,20}\, f_{19,20}$ in Eq. (18).

are denoted by lines connecting circles. If $N = 20$, Figure 1 corresponds to the term $f_{2,3}\, f_{4,10}\, f_{4,5}\, f_{5,10}\, f_{6,7}\, f_{6,11}\, f_{11,12}\, f_{8,13}\, f_{13,17}\, f_{14,18}\, f_{14,15}$ $f_{14,20}\, f_{19,20}$. Every term in Eq. (18) can be represented by a new figure analogous to Figure 1. The first term of Eq. (18), unity, is represented by a figure in which none of the circles are connected. A total of $\frac{1}{2}N(N-1)$ figures must be drawn, each with a single connecting line to represent the terms arising from the second term, $\sum f_{ij}$, of Eq. (18). The term 'cluster' arises from the fact that there are groups of molecules in Figure 1 which are connected to one another, in some cases indirectly as 7 and 11, but none of which are connected to the remainder of the 20 molecules. In Figure 1 there are $m_1 = 3$ clusters consisting of single molecules. There is only $m_2 = 1$ cluster consisting of 2 molecules. A cluster of three molecules can be formed in four different ways as indicated in Figure 2. There are

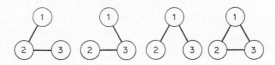

Figure 2. All possible different clusters involving only three molecules.

two such clusters in Figure 1. The simplification of Eq. (18) is facilitated by the concept of the cluster sum $S_{i,\, j,\, k\, \ldots}$ (sometimes referred to as the Ursell or U-function). $S_{i,\, j,\, k,\, \ldots}$ is defined as the sum of all terms in Eq. (18) which connect in a cluster either directly or indirectly the molecules $i, j, k, \ldots$ with none of the remaining molecules connected to any molecule in the cluster. To complete the definition of $S_{i,\, j,\, k,\, \ldots}$ we add that $S_i = 1$. Figure 2 provides an illustration of the cluster sum: $S_{1,2,3} = f_{2,1}f_{3,2} + f_{3,1}f_{3,2} + f_{2,1}f_{3,1} + f_{2,1}f_{3,1}f_{3,2}$. We are actually interested in only those products of cluster sums in which each molecule appears as a subscript to the symbol for only one of the cluster sums, i.e.

$$S_1 S_9 S_{16} S_{3,2} S_{10,5,4} S_{17,13,8} S_{12,11,7,6} S_{20,19,18,15,14} \tag{20}$$

This is a shorthand notation for the product

$$(1)(1)(1)(f_{3,2})(f_{5,4}f_{10,5} + f_{10,4}f_{10,5} + f_{5,4}f_{10,4}$$
$$+ f_{5,4}f_{10,4}f_{10,5})(\ldots)(\ldots)(\ldots) \tag{21}$$

which if expanded would contain among its sum of terms the term represented in Figure 1. It should be remarked that no term is present in the sum that is inconsistent with the following restrictions: molecules 1, 9, and 16 are each unit clusters, molecules 2 and 3 are in a two-molecule cluster and in no other cluster, molecules 4, 5 and 10 are in a three-molecule cluster that can be formed in any one of four different ways, etc.

Every term in Eq. (18) is generated by taking the sum of all the different possible products of the cluster sums consistent with the restriction that each such product of the S's has every one of the N possible subscripts once and only once. By definition each of the products of S's corresponds to a different assignment of the N molecules to clusters. The cluster integral b_l is defined by the relation

$$b_l(V, T) = \frac{1}{l! V} \int \cdots \int_V S_{1,2,\ldots,l} \, dr_1 \ldots dr_l \tag{22}$$

where l is the number of molecules per cluster. For example, the cluster integral b_1 is given by

$$b_1 = \frac{1}{V} \int_V S_1 \, dr_1 = 1 \tag{23}$$

Equation (22) has several interesting properties. If the volume V containing the imperfect gas is large and the gas density is low, i.e. $l \ll V/r_0^3$, where r_0 is approximately a molecular diameter, b_l is independent of V and a function of T only. This conclusion is supported by a comparatively simple argument. Unless all members of a cluster are physically close together, $f_{i,j,\ldots,l}$ is negligible. Since the cluster sum S in Eq. (22) is a sum of products of f's, each product in S is non-zero only when the member molecules of each cluster lie near one another. If this condition is satisfied, the lth molecule in one of the clusters must also lie within a few molecular diameters of the container wall in order for the volume V to affect the evaluation of b_l. For a macroscopic volume and low gas density such a location of the lth molecule is improbable, integration over $r_1, \ldots, r_{l-1}$ is independent of r_l and V, and b_l is a function of T alone. While we shall have occasion to refer to this property of b_l later, we do not use it in this section in deriving an expression for the configuration integral Q_N, Eq. (30), that is volume dependent.

The fact that integration of Eq. (22) yields the same function of V and T for the value of b_l regardless of which particular molecules occur in the subscript to S is also important. That this is true can be seen from the following simple case:

$$\iint S_{ij}\,dr_i\,dr_j = \iint S_{kl}\,dr_k\,dr_l \tag{24}$$

since S_{kl} is the same function of the distance r_{kl} as S_{ij} is of r_{ij}. The consequence of this property and the fact that a molecule occurs in only one of the cluster sums of the product Eq. (20) is that the integral of Eq. (20) over the twenty different coordinates is

$$\int \cdots \int_V S_1 S_9 S_{16} S_{3,2} \ldots S_{20,19,18,15,14}\,dr_1 \ldots dr_{20}$$
$$= (1!\,Vb_1)^3(2!\,Vb_2)(3!\,Vb_3)^2(4!\,Vb_4)(5!\,Vb_5) \tag{25}$$

The general expression for this result is

$$(1!\,Vb_1)^{m_1}(2!\,Vb_2)^{m_2} \ldots (l!\,Vb_l)^{m_l} \tag{26}$$

where m_l is the number of clusters composed of l molecules in the gas of N molecules. Necessarily N must be given by

$$N = \sum_{l=1}^{N} lm_l \tag{27}$$

The expression Eq. (26) is the contribution to the configuration integral Q_N of all the terms for which the same (numbered) molecules occur together in clusters.

The product of cluster sums Eq. (20) is not the only possible product that would give rise on integration to Eq. (25). We need to know the number of ways the N molecules can be split up into clusters so that there are m_1 single molecules, m_2 two-molecule clusters, m_3 three-molecule clusters, ... and m_l clusters each composed of l molecules. We derive this result by first imagining the N numbered (i.e. distinguishable) molecules arranged along a line in $N!$ different ways. The molecules can then be divided into clusters, i.e. the first m_1 molecules are taken singly, the next $2m_2$ are paired, the following $3m_3$ are taken as successive triplets, etc. Since any one of the m_l l-molecular clusters is indistinguishable from the remaining (m_l-1), no particular order is attached to them and we must divide by $m_l!$. Similarly no particular order is attached to the molecules within a cluster, so we must also divide by $l!$ for every cluster containing l molecules. The resulting expression is

$$\frac{N!}{\prod_l m_l!\,(l!)^{m_l}} \tag{28}$$

The product of Eq. (26) and Eq. (28) is the contribution to the configuration integral Q_N made by all terms in Eq. (18) expressible by the cluster sums $S_{i, j, k} \ldots$ derived from the particular cluster distribution $m_1, m_2, m_3, \ldots m_l$. Since each set of m_l's gives rise to an analogous product, the complete expression for the configurational partition function is

$$Q_N = \frac{1}{N!} \sum_{m_l(\Sigma \, lm_l = N)} \left[\frac{N!}{\prod_{l=1}^{N} m_l! \, (l!)^{m_l}} \prod_{l=1}^{N} (l! \, V b_l)^{m_l} \right] \tag{29}$$

$$= \sum_{m_l(\Sigma \, lm_l = N)} \left[\prod_{l=1}^{N} \frac{(V b_l)^{m_l}}{m_l!} \right] \tag{30}$$

where the subscripts on the large sigmas denote summation over all possible sets $m_1, m_2, m_3, \ldots, m_l$ consistent with Eq. (27).

Introducing Eq. (30) into Eq. (13), we have for the grand partition function

$$\Xi = e^{pV/kT} = \sum_{N \geqslant 0} a^N \sum_{m_l(\Sigma \, lm_l = N)} \prod_{l} \frac{(V b_l)^{m_l}}{m_l!} \tag{31}$$

$$\Xi = \prod_{l} \sum_{m_l} \frac{(V b_l a^l)^{m_l}}{m_l!} \tag{32}$$

$$\Xi = exp \, V \sum_{l \geqslant 0} b_l a^l \tag{33}$$

whence

$$p = kT \sum_{l \geqslant 1} b_l a^l \tag{34}$$

in the limit as $V \to \infty$ and hence b_l is independent of volume. Ono[3] has outlined an argument by which Eq. (34) may be derived without assuming the intermolecular potential to be pair-wise additive. Yang and Lee[4] have derived Eq. (34) from Eq. (5) by an entirely different method.

In Eq. (32) the term on the right for a given value of m_l is proportional to the probability of there being m_l clusters of l molecules in excess of the number that would exist in the gas in the absence of an intermolecular potential.[5] Furthermore, the average number $\bar{m}_l$ of l-molecular clusters is $V b_l a^l$. The consequence of this fact is that Eq. (34) may be rewritten as

$$pV = kT \sum_{l \geqslant 1} \bar{m}_l = \bar{m}_c kT \tag{35}$$

where $\bar{m}_c = \sum_i m_l$ is the average total number of clusters of all sizes. For a gas in which the intermolecular potential is attractive $\bar{m}_c < N$ and

3 S. Ono, *J. Chem. Phys.*, **19**, 504 (1951).
4 C. N. Yang and T. D. Lee, *Phys. Rev.*, **87**, 404, 410 (1952).
5 J. E. Mayer, *op. cit.*, pp. 131, 132.

the pressure will, of course, be less than that of a perfect gas. In view of the fact that $\bar{m}_l$ is the excess of l-molecular clusters in the gas over the number expected randomly, the $\bar{m}_l$'s will sometimes assume negative values. For instance, if the intermolecular potential were due to repulsive forces between molecules, the probability of finding bimolecular clusters, trimolecular clusters, etc. would be less than in the absence of all inter-molecular potentials. Hence, $\bar{m}_2$, $\bar{m}_3$, etc. would be negative, and $\bar{m}_1$ would be greater than the total number of molecules. The possibility of $\bar{m}_l$ being negative suggests that the clusters in all the above arguments must not be taken literally as physical aggregates.[5, 6]

6. Equation of State in Powers of the Density

Since the experimental description of a gas is commonly given in terms of temperature and volume or concentration, an expansion of p/kT in powers of the density, $\rho = \bar{N}/V$, will generally be more useful than Eq. (5.34). From Sect. 4.15 we have

$$\bar{N} = kT \left(\frac{\partial \ln \Xi}{\partial \mu} \right)_{T,V} \tag{1}$$

Introducing Eqs. (5.1) and Eq. (4.15.10), this becomes

$$\frac{\bar{N}}{V} = \rho = a \left(\frac{\partial p/kT}{\partial a} \right)_{T,V} \tag{2}$$

Substitution in this expression of $p/kT = \sum_{l \geqslant 1} b_l a^l$, Eq. (5.34), then yields

$$\rho = \sum_{l \geqslant 1} l b_l a^l \tag{3}$$

This series can be inverted to give the activity a as a power series in ρ, and the new series can then be substituted in Eq. (5.34) to yield $p/kT = \rho + B_2(T)\rho^2 + \ldots$, Eq. (4.1). The details of such a calculation are the following:

$$\rho = \sum_{l \geqslant 1} l b_l (\rho + c_2 \rho^2 + c_3 \rho^3 + \ldots)^l \tag{4}$$

$$\rho = b_1(\rho + c_2 \rho^2 + c_3 \rho^3 + \ldots) + 2b_2(\rho^2 + 2c_2 \rho^3 + \ldots) + 3b_3(\rho^3 + \ldots) \tag{5}$$

Equating coefficients of powers of ρ in Eq. (5), we obtain

$$1 = b_1$$
$$0 = b_1 c_2 + 2b_2 \tag{6}$$
$$0 = b_1 c_3 + 4b_2 c_2 + 3b_3$$

[6] T. L. Hill, *op. cit.*, pp. 132–134.

Solving these equations for the c's, we have

$$c_2 = -2b_2$$
$$c_3 = -3b_3 + 8b_2^2 \tag{7}$$

Inserting these coefficients in the equation for the activity a as a power series in the density ρ, substituting this relation for a in Eq. (5.34), expanding and finally collecting terms, we obtain the virial equation of state with the virial coefficients expressed in terms of the cluster integrals

$$\frac{p}{kT} = \rho + (-b_2)\rho^2 + (-2b_3 + 4b_2^2)\rho^3 + \ldots \tag{8}$$

Equation (8) can be expressed in a more elegant form by introducing the concept of 'irreducible clusters'. Such a cluster is defined to be the product of f_{ij}'s, represented by diagrams analogous to Figure 5.1, in which any molecule can be reached from any other molecule in the irreducible cluster by two independent paths that do not intersect at any intermediate molecules. In addition, all two-molecule clusters are considered to be irreducible. Figure 1 depicts a nine-molecule cluster composed of five

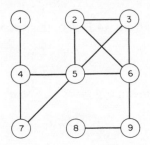

Figure 1. Cluster of nine molecules composed of five irreducible clusters.

irreducible clusters. Molecules 1 and 4, 6 and 9, and 8 and 9 constitute three separate bimolecular irreducible clusters. Molecules 4, 5, and 7 form a trimolecular irreducible cluster, and molecules 2, 3, 5, and 6 are members of a termolecular irreducible cluster.

The irreducible cluster sum $S'_{i,\,j,\,k}\ldots$ is defined as the sum of all the different products of f's that connect molecules $i, j, k \ldots$ into a single irreducible cluster. Referring to Figure 2, we see that

$$S'_{1,2} = f_{1,2}$$
$$S'_{1,2,3} = f_{1,2}f_{1,3}f_{2,3} \tag{9}$$
$$S'_{1,2,3,4} = f_{1,2}f_{2,3}f_{3,4}f_{1,4} + f_{1,3}f_{2,3}f_{2,4}f_{1,4} + \ldots$$
$$+ f_{1,4}f_{3,4}f_{2,3}f_{1,2}f_{1,3}f_{2,4}$$

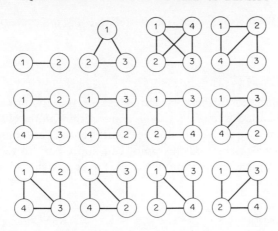

Figure 2. All possible irreducible clusters of two, three, and four molecules.

where $S'_{1, 2, 3, 4}$ is the sum of all ten products indicated in Figure 2.

We now define the irreducible cluster integral to be

$$\beta_k = \frac{1}{k! V} \int \cdots \int_V S'_{1, 2, \ldots k+1} dr_1 \cdots dr_{k+1} \tag{10}$$

As was also the case for the cluster integral b_l, the choice of the $k+1$ specific molecules appearing in the subscript to S' of Eq. (10) does not alter the value of the resulting integral. Furthermore, β_k is independent of volume for $k \ll V/r_0^3$.

We begin the now familiar process of simplifying Eq. (10) by considering the product of irreducible sums

$$S'_{1, 4} S'_{6, 9} S'_{8, 9} S'_{4, 5, 7} S'_{2, 3, 5, 6} \tag{11}$$

This product has a deceptively simple appearance since it contains all the terms, i.e. the products of the f's, in the cluster sum $S_{1, 2, \ldots 9}$, that satisfy the condition that the following parenthesized molecules constitute irreducible clusters: (1, 4), (6, 9), (8, 9), (4, 5, 7) and (2, 3, 5, 6). Figure 1 depicts only one of the many terms in $S_{1, 2, \ldots 9}$.

The cluster integral b_9 can be represented by a sum of integrals one of which is

$$I = \frac{1}{9! V} \int \cdots \int_V S'_{1, 4} S'_{6, 9} S'_{8, 9} S'_{4, 5, 7} S'_{2, 3, 5, 6} dr_1 \cdots dr_9 \tag{12}$$

Referring to Figure 1 or, for that matter, any other figure that allocates the same molecules to the same size irreducible clusters, we can split (12) up into a product of irreducible cluster integrals by changing to relative coordinates. Taking our coordinates relative to molecule 4, Eq. (12) becomes

$$I = \frac{1}{9!\,V} \int \cdots \int_V S'_{1,4} S'_{6,9} S'_{8,9} S'_{4,5,7} S'_{2,3,5,6}\, dr_4\, dr_{14}\, dr_{24} \ldots dr_{49} \quad (13)$$

In order to proceed further, we make use of the condition $k \ll V/r_0^3$. This condition, alluded to previously in connection with the cluster integral b_l, has not been used to this point. The consequence of assuming $k \ll V/r_0^3$ is that all our results beyond this point can apply only to the gas phase. Taking $k \ll V/r_0^3$, the integration of Eq. (13) over r_4 yields V, and Eq. (13) therefore becomes

$$I = \frac{1}{9!}\left(\int_V S'_{1,4}\, dr_{14}\right)\left(\int \cdots \int_V S'_{6,9} S'_{8,9} S'_{4,5,7} S'_{2,3,5,6}\, dr_{24} \ldots dr_{49}\right) \quad (14)$$

$$= \frac{1}{9!}\left(\frac{1}{V}\int_V S'_{1,4}\, dr_1\, dr_4\right)\left(\frac{1}{V}\int \cdots \int_V S'_{6,9} S'_{8,9} S'_{4,5,7} S'_{2,3,5,6}\, dr_2 \ldots dr_9\right)$$

$$(15)$$

From Eq. (10) we have β_1 for the first parenthesized term and Eq. (15) can be rewritten as

$$I = \frac{\beta_1}{9!}\frac{1}{V}\int \cdots \int_V S'_{6,9} S'_{8,9} S'_{4,5,7} S'_{2,3,5,6}\, dr_2 \ldots dr_9 \quad (16)$$

We have succeeded in breaking off one of the irreducible clusters from the nine-molecule cluster of Figure 1. The trimolecular cluster is separated next by taking coordinates relative to molecule 5. Equation (16) then becomes

$$I = \frac{\beta_1}{9!}\left(\frac{1}{V}\int \cdots \int_V S'_{4,5,7}\, dr_4\, dr_5\, dr_7\right)$$

$$\times \left(\frac{1}{V}\int \cdots \int_V S'_{6,9} S'_{8,9} S'_{2,3,5,6}\, dr_2\, dr_3\, dr_5\, dr_6\, dr_8\, dr_9\right) \quad (17)$$

$$= \frac{\beta_1}{9!}(2!\,\beta_2)\frac{1}{V}\int \cdots \int_V S'_{6,9} S'_{8,9} S'_{2,3,5,6}\, dr_2\, dr_3\, dr_5\, dr_6\, dr_8\, dr_9 \quad (18)$$

We notice that each time we separate an S' with $k+1$ molecular indices in its subscript from the main integral, k of the molecular indices no longer appear among the remaining irreducible cluster sums. This is a consequence of the fact that an irreducible cluster, by definition, may be joined to another through only one molecule. The last S' of Eq. (13) is an exception since its integration must necessarily remove all the remaining $k+1$

molecular indices. Pruning the remaining three irreducible clusters from the nine-molecule cluster in the same fashion, we finally obtain

$$I = \frac{1}{9!}(1!\beta_1)^3(2!\beta_2)(3!\beta_3) \tag{19}$$

In general, the contribution made to a cluster integral b_l by a product of irreducible cluster sums corresponding to n_1 irreducible bimolecular clusters, n_2 irreducible trimolecular clusters,... and n_k irreducible clusters of $k+1$ molecules is

$$\frac{1}{l!}(1!\beta_1)^{n_1}(2!\beta_2)^{n_2} \ldots (k!\beta_k)^{n_k} \tag{20}$$

As was mentioned earlier, a large number of products of irreducible cluster sums contribute to b_l. The exact number of such contributing products is equal to the number of ways l distinguishable molecules can be assigned to n_1 sets of two molecules, n_2 sets of three molecules,..., and n_k sets of $k+1$ doubly connected molecules so that every molecule appears in at least one set. In those cases where a molecule occurs in more than one set, these sets must be connected only through the one molecule in question. This combinatorial problem was solved by S. F. Harrison and J. E. Mayer. We shall not reproduce their 'bolt-washer-frame' proof that is readily available elsewhere.[1] Their final result is

$$\frac{l!}{l^2}\prod_{k=1}^{l-1}\left(\frac{l}{k!}\right)^{n_k}\frac{1}{n_k!} \tag{21}$$

The product of Eqs. (20) and (21) is the contribution made to b_l by all products of irreducible cluster sums corresponding to a particular choice of $n_1, n_2, \ldots n_k$. The cluster integral is therefore given by

$$b_l = \frac{1}{l^2}\sum_{n_k\left(\sum\limits_{k=1}^{l-1}kn_k=l-1\right)}\prod_{k=1}^{l-1}\frac{(l\beta_k)^{n_k}}{n_k!} \tag{22}$$

where the summation is over all possible choices of $n_1, n_2, \ldots, n_k$ consistent with the parenthesized condition. The first few cluster integrals are

$$b_2 = \tfrac{1}{2}\beta_1 \tag{23}$$

$$b_3 = \tfrac{1}{3}\beta_2 + \tfrac{1}{2}\beta_1^2 \tag{24}$$

$$b_4 = \tfrac{1}{4}\beta_3 + \beta_1\beta_2 + \tfrac{2}{3}\beta_1^3 \tag{25}$$

From these last three equations it is apparent that the virial equation, Eq. (8), may be rewritten as

$$\frac{p}{kT} = \rho - \tfrac{1}{2}\beta_1\rho^2 - \tfrac{2}{3}\beta_2\rho^3 - \ldots \tag{26}$$

[1] J. E. Mayer and M. G. Mayer, *Statistical Mechanics*, Wiley, New York, 1940, pp. 455–459.

The general result for sufficiently small values of the activity a and density ρ is

$$\frac{p}{kT} = \rho\left[1 - \sum_{k \geq 1} \frac{k}{k+1}\beta_k \rho^k\right] \tag{27}$$

Since we are only interested in numerical calculations of the first few virial coefficients, we shall omit the proof of Eq. (27).[2, 3]

A startling property of the virial coefficients of Eqs. (4.1) and (26) is revealed by a consideration of the inverse of Eq. (22)[4]

$$\beta_k = \sum_{\substack{m_l \geq 0 \left(\sum\limits_{l=2}^{k+1}(l-1)m_l = k\right)}} (-1)^{\sum_l m_l - 1} \frac{\left(k-1+\sum\limits_l m_l\right)!}{k!} \prod_l \frac{(lb_l)^{m_l}}{m_l!} \tag{28}$$

$$\beta_1 = 2b_2$$
$$\beta_2 = 3b_3 - 6b_2^2 \tag{29}$$
$$\beta_3 = 4b_4 - 24b_2 b_3 + \tfrac{80}{3}b_2^2$$

and the inverse of Eq. (5.30)[5]

$$b_l = \frac{1}{V}\sum_{\substack{n_i \geq 0 \\ (in_i = l)}} (-1)^{\sum_i n_i - 1}\left(\sum_i n_i - 1\right)!\prod_i \frac{(Q_i)^{n_i}}{n_i!} \tag{30}$$

$$b_2 = \frac{1}{2V}(2Q_2 - Q_1^2)$$

$$b_3 = \frac{1}{3V}(3Q_3 - 3Q_1 Q_2 + Q_1^3) \tag{31}$$

$$b_4 = \frac{1}{4V}(4Q_4 - 4Q_1 Q_3 - 2Q_2^2 + 4Q_1^2 Q_2 - Q_1^4)$$

where Q_2, for instance, is the configurational partition function in f_2, the canonical ensemble partition function for two molecules in a volume V. It is apparent from Eqs. (28) through (31) that even if the imperfect gas consists of as many as 10^{20} molecules, the use of the grand canonical ensemble has reduced the problem of calculating the second virial coefficient,

$$B_2(T) = -\tfrac{1}{2}\beta_1 = -b_2 = \frac{1}{2V}(Q_1^2 - 2Q_2) \tag{32}$$

to one of calculating the quantum mechanical energy levels of one and

[2] J. E. Mayer, op. cit., pp. 137, 138.
[3] T. L. Hill, op. cit., pp. 141–143.
[4] J. E. Mayer, J. Chem. Phys., 10, 629 (1942); J. E. Kilpatrick, J. Chem. Phys., 21, 274 (1953).
[5] S. Ono, op. cit., p. 504.

two molecules in a box of volume V, the ingredients of the canonical ensemble partition functions f_1 and f_2 for one and two molecules in V. In general, the n canonical ensemble partition functions for 1, 2,..., n molecules in the volume V are required to calculate the nth virial coefficient $B_n(T)$.

We should make one further remark regarding the equations of state expressed as a power series in the activity a or the density ρ. As long as the volume V occupied by the gas is finite, these series are convergent.[6] The phenomenon of condensation is closely associated with the divergence of these series that occurs when the gas clusters become part of the infinite cluster of the liquid state.

7. Numerical Evaluation of the Virial Coefficients

Numerical calculations of the second and third virial coefficients in Eq. (6.26) have been compiled for a wide variety of intermolecular potentials by Hirschfelder, Curtiss, and Bird.[1] We shall discuss the calculation of the second and third virial coefficients for only two potentials: first, a hard sphere potential

$$u(r_{ij}) = \infty, \qquad r < \sigma$$
$$u(r_{ij}) = 0, \qquad r \geqslant \sigma \tag{1}$$

where σ is the diameter of a sphere, and second, the Lennard-Jones 6–12 potential, Eq. (3.3).

From Eqs. (6.8), (5.22), and (5.16) we have for the second virial coefficient in the equation of state of a monatomic, one-component gas

$$B_2(T) = -b_2 = -\frac{1}{2V} \iint f_{1,2} \, d\mathbf{r}_1 \, d\mathbf{r}_2 \tag{2}$$

$$= -\frac{1}{2V} \iint_V (e^{-u(r_{12})/kT} - 1) \, d\mathbf{r}_1 \, d\mathbf{r}_2 \tag{3}$$

Since the intermolecular potential rapidly drops to zero for large intermolecular separations, the integrand in Eq. (3) will be non-zero only if the volume elements $d\mathbf{r}_1$ and $d\mathbf{r}_2$ are close together. This suggests changing the variables of integration from $\mathbf{r}_1$ and $\mathbf{r}_2$ to $\mathbf{r}_1$ and $\mathbf{r}_{12}$ where $\mathbf{r}_{12} = \mathbf{r}_1 - \mathbf{r}_2$. As we have stated earlier, the only time that integration over $\mathbf{r}_{12}$ yields a result that is dependent on $\mathbf{r}_1$ is when molecule 1 is within a few molecular

[6] J. Yvon, *J. Physique*, **10**, 373 (1949).
[1] J. O. Hirschfelder *et al.*, *op. cit.*, Chapter 3.

diameters of the vessel wall. For a small cluster in a macroscopic volume such a dependence on $\mathbf{r}_1$ is very improbable, and Eq. (3) becomes

$$B_2(T) = -\frac{1}{2V} \int d\mathbf{r}_1 \int (e^{-u(r_{12})/kT} - 1) \, d\mathbf{r}_{12} \tag{4}$$

Since the forces between monatomic molecules depend only on their separation, we may set $d\mathbf{r}_{12} = 4\pi r^2 dr$. We may also take the upper limit of integration to be infinity since the only contributions to the integral come in the first few molecular diameters. Equation (4) thus reduces to

$$B_2(T) = -\tfrac{1}{2} \int_0^\infty (e^{-u(r)/kT} - 1) 4\pi r^2 \, dr \tag{5}$$

This is, of course, the long promised duplicate of Eq. (4.16), which was derived from the virial theorem of Clausius. If the function $(e^{-u(r)/kT} - 1)$ is expanded as a series and the first term is integrated, it develops that the integral cannot converge unless $u(r)$ decreases more rapidly than r^{-3}, hence the reservation regarding the choice of $u(r_{ij})$ made following Eq. (5.14).

For the hard sphere potential of Eq. (1), the integral of Eq. (5) is -1 for $r < \sigma/2$ and zero for $r \geq \sigma/2$, and the second virial coefficient

$$B_2 = \frac{2\pi}{3} \sigma^3 \tag{6}$$

is independent of temperature. Thus B_2 is just four times the volume of one of the hard sphere molecules. At high temperatures for which intermolecular attractive forces are negligible this model should be a good approximation. However, there are several alternative ways of assigning a numerical value to the collision diameter σ, all of which seem equally plausible.[2]

In discussing the Lennard-Jones 6–12 potential, Eq. (3.3), let us use the last term of Eq. (4.13)

$$-\frac{2\pi}{3kT} \int_0^\infty r^3 \frac{\partial u}{\partial r} e^{-u/kT} \, dr$$

as the second virial coefficient of Eq. (6.26) rather than what we have seen to be its equivalent, Eq. (5). We shall also rewrite Eq. (3.3) in the entirely equivalent form

$$u(r) = 4\varepsilon \left[-\left(\frac{\sigma}{r}\right)^6 + \left(\frac{\sigma}{r}\right)^{12} \right] \tag{8}$$

---

[2] J. O. Hirschfelder *et al.*, *op. cit.*, p. 157.

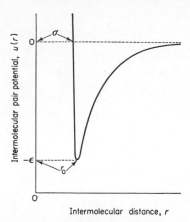

Figure 1. Lennard-Jones 6–12 potential.

where $u(r) = 0$ at $r = \sigma$, and $r_0 = 2^k\sigma$ (see Figure 1). It is then convenient to define the following reduced quantities:

$$r^* = \frac{r}{\sigma} \qquad T^* = \frac{kT}{\varepsilon} \tag{9}$$

The relation for the second virial coefficient resulting from the substitution of Eq. (8) in Eq. (7) is therefore

$$B_2(T) = -\frac{2\pi}{3}\left\{\frac{4\sigma^3}{T^*}\int_0^\infty r^{*2}\left[-\frac{12}{r^{*12}} + \frac{6}{r^{*6}}\right]e^{-(4/T^*)(1/r^{*12}-1/r^{*6})}dr^*\right\} \tag{10}$$

By expanding $\exp[(4/T^*)\,r^{*-6}]$ as an infinite series, Eq. (10) can be given a form that is integrable analytically. The result[3] is

$$B_2(T) = \frac{2\pi\sigma^3}{3}\,T^{*-\frac{1}{4}}\sqrt{2}\sum_{j\geq 0}-\frac{2^j}{4j!}\Gamma\left[\frac{2j-1}{4}\right]T^{*-j/2}$$

$$= \frac{2\pi\sigma^3}{3}\,T^{*-\frac{1}{4}}[1.733 - 2.564T^{*-\frac{1}{2}} - 8.66T^{*-1} - 4.27T^{*-\frac{3}{2}} - \ldots] \tag{11}$$

For reduced temperatures, $T^* = kT/\varepsilon$, greater than four this series converges rapidly. Equation (11) predicts a law of corresponding states for all gases for which the Lennard-Jones 6–12 intermolecular pair potential applies, i.e. B_2/σ^3 is a universal function of the reduced temperature T^*. Examples of gases which fit such a curve experimentally are argon, neon and N_2 and CH_4 for which the intermolecular pair potential is also spherically symmetric to a good approximation. The Boyle point is defined

[3] J. O. Hirschfelder *et al.*, *op. cit.*, pp. 163, 1119.

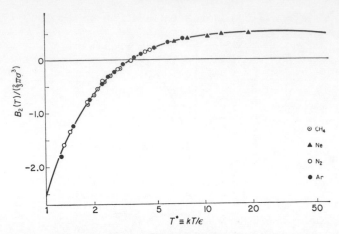

Figure 2. The reduced second virial coefficient for the Lennard-Jones 6–12 potential plotted from Eq. (11) as a function of the reduced temperature T^*. The experimental points are for the gases methane, neon, nitrogen, and argon, which behave classically. (After Lunbeck, 1950, and Hirschfelder *et al.*, 1954.)

as the point at which an isotherm goes through a minimum in a plot of pV *vs.* p. Raising the temperature shifts the Boyle point to lower and lower pressures until it finally disappears at the Boyle temperature. The Boyle temperature of air, for instance, is 347°K. At higher temperatures there is no point along an isotherm for which $d(pV)/dp = 0$. At the Boyle temperature the second virial coefficient is zero. As can be seen from Figure 2, the reduced Boyle temperature is $T^* = 3.42$. The curve of Figure 2 can be explained qualitatively in terms of the Lennard-Jones potential function. At low temperatures a molecular pair has, in general, insufficient energy to get out of the potential well of Figure 1; the imperfect gas pressure is therefore lower than that of a perfect gas, and B_2 is negative. As the temperature rises, the shallow potential well of Figure 1 becomes unimportant, the repulsive or hard sphere potential predominates, the pressure of the gas is greater than that of an ideal gas, and B_2 is positive. Finally, at sufficiently high temperatures the colliding spheres should 'soften' with a consequent decrease in the apparent volume of the gas molecules, the pressure, and the second virial coefficient. A maximum in the quantum mechanical analogue of the classical theoretical curve of Figure 2 has been duplicated experimentally with helium.

From Eqs. (6.26), (6.10), and (6.9) we have for the third virial coefficient

$$B_3(T) = -\tfrac{2}{3}\beta_2 = -\frac{1}{3V} \iiint f_{12} f_{13} f_{23} \, dr_1 \, dr_2 \, dr_3 \tag{12}$$

where the f's are, of course, defined by Eq. (5.16). When Eq. (12) is integrated for the hard sphere potential of Eq. (1) the result is

$$B_3 = \frac{5}{8}\left(\frac{2\pi\sigma^3}{3}\right)^2 = \tfrac{5}{8}B_2^2 \tag{13}$$

When the Lennard-Jones 6–12 potential is used and Eq. (12) is integrated the resulting expression for B_3 suggests a law of corresponding states which experimentally is followed much less satisfactorily than Eq. (11).[4] The theoretical B_3/σ^6 vs. T^* curve is only negative at lower temperatures than the B_2/σ^3 curve, passes through zero at $T^* \simeq 0.9$, and attains a fairly sharp maximum at $T^* \simeq 1.3$.

8. The Critical Point

In a plot of pressure versus temperature for a single-component system the point at which the liquid–gas phase equilibrium curve terminates is called critical. The temperature and pressure at this point are called the

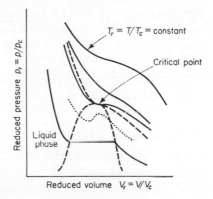

Figure 1. Isotherms of a one-component system near the critical point. Dotted lines are isotherms calculated from van der Waals' equation.

critical temperature, T_c, and the critical pressure, p_c. In a plot of pressure versus volume, Figure 1, the isothermal curve for the critical temperature T_c will have a single point at which

$$\left(\frac{\partial p}{\partial V}\right)_T = 0 \tag{1}$$

and

$$\left(\frac{\partial^2 p}{\partial V^2}\right)_T = 0 \tag{2}$$

[4] J. O. Hirschfelder et al., op. cit., p. 171.

The pressure and volume corresponding to this point will be the critical values p_c and V_c. At higher temperatures the isotherms will be smooth continuous curves corresponding to a single vapor phase. Below the critical temperature each isotherm will consist of three distinct parts joined at points at which the slope is discontinuous. The middle, horizontal portion of these isotherms corresponds to the saturated gas in equilibrium with the liquid. The other two portions of such a curve correspond to the liquid and gas respectively.

Our interest in the critical point stems from the fact that the description of critical phenomena provides a particularly challenging test of theoretical equations of state intended to describe both gases and liquids. As we shall see later in discussing liquids, equations of state can also be tested by comparing calculated and observed compressibility factors (pV/RT), vapor pressures, boiling points, and entropies of evaporation at the boiling point.

9. Semi-empirical Equations of State

Many semi-empirical equations of state have been devised to represent the behavior of gases and liquids throughout the pVT domain.[1] We shall consider here only two of these relations: van der Waals' equation of state[2]

$$\left(p + \frac{N^2 a}{V^2}\right)(V - Nb) = NkT \tag{1}$$

and Dieterici's equation of state[3]

$$p(V - Nb) = RT\, e^{-Na/kTV} \tag{2}$$

Although neither equation has a sound theoretical foundation except at low pressures and high temperatures, both exhibit critical and gas–liquid phase transition behavior. In practical use the two adjustable parameters in each of these equations are chosen to give a best fit of the experimental data over a narrow range of temperatures and pressures.

We begin an evaluation of the constants in Eq. (1) by assuming that each molecule of the gas moves in a field generated by all the molecules and that molecular interactions can be described on a pairwise basis by the following potential function:

$$u(r_{ij}) = \infty, \qquad\qquad r < r_0 \tag{3}$$

$$= -\varepsilon\left(\frac{r_0}{r}\right)^6, \qquad r \geq r_0 \tag{4}$$

[1] J. O. Hirschfelder et al., op. cit., p. 250.

[2] J. D. van der Waals, *Die Continuität des gasförmigen und flüssigen Zustandes,* Barth, Leipzig, 1881.

[3] C. Dieterici, *Ann. Phys.,* **69,** 685 (1899); **5,** 51 (1901).

where r_0 is a 'molecular diameter' and not a 'radius'. The potential minimum of this hard sphere weak attraction potential occurs at $r = r_0$. The appropriate canonical ensemble partition function for our model is

$$f_N = \left[\frac{1}{N!} \left(\frac{2\pi m k T}{h^2} \right)^{\frac{3}{2}N} V_f^N \right] e^{-N(\phi/2)(1/kT)} \qquad (5)$$

Except for the replacement of the total volume V by the empty volume V_f the parenthesized term is just the partition function of the perfect gas, Eq. (4.12.5). In our model each pair of colliding gas molecules excludes a volume $4\pi r_0^3/3$ (see Figure 1) and hence for N molecules the excluded volume is $(N/2) (4\pi r_0^3/3)$.

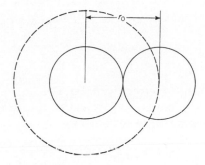

Figure 1. Excluded volume, $V = \frac{4}{3}\pi r_0^3$.

The empty volume is therefore

$$V' = V - Nb \qquad \text{where } b = 2\pi r_0^3/3 \qquad (6)$$

The energy ϕ in the Boltzmann exponential factor of Eq. (5) is the potential energy of interaction between one molecule and all the other molecules of the gas. Division by two is necessary to prevent overcounting. Since in Eqs. (3) and (4) we have postulated intermolecular interactions, we should expect a certain amount of short range ordering of the dense gas in the vicinity of any particular gas molecule. However, in evaluating the constant a of Eq. (1), we shall make the unfounded assumption that the molecules are randomly distributed throughout the volume and the number of molecules lying near a particular molecule in a concentric shell ranging from r to $r + dr$ is

$$\frac{N}{V} \cdot 4\pi r^2 \, dr \qquad \text{where } r \geqslant r_0 \qquad (7)$$

The interaction energy of all the other gas molecules with the particular molecule in question is therefore from Eq. (4) just

$$\phi = -\int_{r_0}^{\infty} \varepsilon \left(\frac{r_0}{r}\right)^6 \frac{N}{V} 4\pi r^2 \, dr = -\frac{2Na}{V} \tag{8}$$

where

$$a = 2\pi \varepsilon r_0^3 / 3 \tag{9}$$

Using Eq. (1.2.26) and Stirling's approximation, we then have

$$A = -kT \ln f_N$$

$$= -kT \left[-N \ln N + N + \tfrac{3}{2} N \ln \left(\frac{2\pi m kT}{h^2}\right) + N \ln (V - Nb) + \frac{N^2 a}{V kT} \right] \tag{10}$$

From the relation $p = -(\partial A / \partial V)_T$, Eq. (1.2.28), we then have

$$p = \frac{NkT}{(V - Nb)} - \frac{N^2 a}{V^2} \tag{11}$$

A trivial rearrangement of terms yields Eq. (1).

By expanding p/kT in powers of the density $\rho = N/V$, we can obtain an expression for the second virial coefficient:

$$\frac{p}{kT} = (\rho + b\rho^2 + b^2\rho^3 + \ldots) - \frac{N^2 a}{V^2 kT}$$

$$= \rho + \left(b - \frac{a}{kT}\right)\rho^2 + b^2\rho^3 + \ldots \tag{12}$$

Dieterici's equation, (2), yields the same value of $B_2(T)$. In the limit of high temperatures we can obtain this same expression for the second virial coefficient by substituting the potential function of Eqs. (3) and (4) in Eq. (4.16). For T large we may write $e^{-u(r)/kT} = 1 - u(r)/kT$ and hence

$$B_2 = 2\pi \int_0^{\infty} r^2 (1 - 1 + u(r)/kT) \, dr$$

$$= 2\pi \int_0^{r_0} r^2 \, dr + 2\pi \int_{r_0}^{\infty} r^2 \left(-\frac{\varepsilon r_0^6}{kT r^6}\right) dr$$

$$= b - a/kT \tag{13}$$

Since the random distribution of molecules assumed in deriving Eq. (12) will in fact obtain at sufficiently high temperatures and since the other serious approximation of no interpretation of molecular volumes is also good for low densities, the agreement between Eqs. (12) and (13) comes as no great surprise.

In order to define the van der Waals constants a and b in terms of the critical temperature and volume we substitute Eq. (11) in Eqs. (8.1) and (8.2) and obtain

$$-\frac{NkT_c}{(V_c-Nb)^2} + \frac{2N^2a}{V_c^3} = 0 \tag{14}$$

$$\frac{2NkT_c}{(V_c-Nb)^3} - \frac{6N^2a}{V_c^4} = 0 \tag{15}$$

The solution of these simultaneous equations is

$$b = \frac{V_c}{3N}, \qquad a = \frac{9}{8}\left(\frac{kT_cV_c}{N}\right) \tag{16}$$

The van der Waals constants are more commonly expressed as molar rather than molecular quantities, i.e.

$$b' = \tfrac{1}{3}V_c, \qquad a' = \tfrac{9}{8}RT_cV_c \tag{17}$$

The corresponding form of van der Waals equation of state is

$$\left(p + \frac{a'}{\tilde{V}^2}\right)(\tilde{V}-b') = RT \tag{18}$$

Substituting Eq. (17) in Eq. (18), and setting $\tilde{V} = V_c$ and $T = T_c$, we obtain

$$\frac{pV_c}{RT_c} = \tfrac{3}{8} = 0.375 \tag{19}$$

The same result can be obtained, of course, by substituting Eq. (16) in Eq. (1) and setting $\tilde{V} = V_c$ and $T = T_c$.

The analogues of Eqs. (17), (18), and (19) for Dieterici's equation of state are

$$b' = \tfrac{1}{2}V_c \qquad\qquad a' = 2RT_cV_c \tag{20}$$

$$p^{(\tilde{V}-b')} = RT\, e^{-a'/RT\tilde{V}} \tag{21}$$

and

$$\frac{pV_c}{RT_c} = 2e^{-2} = 0.271 \tag{22}$$

respectively. Note that at low pressures both Eqs. (18) and (21) reduce to

$$\tilde{V} = \frac{RT}{p} + b' - \frac{a'}{RT} \tag{23}$$

when small second-order terms are neglected.

The experimental compressibility factor at the critical point, p_cV_c/RT_c, is given for a number of molecules in Table 1.[4]

[4] J. O. Hirschfelder *et al.*, *op. cit.*, p. 237.

TABLE 1. Experimental compressibility factors at the critical point

Substance	$p_c V_c/RT_c$	Substance	$p_c V_c/RT_c$
H_2	0.304	n-Octane	0.258
Ne	0.296	Ethylene	0.291
Ar	0.291	CH_3CN	0.181
N_2	0.292	H_2O	0.224
CO_2	0.287	NH_3	0.238
CH_4	0.290	C_2H_5Cl	0.269

The essentially spherical, non-polar molecules of the first column in Table 1 have an average compressibility factor of 0.293. Evidently, Dieterici's equation of state gives at least a rough representation of the relationship between p_c, V_c, and T_c whereas van der Waals' equation fails to do so. It is further apparent from Table 1 that a law of corresponding states can be expected to apply in only the roughest sort of way when the substances compared have different shapes, masses, and dipole moments.

10. Corresponding States

Figure 7.2 and Eqs. (9.19) and (9.22) suggest that many substances at equal reduced temperatures, $T_r = T/T_c$, have equal reduced saturated vapor pressures, equal reduced specific volume for the saturated vapor, and equal reduced specific volume of the liquid in equilibrium with the saturated vapor. This law of corresponding states can be obtained from any two-parameter intermolecular potential that is pairwise additive and has the form (energy) × (reciprocal distance). Let us consider Hill's elaboration of Pitzer's proof of this statement.[1]

We begin by assuming that the translational partition function is classical thereby excluding hydrogen, helium, and to a lesser degree neon at low temperatures. We also assume that the internal degrees of freedom of the molecules are the same in the liquid as in the gas phase, and the intermolecular potential energy is a function only of intermolecular distances. This latter assumption excludes highly polar molecules, metals, and hydrogen bonded molecules from consideration. Our attention is restricted then to essentially spherically symmetric molecules interacting only through van der Waals forces. Finally, we assume that we may write the potential function for a pair of molecules in the general form

$$\varepsilon\Phi(r/r_0) \qquad (1)$$

where r is the intermolecular distance, ε and r_0 are constants characteristic

[1] K. S. Pitzer, *J. Chem. Phys.*, **7**, 583 (1939); T. L. Hill, *Statistical Thermodynamics*, Addison-Wesley, Reading, Mass., 1960, p. 298.

of a particular substance, and Φ is the same function for all substances under consideration. The Lennard-Jones 6–12 potential is just one of many conceivable potential functions that would satisfy these requirements.

On the basis of the foregoing assumptions we have the following partition function

$$f_N = \left(\frac{2\pi mkT}{h^2}\right)^{\frac{3}{2}N} (f_{\text{int}})^N Q_N \tag{2}$$

where the configuration partition function is

$$Q_N = \frac{1}{N!} \int_V \cdots \int e^{-U/kT} \, dr_1 \ldots dr_N = \frac{r_0^{3N}}{N!} \int_V \cdots \int e^{-U/kT} \, d\left(\frac{r_1}{r_0^3}\right) \ldots d\left(\frac{r_N}{r_0^3}\right) \tag{3}$$

and

$$\frac{U}{kT} = \sum_{1 \leqslant i < j \leqslant N} \frac{u(r_{ij})}{kT} = \sum_{i<j} \frac{\varepsilon}{kT} \Phi\left(\frac{r_{ij}}{r_0}\right) \tag{4}$$

We make no attempt at evaluating Eq. (3) but simply rewrite the configurational partition function in an equivalent form

$$Q_N = \frac{r_0^{3N}}{N!} \psi_1 \left(\frac{\varepsilon}{kT}, \frac{V}{r_0^3}, N\right) \tag{5}$$

where ψ_1 is a universal function for all substances under consideration. The quantity $-A/NkT$ is intensive according to thermodynamics and is therefore a function of $\tilde{V} = V/N$ and T only. From the relations $A = -kT \ln f_N$ and Eq. (2), it necessarily follows that both $N^{-1} \ln f_N$ and $N^{-1} \ln Q_N$ are also functions of $\tilde{V}$ and T alone, i.e.

$$Q_N = e^{N\psi_2(\tilde{V}, T)} = \psi_3(\tilde{V}, T)^N \tag{6}$$

Now if we compare Eqs. (5) and (6) we see that

$$\psi_1 = \Psi\left(\frac{\varepsilon}{kT}, \frac{\tilde{V}}{r_0^3}\right)^N \tag{7}$$

where Ψ is again a universal function for all substances in question. From Eqs. (2), (5), and (7) we then have

$$f_N = \left(\frac{2\pi mkT}{h^2}\right)^{\frac{3}{2}N} (f_{\text{int}})^N r_0^{3N} \Psi\left(\frac{\varepsilon}{kT}, \frac{\tilde{V}}{r_0^3}\right)^N \tag{8}$$

It follows from Eqs. (1.2.26) and (1.2.28) that

$$\frac{p\tilde{V}}{kT} = \frac{\tilde{V}}{r_0^3} \left(\frac{\partial \ln \Psi}{\partial \tilde{V}/r_0^3}\right)_{\varepsilon/kT} \tag{9}$$

and we have demonstrated that $p\tilde{V}/kT$ is a universal function of the quantities $\tilde{V}/r_0^3$ and ε/kT.

12

EQUILIBRIUM PROPERTIES OF LIQUIDS

1. Introduction

The liquid state is intermediate between the solid and gas states and, therefore, it is to be expected that the thermodynamic properties of a liquid will be intermediate between those of its gaseous and solid states.

X-ray studies of liquids[1] indicate considerable short-range order with nearest neighbor distances only slightly different from those of solids. This is unlike the almost complete randomness of the gaseous state, in which only an occasional dimer or trimer reminds us of the all but vanished short-range order so conspicuous in the condensed phases. For liquids one can, therefore, speak of a quasi-lattice structure with the typical twelve per cent expansion of a liquid due to the introduction of vacancies or holes into the structure. The atypical ten per cent contraction of ice on melting is due to a structural contraction superimposed on the usual expansion of the solid to liquid transition. Indeed, this contraction disappears if one first applies some 2100 atmospheres pressure at $-22°c$ to the hydrogen-bonded tetrahedral ice I and so transforms it to ice III, which is a fifth more dense. Ice III then melts with a normal ten per cent expansion.

To remove a molecule from a lattice and leave a hole behind involves breaking all the bonds binding the molecule to its neighbors. To evaporate molecules requires only half this energy since again all bonds to neighbors are broken but each bond joins two molecules and therefore only half of the energy of a bond should be charged against each neighbor. Thus, the energy of vaporization of a molecule is just half of the sum of the bond energies joining it to its neighbors. Clearly, the energy of vaporization could be regained by letting the hole disappear by migrating to the liquid surface or by returning the molecule to the surface. Therefore, it follows that the introduction of a molecular-sized hole requires an energy equal to the heat of vaporization. Thus, approximately, a molecular-sized hole in the liquid contributes the same enthalpy and entropy as does a molecule in the vapor. It is, therefore, to be expected that there should be as many molecular-sized holes per unit volume of liquid as there are molecules per

---

[1] A. Eisenstein and N. S. Gingrich, *Phys. Rev.*, **62**, 261 (1942).

unit volume of vapor, so that the sum of the densities of the liquid and vapor should be constant except for a drift toward lower mean densities of the vapor with rising temperature because of the thermal expansion of the lattice. This qualitative explanation of the experimental law of rectilinear diameters[2] was first pointed out long ago.[3]

2. The Method of Significant Structures

The above considerations may be quantitatively formulated in the following manner. Neglecting the effect of holes other than those of molecular size, the number of holes present in a liquid is $N(V-V_s)/V_s$, where V_s and V are, respectively, the molar volumes of the solid and liquid phases. Such a molecular-sized hole will confer gas-like properties on a neighboring molecule which jumps into it. Assuming a random distribution of holes and molecules, $N(V-V_s)/V$ of the molecules will possess solid-like properties. If the above argument is valid then the specific heat at constant volume of a classical liquid would be[1]

$$C_V = 6\frac{V_s}{V} + 3\frac{V-V_s}{V} \qquad (1)$$

Equation (1) is plotted in Figure 1 for liquid argon and is seen to be in good agreement with the experimental points.

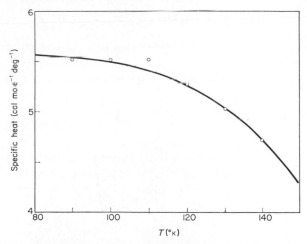

Figure 1. The specific heat of liquid argon (after Eyring and Ree [2]). The points represent the experimental values.

[2] L. Cailletet and E. Mathias, *C. R. Acad. Sci., Paris*, **102**, 1202 (1886); **104**, 1563 (1887).

[3] H. Eyring, *J. Chem. Phys.*, **4**, 283 (1936).

[1] J. Walter and H. Eyring, *J. Chem. Phys.*, **9**, 393 (1941).

[2] H. Eyring, T. Ree and N. Hirai, *Proc. Natl. Acad. Sci. U.S.*, **44**, 683 (1958); H. Eyring and T. Ree, *ibid.*, **47**, 526 (1961).

The presence of holes in the liquid will not only confer gas-like properties on some of the molecules but will also provide, for a solid-like molecule, a positional degeneracy equal to the number of neighboring holes, n_h, multiplied by the probability of the molecule and a hole exchanging positions. If we let ε be the energy required for a molecule–hole pair to exchange positions, then the partition function for a liquid is[2]

$$f_N = \{f_s(1 + n_h e^{-\varepsilon/RT})\}^{N(V_s/V)}\{f_g\}^{N(V-V_s)/V}\left\{\left(N\frac{V-V_s}{V}\right)!\right\}^{-1} \qquad (2)$$

where f_s and f_g are the partition functions for a solid-like and for a gas-like molecule, respectively. Assuming a random distribution of holes and molecules

$$n_h = z\frac{V-V_s}{V} \qquad (3)$$

where $z = 12$ is the coordination number of the lattice. All liquids but helium and hydrogen, and to a much lesser extent neon, exist at comparatively high temperatures where a large entropy will be important in minimizing the free energy and, therefore, the molecules will tend to surround themselves with their full complement of holes. For this situation Eq. (3) should be replaced by

$$n_h = n\frac{V-V_s}{V_s} \qquad (4)$$

The energy ε is assumed to be proportional to the potential energy of the lattice and inversely proportional to n_h. Figure 2 illustrates the energetic

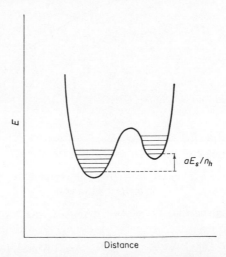

Figure 2. Potential energy curve for a molecule occupying the most favored position as compared with a neighboring vacancy (after Eyring and Ree[2]).

situation for a solid-like molecule comparing the most favored position with a neighboring vacancy.

Once the partition function has been formulated the thermodynamic properties may be calculated in the usual way. To find the phases in equilibrium with each other the Helmholtz free energy is plotted, for a given temperature, as a function of the volume (see Figure 3). The volumes at the points of common tangency are the volumes of the corresponding phases and the pressure is given by the slope of the tangent. The tangent intercepts the A axis at the common Gibbs' free energy, G, for the various phases. Except at the triple point, a tangent line has at most two points of tangency. Tangents which cut the curve, A versus V, at any point correspond to a metastable state but may be realizable kinetically. Figure 3 is schematic since the volume of the gas, V_g, is actually of the order of thousands of times the volume of the liquid, V_l.

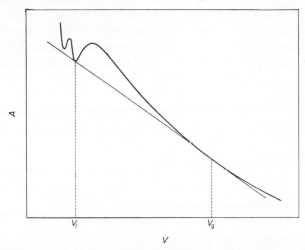

Figure 3. Schematic plot of the Helmholtz free energy as a function of volume for some temperature.

Since the critical point is a point of inflection in a plot of isotherms, the critical properties can be calculated from the relations

$$-\left(\frac{\partial A}{\partial V}\right)_T = p, \qquad \left(\frac{\partial p}{\partial V}\right)_T = 0, \qquad \left(\frac{\partial^2 p}{\partial V^2}\right)_T = 0 \qquad (5)$$

It is to be emphasized that the significant structure theory of liquids does not imply that a liquid is a mixture of solid and gas. A molecule has solid-like properties for the time it vibrates about an equilibrium position, then it may instantaneously transform into gas-like behavior in one or more of its degrees of freedom as it jumps into a neighboring hole.

3. Application to Simple Classical Liquids

In this section we shall consider the application of the significant structures method to representative relatively simple classical liquids such as the inert gases and chlorine.

In as much as the molecules of the inert gases are monatomic we have for their partition function

$$f_N = \left\{ \frac{e^{E_s/RT}}{(1 - e^{-\theta/T})^3} (1 + n_h e^{-aE_s/n_hRT}) \right\}^{N(V_s/V)}$$

$$\times \left\{ \left(\frac{2\pi mkT}{h^2} \right)^{\frac{3}{2}} (V - V_s) \right\}^{N(V-V_s)/V} \left\{ \left(N\frac{V - V_s}{V} \right)! \right\}^{-1}$$

$$= \left\{ \frac{e^{E_s/RT}}{(1 - e^{-\theta/T})^3} (1 + n_h e^{-aE_s/n_hRT}) \right\}^{N(V_s)/V} \left\{ \left(\frac{2\pi mkT}{h^2} \right)^{\frac{3}{2}} \frac{eV}{N} \right\}^{N(V-V_s)/V} \quad (1)$$

where n_h is given by Eq. (2.4) and θ, E_s, and V_s are the Einstein characteristic temperature, the energy of sublimation, and the volume of the solid, all measured at the melting point. We can regard these three quantities as parameters calculated from a quantum mechanical treatment of the solid state or as experimental solid state parameters. Values for n and a can be determined by requiring the free energy to be a minimum at the observed triple point. The term eV/N arises from the application of Stirling's approximation $x! = (x/e)^x$. Such considerations involve assuming that the gas-like degrees of freedom distribute themselves in such a way as to share communally the available volume, $V - V_s$.

The values of the parameters used in the calculation of the thermodynamic properties of the liquid inert gases[1] are given in Table 1 and the calculated and observed thermodynamic properties of these liquids at their melting, boiling, and critical points are listed in Table 2.

TABLE 1. Values of the parameters for the inert gases

	Ne	Ar	Kr	Xe
Energy of sublimation, E_s (cal mole^{-1})	447.4	1888.6	2710.6	3897.7
Solid molar volume, V_s (cm^3 mole^{-1})	13.98	24.98	28.4	36.5
Einstein characteristic temperature, θ (°K)	44.7	60.0	45.0	39.2
n	11	10.80	11.70	12.27
a	0.00802	0.00534	0.00580	0.005632

[1] E. J. Fuller, T. Ree and H. Eyring, *Proc. Natl. Acad. Sci. U.S.*, **45**, 1594 (1959).

TABLE 2. Calculated and observed thermodynamic properties of the inert gases

	Ne	Ar	Kr	Xe	
V_m (cm^3 mole^{-1})	16.43	28.90	33.11	42.30	calc.
	16.15	28.03	34.13	42.68	obs.
p_m (atm)	0.437	0.732	0.756	0.399	calc.
	0.417	0.674	0.722	0.804	obs.
S_m (e.u.)	3.244	3.263	3.456	3.415	calc.
	3.259	3.35	3.35	3.40	obs.
T_b (°K)	27.13	87.29	119.28	167.5	calc.
	27.16	87.29	119.93	165.1	obs.
V_b (cm^3 mole^{-1})	17.17	29.33	—	—	calc.
	16.80	28.69	—	—	obs.
S_b (e.u.)	15.68	19.04	19.27	19.43	calc.
	15.81	17.85	17.99	18.29	obs.
T_c (°K)	46.29	149.7	208.33	287.8	calc.
	44.47	150.66	210.6	289.8	obs.
V_c (cm^3 mole^{-1})	47.11	83.68	88.32	113.52	calc.
	41.74	75.26	—	113.8	obs.
p_c (atm)	29.12	52.93	69.68	74.89	calc.
	26.86	48.00	54.24	58.2	obs.

An essential point in any model of the liquid is that it explains the utilization of the excess volume introduced upon melting. A model which omits this explanation applies to either a superheated liquid or a super-cooled gas and not to a liquid. As we have seen, melting introduces the degeneracy factor

$$\left\{1 + n \frac{V - V_s}{V_s} \exp\left(-\frac{aE_sV_s}{(V-V_s)RT}\right)\right\}.$$

Simply stated, the excess volume introduces alternative positions proportional to the number of holes, and the energy required for a molecule to pre-empt these positions from competing neighbor molecules is proportional to the energy of vaporization and inversely proportional to the number of holes. Near the melting point where the liquid still approximates a lattice, we can evaluate $n(V-V_s)/V_s$ and $\exp[-aE_sV_s/(V-V_s)RT]$. Thus, near melting the fraction of the neighboring points z which are empty and therefore available for occupancy is

$$z\frac{V-V_s}{V_s} = \left(\frac{zV_s}{V}\right)\frac{V-V_s}{V} = n\frac{V-V_s}{V_s}.$$

Hence $n = zV_s/V = 12 \times (1/1.12) = 10.7$ to be compared with the value $n = 10.6$ required to fit experimental data. Now these positions would be available without extra energy to a neighbor except that in melting the other neighbors to the position have gained the kinetic energy of melting by spreading into the vacancies. According to the virial theorem the kinetic energy of melting is half the total energy of melting. Thus, at or very near the melting point

$$\frac{aE_s V_s}{V - V_s} = \frac{n-1}{z} \frac{1}{2} E_m = \frac{n-1}{z} \frac{1}{2} \frac{V - V_s}{V} E_s.$$

Hence

$$a = \frac{n-1}{z} \frac{1}{2} \frac{V - V_s}{V} \frac{V - V_s}{V_s} = 0.0052$$

which is to be compared with the value 0.00534 which was chosen to fit experimental data. The factor $(n-1)/z$ results from the fact that a molecule expanding into the vacancy acquires $1/z$ of its kinetic energy of melting and there are only $n-1$ molecules to compete with the molecule in question. Our model thus fixes all the parameters in liquid theory except those characteristic of the solid.

The partition function for the rare gases successfully represents the equation of state of methane and nitrogen[1] since these latter substances freely rotate in the liquid state. Benzene and chlorine on the other hand do not rotate freely in the liquid state. When restricted rotation is introduced into the partition function equally satisfactory results are obtained for benzene[1] and chlorine.[2] We shall consider the case of chlorine as illustrative of this procedure.

It may be inferred from the unusually high entropy of fusion of chlorine[3] that the chlorine molecules do not freely rotate in the solid state. This view is supported by the absence of transition peaks in the heat capacity curve of solid chlorine and from the density data for liquid chlorine.[4, 5] Rather than complicate the partition function by considering libration type degrees of freedom, the solid-like part is treated as a five-degree Einstein oscillator, with internal vibration being the sixth degree of freedom. Free rotation is assumed in the gas-like part of the partition function. Hence

$$f_N = \left\{ \frac{e^{E_s/RT}}{(1 - e^{-\theta/T})^5} (1 + n_h e^{-aE_s/n_h RT}) \right\}^{N(V_s/V)}$$

$$\times \left\{ \left(\frac{2\pi mkT}{h^2}\right)^{\frac{3}{2}} \frac{8\pi^2 IkT}{2h^2} \frac{eV}{N} \right\}^{N(V - V_s)/V} \left\{ \frac{1}{1 - e^{-hv/kT}} \right\}^N \quad (2)$$

In order to obtain reasonable agreement it was found necessary to choose a value of V_s somewhat larger than the observed value ($V_s = 34.341$).

2 T. R. Thomson, H. Eyring and T. Ree, *Proc. Natl. Acad. Sci. U.S.*, **46**, 336 (1960).
3 W. F. Giauque and T. M. Powell, *J. Am. Chem. Soc.*, **61**, 1970 (1939).
4 M. Pellaton, *J. Chim. Phys.*, **13**, 426 (1915).
5 F. M. G. Johnson and D. McIntosh, *J. Am. Chem. Soc.*, **31**, 1142 (1909).

This anomaly is probably due to some transition in the solid beginning at a temperature near or at the melting point. The parameters for liquid chlorine were obtained by a trial and error method and are listed in Table 3. The calculated and observed thermodynamic properties of liquid chlorine at its boiling and critical points are given in Table 4.

TABLE 3. Values of the parameter for liquid chlorine

Energy of sublimation, E_s (cal mole^{-1})	6075.9
Molar volume of solid, V_s (cm^3 mole^{-1})	39.1757
Einstein characteristic temperature, θ (°K)	41.48
n	14.3
a	0.0012977

TABLE 4. Calculated and observed thermodynamic properties of liquid chlorine

	Calculated	Observed	Δ
T_b (°K)	(239.05)	239.05	—
V_b (cm^3 mole^{-1})	44.856	45.321	-1.03%
p_b (atm)	0.9984	1.0000	-0.161%
S_b (e.u.)	20.46	20.40	-0.27%
T_c	463.5	417.16	-11.1%
V_c	131.2	123.8	-5.98%
p_c	104.74	76.1	-37.7%

The calculated and observed vapor pressures of liquid chlorine as functions of the temperature are plotted in Figure 1. The agreement is very good

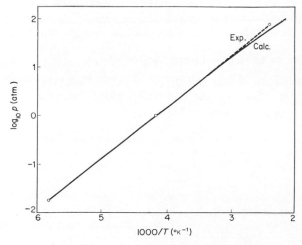

Figure 1. Vapor pressure of liquid chlorine.

indeed although a departure from the experimentally observed linear relationship between $\log_{10} p$ and $1/T$ is to be noted in the region of the critical point.

The specific heat may be calculated from the partition function. Experimental values are available for C_p, which is related to C_V by Eq. (3.5.42)

$$C_p - C_V = \frac{TV\alpha^2}{\beta} \tag{3}$$

where α is the coefficient of thermal expansion and β is the compressibility

$$\alpha = \frac{1}{V}\left(\frac{\partial V}{\partial T}\right)_p, \qquad \beta = -\frac{1}{V}\left(\frac{\partial V}{\partial p}\right)_T \tag{4}$$

which may also be calculated from the partition function for liquid chlorine. The calculated values of α, β, C_V, and C_p and the experimental values of C_p are given in Table 5 for various temperatures. This constitutes an extreme test of the partition function since any errors in C_V, α, and β are compounded.

TABLE 5. Calculated values for α, β, C_V, and C_p and observed values of C_p for liquid chlorine (after Thomson et al.)

$T(°K)$	$\alpha \times 10^3$	$\beta \times 10^6$	C_V	C_p(calc.)	C_p(obs.)	Δ
180.000	1.301	47.4	10.12	16.59	16.02	3.56%
190.513	1.219	50.0	10.03	15.81	15.99	−1.13%
200.413	1.216	55.3	10.13	15.67	15.95	−1.76%
210.000	1.241	62.1	10.11	15.56	15.89	−1.45%
219.909	1.254	68.3	10.11	15.47	15.84	−2.34%
229.958	1.304	82.2	10.11	15.47	15.77	−1.90%
240.050	1.356	88.9	10.11	15.51	15.70	−1.21%

4. Application to Molten Salts and Molten Metals

The observed percentage change in volume of argon upon melting is twelve per cent. However, for the molten alkali halides the expansion is much greater as can be seen in Table 1.

TABLE 1. Volume changes at the melting point (after Carlson et al.[1])

	NaCl	KCl	NaBr	KBr
Liquid volume (cm³ mole⁻¹)	37.74	48.80	44.08	56.03
Solid volume (cm³ mole⁻¹)	30.19	41.57	36.02	48.05
Per cent change	25.0	17.4	22.4	16.6

[1] C. M. Carlson, H. Eyring and T. Ree, *Proc. Natl. Acad. Sci. U.S.*, **46**, 333 (1960).

Evidently the expansion of the alkali halides upon melting is about twice that of a normal liquid such as argon. This is to be expected since the entropy of melting comes from the randomness introduced by holes. Since the positive ions can occupy only half the vacancies while the negative ions occupy the other half, it should require twice the percentage expansion to get the same entropy increase for each kind of ion. The fact that only half of the extra volume $(V - V_s)$ provides vacancies for each kind of ion means that the parameter n in the degeneracy term should be only about half as large for the molten alkali halides as for the liquid inert gases. This too is in accord with the findings, as is seen below.

The energy of vaporization for liquid inert gases falls off as $E_s V_s / V$, that is, inversely as the volume, as was suggested by van der Waals long ago. This is not true for the molten alkali halides since in one of the three dimensions, a positive and negative ion cling together and there is expansion only in the other two dimensions. Thus the energy should fall off more nearly inversely proportional to $V^{\frac{2}{3}}$.

Such considerations provide the justification for the following partition function used by Carlson et al.[1] for molten alkali halides.

$$f_N = \left\{ \frac{\exp \dfrac{E_s}{2RT} \left(\dfrac{V}{V_s} \right)^{\frac{1}{3}}}{(1 - e^{-\theta/T})^3} (1 + n_h e^{-aE_s(V/V_s)^{\frac{1}{3}}/n_h RT}) \right\}^{2NV_s/V}$$

$$\times \left\{ \left(\frac{2\pi m k T}{h^2} \right)^{\frac{3}{2}} \frac{eV}{N} \frac{8\pi^2 IkT}{h^2} \frac{1}{1 - e^{-h\nu/kT}} \right\}^{N(V - V_s)/V} \qquad (1)$$

The results of this theory for potassium chloride are shown in Table 2.

TABLE 2. Properties of molten KCl (after Carlson et al.[1])

T_m (°K)	V_m (cm³ mole⁻¹)	ΔS_m	T_b (°K)	V_b (cm³ mole⁻¹)	ΔS_b (e.u.)	T_c (°K)	V_c (cm³ mole⁻¹)	p_c (atm)
Calc. 1023	49.06	5.40	1684	71.20	21.63	3092	432	135.5
Obs. 1049	48.80	5.8	1680	—	23.1	—	—	—
Δ −2.6%	−0.53%	−6.90%	−0.24%	—	−6.36%	—	—	—

$$n \quad 6 \qquad\qquad a \quad 0.03000 \qquad\qquad E_s \quad 54.15 \text{ kcal mole}$$
$$V_s \quad 41.57 \text{ cm}^3 \text{ mole}^{-1} \qquad \theta \quad 170°\text{K} \qquad\qquad I \quad 2.195 \times 10^{-36} \text{ gm cm}^2$$
$$\omega \quad 305 \text{ cm}^{-1}$$

This theory applies with equal faithfulness to molten metals[2] if it is recognized that the necessary vacancies need only be large enough to accommodate the ion stripped of the valence electrons and that these ions are only about a third of the volume of the atom. Metals will, therefore, expand upon melting roughly one-third as much as the liquid inert gases. Taking this into account by choosing values of n about three times as large as for the liquid inert gases and allowing for both atoms and diatomic molecules in the gas-like part of the partition function, the same faithful representation of the thermodynamic properties is obtained. Again the model seems to be powerfully supported.

5. Application to Liquid Hydrogen

In applying the above theory to liquid hydrogen[1] a Debye partition function was used for the solid-like molecules. At the temperatures of interest, the gas-like molecules are slightly degenerate and therefore a Bose–Einstein partition function was used for the hydrogen and deuterium molecules and a Fermi–Dirac partition function was used for the hydrogen deuteride molecules. The resulting partition function for liquid hydrogen is then

$$\ln f_N = N \frac{V_s}{V} \left\{ \frac{E_p}{RT} - \frac{9}{8} \left(\frac{\theta_D}{T} \right) - 9 \left(\frac{T}{\theta_D} \right)^3 \int_0^{\theta_D/T} u^2 \ln(1 - e^{-u}) \, du \right.$$

$$\left. + \ln(1 + n_h e^{-aE_p/n_h RT}) \right\} + N \frac{V - V_s}{V} \left\{ 1 - \ln y \pm \frac{y}{2^{\frac{3}{2}}} \right\} + N \ln f_r \quad (1)$$

where the top sign applies to the Bose–Einstein gas and the bottom sign applies to the Fermi–Dirac case, E_p is the potential energy of the solid-like lattice, $y = \frac{N}{V} \left(\frac{h^2}{2\pi m k T} \right)^{\frac{3}{2}}$, θ_D is the Debye temperature of the solid-like lattice, and f_r is the rotational partition function for the molecules. If $\theta_r = h^2/8\pi^2 Ik$ then the rotational partition functions for ortho-hydrogen (o-H_2) and para-hydrogen (p-H_2), respectively, are given by the expressions

$$f_r^o = 3 \sum_{n=1,3}^{\infty} (2n+1) e^{-n(n+1)\theta_r/T}$$

$$f_r^p = \sum_{n=0,2}^{\infty} (2n+1) e^{-n(n+1)\theta_r/T}$$

(2)

[2] C. M. Carlson, H. Eyring and T. Ree, *Proc. Natl. Acad. Sci. U.S.*, **46**, 649 (1960).
[1] D. Henderson, H. Eyring and D. Felix, *J. Phys. Chem.*, **66**, 1128 (1962).

For ortho-deuterium (o-D_2) and para-deuterium (p-D_2) the corresponding expressions are

$$f_r^o = 6 \sum_{n=0,2}^{\infty} (2n+1) e^{-n(n+1)\theta_r/T}$$

$$f_r^p = 3 \sum_{n=1,3}^{\infty} (2n+1) e^{-n(n+1)\theta_r/T} \tag{3}$$

For mixtures of ortho and para molecules the rotational partition function is given by the usual expression

$$\ln f_r = \eta \ln f_r^o + (1-\eta) \ln f_r^p \tag{4}$$

where η is the fraction of the molecules which are in the ortho state. For normal hydrogen $\eta = \frac{3}{4}$ while for normal deuterium $\eta = \frac{2}{3}$. Finally for hydrogen deuteride (H—D) the rotational partition function is

$$f_r = 6 \sum_{n=1,2}^{\infty} (2n+1) e^{-n(n+1)\theta_r/T} \tag{5}$$

Equations (3) through (5) have been justified in Sect. 11.1.

Equation (2.3) was used in calculating the thermodynamic properties for temperatures up to and somewhat above the boiling temperatures. However, at the comparatively high temperatures and low densities of the critical points of the various forms of liquid hydrogen Eq. (2.4) was assumed valid, i.e. $n = zV_s/V$ is a constant. In the calculation of critical constants it was assumed that $\frac{1}{2}z$ was a sufficiently good value for n. Since n appears logarithmically its exact value does not greatly affect the value of the critical constants.

The values of the parameters used in these calculations are listed in Table 1 and the calculated and observed boiling point and critical point properties are listed in Table 2. The vapor pressures of p-H_2, H—D, and o-D_2 are plotted as functions of the temperature in Figure 1.

TABLE 1. Values of parameters for liquid hydrogen (after Henderson et al.[1])

	p-H_2	n-H_2	H—D	o-D_2	n-D_2
V_s (cm³ mole⁻¹)	23.34	23.25	21.84	20.58	20.48
θ (°K)	91	91	90	89	89
E_p (cal mole⁻¹)	384.9	386.3	435.7	475.2	476.8
I (gm cm²) × 10⁴¹	4.67	4.67	6.21	9.31	9.31
θ_r (°K)	85.4	85.4	64.2	42.8	42.8
$a \times 10^2$	0.547	0.554	0.565	0.640	0.647

TABLE 2. Thermodynamic properties of liquid hydrogen

	p-H_2	n-H_2	H—D	o-D_2	n-D_2	
T_b (°K)	20.58	20.70	22.29	23.65	23.75	calc.
	20.261	20.365	22.14	23.59	23.67	obs.
V_b (cm³ mole⁻¹)	28.829	28.692	26.525	24.955	24.830	calc.
	28.482	28.393	—	—	—	obs.
S_b (e.u.)	10.553	10.564	11.868	12.741	12.737	calc.
	10.602	—	—	12.459	—	obs.
T_c (°K)	35.9	36.2	37.6	39.4	39.7	calc.
	32.994	33.24	35.908	38.262	38.24	obs.
V_c (cm³ mole⁻¹)	77.7	77.3	71.5	68.3	68.0	calc.
	65.5	—	62.8	60.3	—	obs.
p_c (cm³ mole⁻¹)	13.6	13.8	15.5	17.1	17.3	calc.
	12.770	12.797	14.645	16.282	16.421	obs.

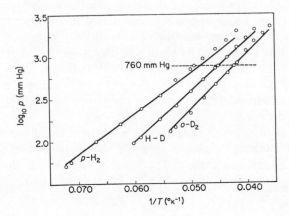

Figure 1. Vapor pressure of liquid hydrogen. The points represent experimental values (after Henderson *et al.*[1]).

The most recent and probably the most accurate specific heat data for liquid hydrogen is for the specific heat at saturated vapor pressures, C_s, which is related to C_V by the expression

$$C_s = C_V + T\left(\frac{\partial S}{\partial V}\right)_T \left(\frac{\mathrm{d}V}{\mathrm{d}T}\right)_{\text{sat.}} \tag{6}$$

The calculated and observed values of C_s for p-H_2, H—D, and o-D_2 are compared in Figure 2.

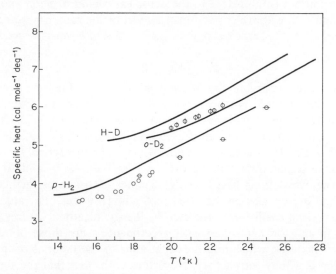

Figure 2. Specific heat of liquid hydrogen at saturated vapor pressures. Points represent experimental values (after Henderson *et al.*[1]).

It is evident from the above that a straightforward application of the significant structures method leads to results in good agreement with experiment. Despite this the theory is not entirely satisfactory since two expressions were needed for the positional degeneracy term in the limits of low and high temperatures. It would be desirable to obtain an expression which is applicable at all temperatures and volumes. This is presently being considered.

6. Application to Dense Gases

In deriving the solid-like partition function it has been assumed that the Einstein oscillator satisfies the condition $l\theta \gg T$, where l is the vibrational quantum number of the energy level at which the solid molecule sublimes, i.e. $l = E_s/3R\theta$. The condition $l\theta \gg T$, however, does not hold at the comparatively high temperatures of the dense gas region. This is particularly true for substances with a low value of E_s, i.e. neon and argon. Thus a more general partition function has been introduced:[1]

$$f_s = e^{E_s/RT}\left\{\frac{1-e^{-l\theta/T}}{1-e^{-\theta/T}} + e^{-l\theta/T}\left[\left(\frac{2\pi mkT}{h^2}\right)^{\frac{1}{2}}\left(V_s^{\frac{1}{3}} - \frac{b^{\frac{1}{3}}}{4^{\frac{1}{3}}}\right)\right]\right\}^3 \tag{1}$$

[1] T. S. Ree, T. Ree and H. Eyring, *Proc. Natl. Acad. Sci. U.S.*, **48**, 501 (1962).

where b is the van der Waals constant, $b/4$ being the net volume of the molecule. This refinement does not appreciably affect the results in the liquid region but is important in the dense gas region of neon and argon. In addition to the above correction the effect of the rather large pressures characteristic of the dense gas regions on the value of V_s must be considered, i.e.

$$V_{sp} = V_s(1 - K\Delta p) \tag{2}$$

where K is the compressibility of the solid phase. In Figure 1 the experimental values for the compressibility factor, pV/NkT, of argon at $0°c$ are plotted as a function of the density in Amagat units, i.e. $1/22,400 \text{ cm}^{-3}$, and compared with Ree's results based on Eq. (1), with the calculations of Wentorf *et al.*,[2] Henderson,[3] and Kirkwood.[4] The theoretical bases of the latter three calculations will be discussed in Sects. 8, 9, and 10 respectively. The calculations based on the significant structures method agree better than those based on the other methods. However, the values of the individual virial coefficients predicted by the significant structures method are not in as good agreement with experiment as are those obtained by the other methods, which indicates that none of the theories of the dense gas region is wholly satisfactory. Nevertheless the fact that the significant

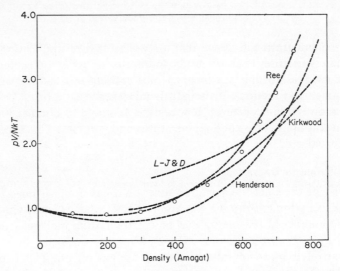

Figure 1. Compressibility factor of argon at $0°c$. The points represent the experimental values.

[2] R. H. Wentorf, R. J. Buehler, J. O. Hirschfelder and C. F. Curtiss, *J. Chem. Phys.*, **18**, 1484 (1950).
[3] D. Henderson, *J. Chem. Phys.*, **37**, 631 (1962).
[4] J. G. Kirkwood, V. A. Lewinson and B. J. Alder, *J. Chem. Phys.*, **20**, 929 (1952).

structures method does yield satisfactory predictions throughout the entire liquid and gas regions is a powerful argument in its favor.

7. Free Volume Theories of the Liquid State

In the preceding sections we have considered an approach in which the properties of a liquid are related to the properties of its solid phase. In the remaining four sections of this chapter we shall discuss two approaches in which the liquid properties are calculated from the intermolecular forces.

In this and the two following sections the free volume theory of liquids will be considered. This approach is not unlike the significant structure theory of liquids in as much as the similarity between a solid and a liquid is emphasized. For simplicity, this discussion will be limited to liquids consisting of monatomic molecules of non-metallic character which are sufficiently heavy and which exist at temperatures which are sufficiently high so that quantum effects need not be considered. The incorporation of quantum liquids into this theory will, however, be briefly discussed.

A rigorous theory of liquids would involve the evaluation of the partition function

$$f_N = \frac{1}{N! h^{3N}} \int e^{-H/kT} \, d\mathbf{r}_1 \ldots d\mathbf{r}_N \, d\mathbf{p}_1 \ldots d\mathbf{p}_N \tag{1}$$

where the integration is over all possible values of the momenta and coordinates. In order to facilitate the evaluation of this integral the forces between molecules will be assumed to be central forces which are derivable from a potential function $u(r)$ and it will be further assumed that the potential function is independent of the positions of the other molecules. Under these assumptions

$$H = \sum_i \frac{p_i^2}{2m} + \sum_{i>j} u(r_{ij}) \tag{2}$$

The integration over momenta may be immediately performed and yields

$$f_N = \frac{1}{N!} \left(\frac{2\pi mkT}{h^2} \right)^{\frac{3}{2}N} \int \exp\left\{ -\frac{1}{kT} \sum_{i>j} u(r_{ij}) \right\} d\mathbf{r}_1 \ldots d\mathbf{r}_N$$

$$= \left(\frac{2\pi mkT}{h^2} \right)^{\frac{3}{2}N} Q_N \tag{3}$$

where Q_N is called the configurational partition function.

The intermolecular potential is reasonably well described by the Lennard-Jones (6–12) potential

$$u(r) = 4\varepsilon \left[\left(\frac{\sigma}{r} \right)^{12} - \left(\frac{\sigma}{r} \right)^{6} \right] \tag{4}$$

where ε is the maximum depth of the potential and σ is the *collision diameter*, the distance at which $u(r)$ is zero. The justification for this potential has been discussed in Sect. 11.3 and the potential is plotted in Figure 11.7.1. The values of ε and σ can be determined from data on the second virial coefficient and are tabulated for the inert gases in Table 1. Further tabulations of these parameters for other substances may be found in the informative book by Hirschfelder, Curtiss and Bird.[1]

TABLE 1. Force constants for the Lennard-Jones (6–12) potential

Substance	ε/k (°K)	σ (Å)
Ne	35.60	2.749
Ar	119.8	3.405
Kr	171	3.60
Xe	221	4.100

The parameters ε and σ can be used to define the following dimensionless reduced quantities

$$T^* = \frac{kT}{\varepsilon}, \qquad v^* = \frac{V}{N\sigma^3} \tag{5}$$

The pressure is given by

$$p = kT \frac{\partial}{\partial V} \ln \int \exp\left\{ -\frac{1}{kT} \sum_{i>j} u(r_{ij}) \right\} d\mathbf{r}_1 \ldots d\mathbf{r}_N \tag{6}$$

which depends only on the quantities V, kT, ε and σ. If the dimensionless reduced pressure

$$p^* = \frac{p\sigma^3}{\varepsilon} \tag{7}$$

is formed, then the law of corresponding states (Sect. 11.10)

$$p^* = p^*(v^*, T^*) \tag{8}$$

follows since a dimensionless quantity can only be a function of dimensionless quantities. For a quantum liquid the pressure will also depend on h and a new dimensionless quantity

$$\Lambda^* = \frac{h}{\sigma(m\varepsilon)^{\frac{1}{2}}} \tag{9}$$

must be introduced. Hence, Eq. (8) must be corrected to

$$p^* = p^*(v^*, T^*, \Lambda^*) \tag{10}$$

[1] J. O. Hirschfelder, C. F. Curtiss and R. B. Bird, *Molecular Theory of Gases and Liquids*, Wiley, New York, 1954.

The classical law of corresponding states is, therefore, correct only for substances whose molecules have sufficiently large mass so that Λ^* is negligibly small and may be neglected.

If it is assumed that each molecule is confined to a singly occupied cell formed by its nearest neighbors and that within its cell each molecule moves in a field $\psi(r)$, where $r = 0$ is located at the minimum in $\psi(r)$, then the partition function becomes

$$f_N = \left(\frac{2\pi mkT}{h^2}\right)^{\frac{3}{2}N} e^{-N\psi(0)/2kT} v_f^N \tag{11}$$

where v_f is called the *free volume* and is given by

$$v_f = \int_{\text{Cell}} e^{-[\psi(r)-\psi(0)]/kT} 4\pi r^2 \, dr \tag{12}$$

A characteristic difficulty arises when the limit of low densities ($V \to \infty$) is considered. In this limit $\psi(r) \to 0$ and $v_f \to V/N$ giving

$$f_N = \left(\frac{2\pi mkT}{h^2}\right)^{\frac{3}{2}N} \left(\frac{V}{N}\right)^N \tag{13}$$

whereas the partition function for a perfect gas is

$$f_N = \left(\frac{2\pi mkT}{h^2}\right)^{\frac{3}{2}N} \left(\frac{eV}{N}\right)^N \tag{14}$$

The extra factor e^N arises because the gas molecules are indistinguishable whereas in the free volume model of a liquid the molecules are confined to their respective cells and, therefore, are distinguishable. The extra factor e^N gives rise to an additional contribution Nk to the entropy which is called the *communal entropy*. Eyring[2] has suggested that the extra factor e^N should be included in Eq. (11) and that the communal entropy provides most of the entropy of melting. The extra entropy of liquids may be accounted for in more satisfactory ways by allowing for either multiple occupancy of cells or by considering the randomness introduced by empty cells or holes. These modifications of the free volume theory will be considered in Sect. 9.

8. The Lennard-Jones and Devonshire Calculation of the Free Volume

Lennard-Jones and Devonshire[1] have calculated $\psi(r)$ by assuming that each molecule moves within its cell in the potential field of its nearest neighbors fixed at the centers of their respective cells. To simplify the prob-

[2] H. Eyring, *J. Chem. Phys.*, **4**, 283 (1936); H. Eyring and J. O. Hirschfelder, *J. Phys. Chem.*, **41**, 249 (1937).

[1] J. E. Lennard-Jones and A. F. Devonshire, *Proc. Roy. Soc. (London)*, **A163**, 53 (1937); **A165**, 1 (1938).

lem the z nearest neighbors are treated as uniformly smeared over a spherical surface of radius a equal to the nearest neighbor distance. Under these assumptions the field $\psi(r)$ in which a molecule moves in its cell is the field of the surrounding molecules averaged over all directions. The cell geo-

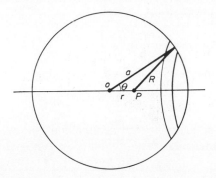

Figure 1. Cell geometry in the Lennard-Jones and Devonshire model.

metry is depicted in Figure 1. The area of the ring is $2\pi a^2 \sin\theta\, d\theta$ and therefore the number of smeared nearest neighbors in the ring is $(z/2)\sin\theta\, d\theta$. Hence

$$\psi(r) = \int_0^\pi 4\varepsilon\left\{\left(\frac{\sigma}{R}\right)^{12} - \left(\frac{\sigma}{R}\right)^6\right\}\frac{z}{2}\sin\theta\, d\theta \tag{1}$$

where $R^2 = r^2 + a^2 - 2ar\cos\theta$. For fixed r, $2R\, dR = 2ar\sin\theta\, d\theta$ and

$$\psi(r) = \frac{2z\varepsilon}{ar}\int_{a-r}^{a+r}\left\{\left(\frac{\sigma}{R}\right)^{12} - \left(\frac{\sigma}{R}\right)^6\right\}R\, dR \tag{2}$$

Performing this integration and using the fact that

$$\psi(0) = 4z\varepsilon\left\{\left(\frac{\sigma}{a}\right)^{12} - \left(\frac{\sigma}{a}\right)^6\right\} \tag{3}$$

yields

$$\psi(r) - \psi(0) = z\varepsilon\sigma^{12}\left\{\frac{1}{5ar}\left[\frac{1}{(a-r)^{10}} - \frac{1}{(a+r)^{10}}\right] - \frac{4}{a^{12}}\right\}$$

$$+ z\varepsilon\sigma^6\left\{\frac{1}{2ar}\left[\frac{1}{(a+r)^4} - \frac{1}{(a-r)^4}\right] + \frac{4}{a^6}\right\} \tag{4}$$

For a cubic close-packed structure $z = 12$ and $V/N = a^3/\sqrt{2}$. Under these circumstances Eq. (4) can be expressed in the following more usual form

$$\psi(r) - \psi(0) = z\varepsilon \left\{ \frac{l(y)}{v^{*4}} - \frac{2m(y)}{v^{*2}} \right\} \tag{5}$$

where

$$l(y) = (1 + 12y + 25.2y^2 + 12y^3 + y^4)(1-y)^{-10} - 1 \tag{6}$$
$$m(y) = (1+y)(1-y)^{-4} - 1 \tag{7}$$

and

$$y = \left(\frac{r}{a}\right)^2 = \left(\frac{r^*}{a^*}\right)^2, \qquad r^* = r/\sigma, \qquad a^* = a/\sigma$$

and

$$v^* = v/\sigma^3 = V/N\sigma^3$$

The partition function is then

$$f_N = \left(\frac{2\pi mkT}{h^2}\right)^{\frac{3}{2}N} e^{-N\psi(0)/2kT} (ev_f)^N \tag{8}$$

Choosing the volume of the cell so that it equals V/N, the free volume becomes

$$v_f = \int_0^{r_m} e^{-[\psi(r)-\psi(0)]/kT} 4\pi r^2 \, dr$$
$$= 2\pi a^3 g(v^*, T^*) \tag{9}$$

where

$$g(v^*, T^*) = \int_0^{y_m} \sqrt{y} \exp\left\{ -\frac{z}{T^*} \left[\frac{l(y)}{v^{*4}} - \frac{2m(y)}{v^{*2}} \right] \right\} dy \tag{10}$$

and

$$y_m = \left(\frac{3}{4\pi\sqrt{2}}\right)^{\frac{2}{3}} \tag{11}$$

The equation of state is then

$$\frac{pV}{NkT} = -\frac{v}{2kT}\left(\frac{\partial\psi(0)}{\partial v}\right)_T + v\left(\frac{\partial \ln v_f}{\partial v}\right)_T \tag{12}$$

The first term is the potential part of the pressure resulting from the potential energy of all the molecules placed at the centers of their cells and the second term is the thermal part of the pressure resulting from the motion of the molecules in their cells. Performing these differentiations yields, since $a^3 = \sqrt{2}v$,

$$\frac{pV}{NkT} = 1 + \frac{2z}{T^*}\left[\frac{1}{v^{*4}}\left(1 + \frac{2g_l}{g}\right) - \frac{1}{v^{*2}}\left(1 + \frac{2g_m}{g}\right)\right] \tag{13}$$

where g is given by Eq. (10) and

$$g_l(v^*, T^*) = \int_0^{y_m} l(y)\sqrt{y}\, \exp\left\{-\frac{z}{T^*}\left[\frac{l(y)}{v^{*4}} - \frac{2m(y)}{v^{*2}}\right]\right\} dy \qquad (14)$$

$$g_m(v^*, T^*) = \int_0^{y_m} m(y)\sqrt{y}\, \exp\left\{-\frac{z}{T^*}\left[\frac{l(y)}{v^{*4}} - \frac{2m(y)}{v^{*2}}\right]\right\} dy \qquad (15)$$

These integrals have been tabulated by several authors.[1, 2, 3] In the original papers of Lennard-Jones and Devonshire the effect of the 6 second nearest neighbors at a distance of $\sqrt{2}a$ and the 24 third nearest neighbors at a distance $\sqrt{3}a$ on the lattice energy (but not on the free volume) was included resulting in a change in the coefficient of $1/v^{*2}$ in the equation of state to $(1.2 + 2g_m/g)$. The most extensive calculations of the Lennard-Jones and Devonshire equation of state are those of Wentorf *et al.*,[4] who have included the effect of the three neighboring shells on both the lattice energy and the free volume and obtained the following equation of state

$$\frac{pV}{NkT} = 1 + \frac{2z}{T^*}\left[\frac{1}{v^{*4}}\left(1.0110 + \frac{2G_L}{G}\right) - \frac{1}{v^{*2}}\left(1.2045 + \frac{2G_M}{G}\right)\right] \qquad (16)$$

where G, G_L, and G_M are integrals like g, g_l, and g_m except that $l(y)$ and $m(y)$ are replaced by the functions

$$L(y) = l(y) + \tfrac{1}{128}l(\tfrac{1}{2}y) + \tfrac{2}{129}l(\tfrac{1}{3}y) \qquad (17)$$

$$M(y) = m(y) + \tfrac{1}{16}m(\tfrac{1}{2}y) + \tfrac{2}{27}m(\tfrac{1}{3}y) \qquad (18)$$

Equation (16) is plotted for argon at 0°c in Figure 6.1.

The expansion of Eq. (13) in powers of v^*/v has no first power term so that the second virial coefficient is zero.

The molar volumes of the liquid at saturated vapor pressures may be obtained, for low vapor pressures, from Eq. (13) by setting $p = 0$. In Figure 2 the results of this calculation are compared with experimental results and with the recent calculations of Henderson (which are discussed in the next section). The predictions of the Lennard-Jones and Devonshire theory can be improved by using a smaller coordination number, say $z = 10$, which is reasonable since the effect of holes is to lower the number of nearest neighbors.

2 I. Prigogine and S. Raulier, *Physica*, **9**, 396 (1942); I. Prigogine and G. Garikian, *J. Chim. Phys.*, **45**, 273 (1948).

3 T. L. Hill, *J. Phys. and Colloid Chem.*, **51**, 1219 (1947).

4 R. H. Wentorf, Jr., R. J. Buehler, J. O. Hirschfelder and C. F. Curtiss, *J. Chem. Phys.*, **18**, 1484 (1950).

The vapor pressure of the liquid can be calculated by equating the Gibbs' free energy of the liquid to that of the vapor. The contribution pV_{liq} to the Gibbs' free energy may be neglected and therefore

$$G_l = \tfrac{3}{2}NkT\ln\left(\frac{h^2}{2\pi mkT}\right) + \frac{N\psi(0)}{2} - NkT\ln v_f - NkT \qquad (19)$$

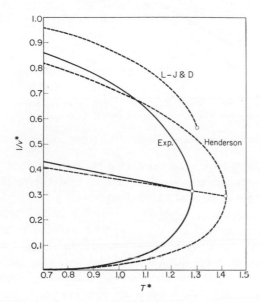

Figure 2. Rectilinear diameters plot for the inert gases (after Henderson[6.3]).

Except in the critical region the vapor may be assumed to be ideal and therefore

$$G_g = \tfrac{3}{2}NkT\ln\left(\frac{h^2}{2\pi mkT}\right) - NkT\ln\frac{eV}{N} + pV$$

$$= \tfrac{3}{2}NkT\ln\left(\frac{h^2}{2\pi mkT}\right) + NkT\ln p - NkT\ln kT \qquad (20)$$

Equating the two free energies gives

$$\ln p = \ln kT - \ln v_f + \frac{\psi(0)}{2kT} - 1 \qquad (21)$$

Despite the fact that the theory correctly predicts the linear dependence of $\ln p$ on $1/T$, the agreement with experiment is not satisfactory as may be seen in Figure 3. Using $z = 10$ does not improve the agreement.

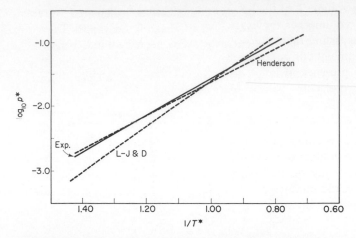

Figure 3. Vapor pressures of the inert gases (after Henderson[6.3]).

Critical constants have been calculated by Wentorf *et al.* for the three-shell modification and are listed in Table 1 of the following section. Only for T_c^* is the agreement satisfactory.

The above theory can be applied to quantum liquids. The only modification is that the integral in Eq. (7.1) must be replaced by a sum and the energy levels calculated by solving Schrödinger's equation. Levelt and Hurst[5] have recently done this for liquid hydrogen for the single volume $v^* = 5/3$ and have calculated the internal energy, the specific heat, and entropy as a function of T^* for this volume. However, the energy levels would have to be determined for other values of v^* before the equation of state could be calculated and a comparison with experiment undertaken.

9. Modifications of the Free Volume Theory of Liquids

The free volume theory of liquids is really a one-particle theory of the solid state which is assumed applicable to the liquid state if the communal entropy factor, e^N, is somewhat arbitrarily introduced. In as much as the free volume theory emphasizes the similarities between the solid and liquid states it is conceptually not unlike the significant structure theory of liquids which has been discussed earlier in this chapter. In view of this one might reasonably ask if the free volume theory might not be improved if the effect of empty cells or holes is considered. Such a modification has indeed been formulated by Cernuschi and Eyring[1] and admirably reviewed by Rowlinson and Curtiss.[2]

[5] J. M. H. Levelt and R. P. Hurst, *J. Chem. Phys.*, **32**, 96 (1960).
[1] F. Cernuschi and H. Eyring, *J. Chem. Phys.*, **7**, 547 (1939).
[2] J. S. Rowlinson and C. F. Curtiss, *J. Chem. Phys.*, **19**, 1519 (1951).

The volume V of the liquid is divided into $L > N$ cells so that $v = V/N$ is the volume per molecule and $\omega = V/L$ is the volume per cell. Let us further assume that these cells are large enough so that we need only consider nearest neighbor interactions. If we define $x = N/L$, then $\omega = xv$. Because of the presence of holes in the liquid the coordination number of a particular molecule i will be decreased. That is

$$z_i = y_i z \tag{1}$$

where y_i is some number between zero and unity. We shall assume that the free volume of the molecule i at a particular temperature and volume depends only on the value of y_i, that is the potential energy depends only on the number of neighboring holes and not on their arrangement. Under these circumstances Eq. (7.11) becomes

$$f_N = \left(\frac{2\pi mkT}{h^2}\right)^{\frac{3}{2}N} \sum_{\langle y_i \rangle} \prod_{i=1}^{N} e^{-y_i\psi(0)/2kT} v_f(y_i) \tag{2}$$

The sum in Eq. (2) is much like the sum which arose in our discussion of ferromagnetism in Chapter 10. In that case we were, in effect, considering the results of mixing $+$ and $-$ spins whereas in the present considerations we are considering the results of mixing holes and molecules. The sum in Eq. (2) may, therefore, be evaluated by the methods discussed in Chapter 10, as for example, the Bragg–Williams or quasi-chemical approximations. In either of these approximations if Eq. (2) is considered in the limit $v \to \infty$, the perfect gas partition function results so that the extra entropy of the liquid arises from the randomness introduced by the holes. Thus, this theory is capable, in principle, of describing both the liquid and gaseous states.

Before the partition function can be explicitly evaluated the dependence of v_f on y_i must be known. The Lennard-Jones and Devonshire values for the free volume are the only widely tabulated free volumes and have therefore been exclusively used. Until recently a linear dependence of the logarithm of the free volume on y_i was thought necessary in order that Eq. (2) be evaluated in the quasi-chemical approximation and therefore the earlier investigations differed only in the choice of the linear relationship. The five approximations of Cernuschi and Eyring,[1] Ono,[3] Peek and Hill,[4] Rowlinson and Curtiss,[2] and de Boer[5] are illustrated in Figure 1.

[3] S. Ono, *Mem. Fac. Eng. Kyushu Univ.*, **10**, 190 (1947).
[4] H. M. Peek and T. L. Hill, *J. Chem. Phys.*, **18**, 1252 (1950).
[5] J. de Boer, *Proc. Roy. Soc. (London)*, **A215**, 4 (1952).

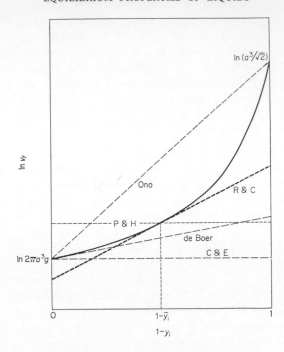

Figure 1. Dependence of the free volume on y_i.

The approximations of Cernuschi and Eyring, Ono, and de Boer are alike in that ω is chosen as equal to the cell volume of the solid at the melting point, that is $\omega^* = 1$, whereas in the approximations of Peek and Hill and Rowlinson and Curtiss the value of ω is chosen so that the Helmholtz free energy is a minimum for each volume and temperature. The latter procedure is somewhat preferable theoretically but on performing the calculations it is found that the ω increases much too rapidly with increasing volume, with the result that much too small a proportion of holes is predicted. The predicted critical point properties for these approximations are listed in Table 1. No results are reported for the approximation of Rowlinson and Curtiss since the critical point appears to lie at a cell size of about 5 which lies outside the tabulated values of g, g_l, and g_m.

Grindlay[6] has recently been able to evaluate explicitly the partition function in the quasi-chemical approximation without assuming a linear dependence of $\ln v_f$ on y. In this investigation ω was determined by

6 J. Grindlay, *Proc. Phys. Soc.* (*London*), **77**, 1001 (1961).

Table 1. Calculated values of critical point properties

Mean value for	T_c^*	v_c^*	p_c^*	$p_c^* v_c^*/T_c^*$	y_c
Ne, Ar, N_2	1.28	3.15	0.119	0.293	~0.5
L-J & D	1.30	1.77	0.434	0.591	1.000
C & E	2.75	2.00	0.470	0.342	0.544
Ono	0.75	2.00	0.128	0.342	0.544
P & H	1.18	3.25	0.261	0.825	0.825
R & C	—	—	—	—	—
de Boer	1.89	2.00	0.322	0.342	0.544
Grindlay	1.30	1.77	0.434	0.591	1.000
Henderson	1.41	3.39	0.139	0.333	0.321
Kirkwood	1.68	2.02	0.298	0.358	—

minimizing the free energy and it was found that ω was virtually equal to v so that the theory did not differ appreciably from the unmodified theory of Lennard-Jones and Devonshire. This can be seen from Table 1. The reason for this difficulty, which is common to all the above approximations, is due to the use of the Lennard-Jones and Devonshire procedure of smearing the nearest neighbors over the surface of a sphere of radius a. This approximation is even more inadequate if holes are present than it is for the original theory of Lennard-Jones and Devonshire. The result of this approximation is that the free volume can be increased more rapidly by an expansion of the cell dimensions than it can by the introduction of holes and that therefore minimization of the free-energy predicts a negligible number of holes.

If one adopts the view that the neighboring molecules are instead confined to the centers of their respective cells then when a neighboring molecule is removed the free volume in the cell will increase in the neighborhood of the hole. This leads to the idea of a linear dependence of the free volume (rather than its logarithm) on the number of neighboring holes. Accordingly, Henderson[6.3] has considered the relation

$$v_f(y_i) = y_i v_f^0 + (1 - y_i)\omega \tag{3}$$

which is in accord with the concepts of the significant structure theory in which the molecules are viewed as acquiring gas-like properties in strict proportion to the number of neighboring holes. Preliminary calculations have been performed on the basis of the Bragg–Williams approximation, the value of ω being determined by a minimization of the free energy. The calculated values of the densities and vapor pressures of the inert gases are plotted in Figures 8.2 and 8.3, respectively, and the calculated critical point properties are shown in Table 1. The results are quite good and represent a significant improvement over previous attempts to incorporate the effects of holes into the free volume theory. This theory works quite well in the dense gas region also as can be seen in Figure 2, where the calculated values of the second virial coefficient are compared with the experimental results and the calculations of Rowlinson and Curtiss.

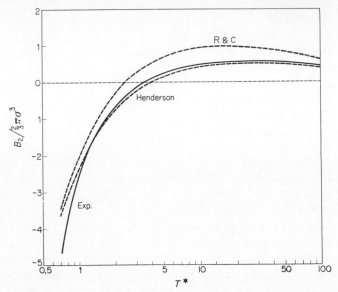

Figure 2. Calculated and experimental values of the second virial coefficient (after Henderson[6.3]).

Calculated values for the compressibility factor of argon at 0°C can be found in Figure 6.1.

A number of other modifications of the free volume theory of Lennard-Jones and Devonshire have been considered. However, they have not generally been as successful as the hole theories outlined above. Kirkwood[7] has shown that the Lennard-Jones and Devonshire theory is a first approximation of a variational treatment for the calculation of the free energy. The more recent investigations of Mayer and Careri,[8] Dahler, Hirschfelder and Thacker,[9] and Barker[10] suggest that this method is not satisfactory.

Another approach is to correct, by direct calculation, the defects of the Lennard-Jones and Devonshire theory. These are the sphericalization of

7 J. Kirkwood, *J. Chem. Phys.*, **18**, 380 (1950).

8 J. E. Mayer and G. Careri, *J. Chem. Phys.*, **20**, 1001 (1952).

9 J. S. Dahler, J. O. Hirschfelder and H. C. Thacker, *J. Chem. Phys.*, **25**, 249 (1956).

10 J. A. Barker, *Proc. Roy. Soc.* (*London*), **A230**, 390 (1955); **A237**, 63 (1956); **A240**, 265 (1957); **A241**, 547 (1958).

the cell, the incorrect calculation of the communal entropy, and the neglect of correlations of neighboring molecules. The first correction involves a straightforward numerical integration over the dodecahedral cell and has been performed by Buehler et al.[11] for unattracting rigid sphere molecules and by Barker for molecules obeying the Lennard-Jones 6–12 potential. This correction increases the free volume by a factor of up to 1.4 in the critical region. The correction for the communal entropy has been made by Pople[12] and by Janssens and Prigogine[13] by estimating the probability of finding two molecules in one cell. Pople has calculated the communal entropy for a system of rigid spheres and found that even in the dense gas region double occupancy makes little contribution to the free energy. Barker has calculated the correction for a 6–12 potential and found a much greater contribution to the communal entropy, as would be expected from the softer nature of the potential. The third correction consists in calculating the correlation of the motions of molecules in neighboring cells. The effect of these corrections is to improve considerably the predictions of the theory for low temperatures but unfortunately the agreement in the critical region is worse, with the reduced critical temperature lying well above 1.6. This would indicate that further refinement is necessary. In particular, higher terms for the multiple occupancy and molecular correlation terms should be included. It is interesting to note that the inclusion of the correlation term leads to a second phase at low temperatures and high densities. Barker obtains 0.90 for the reduced triple point temperature, which is appreciably higher than the observed value of 0.70. However, since none of the other modifications of the free volume theory lead to a solid–liquid transition, this has interesting implications.

Similar considerations are being investigated by de Boer, Cohen and colleagues.[14] In de Boer's treatment the multiple occupancy and correlation corrections are both included in one term, the cell cluster integral. This would seem to be a less satisfactory procedure than that of Barker who considers the two corrections separately. At present good progress has been made toward calculating the combinatorial factors in the cell-cluster partition function but as yet the free volumes of cells containing more than one molecule have not been calculated for any

[11] R. J. Buehler, R. H. Wentorf, Jr., J. O. Hirschfelder and C. F. Curtiss, J. Chem. Phys., 19, 61 (1951).
[12] J. A. Pople, Phil. Mag., 42, 459 (1951).
[13] P. Janssens and I. Prigogine, Physica, 16, 895 (1950).
[14] J. de Boer, Physica, 20, 655 (1954); E. G. D. Cohen, J. de Boer and Z. W. Salsburg, ibid., 21, 137 (1955); 23, 389 (1957); Z. W. Salsburg, E. G. D. Cohen, B. C. Rethmeier and J. de Boer, ibid., 23, 407 (1957); E. G. D. Cohen and B. C. Rethmeier, ibid., 24, 959 (1958); J. S. Dahler and E. G. D. Cohen, ibid., 26, 81 (1960).

realistic intermolecular potentials. However, the method seems, at least formally, capable of providing an exact theory of the liquid state. It is interesting to note that in the most recent paper of this series the effect of holes is considered with considerable improvement in the results.

10. Thermodynamics of a Liquid in Terms of the Pair Distribution Function

In the preceding sections a liquid has been pictured as a disordered solid. Another, entirely different, approach to the theory of liquids which has been illuminating is based on the evaluation of the so-called molecular distribution functions.

The importance of these molecular distribution functions may be seen from the virial theorem. If Eqs. (11.4.8, 9) are combined and if the potential is assumed to be due to the additive contributions of all the pairs of molecules, i.e.

$$H = \sum_i \frac{p_i^2}{2m} + \sum_{i>j} u(r_{ij}) \tag{1}$$

then the equation of state becomes

$$pV = NkT - \tfrac{1}{3} \overline{\sum_{i>j} r_{ij} \frac{\partial u}{\partial r_{ij}}} \tag{2}$$

If the time average in Eq. (2) is replaced by an average over a canonical ensemble then one obtains on integrating over the momenta

$$pV = NkT - \frac{1}{3N!Q_N} \int \sum_{i>j} r_{ij} \frac{\partial u}{\partial r_{ij}} \exp\left\{-\frac{1}{kT}\sum_{i>j} u(r_{ij})\right\} d\mathbf{r}_1 \ldots d\mathbf{r}_N \tag{3}$$

where Q_N is the configurational partition function and is given by

$$Q_N = \frac{1}{N!} \int \exp\left\{-\frac{1}{kT}\sum_{i>j} u(r_{ij})\right\} d\mathbf{r}_1 \ldots d\mathbf{r}_N \tag{4}$$

At this point it is convenient to define the molecular pair distribution function

$$n^{(2)}(\mathbf{r}_1, \mathbf{r}_2) = n^{(2)}(r_{12}) = \frac{N!}{(N-2)!} \frac{\int e^{-U/kT} d\mathbf{r}_3 \ldots d\mathbf{r}_N}{\int e^{-U/kT} d\mathbf{r}_1 \ldots d\mathbf{r}_N} \tag{5}$$

which is the probability of finding an arbitrary pair of molecules in the configuration $\mathbf{r}_1$, $\mathbf{r}_2$. The integration of the second term on the right-hand side of Eq. (3) over the coordinates of all molecules except molecules i and j leads to $\tfrac{1}{2}N(N-1)$ terms of the form

$$\iint r_{ij} \frac{\partial u}{\partial r_{ij}} n^{(2)}(r_{ij}) d\mathbf{r}_i d\mathbf{r}_j \tag{6}$$

Therefore, the equation of state becomes

$$pV = NkT - \tfrac{1}{6} \iint n^{(2)}(r_{12}) r_{12} \frac{\partial u}{\partial r_{12}} \, d\mathbf{r}_1 \, d\mathbf{r}_2 \tag{7}$$

The internal energy may also be related to the pair distribution function

$$E = \frac{1}{N! f_N} \int \left\{ \sum_i \frac{p_i^2}{2m} + \sum_{i>j} u(r_{ij}) \right\} e^{-H/kT} \, d\mathbf{p}_1 \ldots d\mathbf{p}_N \, d\mathbf{r}_1 \ldots d\mathbf{r}_N \tag{8}$$

Because of the principle of equipartition of energy, the first term becomes $\tfrac{3}{2}NkT$. The integration of the second term may be performed in a manner analogous to that used in obtaining Eq. (7) and, therefore,

$$E = \tfrac{3}{2}NkT + \tfrac{1}{2} \iint n^{(2)}(r_{12}) u(r_{12}) \, d\mathbf{r}_1 \, d\mathbf{r}_2 \tag{9}$$

Hence a determination of the pair distribution function leads directly to the thermodynamic properties of a liquid.

Other distribution functions $n^{(h)}$ can be defined analogously

$$n^{(h)}(\mathbf{r}_1 \ldots \mathbf{r}_h) = \frac{N!}{(N-h)!} \frac{\int e^{-U/kT} \, d\mathbf{r}_{h+1} \ldots d\mathbf{r}_N}{\int e^{-U/kT} \, d\mathbf{r}_1 \ldots d\mathbf{r}_N} \tag{10}$$

The pair distribution function can, at least in principle, be determined from X-ray studies since it is related to the radial distribution function, $g(r)$, by

$$n^{(2)}(r_{12}) = \frac{N(N-1)}{V^2} g(r_{12}) \tag{11}$$

However, at the present time, the experimental determinations of $g(r)$ are not of sufficient accuracy nor have they been performed over a sufficiently wide temperature and volume range to make such a procedure fruitful.

One analytic procedure is to develop $n^{(2)}(r)$, and thus p, in a power series in ρ. This leads to the familiar virial expansion discussed in Chapter 11. This method, although rigorous, suffers from the slow convergence of the series and from the fact that the virial coefficients are extremely hard to evaluate. In the remainder of this section we shall be solely concerned with another method in which an integral equation is obtained for $n^{(2)}(r)$.

These distribution functions can be related to the average force exerted on one molecule, in a configuration of h molecules, by all of the other molecules. If we consider a pair of molecules, 1 and 2, then the average

·force on molecule 1 due to all the other molecules is obtained by taking the ensemble average of $-\partial v/\partial \mathbf{r}_1$:

$$\overline{\mathbf{F}_1(\mathbf{r}_1, \mathbf{r}_2)} = -\frac{\partial \Psi(\mathbf{r}_1, \mathbf{r}_2)}{\partial \mathbf{r}_1} = \frac{\int \left(-\dfrac{\partial U}{\partial \mathbf{r}_1}\right) e^{-H/kT}\, d\mathbf{p}_1 \ldots d\mathbf{p}_N\, d\mathbf{r}_3 \ldots d\mathbf{r}_N}{\int e^{-H/kT}\, d\mathbf{p}_1 \ldots d\mathbf{p}_N\, d\mathbf{r}_3 \ldots d\mathbf{r}_N}$$

$$= \frac{\int \left(-\dfrac{\partial U}{\partial \mathbf{r}_1}\right) e^{-U/kT}\, d\mathbf{r}_3 \ldots d\mathbf{r}_N}{\int e^{-U/kT}\, d\mathbf{r}_3 \ldots d\mathbf{r}_N} \tag{12}$$

where $\Psi(\mathbf{r}_1, \mathbf{r}_2)$ is, by definition, the potential of the average force. Taking into account the definition of $n^{(2)}(r_{12})$, Eq. (5), we have the differential equation

$$\overline{\mathbf{F}_1(\mathbf{r}_1, \mathbf{r}_2)} = -\frac{\partial \Psi(\mathbf{r}_1, \mathbf{r}_2)}{\partial \mathbf{r}_1} = kT \frac{\partial \ln n^{(2)}(\mathbf{r}_1, \mathbf{r}_2)}{\partial \mathbf{r}_1} \tag{13}$$

which when integrated gives

$$n^{(2)}(\mathbf{r}_1, \mathbf{r}_2) = n^2\, e^{-\Psi(\mathbf{r}_1,\, \mathbf{r}_2)/kT} \tag{14}$$

The factor n^2 arises because in the low density limit ($r_{12} \to \infty$, $\Psi(\mathbf{r}_1, \mathbf{r}_2) \to 0$) $n^{(2)} = N(N-1)/V^2 \simeq n^2$. Similar expressions may be obtained for the other distribution functions

$$n^{(h)}(\mathbf{r}_1, \ldots, \mathbf{r}_h) = n^h\, e^{-\Psi(\mathbf{r}_1,\ldots,\mathbf{r}_h)/kT} \tag{15}$$

An integro-differential equation for $n^{(2)}$ is obtained by substituting

$$\frac{\partial U}{\partial \mathbf{r}_1} = \frac{\partial u(r_{12})}{\partial \mathbf{r}_1} + \sum_{i=1}^{3} \frac{\partial u(r_{1i})}{\partial \mathbf{r}_1} \tag{16}$$

into Eqs. (12) and (13) obtaining

$$kT \frac{\partial \ln n^{(2)}(r_{12})}{\partial \mathbf{r}_1} = -\frac{\partial u(r_{12})}{\partial \mathbf{r}_1} - \int \frac{\partial u(r_{13})}{\partial \mathbf{r}_1} \frac{n^{(3)}(\mathbf{r}_1, \mathbf{r}_2, \mathbf{r}_3)}{n^{(2)}(\mathbf{r}_1, \mathbf{r}_2)}\, d\mathbf{r}_3$$

$$kT \frac{\partial n^{(2)}(r_{12})}{\partial \mathbf{r}_1} = -n^{(2)}(r_{12}) \frac{\partial u(r_{12})}{\partial \mathbf{r}_1} - \int n^{(3)}(\mathbf{r}_1, \mathbf{r}_2, \mathbf{r}_3) \frac{\partial u(r_{13})}{\partial \mathbf{r}_1}\, d\mathbf{r}_3 \tag{17}$$

Similar equations may be obtained for the other distribution functions

$$kT \frac{\partial n^{(h)}}{\partial \mathbf{r}_i} = -\sum_{k=1}^{h} n^{(h)} \frac{\partial u(r_{ik})}{\partial \mathbf{r}_i} - \int n^{(h+1)} \frac{\partial u(r_{i,h+1})}{\partial \mathbf{r}_i}\, d\mathbf{r}_{h+1} \tag{18}$$

These equations form a very complicated family of integro-differential equations, the first of which gives $n^{(2)}$ in terms of $n^{(3)}$, the next gives $n^{(3)}$ in terms of $n^{(4)}$, and so forth. There is no hope of obtaining a solution to these equations unless the series is terminated. This is done by substituting into Eq. (17) an approximate solution for $n^{(3)}$ and then solving for $n^{(2)}$. The most usual approximation for $n^{(3)}$ is

$$n^{(3)}(\mathbf{r}_1, \mathbf{r}_2, \mathbf{r}_3) = \frac{n^{(2)}(\mathbf{r}_1, \mathbf{r}_2)n^{(2)}(\mathbf{r}_1, \mathbf{r}_3)n^{(2)}(\mathbf{r}_2, \mathbf{r}_3)}{n^3} \tag{19}$$

which is the *superposition approximation* of Kirkwood.[1] This approximation asserts that the probability of any triplet configuration is equal to that of the three constituent pairs occurring separately. This is correct at low densities but its consequences at high densities have not been assessed. Substitution of (19) into (17) gives

$$kT\frac{\partial \ln n^{(2)}(r_{12})}{\partial \mathbf{r}_1} = -\frac{\partial u(r_{12})}{\partial \mathbf{r}_1} - \frac{1}{n^3}\int \frac{\partial u(r_{13})}{\partial \mathbf{r}_i} n^{(2)}(r_{13})n^{(2)}(r_{23}) \, d\mathbf{r}_3 \tag{20}$$

Born and Green[2] and Yvon[3] have shown by means of straightforward, but lengthy, manipulations that this equation can be integrated over $\mathbf{r}_1$ giving

$$kT \ln \frac{n^{(2)}(r_{12})}{n^2} = -u(r_{12}) + 2\pi n \int_0^\infty \int_{r-r_{13}}^{r+r_{13}} \frac{\partial u(r_{13})}{\partial r_{13}} \frac{n^{(2)}(r_{13})}{n^2}$$
$$\times \left(\frac{n^{(2)}(r_{23})}{n^2} - 1\right)\left[\frac{r_{13}^2 - (r_{23}-r_{12})^2}{2r}\right] r_{23} \, dr_{23} \, dr_{13} \tag{21}$$

where $u(-\mathbf{r}) = u(\mathbf{r})$ and $n^{(2)}(-\mathbf{r}) = n^{(2)}(\mathbf{r})$, by definition.

Kirkwood[1] has used a different method to obtain an equation for $n^{(2)}$. Molecule 1 is supposed to be loosely coupled with the other molecules so that

$$U = \xi \sum_{j=2}^{N} u(\mathbf{r}_1, \mathbf{r}_j) + \sum_{j>k=2}^{N} u(r_{jk}) \tag{22}$$

Substitution of Eq. (22) into Eq. (5) and differentiation with respect to ξ gives

$$kT\frac{\partial \ln n^{(2)}(r_{12})}{\partial \xi} = -u(r_{12}) - \int u(r_{13})\left[\frac{n^{(3)}(\mathbf{r}_1, \mathbf{r}_2, \mathbf{r}_3)}{n^{(2)}(\mathbf{r}_1, \mathbf{r}_2)} - \frac{n^{(2)}(\mathbf{r}_1, \mathbf{r}_2)}{n}\right] d\mathbf{r}_3 \tag{23}$$

Applying the superposition approximation yields Kirkwood's approximate integral equation

$$kT \ln \frac{n^{(2)}(r_{12}, \xi)}{n^2} = -\xi u(r_{12})$$
$$+ 2\pi n \int_0^\infty \int_0^\xi \int_{|r-r_{13}|}^{r+r_{13}} u(r_{13})\frac{n^{(2)}(r_{13})}{n^2}(n^{(2)}(r_{23})-1)\frac{r_{13}r_{23}}{r_{12}} \, dr_{23} \, d\xi \, dr_{13} \tag{24}$$

[1] J. G. Kirkwood, *J. Chem. Phys.*, **3**, 300 (1935).
[2] M. Born and H. S. Green, *Proc. Roy. Soc. (London)*, **A188**, 10 (1946).
[3] J. Yvon, *Actualités scientifiques et industrielles*, Herman & Cie., Paris, 1935.

Both the Born–Green–Yvon integral equation (21) and the Kirkwood integral equation are approximate. Indeed if $n^{(2)}$ is now expanded in a power series in the density it is found[4] that the resulting equation of state is correct for the second and third virial coefficients but not for the fourth and higher coefficients. This is not surprising since the superposition approximation is probably inadequate at high densities. Modifications of the superposition approximation have been proposed[5] which yield improved results for the fourth virial coefficient.

The equation of state for a system of rigid spheres has been calculated from the Born–Green–Yvon equation[6] and from the Kirkwood equation.[7] The agreement of the two results is excellent at low densities but only moderately good at high densities. This, too, indicates the inadequacies of the superposition principle at high densities. Kirkwood[8] has also calculated from the Born–Green–Yvon equation the equation of state for a system of molecules obeying a Lennard-Jones 6–12 potential which has been modified so that the potential is infinite for $r < \sigma$. The critical point properties calculated by Kirkwood are tabulated in Table 9.1 and the calculated compressibility factor of argon at $0°$c is plotted in Figure 6.1.

It has recently been possible[9, 10, 11] to obtain an exact integral equation for the pair distribution function. In order to solve this equation it is necessary to make some approximations. These approximations appear to be better than the superposition approximation because they are self consistent and have the further advantage of being introduced after the derivation of the integral equation rather than before. Detailed numerical investigations have, however, not yet been undertaken so that a proper appraisal is not yet possible.

In this chapter we have discussed two quite different approaches to the theory of liquids. The significant structure and free volume theories, although differing in their formalism, are both based on the same model: a disordered lattice structure. The radial distribution function method is formulated in analogy to the gaseous state and is, in principle, an exact

4 R. W. Hart, R. Wallis and L. Pode, *J. Chem. Phys.*, **19**, 139 (1951); G. R. Rushbrooke and H. I. Scoins, *Phil. Mag.*, **42**, 582 (1951); B. R. A. Nijboer and L. van Hove, *Phys. Rev.*, **85**, 777 (1952).

5 A. E. Rodriguez, *Proc. Roy. Soc. (London)*, **A239**, 373 (1957); G. H. A. Cole, *J. Chem. Phys.*, **34**, 2016 (1961).

6 J. G. Kirkwood and E. M. Boggs, *J. Chem. Phys.*, **10**, 394 (1942).

7 J. G. Kirkwood, E. K. Maun and B. J. Alder, *J. Chem. Phys.*, **18**, 1040 (1950).

8 J. G. Kirkwood, V. A. Lewinson and B. J. Alder, *J. Chem. Phys.*, **20**, 929 (1952).

9 E. Meeron, *Phys. Fluids*, **1**, 139 (1958); E. Meeron and E. R. Rodemich, *ibid.*, **1**, 246 (1958); E. Meeron, *J. Math. Phys.*, **1**, 192 (1960); *Physica*, **26**, 445 (1960).

10 J. M. J. van Leeuwen, J. Groenweld and J. de Boer, *Physica*, **25**, 792 (1959).

11 T. Morita and K. Hiroike, *Progr. Theoret. Phys., Kyoto*, **23**, 1003 (1960); K. Hiroike, *ibid.*, **24**, 317 (1960); T. Morita and K. Hiroike, *ibid.*, **25**, 537 (1961).

theory. That both approaches are capable of describing the liquid state should not be surprising since, for example, the free electron model of a metal and the more exact band theory yield substantially the same results for metals despite their different bases. Although the distribution function method is more general, the authors frankly consider the other approach as being more useful for practical calculations, just as the free electron model, although less general than band theory, is more easily applied to practical problems in solid state theory.

13

LIQUID MIXTURES

1. Introduction

The statistical thermodynamics of mixtures has been one of the most interesting problems in physical chemistry. The earliest approach was that of van der Waals[1] who applied his well-known equation of state to binary mixtures by replacing the quantities a and b by the following composition-dependent averages:

$$a = x_A^2 a_A + 2x_A x_B a_{AB} + x_B^2 a_B$$
$$b = x_A b_A + x_B b_B \tag{1}$$

where $a_{AB} = \sqrt{a_A a_B}$; a_A, b_A are the values appropriate to the first component and a_B, b_B are the values appropriate to the second component. Although deceptively simple, we shall see that this procedure of replacing parameters by composition-dependent averages has underlain much of the subsequent work on the theory of mixtures.

In the next section a brief discussion of the properties of perfect mixtures will be given and in the following sections various theories which explain deviations from the laws of perfect mixtures will be presented. The present discussion will be primarily concerned with the theory of concentrated solutions. Therefore, the interesting work of McMillan and Mayer[2] which is based on the theory of imperfect gases and appears practicable only for very dilute solutions will not be presented. For simplicity, the discussion will be limited to binary mixtures.

2. Perfect Mixtures; Excess Thermodynamic Quantities

If the molecules of the components of a binary mixture are sufficiently similar, then the partition function of the mixture will be given by

$$\frac{N!}{N_A! N_B!} f_A^{N_A} f_B^{N_B} \tag{1}$$

where $N = N_A + N_B$. Such a mixture is called a *perfect mixture*. Clearly

---

[1] J. D. van der Waals, *Die Continuität des gasförmigen und flüssigen Zustandes*, Barth, Leipzig, 1899.
[2] W. G. McMillan, Jr., and J. E. Mayer, *J. Chem. Phys.*, **13**, 276 (1945).

the concept of a perfect mixture is an idealization. If the component molecules were completely similar no distinction could be made between configurations which differ only by permutations and Eq. (1) would not be correct. However, there are many systems, such as mixtures of isotopes and enantiomers, where the differences between the component molecules are slight and Eq. (1) is a good approximation.

The *thermodynamic functions of mixing*, which will be denoted by the superscript M, are the differences between the thermodynamic properties of the mixture and those of the pure components *taken at the same temperature and pressure*. For example, the Helmholtz free energy of mixing is

$$A^M = A(p, T, N_A, N_B) - A_A(p, T, N_A) - A_B(p, T, N_B) \qquad (2)$$

For a perfect mixture, the Helmholtz free energy of mixing is given by

$$A^M = NkT x_A \ln x_A + NkT x_B \ln x_B \qquad (3)$$

where $x_A = N_A/N$, etc. The entropy of mixing is

$$S^M = -Nk x_A \ln x_A - Nk x_B \ln x_B \qquad (4)$$

Note that A^M is negative and S^M is positive. The other thermodynamic functions of mixing, such as the heat of mixing and the volume of mixing, are all zero for a perfect mixture.

From Eq. (3) we may deduce the difference between the chemical potential μ_i of the ith component in the mixture and its chemical potential μ_i^0 in the pure state:

$$\mu_i - \mu_i^0 = kT \ln x_i \qquad (5)$$

Hence, for the absolute activity,

$$\lambda_i / \lambda_i^0 = x_i \qquad (6)$$

If the vapor phase in equilibrium with the mixture can be regarded as a perfect gas then the vapor pressures p_i of the mixture are related to the vapor pressures p_i^0 of the pure substances by

$$p_i / p_i^0 = x_i \qquad (7)$$

Equation (7) is referred to as *Raoult's law*.

In the remainder of this chapter we shall be concerned not with perfect mixtures but with deviations from the properties of perfect mixtures. For this reason we shall not talk about thermodynamic functions of mixing. Instead we shall use *excess thermodynamic functions*, denoted by a superscript E, which are defined as the difference between the thermodynamic function of mixing and the value corresponding to a perfect mixture at the same temperature, pressure, and composition. The excess thermodynamic functions differ from the thermodynamic functions of mixing only for quantities which involve the entropy. Thus the excess volume is identical with the volume of mixing, etc.

In order to discuss deviations from the properties of perfect mixtures, the potential energy of interaction between the component molecules must be known. Therefore, in the next section we shall discuss the second virial coefficient of a gaseous mixture before returning to the subject of liquid mixtures.

3. Second Virial Coefficient of Mixtures; Combining Rules

For a mixture of N_A molecules of type A and N_B molecules of type B, the configurational partition function is given by

$$Q_N = \frac{1}{N_1! N_2!} \int e^{-U/kT} dr_1 \ldots dr_{N_A} ds_1 \ldots ds_{N_B} \tag{1}$$

Assuming that the potential energy is a sum of pair interactions then

$$U(r_1, \ldots, r_{N_A}, s_1, \ldots, s_{N_B}) = \sum_{ij} u_{AA}(r_{ij}) + \sum_{kl} u_{BB}(s_{kl}) + \sum_{ik} u_{AB}(t_{ik}) \tag{2}$$

There are $\frac{1}{2}N_A(N_A-1) \simeq N_A^2/2$ terms in the first sum, $\frac{1}{2}N_B(N_B-1) \simeq N_B^2/2$ terms in the second sum, and $N_A N_B$ terms in the third sum. Proceeding as in Sect. 11.5 we introduce the functions

$$f_{ij}^{AA} = e^{-u_{AA}(r_{ij})/kT} - 1, \qquad f_{kl}^{BB} = e^{-u_{BB}(s_{kl})/kT} - 1$$

$$f_{ik}^{AB} = e^{-u_{AB}(t_{ik})/kT} - 1 \tag{3}$$

Thus

$$e^{-U/kT} = \prod_{ijkl} (1 + f_{ij}^{AA})(1 + f_{kl}^{BB})(1 + f_{ik}^{AB})$$

$$= 1 + \sum_{ij} f_{ij}^{AA} + \sum_{kl} f_{kl}^{BB} + \sum_{ik} f_{ik}^{AB} \tag{4}$$

where only the zero and first order terms have been kept. Introduce the definitions

$$B_{AA} = -\frac{1}{2V} \int (e^{-u_{AA}/kT} - 1) dr_1 dr_2 = 2\pi \int_0^\infty (1 - e^{u_{AA}/kT}) r^2 dr \tag{5}$$

$$B_{BB} = -\frac{1}{2V} \int (e^{-u_{BB}/kT} - 1) ds_1 ds_2 = 2\pi \int_0^\infty (1 - e^{u_{BB}/kT}) r^2 dr \tag{6}$$

$$B_{AB} = -\frac{1}{2V} \int (e^{-u_{AB}/kT} - 1) dr_1 ds_2 = 2\pi \int_0^\infty (1 - e^{u_{AB}/kT}) r^2 dr \tag{7}$$

The configurational integral becomes

$$Q_N = \frac{V^{N_A + N_B}}{N_A! N_B!} \left[\frac{1 - N_A^2 B_{AA} + 2N_A N_B B_{AB} + N_B^2 B_{BB}}{V} \right] \tag{8}$$

Hence

$$A = -kT \ln f_N$$

$$= -(N_B + N_A)kT \ln V + \frac{N_1^2 B_{AA} + 2N_A N_B B_{AB} + N_B^2 B_{BB}}{V} kT$$

$$+ \text{terms independent of } V \tag{9}$$

In obtaining (9) the expansion $\ln(1+x) = x$ has been used. The pressure is given by

$$p = -\left(\frac{\partial A}{\partial V}\right)_T$$

$$= \frac{(N_A + N_B)kT}{V} + \frac{N_A^2 B_{AA} + 2N_A N_B B_{AB} + N_B^2 B_{BB}}{V^2} kT \tag{10}$$

Therefore

$$\frac{pV}{NkT} = 1 + \frac{N}{V}(x_A^2 B_{AA} + 2x_A x_B B_{AB} + x_B^2 B_{BB}) \tag{11}$$

If a Lennard-Jones 6–12 intermolecular potential is assumed, it has been experimentally observed that (11) gives fairly satisfactory agreement with experiment if the following combining rules are used

$$\varepsilon_{AB} = \sqrt{\varepsilon_A \varepsilon_B}, \qquad \sigma_{AB} = \tfrac{1}{2}(\sigma_A + \sigma_B) \tag{12}$$

The first relation follows from the theory of dispersion forces and the second is correct for hard core interactions. The name *Lorentz–Berthelot mixture* is often given to a mixture of Lennard-Jones molecules in which the parameters for the interaction between the unlike molecules are given by Eq. (12).

4. Strictly Regular Solutions

We are now in a position to study the statistical thermodynamics of liquid mixtures. The earliest model to be developed was the lattice or the theory of strictly regular solutions which is primarily due to Guggenheim.[1] The term strictly regular solution (or s-regular solution) is used to avoid confusion with the term regular solution introduced by Hildebrand in a different context.

The basic assumptions of this model are:

(1) A quasi-lattice is assumed with each molecule occupying a single lattice site. It is further assumed that the lattice is rigid. As a result the volume is not an independent thermodynamic quantity but is simply proportional to $N = N_A + N_B$. The excess volume is zero in this model.

(2) It is assumed that the partition function can be factored into a product of the internal partition function, f_{int}, and the translational partition function, f_{tr},

$$f_N = f_{\text{tr}} f_{\text{int}} \tag{1}$$

As usual,

$$f_{\text{tr}} = \left(\frac{2\pi m_A kT}{h^2}\right)^{\frac{3}{2}N_A} \left(\frac{2\pi m_B kT}{h^2}\right)^{\frac{3}{2}N_B} Q_N \tag{2}$$

[1] E. A. Guggenheim, *Mixtures*, Oxford University Press, Oxford, 1952.

where Q_N is the configurational partition function. It is further assumed that the free energy of mixing depends only on Q_N and that the potential energy can be factored into two independent terms. The first term is the energy of the system when each atom is at rest at a lattice site and the second term is the energy of vibration about the sites. Thus

$$Q_N = Q_{\text{latt}}Q_{\text{vib}} \tag{3}$$

It is assumed that Q_{vib} is unaffected by the composition of the system and, therefore, we need focus our attention only on Q_{latt}.

If w_{AA}, w_{AB}, and w_{BB} are the energies of each AA, AB, and BB pair then the lattice energy is given by

$$E_{\text{latt}} = N_{AA}w_{AA} + N_{AB}w_{AB} + N_{BB}w_{BB} \tag{4}$$

where N_{AA}, N_{AB}, and N_{BB} are the number of AA, AB, and BB pairs and are given by

$$zN_A = 2N_{AA} + N_{AB}$$
$$zN_B = 2N_{BB} + N_{AB} \tag{5}$$

As usual z is the coordination number of the lattice. Substituting Eqs. (5) and (4) gives

$$E_{\text{latt}} = \tfrac{1}{2}zN_A w_{AA} + \tfrac{1}{2}zN_B w_{BB} + N_{AB}(w_{AB} - \tfrac{1}{2}w_{AA} - \tfrac{1}{2}w_{BB}) \tag{6}$$

If we introduce the following definitions

$$E_{AA} = \tfrac{1}{2}zN_A w_{AA}, \qquad E_{BB} = \tfrac{1}{2}zN_B w_{BB} \tag{7}$$

$$w = w_{AB} - \tfrac{1}{2}w_{AA} - \tfrac{1}{2}w_{BB} \tag{8}$$

then (6) becomes

$$E_{\text{latt}} = E_{AA} + E_{BB} + N_{AB}w \tag{9}$$

The lattice partition function is

$$Q_{\text{latt}} = \sum_{\langle N_{AB} \rangle} g(N_A, N_B, N_{AB}) \exp\left\{ -\frac{E_{AA} + E_{BB} + N_{AB}w}{kT} \right\}$$
$$= \exp\left\{ -\frac{E_{AA} + E_{BB}}{kT} \right\} \sum_{\langle N_{AB} \rangle} g(N_A, N_B, N_{AB}) \exp\left\{ -\frac{N_{AB}w}{kT} \right\} \tag{10}$$

where $g(N_A, N_B, N_{AB})$ is the number of arrangements of N_A molecules of the first species and N_B molecules of the second species subject to the requirement that there be N_{AB} pairs. The contribution of Q_{latt} to the Helmholtz free energy is

$$-kT \ln Q_{\text{latt}} = E_{AA} + E_{BB} - kT \ln \sum_{\langle N_{AB} \rangle} g(N_A, N_B, N_{AB}) \exp\left\{ -\frac{N_{AB}w}{kT} \right\} \tag{11}$$

Thus the free energy of mixing is given by

$$A^M = -kT \ln \sum_{\langle N_{AB} \rangle} g(N_A, N_B, N_{AB}) \exp\left\{ -\frac{N_{AB}w}{kT} \right\} \tag{12}$$

If $w = 0$ (i.e. $w_{AA} + w_{BB} = 2w_{AB}$) then we may use the fact

$$\sum_{\langle N_{AB} \rangle} g(N_A, N_B, N_{AB}) = \frac{N!}{N_A! N_B!}$$

to obtain

$$A^M = -kT \ln \frac{N!}{N_A! N_B!}$$

$$= NkTx_A \ln x_A + NkTx_B \ln x_B \tag{13}$$

Thus, for a strictly regular solution the vanishing of w is a sufficient condition for the solution to be perfect.

If $w \neq 0$ then the sum in (12) must be evaluated. This problem is mathematically identical to the problem of evaluating the sum which arose in the Ising model in Chapter 10. Since we have already discussed several techniques for performing the summation we shall confine our discussion to random mixtures (Bragg–Williams approximation). In this approximation

$$N_{AB} = zN \left(\frac{N_A}{N} \right) \left(\frac{N_B}{N} \right) \tag{14}$$

Therefore

$$A^M = NkTx_A \ln x_A + NkTx_B \ln x_B + Nzwx_Ax_B \tag{15}$$

The excess functions are thus

$$A^E = G^E = Nzwx_Ax_B \tag{16}$$

$$H^E = E^E = Nzwx_Ax_B \tag{17}$$

$$S^E = 0 \tag{18}$$

where pV terms have been assumed to be negligible. These results are not greatly affected if better approximations (such as the quasi-chemical approximation derived in Chapter 10) are used. The excess entropy is small and negative because departures from randomness can only lower the number of available configurations, and the excess enthalpy or heat of mixing is very nearly equal to the excess free energy. However, experimental studies have shown that the excess entropy can be positive or negative and that excess entropy is of the same order as the heat of mixing. More successful models will be considered in the next sections.

In Figure 1 the free energy of mixing is plotted for the two temperatures $zw/kT = 1.5$ and 2.5.

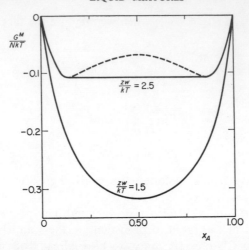

Figure 1. Free energy of mixing according to the Bragg–Williams approximation.

It is evident that at the lower temperature phase separation takes place. This is because for $w > 0$, $2w_{AB} > w_{AA} + w_{BB}$ and AA and BB pairs are energetically favored over AB pairs. Hence, at low enough temperatures the phases will separate. The critical temperature, at which the two phases become identical, is defined by the conditions

$$\frac{\partial^2 G^M}{\partial x_A{}^2} = 0, \qquad \frac{\partial^3 G^M}{\partial x_A{}^3} = 0 \tag{19}$$

Applying these conditions to Eq. (15) yields

$$\frac{zw}{kT_c} = 2, \qquad x_A^c = x_B^c = \tfrac{1}{2} \tag{20}$$

Corrections to the Bragg–Williams approximation appreciably lower the calculated critical point. The results of these higher order approximations are discussed in Guggenheim's book.[1]

Equation (15) may be rewritten as

$$A^M = N_A kT \ln \frac{N_A}{N_A + N_B} + N_B kT \ln \frac{N_B}{N_A + N_B} + z \frac{N_A N_B}{N_A + N_B} w \tag{21}$$

The chemical potential, μ_i, may be obtained by differentiating with respect to N_i. The result is

$$\mu_i - \mu_i^0 = kT \ln x_i + (1 - x_i)^2 zw \tag{22}$$

Hence

$$\frac{\lambda_i}{\lambda_i^0} = x_i e^{(1 - x_i)^2 zw/kT} \tag{23}$$

[1] E. A. Guggenheim, *Mixtures*, Oxford University Press, Oxford, 1952.

The partial vapor pressures are given by

$$\frac{p_i}{p_i^0} = x_i \, e^{(1-x_i)^2 zw/kT} \tag{24}$$

In Figure 2 the partial vapor pressure is plotted for $zw/kT = 1, 0$, and -2. For $w = 0$ we obtain Raoult's law. For $w > 0$ there are positive deviations from Raoult's law whereas for $w < 0$ there are negative deviations from Raoult's law. In Figures 3 and 4 the partial vapor pressures are plotted for $zw/kT = 2$ and 3, respectively.

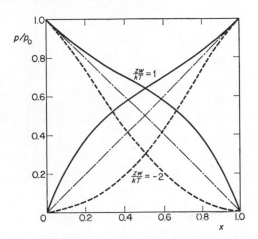

Figure 2. Partial vapor pressures according to the Bragg–Williams approximation for $zw/kT = 1, 0$, and -2.

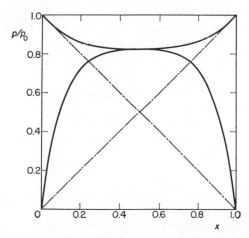

Figure 3. Partial vapor pressures according to the Bragg–Williams approximation for $zw/kT = 2$.

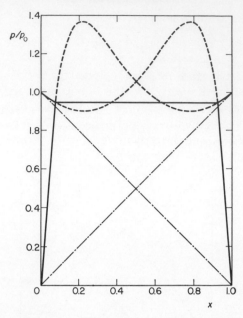

Figure 4. Partial vapor pressures according to the Bragg–Williams approximation for $zw/kT = 3$.

5. Cell Model of Mixtures

In the preceding section we have seen that the theory of strictly regular solutions provides very illuminating qualitative information about a mixture but that it is lacking quantitatively. The free volume or cell model of Lennard-Jones and Devonshire has been widely applied to liquids. This model has been applied to mixtures[1, 2] with fair quantitative success. The use of the cell model to calculate the excess properties of a mixture is a much less drastic approximation than its use to calculate the absolute values of those properties.

Proceeding as in Sect. 12.8, configuration space is divided into N cells of equal size. This assumes that the molecules are similar in size but does not necessarily require that the molecules be of equal size. Assuming a random distribution of the molecules among the cells the configurational partition function is

$$Q_N = \frac{N!}{N_A! N_B!} \{ev_f(A)\}^{N_A} \{ev_f(B)\}^{N_B} \exp\left\{ -\frac{N_A \psi_A(0) + N_B \psi_B(0)}{kT} \right\} \quad (1)$$

[1] I. Prigogine and V. Mathot, *J. Chem. Phys.*, **20**, 49 (1952).

[2] Z. W. Salsburg and J. G. Kirkwood, *J. Chem. Phys.*, **20**, 1538 (1952); **21**, 2169 (1953).

where

$$v_f(A) = \int_{\text{cell}} e^{-[\psi_A(r) - \psi_A(0)]/kT} 4\pi r^2 \, dr \qquad (2)$$

$$v_f(B) = \int_{\text{cell}} e^{-[\psi_B(r) - \psi_B(0)]/kT} 4\pi r^2 \, dr$$

and $\psi_A(r)$ and $\psi_B(r)$ are the mean potentials in a cell occupied by molecules A or B. The communal entropy term $e^{N_A} e^{N_B}$ need not be included since it does not affect excess properties. Assuming the zx_A molecules of species A and the zx_B molecules of species B to be smeared over the surface of a sphere of radius $a = (\sqrt{2}V/N)^{\frac{1}{3}}$ then $\psi_A(r)$ is given by

$$\int_0^{\pi} \{x_A u_{AA}(R) + x_B u_{AB}(R)\} \tfrac{1}{2} z \sin \theta \, d\theta$$

$$= \int_0^{\pi} 4 \left[\frac{1}{R^{12}} \{x_A \varepsilon_{AA} \sigma_{AA}^{12} + x_B \varepsilon_{AB} \sigma_{AB}^{12}\} \right.$$

$$\left. - \frac{1}{R^6} \{x_A \varepsilon_{AA} \sigma_{AA}^6 + x_B \varepsilon_{AB} \sigma_{AB}^6\} \right] \tfrac{1}{2} z \sin \theta \, d\theta \qquad (3)$$

Comparing Eq. (3) with Eq. (12.8.1), we see that $\psi_A(r)$ is equivalent to the cell potential of a single component fluid with average parameters $\langle \varepsilon_A \rangle$ and $\langle \sigma_A \rangle$ given by

$$\langle \varepsilon_A \rangle = \frac{(x_A \varepsilon_{AA} \sigma_{AA}^6 + x_B \varepsilon_{AB} \sigma_{AB}^6)^2}{(x_A \varepsilon_{AA} \sigma_{AA}^{12} + x_B \varepsilon_{AB} \sigma_{AB}^{12})} \qquad (4)$$

$$\langle \sigma_A \rangle = \left(\frac{x_A \varepsilon_{AA} \sigma_{AA}^{12} + x_B \varepsilon_{AB} \sigma_{AB}^{12}}{x_A \varepsilon_{AA} \sigma_{AA}^6 + x_B \varepsilon_{AB} \sigma_{AB}^6} \right)^{\frac{1}{6}} \qquad (5)$$

Similarly for a B molecule

$$\langle \varepsilon_B \rangle = \frac{(x_B \varepsilon_{BB} \sigma_{BB}^6 + x_A \varepsilon_{AB} \sigma_{AB}^6)^2}{(x_B \varepsilon_{BB} \sigma_{BB}^{12} + x_A \varepsilon_{AB} \sigma_{AB}^{12})} \qquad (6)$$

$$\langle \sigma_B \rangle = \left(\frac{x_B \varepsilon_{BB} \sigma_{BB}^{12} + x_A \varepsilon_{AB} \sigma_{AB}^{12}}{x_B \varepsilon_{BB} \sigma_{BB}^6 + x_A \varepsilon_{AB} \sigma_{AB}^6} \right)^{\frac{1}{6}} \qquad (7)$$

The properties of the mixture can then be calculated from the already existing tables of calculated properties for a one-component fluid.

If we wish we can simplify matters somewhat by assuming that, on the average, the cells are equivalent and that a single free volume may be used. We can refer to this as a *single-fluid model*, in contrast to the *two-fluid model* we have considered thus far. The predictions of the two-fluid model are not greatly different than those of the single-fluid model. The configurational partition function is

$$Q_N = \frac{N!}{N_A! N_B!} \{ev_f\}^N \exp \frac{N\psi(0)}{kT} \qquad (8)$$

where

$$v_f = \int_{\text{cell}} \exp\left\{-\frac{\psi(r)-\psi(0)}{kT}\right\} 4\pi r^2 \, dr \tag{9}$$

and

$$\psi(r) = x_A \psi_A(r) + x_B \psi_B(r)$$

$$= \int_0^\pi \{x_A^2 u_{AA}(R) + 2x_A x_B u_{AB}(R) + x_B^2 u_{BB}(R)\}\tfrac{1}{2} z \sin\theta \, d\theta \tag{10}$$

This is equivalent to the cell potential of a single-component fluid with average parameters $\langle\varepsilon\rangle$ and $\langle\sigma\rangle$ given by

$$\langle\varepsilon\rangle = \frac{(x_A^2 \varepsilon_{AA}\sigma_{AA}^6 + 2x_A x_B \varepsilon_{AB}\sigma_{AB}^6 + x_B^2 \varepsilon_{BB}\sigma_{BB}^6)^2}{(x_A^2 \varepsilon_{AA}\sigma_{AA}^{12} + 2x_A x_B \varepsilon_{AB}\sigma_{AB}^{12} + x_B^2 \varepsilon_{BB}\sigma_{BB}^{12})} \tag{11}$$

$$\langle\sigma\rangle = \left(\frac{x_A^2 \varepsilon_{AA}\sigma_{AA}^{12} + 2x_A x_B \varepsilon_{AB}\sigma_{AB}^{12} + x_B^2 \varepsilon_{BB}\sigma_{BB}^{12}}{x_A^2 \varepsilon_{AA}\sigma_{AA}^6 + 2x_A x_B \varepsilon_{AB}\sigma_{AB}^6 + x_B^2 \varepsilon_{BB}\sigma_{BB}^6}\right)^{\frac{1}{6}} \tag{12}$$

The predictions of this theory are in much better agreement with experimental results than are the predictions of the theory of strictly regular solutions. In particular, the signs of the excess thermodynamic functions are given correctly. However, the magnitudes of the excess functions, although of the correct order of magnitude, are usually in error. In Table 6.1 a comparison is made between calculated[2] and measured[3] excess functions for a neopentane–CCl$_4$ mixture. The main significance of the cell theory of mixtures is that the partition function of the mixture can be related to the partition function of a one-component fluid by means of averaged potential parameters. This concept forms the basis of the average potential model of mixtures which we shall consider briefly.

6. Smoothed Potential Model

The main error in the method of Sect. 5 is the use of the Lennard-Jones and Devonshire theoretical thermodynamic functions for the one-component fluid. This could be overcome by the use of one of the more satisfactory theories of the liquid state discussed in Chapter 12. However, a less ambitious, but still very interesting procedure would be to use the experimental corresponding states thermodynamic functions. This procedure has been suggested by Prigogine.[1] For convenience, we may call this the average potential model. We have seen that the theorem of corresponding states for a one-component fluid requires that

$$Q_N = [\sigma^3 q(T^*, v^*)]^N \tag{1}$$

[3] V. Mathot and A. Desmyter, *J. Chem. Phys.*, **21**, 782 (1953); A. Englert-Chowles, *J. Chem. Phys.*, **23**, 1168 (1955).
[1] I. Prigogine, A. Bellemans and A. Englert-Chowles, *J. Chem. Phys.*, **24**, 518 (1956).

where $q(T^*, v^*)$ is a universal function of $T^* = kT/\varepsilon$ and $v^* = V/N\sigma^3$. For a single-fluid model (Prigogine calls this the *crude approximation*)

$$Q_N = \frac{N}{N_A! N_B!} [\langle\sigma\rangle^3 q(\langle T^*\rangle, \langle v^*\rangle)]^N \qquad (2)$$

where $\langle T^*\rangle = kT/\langle\varepsilon\rangle$, $\langle v^*\rangle = V/N\langle\sigma\rangle^3$ and $\langle\varepsilon\rangle$ and $\langle\sigma\rangle$ are given by Eqs. (5.11) and (5.12). Similarly, for a two-fluid model (Prigogine calls this the *refined version*)

$$Q_N = \frac{N!}{N_A! N_B!} [\langle\sigma_A\rangle^3 q(\langle T_A^*\rangle, \langle v_A^*\rangle)]^{N_A} [\langle\sigma_B\rangle^3 q(\langle T_B^*\rangle, \langle v_B^*\rangle)]^{N_B} \qquad (3)$$

where $\langle T_A^*\rangle$, $\langle T_B^*\rangle$, $\langle v_A^*\rangle$, and $\langle v_B^*\rangle$ are defined in terms of $\varepsilon_A, \varepsilon_B, \sigma_A$, and σ_B, which are given by Eqs. (5.4) to (5.7). The difference between the predictions of the single- and two-fluid models is slight. The effect of local inhomogeneities of structure can be taken into account. In addition more sophisticated techniques, such as the quasi-chemical approximation, can be used to take non-randomness into account. These points are treated very lucidly in Prigogine's useful book.[2]

In Table 1 the excess functions predicted by the cell model and the averaged potential model for a neopentane–CCl₄ mixture are compared with the experimental results.[3] Both theories predict the correct sign but the averaged potential model gives much the best quantitative agreement.

TABLE 1. Calculated and measured excess properties of a neopentane–CCl₄ mixture at 0°C ($x = 0.5$)

	G^E(cal mole⁻¹)	H^E(cal mole⁻¹)	TS^E(cal mole⁻¹)	V^E(cm³ mole⁻¹)
Cell model		16	− 98	− 3
Av. potential model	80	71	− 13	− 2.2
Measured	76	75	− 1 ± 5	− 0.5

The average potential model agrees to first order in the differences between the potential parameters of the components with the exact theory of conformal solutions developed by Longuet-Higgins.[4] The theory of conformal solutions is essentially a perturbation approach and the higher-order terms can be calculated only with great difficulty. The cell model, on the other hand, is in error in the first-order term but appears

[2] I. Prigogine, *The Molecular Theory of Solutions*, North-Holland Publishing Company, Amsterdam, 1957.

[3] See reference 3, Sect. 5.

[4] H. C. Longuet-Higgins, *Proc. Roy. Soc.* (*London*), **A205**, 247 (1951).

to give good approximations to the higher terms. The average potential model can be regarded as combining the advantages of the cell model and the theory of conformal solutions.

7. Significant Structure Theory of Mixtures

At the present time work is just beginning on the significant structure theory of mixtures. The partition function which is being considered is

$$f = \frac{N!}{N_A! N_B!} f_A f_B [(1 + n_h e^{-\varepsilon/RT}) e^{\langle E_S \rangle/RT}]^{N \langle V_S \rangle/V} \tag{1}$$

where

$$f_i = \left[\frac{1}{(1 - e^{-\theta_i/T})^3}\right]^{N_i \langle V_S \rangle/V} \left[\left(\frac{2\pi m_i kT}{h^2}\right)^{\frac{3}{2}} \frac{eV}{N_i}\right]^{N_i(V - \langle V_S \rangle)/V} \tag{2}$$

The main problem is to determine the dependence of the parameters $\langle V_S \rangle$ and $\langle E_S \rangle$ on concentration. The parameters V_S and E_S are proportional to the intermolecular parameters σ^3 and ε, respectively. For this reason it would be promising to vary V_S and E_S in the same manner as σ^3 and ε are varied in Eqs. (5.11) and (5.12). Work has begun but, unfortunately, no results are available at this time.

14

DILUTE SOLUTIONS OF STRONG ELECTROLYTES

1. Introduction

In this chapter the chemical potential of a dilute solution of a strong electrolyte is calculated. 'Strong electrolyte' in this context denotes one that can be treated as totally dissociated. A 0.001 molar aqueous solution of NaCl is one example; whether an aqueous solution of a uni-univalent, i.e. $1-1$, electrolyte more concentrated than 0.01 molar fits such a description is debatable.[1]

A solution in which the solute molecules have a greater affinity for one another than for the solvent molecules is said to show positive deviation from Raoult's Law. This tendency is measured quantitatively by the activity a defined by

$$\mu = \mu^0 + RT \ln a \tag{1}$$

where μ is the chemical potential. For the case of a high escaping tendency of the solute the activity a of the solute will be greater than the concentration of the same solute. The ratio a/c is called the activity coefficient γ. For a mixture of CCl_4 in H_2O γ is greater than unity. On the other hand, the activity coefficient for a dilute aqueous solution of a strong electrolyte such as NaCl is less than unity. In this latter case physical interactions between positive and negative ions and between ions and solvent result in a lowered escaping tendency for the ionic solute.

In 1923, Debye and Hückel[2] advanced a theoretical expression for the activity coefficient in a very dilute solution of a strong electrolyte. We shall consider their result for the equilibrium case in which no external field is applied to the solution. For the calculation of conductance, a more general formulation including the effects of external fields is required.[3] The approximate treatment of the electrically neutral solvent as a structureless, continuous medium will also preclude the calculation of effects of tempera-

[1] E. A. Guggenheim, *Discussions Faraday Soc.*, **24**, 53 (1957); H. S. Frank, *ibid.*, p. 66.

[2] P. Debye and E. Hückel, *Physik. Z.*, **24**, 185 (1923); for an English translation see: *The Collected Papers of Peter J. W. Debye*, Interscience Publishers, New York, 1954, pp. 217–263.

[3] H. S. Harned and B. B. Owen, *The Physical Chemistry of Electrolytic Solutions*, 3rd Ed., Reinhold Publishing Corp., New York, 1958.

ture and pressure on the equilibrium properties of the electrolytic solution.[4]

At a sufficiently high temperature, the ions would be in a completely disordered state and the resultant interionic attractive energy would be zero. Under normal conditions, however, attractive and repulsive interionic forces give rise to configurations that are not completely random. In fact, were it not for the thermal motion of solute and solvent particles, an orderly array of positive and negative ions similar to the lattice of an ionic crystal would be expected. Focusing our attention arbitrarily on a given positive ion (denoted hereafter by the letter j), we note that negative ions carried past j by thermal motion are deflected toward j while positive ions swerve away. The superposition of many successive snapshots of the immediate vicinity of the jth ion would show a spherically symmetrical atmosphere of negative charge about the jth ion. The concept of an ionic atmosphere and the assumption that deviations from $\gamma = 1$ are primarily due to electrostatic interactions are fundamental to the Debye–Hückel theory.

There is a superficial resemblance between the imperfect gas model of Chapter 11 and that of a very dilute solution of ions when the solvent in the latter case is treated as a continuum. However, the methods of Chapter 11 are unsuitable for this new problem because of the fundamental difference in the potential functions of the two types of systems. In contrast with the Lennard-Jones 6–12 potential of Eq. (11.3.3), the most important ion pair interaction in a dilute electrolytic solution is coulombic. One possible approximate ion pair potential function is

$$u(r_{ij}) = \frac{z_i z_j e^2}{\varepsilon r}, \qquad r \geqslant \sigma$$
$$= \infty, \qquad r < \sigma \tag{2}$$

where the ions are hard spheres of diameter σ (see Figure 1), the charge

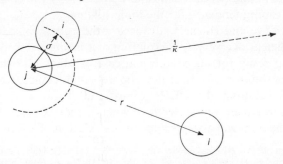

Figure 1. Schematic drawing of the neighborhood of the jth ion with the solvent treated as a continuous medium. σ is an ionic diameter and $1/\kappa$ is the Debye length.

[4] R. H. Fowler and E. A. Guggenheim, *Statistical Thermodynamics*, Cambridge University Press, 1939, Chapter 9.

numbers are denoted by z, e is the charge on an electron, ε is the dielectric constant of the pure solvent (approximately the same as that of the solution), and r is the interionic distance (center to center). This function grossly oversimplifies the short-range non-coulombic interactions by ignoring van der Waals attractive forces altogether. However, this is not a fatal error since in a very dilute solution ion–ion collisions are much less frequent than solvent molecule–solute ion collisions which by our choice of a model have been written out of the picture altogether. When Eq. (2) is substituted for $u(r_{12})$ in the second virial coefficient, Eq. (11.7.5), the resulting integral diverges at the upper limit. As was noted in Sect. 11.5, the potential function must have an r^{-4} dependence or smaller if this integral is to converge. More concisely, the imperfect gas approximation, which considers only binary interactions in a calculation of the second virial coefficient, is invalid when the intermolecular (interionic) forces are effective at considerably greater distances.

Since the ions have a finite radius, they necessarily have a closest distance of approach σ. As one might expect, the equilibrium properties of an electrolytic solution are independent of σ at high dilutions. Thus, the Debye–Hückel limiting law can be derived from a point charge model of the ions.[5] Such a derivation will not be given here. It should be noted in passing that such an assembly of point charges is unstable,[6] and this physical model is, therefore, inherently less interesting than that of ions with finite radii.

The Debye–Hückel treatment given here is also applicable to a plasma, i.e. a gas composed of ions.[7] In such a system the 'solvent' is a vacuum with a dielectric constant of unity.

2. Poisson's Equation

In Sect. 8.1 we derived Poisson's equation, which relates the mean difference of electrostatic potential ϕ in a medium to the mean charge density ρ. The mean charge density $\rho_j(r)$ at a point a distance r from the jth ion in the electrolytic solution is related to the mean number density of ions at the same point by the relation

$$\rho_j(r) = e \sum_i z_i n_i^j(r) \tag{1}$$

where e is the charge on an electron, z_i is the valence of the ith species of ion, and $n_i^j(r)$ is the mean concentration of the ith species of ion at a

[5] H. S. Harned and B. B. Owen, op. cit., Chapter 2.

[6] H. A. Kramers, Proc. Soc. Sci. Amsterdam, 30, 145 (1929); R. H. Fowler and E. A. Guggenheim, op. cit., pp. 397, 406.

[7] L. D. Landau and E. M. Lifshitz, Statistical Physics, Addison-Wesley, Reading, Mass., 1958, p. 229.

distance r from the jth ion. For any point a distance from the center of the jth ion equal to or greater than the diameter σ of the jth ion we may write Poisson's equation (8.1.15) in rectangular coordinates as

$$\nabla^2 \phi_j = \frac{\partial^2 \phi_j}{\partial x^2} + \frac{\partial^2 \phi_j}{\partial y^2} + \frac{\partial^2 \phi_j}{\partial z^2} = -\frac{4\pi\rho_j}{\varepsilon} \tag{2}$$

where ϕ_j is the mean electrostatic potential at the point (x, y, z), ρ_j is the mean charge density at this same point, and the subscript j indicates that the center of the jth ion is the origin of coordinates. Electroneutrality imposes the condition that $\rho_j \to 0$ as the point (x, y, z) becomes infinitely distant from the jth ion. An alternative statement of this condition in polar coordinates is

$$\int_\sigma^\infty 4\pi r^2 \rho_j \, dr = -z_j e \tag{3}$$

The potential ϕ_j will also approach zero as $r \to \infty$.

Since the charge on the jth ion is presumed to lie at its center, the distribution of charge in the atmosphere about the jth ion is spherically symmetric, and a transformation of Eq. (2) to polar coordinates is desirable. The operator ∇^2 in polar coordinates is[1]

$$\nabla^2 = \frac{1}{r^2} \frac{\partial}{\partial r}\left(r^2 \frac{\partial}{\partial r}\right) + \frac{1}{r^2 \sin\theta} \frac{\partial}{\partial \theta}\left(\sin\theta \frac{\partial}{\partial \theta}\right) + \frac{1}{r^2 \sin^2\theta} \frac{\partial^2}{\partial \phi^2} \tag{4}$$

where ϕ is an angle,[2] not a potential difference. Since the distribution of charge in the atmosphere is independent of the angles θ and ϕ, we may use a simplified form of Poisson's equation

$$\frac{1}{r^2} \frac{d}{dr}\left(r^2 \frac{d\phi_j}{dr}\right) = -\frac{4\pi\rho_j}{\varepsilon} \qquad (r \geqslant \sigma) \tag{5}$$

In the above model none of the centers (the charges) of the i ions can approach the center (the charge) of the jth ion more closely than an ionic diameter σ. This amounts to the approximation that all the ions in solution have the diameter σ. This assumption contradicts our knowledge of crystallographic radii and is further complicated in aqueous solutions by the existence of 'hard' hydration sheaths of variable thickness about the cations. This weakness in our argument can be tolerated since in the limit of very great dilution the dependence of the activity coefficient γ upon σ becomes negligible anyway.

---

[1] *Q.C.*, p. 367.
[2] If a position (r, θ, ϕ) on the surface of the earth were re-expressed as (x, y, z) in a right-handed cartesian coordinate system in which the z axis pointed north along the axis of rotation of the earth, the necessary conversion relations would be $x = r\sin\theta\cos\phi$, $y = r\sin\theta\sin\phi$, and $z = r\cos\theta$ and the angle θ would be recognized as a conventional co-latitude while ϕ is an unorthodox longitude.

3. Poisson–Boltzmann Equation

Substitution of Eq. (2.1) in Eq. (2.5) yields

$$\frac{1}{r^2}\frac{d}{dr}\left(r^2\frac{d\phi_j(r)}{dr}\right) = -\frac{4\pi e}{\varepsilon}\sum_i z_i n_i^j(r) \qquad (r \geqslant \sigma) \tag{1}$$

This equation must be solved for $\phi_j(r)$ as the first step in the calculation of the activity coefficient γ.

The frequency of occurrence of the ith ion in a volume element a distance r from the jth ion is given by the Boltzmann formula

$$e^{-W_{ij}/kT}\frac{dr}{V} \tag{2}$$

where dr is the volume element, V is the total volume, and W_{ij} may be defined[1] as either (1) the work expended in bringing the ith ion from infinity to a distance r from the jth ion averaged over all possible configurations of the remaining ions or (2) the potential energy, the first derivative of which is the mean force acting on the ith ion in the volume element dr a distance r from the jth ion. The first of two major approximations in the Debye–Hückel theory is

$$W_{ij} = z_i e\phi_j \tag{3}$$

whence we have for the mean concentration of the ith species of ion a distance r from the jth ion

$$n_i^j(r) = n_i\, e^{-z_i e\phi_j/kT} \qquad (r \geqslant \sigma) \tag{4}$$

where n_i is the mean number density of the ith species for the total volume of solution. The substitution of this Boltzmann relation in Eq. (1) yields the Poisson–Boltzmann equation

$$\frac{1}{r^2}\frac{d}{dr}\left(r^2\frac{d\phi_j(r)}{dr}\right) = -\frac{4\pi e}{\varepsilon}\sum_i z_i n_i\, e^{-z_i e\phi_j(r)/kT} \qquad (r \geqslant \sigma) \tag{5}$$

This differential equation in $\phi_j(r)$ still cannot be solved without resorting to numerical methods unless the second major Debye–Hückel approximation is made

$$z_i e\phi_j \ll kT \tag{6}$$

which permits us to expand the exponential in Eq. (5) using the series $e^{-x} = 1 - x + x^2/2! - x^3/3! + \ldots$ The resulting linear Poisson–Boltzmann equation is

$$\frac{1}{r^2}\frac{d}{dr}\left(r^2\frac{d\phi_j}{dr}\right) = -\frac{4\pi e}{\varepsilon}\sum_i z_i n_i\left(1 - \frac{z_i e\phi_j}{kT}\right) \tag{7}$$

We shall defer an elaborate discussion of the seriousness of the approximations given in Eqs. (3) and (6) until we have obtained the limiting form

[1] R. H. Fowler and E. A. Guggenheim, *op. cit.*, Sections 702 and 908.

of γ. We note, however, in passing that the nature of the approximation made in Eq. (6) depends on the choice of the ionic solute. For a symmetrical electrolyte such as NaCl in which $z_+ = -z_-$ and $n_+ = n_-$, the charge density of Eq. (2.1) becomes from Eq. (4) just

$$\rho_j = 0 - 2z_+ en_+ \left(\frac{z_+ e\phi_j}{kT} \right) + 0 - \tfrac{1}{3} z_+ en_+ \left(\frac{z_+ e\phi_j}{kT} \right)^3 + 0 - \ldots \quad (8)$$

where the first term of the expansion Eq. (7) has vanished because of the electroneutrality condition

$$\sum_i n_i z_i e = 0 \quad (9)$$

In this symmetrical case the use of Eq. (6) has involved no error of order less than $(z_+ e\phi_j/kT)^3$. In the more general case where $|z_1| \neq |z_2| \neq |z_3| \ldots$ and $n_1 \neq n_2 \neq n_3 \ldots$, Eq. (2.1) reduces to

$$\rho_j = -\sum_i z_i en_i \left(\frac{z_i e\phi_j}{kT} \right) \quad (10)$$

when second and higher order terms in $(z_i e\phi_j/kT)$ are neglected. This result presages the wider applicability of the Debye–Hückel limiting law to $1-1$ electrolytes than to more complicated electrolytes.

4. Calculation of the Mean Electrostatic Potential ϕ_j

Application of the electroneutrality condition, Eq. (3.9), to the linear Poisson–Boltzmann equation, Eq. (3.7), yields

$$\frac{1}{r^2} \frac{d}{dr} \left(r^2 \frac{d\phi_j}{dr} \right) = -\frac{4\pi e^2}{\varepsilon kT} \sum_i z_i^2 n_i \phi_j \quad (r \geqslant \sigma) \quad (1)$$

If we let

$$\kappa^2 = \frac{4\pi e^2}{\varepsilon kT} \sum_i n_i z_i^2 \quad (2)$$

Eq. (1) may be rewritten as

$$\frac{d}{dr} \left(r^2 \frac{d\phi_j}{dr} \right) = \kappa^2 r^2 \phi_j \quad (r \geqslant \sigma) \quad (3)$$

The quantity κ has the dimension of reciprocal length, and $1/\kappa$ is called the Debye length. As we shall see later, the Debye length is the approximate thickness of the ionic atmosphere about the jth ion.

Equation (3) can be solved for ϕ_j by substituting x for $r\phi_j$ and thus obtaining

$$\frac{d}{dr} \left(r \frac{dx}{dr} \right) - \frac{dx}{dr} = \kappa^2 rx \quad (4)$$

$$r \frac{d^2 x}{dr^2} = \kappa^2 rx \quad (5)$$

and

$$\frac{d^2x}{dr^2} = \kappa^2 x \qquad (6)$$

whence

$$\phi_j = \frac{A_1}{r} e^{-\kappa r} + \frac{A_2}{r} e^{\kappa r} \qquad (7)$$

where A_1 and A_2 are constants of integration. By applying the boundary conditions we can obtain particular solutions from this general form.

The constant A_2 is readily evaluated by considering the consequence of the convention that $\phi_j \to 0$ as $r \to \infty$. In this limit the second term on the right-hand side of Eq. (7) is unbounded unless

$$A_2 = 0 \qquad (8)$$

Thus we have

$$\phi_j = \frac{A_1}{r} e^{-\kappa r} \qquad (9)$$

To evaluate A_1 we investigate the interior of the sphere of radius σ concentric with the jth ion (see Figure 1.1). With the charge of the jth ion localized at $r = 0$ and no other charge lying within the sphere of radius σ about the point $r = 0$, we conclude that Laplace's equation

$$\frac{1}{r^2} \frac{d}{dr}\left(r^2 \frac{d\Phi_j}{dr} \right) = \frac{1}{r} \frac{d^2}{dr^2}(r\Phi_j) = 0 \qquad (r < \sigma) \qquad (10)$$

is valid for the interior of this hypothetical sphere, where Φ_j denotes the electrostatic potential within the sphere. Integrating twice, we obtain first

$$\frac{d(r\Phi_j)}{dr} = A_3 \qquad (11)$$

and then

$$\Phi_j = A_3 + \frac{A_4}{r} \qquad (12)$$

Since the electrostatic potential Φ_j must approach the coulombic potential $z_j e/\varepsilon r$ as $r \to 0$, it is evident that

$$A_4 = z_j e/\varepsilon \qquad (13)$$

To preserve continuity at $r = \sigma$ it follows that

$$\left.\begin{array}{c} \Phi_j = \phi_j \\ d\Phi_j/dr = d\phi_j/dr \end{array}\right\} r = \sigma \qquad (14)$$

Substituting Eqs. (9) and (12) in Eq. (14), we obtain the simultaneous equations

$$\frac{A_1 e^{-\kappa\sigma}}{\sigma} = A_3 + \frac{z_j e}{\varepsilon\sigma} \qquad (15)$$

and

$$\frac{A_1 e^{-\kappa\sigma}}{\sigma^2} + \frac{A_1 \kappa e^{-\kappa\sigma}}{\sigma} = \frac{z_j e}{\varepsilon\sigma^2} \tag{16}$$

the solutions of which are

$$A_1 = \frac{z_j e\, e^{\kappa\sigma}}{\varepsilon(1+\kappa\sigma)} \tag{17}$$

and

$$A_3 = -\frac{z_j e\kappa}{\varepsilon(1+\kappa\sigma)} \equiv \phi_j^* \qquad (r \leqslant \sigma) \tag{18}$$

Substitution of Eq. (17) in Eq. (9) yields

$$\phi_j = \frac{z_j e}{\varepsilon} \cdot \frac{e^{\kappa\sigma}}{1+\kappa\sigma} \cdot \frac{e^{-\kappa r}}{r} \qquad (r \geqslant \sigma) \tag{19}$$

the time average electrostatic potential at any point within the dilute electrolyte a distance $r \geqslant \sigma$ from the center of the jth ion. From our previous observation that A_4/r in Eq. (12) is the contribution to Φ_j made by the jth ion alone we deduce that Eq. (18), hereafter denoted by ϕ_j^*, is the constant contribution made by the ionic atmosphere about the jth ion to the electrostatic potential Φ_j within the sphere of radius σ.

From a comparison of ϕ_j^* with A_4/r it is apparent that the net effect on the potential of the jth ion of all the other ions in solution could be duplicated by placing all the i ions on a concentric spherical surface a distance $r = \sigma + 1/\kappa$ from the center of the jth ion (or by placing a single ion of opposite charge and equal magnitude to that of the jth ion at this same distance). This is the reason for calling $1/\kappa$ 'the radius of the ionic atmosphere'. It is clear from Figure 1.1 that this concept is entirely satisfactory for values of $1/\kappa < \sigma$ as long as the ionic atmosphere is understood to begin a distance $r = \sigma$ from the center of the jth ion. By substituting ϕ_j of Eq. (19) in Poisson's Eq. (3) and noting that the right-hand side must equal $-4\pi\rho_i/\varepsilon$ we obtain a relation with which we can plot the distribution of charge ρ in the atmosphere about the jth ion (ordinate) as a function of the distance r (abscissa). The resulting asymmetric curve with its maximum at $r = 1/\kappa$ resembles an inverted Morse curve.

The internal consistency of the Debye–Hückel argument leading to Eq. (19) can be checked in several ways. Consider first the charge neutrality condition, Eq. (2.3). In the Debye–Hückel approximation, Poisson's equation yields

$$\rho_j = -\frac{\varepsilon}{4\pi} \kappa^2 \phi_j \tag{20}$$

When the value of ϕ_j given by Eq. (19) is substituted in Eq. (20), the right-hand side of this identity is substituted for the charge density ρ_j in Eq. (2.3), and the indicated integration is carried out, the anticipated value $-z_j e$ is obtained. A second equally critical check of self-consistency follows from Eq. (3.3). By their very definition (Sect. 3) we have the identity

$$W_{ij} = W_{ji} \tag{21}$$

Thus if Eq. (3.3) is to hold, it must follow that

$$z_i \phi_j = z_j \phi_i \tag{22}$$

It is therefore reassuring to observe that ϕ_j of Eq. (19) is indeed a linear function of z_j as is required by Eq. (22).

5. Free Energy and Chemical Potential of the Solution

A dilute aqueous solution of a strong electrolyte would be more easily maintained isothermal than thermally isolated, hence our attention is directed to the Helmholtz free energy A rather than the internal energy $\mathcal{E}$. Since in the Debye–Hückel model the solvent is an incompressible, continuous fluid, no real distinction is made between the Gibbs and Helmholtz free energies.[1] Our first order of business is the derivation of a relationship between the potential ϕ_j^* of Eq. (4.18) and the free energy.[2]

According to Eqs. (4.11.7) and (4.11.8), the Helmholtz free energy of a canonical ensemble of non-localized monatomic ions is

$$A = -kT \ln \left(\frac{1}{N! \, h^{3N}} \int e^{-\mathcal{E}/kT} \, d\Omega \right) \tag{1}$$

where $\mathcal{E}$ is the sum in our model of the coulombic and hard sphere repulsive energies, $N!$ represents the product $(N_1! \, N_2! \, .. \, N_n!)$ where N_1 is the number of ions of species 1 present, etc., and $d\Omega$ is the volume of phase space corresponding to energies between $\mathcal{E}$ and $\mathcal{E} + \delta\mathcal{E}$. The factors involving the number of ions and Planck's constant are constant throughout and may be omitted hereafter. The energy $\mathcal{E}$ can be written as

$$\mathcal{E} = \mathcal{E}_c + \mathcal{E}_s = \mathcal{E}_s + \tfrac{1}{2} \sum_j \sum_k (q_j q_k / \varepsilon r_{jk}) \tag{2}$$

where $\mathcal{E}_c$ is the coulombic energy and $\mathcal{E}_s$ is the hard sphere repulsive energy. Self energy terms $q_j^2 / \varepsilon r_j$ are omitted since they are constant. Equation (2) can be rewritten as

$$\mathcal{E} = \mathcal{E}_s + \tfrac{1}{2} \sum_j q_j \psi_j \tag{3}$$

[1] In the original derivation (Ref. 1.2) neither was used; instead, a free energy $G' = S - (E/T)$ was employed.

[2] H. Falkenhagen and G. Kelbg, 'The Present State of the Theory of Electrolytic Solutions' (J. O'M. Bockris, Ed.). *Modern Aspects of Electrochemistry No. 2*, Butterworths, London, 1959, pp. 3–5.

where

$$\psi_j = \sum_k q_k / \varepsilon r_{jk} = (\partial \mathcal{E}_c / \partial q_j) \qquad (4)$$

is the instantaneous potential at the jth ion resulting from coulombic interactions with all the other ions in solution. To obtain the mean value $\bar{\psi}_j$ of this potential we must calculate the statistical mean value of $\partial \mathcal{E}_c / \partial q_j$. This can be accomplished by differentiating Eq. (1) with respect to the charge q_j. We thus obtain

$$e^{-A/kT} \delta A = \int \delta \mathcal{E} \, e^{-\mathcal{E}/kT} \, d\Omega \qquad (5)$$

In this particular case of adiabatic variation of charge it is evident that

$$\delta \mathcal{E} = \delta \mathcal{E}_c \qquad (6)$$

and for the parameter q as for any other parameter of the state function $\mathcal{E}_c$

$$\delta \mathcal{E}_c = \sum_j (\partial \mathcal{E}_c / \partial q_j) \, \delta q_j \qquad (7)$$

From Eqs. (1) and (7) we see that Eq. (5) may be rewritten as

$$\delta A = \sum_j q_j \left[\frac{\int (\partial \mathcal{E}_c / \partial q_j) \, e^{-\mathcal{E}/kT} \, d\Omega}{\int e^{-\mathcal{E}/kT} \, d\Omega} \right] \qquad (8)$$

Looking back at Eq. (4), we see that the bracketed expression in Eq. (8) is just $\bar{\psi}_j$, the mean value of the electrical potential at the jth ion resulting from coulombic interactions with its ionic atmosphere. Since we have already derived $\bar{\psi}_j \equiv \theta_j^*$ in Sect. 4, the electrostatic contribution to the free energy of an electrolyte can be calculated from

$$A_c = \sum_j N_j q_j \int_0^1 \bar{\psi}_j(\xi) \, d\xi \qquad (9)$$

where ξ is a 'charging parameter' that is permitted to vary from 0 to 1 (i.e. the charge on each ion is increased from a very small fraction of the protonic charge up to its normal value $q_i = z_i e$). The summation is over all species of ions in solution. In this, the so-called Debye charging process, the ions may be charged one at a time in any order or all simultaneously without altering the result.

In the alternative Guntelberg[3] charging process only one ion is charged in the presence of a fully charged atmosphere of ions. This calculation yields the coulombic contribution to the chemical potential directly without an intermediate calculation of the Helmholtz free energy, i.e.

$$\mu_j^c = \left(\frac{\partial A_c}{\partial N_j} \right)_{V,T} = \int_0^1 q_j \bar{\psi}_j(\xi) \, d\xi \qquad (10)$$

[3] See N. Bjerrum, Z. Physik. Chem., 119, 145 (1926).

where it has been assumed that a negligible change in volume occurs during the charging process.[4] The two charging processes yield the same value of μ_j^c provided that the condition of integrability

$$(\partial \psi_k / \partial q_j) = (\partial \psi_j / \partial q_k) \tag{11}$$

is fulfilled.[5] Equation (11) is the Euler reciprocity relation for the exact differential

$$dA_c = \psi_k \, dq_k + \psi_j \, dq_j + \ldots \tag{12}$$

The self-consistency of Eq. (4.19) as an approximate solution of the Poisson–Boltzmann equation is again confirmed by the fact that it satisfies Eq. (11). In fact, Eq. (11) is the most searching test of self-consistency of solutions to the Poisson–Boltzmann equation and is the undoing of the more 'accurate' solutions due to Müller[6] and Gronwall, LaMer, and Sandved.[7]

Using the less expeditious Debye charging process, we substitute θ_j^* of Eq. (4.18) in Eq. (9) recalling that κ, Eq. (4.2), is also a function of the electrostatic charge; the result of this substitution is

$$A_c = -\frac{\kappa}{\varepsilon} \left(\sum_j N_j z_j^2 \varepsilon^2 \right) \int_0^1 \frac{\xi^2}{1 + \xi \kappa \sigma} \, d\xi \tag{13}$$

Performing the integration, we obtain

$$A_c = -\frac{\kappa}{3\varepsilon} \left\{ \frac{3}{(\kappa\sigma)^3} \left[\ln(1 + \kappa\sigma) - \kappa\sigma + \tfrac{1}{2}(\kappa\sigma)^2 \right] \right\} \sum_j N_j z_j^2 e^2 \tag{14}$$

which according to the expansion $\ln x = (x-1) - (x-1)^2/2 + \ldots$ is

$$A_c = -\frac{\kappa}{3\varepsilon} \left\{ 1 - \tfrac{3}{4}\kappa\sigma + \tfrac{3}{5}\kappa^2\sigma^2 - \tfrac{3}{6}\kappa^3\sigma^3 + \ldots \right\} \sum_j N_j z_j^2 e^2 \tag{15}$$

Noting the dependence of κ, Eq. (4.2), on the number of ions, we see that the coulombic contribution to the chemical potential, $\mu_j^c = (\partial A_c / \partial N_j)_{V,T}$ is

$$\mu_j^c = -\frac{z_j^2 e^2 \kappa}{2\varepsilon(1 + \kappa\sigma)} \tag{16}$$

where higher terms have been neglected as is clearly justified for high dilutions.

The chemical potential of a mole of the jth species of ion in an ideal solution in which interionic distances are extremely large is

$$\mu_j = \mu^0 + RT \ln X_j \tag{17}$$

[4] R. H. Fowler and E. A. Guggenheim, op. cit., p. 398.
[5] L. Onsager, Chem. Rev., 13, 73 (1933); O. Halpern, J. Chem. Phys., 2, 85 (1934).
[6] H. Müller, Physik. Z., 28, 324 (1927).
[7] T. H. Gronwall, V. K. LaMer and K. Sandved, Physik. Z., 29, 358 (1928).

where X_j is the mole fraction of the jth species. In a non-ideal solution the analogous expression is [see Eq. (1.1)]

$$\mu_j = \mu^0 + RT \ln a_j = \mu^0 + RT \ln X_j + RT \ln \gamma_j \tag{18}$$

$RT \ln \gamma_j$, the difference between Eqs. (17) and (18), is in the present model a sum of two terms

$$\ln \gamma_j = -\frac{z_j^2 e^2 \kappa}{2\varepsilon kT(1+\kappa\sigma)} + \frac{\mu_j^s}{kT} \tag{19}$$

The calculation of μ_j^s, the hard sphere contribution, necessitates the extension of the imperfect gas theory of Chapter 11 to multicomponent systems.[8] Since at low concentrations the coulombic term is of overriding importance and since the hard sphere model of the ions in solution is a very crude one, the resulting expression for μ_j^s does not significantly improve the agreement between theory and experiment. An empirical additive repulsive potential factor is more commonly substituted for μ_j^s/kT when an attempt is made to fit experimental data for moderately concentrated electrolytic solutions to which the Debye–Hückel limiting law no longer applies. The justification for having carried the concept of a non-coulombic potential throughout the above derivation is that without such a term included in the energy $\mathscr{E}$ of Eq. (1) the phase integral of that relation will not converge.[9] The activity coefficient for an individual ion as given by Eq. (19) does have a genuine physical significance[10] but for convenience is usually expressed in terms of a mean activity coefficient that can be readily measured experimentally.

6. Debye–Hückel Limiting Law

The derivation of the Debye–Hückel limiting equation for the mean activity coefficient from Eq. (5.19) begins with a re-evaluation of κ, Eq. (4.2). Heretofore, we have treated n_i, the mean number density of the ith species of ion, as the number of ions per cc. We may replace n_i in Eq. (4.2) by $Nc_i/1000$, where c_i is the number of gram ions per liter of solution and N is Avogadro's number and thus obtain

$$\kappa = \left(\frac{4\pi Ne^2}{1000\varepsilon kT} \sum_i c_i z_i^2 \right)^{\frac{1}{2}} \tag{1}$$

The ionic strength of a solution

$$I = \sum_i \tfrac{1}{2} m_i z_i^2 \tag{2}$$

---

[8] T. L. Hill, *An Introduction to Statistical Thermodynamics*, Addison-Wesley, Reading, Mass., 1960, pp. 274, 275 and 327.

[9] L. Onsager, *op. cit.*

[10] H. S. Frank, *J. Phys. Chem.*, **67**, 1554 (1963).

where m_i is the molality and z_i is the charge number of the ith species of ion, is a familiar quantity in electrochemistry. Since the solutions under consideration are very dilute, the number of moles per liter, c_i, closely approximates the product $m_i\rho$, where ρ in this case is the solvent density (rather than a charge density). Hence, we may rewrite Eq. (1) as

$$\kappa = \left(\frac{8\pi N e^2 \rho}{1000\varepsilon kT}\right)^{\frac{1}{2}} I^{\frac{1}{2}} \tag{3}$$

where ρ in aqueous solutions is, of course, unity or close to it.

For a binary electrolyte that dissociates into v ions of which v_+ are cations and v_- are anions the mean activity coefficient $\gamma_\pm$ is

$$\gamma_\pm = (\gamma_+^{v_+}\gamma_-^{v_-})^{1/v} \tag{4}$$

Taking the natural logarithm of both sides of Eq. (4), we obtain

$$(v_+ + v_-)\ln\gamma_\pm = v_+ \ln\gamma_+ + v_-\ln\gamma_- \tag{5}$$

Considering only coulombic contributions, it is then apparent from Eq. (5.19) that

$$\ln\gamma_\pm = -\left(\frac{v_+ z_+^2 + v_- z_-^2}{v_+ + v_-}\right)\left(\frac{e^2}{2\varepsilon kT}\right)\left(\frac{\kappa}{1+\kappa\sigma}\right) \tag{6}$$

The relationship between valence and number of ions in a solution of a binary electrolyte is defined by the equations

$$v_+ z_+ + v_- z_- = 0$$

and

$$v_+ + v_- = v \tag{7}$$

Solving this pair of simultaneous equations for v_+ and v_-, we have

$$v_+ = -\left(\frac{z_-}{z_+ - z_-}\right)v$$

and

$$v_- = \left(\frac{z_+}{z_+ - z_-}\right)v \tag{8}$$

These two relations permit us to rewrite Eq. (6) as

$$\ln\gamma_\pm = (z_+ z_-)\left(\frac{e^2}{2\varepsilon kT}\right)\left(\frac{\kappa}{1+\kappa\sigma}\right) \tag{9}$$

Substituting with Eq. (3) for κ and converting to logarithms to the base 10, we see that Eq. (9) takes the simplified form

$$\log_{10}\gamma_\pm = \frac{A z_+ z_- \sqrt{I}}{1 + B\sigma\sqrt{I}} \tag{10}$$

where

$$A = 1.825 \times 10^6 \frac{\rho^{\frac{1}{2}}}{(\varepsilon T)^{\frac{3}{2}}} \text{ mole}^{-\frac{1}{2}} \text{ liter}^{\frac{1}{2}} \text{ deg}^{\frac{3}{2}} \tag{11}$$

and

$$B = 50.29 \frac{\rho^{\frac{1}{2}}}{(\varepsilon T)^{\frac{3}{2}}} \text{Å}^{-1} \text{ mole}^{-\frac{1}{2}} \text{ liter}^{\frac{1}{2}} \text{ deg}^{\frac{1}{2}} \tag{12}$$

The familiar Debye–Hückel limiting law

$$\log_{10} \gamma_\pm = A z_+ z_- \sqrt{I} \tag{13}$$

is an approximate form of Eq. (10) applicable to very dilute solutions that circumvents the awkward question of the numerical value of σ. Since $\varepsilon = 78.54$ and $\rho = 0.997$ for water at 25°C, the coefficient A in Eq. (13) for dilute aqueous solutions is 0.509.

7. Nature of Some of the Approximations

When an attempt is made to fit experimental data with Eq. (6.10) the parameter σ must sometimes be chosen considerably smaller than the closest distance of approach calculated from crystallographic radii. In such cases σ is certainly being used to correct for the short-range non-electrostatic forces. This being true, there is no justification for interpreting all variations in numerical values of the parameter σ as real changes in ionic diameters.

Difficulties with the parameter σ can be ascribed partially to the approximation $z_i e \phi_j \ll kT$, Eq. (3.6). By assembling some of the information accumulated since making this approximation, we can make a quantitative assessment of its seriousness. We recall from Sect. 4 that most of the ions in the atmosphere of the jth ion lie on or near an imaginary concentric spherical surface of radius $r = 1/\kappa$. From Eq. (6.3) we calculate $1/\kappa$ for a 10^{-2} molar aqueous solution of a uni-univalent salt at 25°C to be approximately 30 Å. According to Eq. (4.19), the potential ϕ_j at a distance $r = 1/\kappa$ from the jth ion of a uni-univalent salt (such as NaCl for which $\sigma \approx 4 \text{ Å}^1$) is

$$\phi_j = \frac{e\kappa \, e^{(\kappa\sigma - 1)}}{\varepsilon(1 + \kappa\sigma)} \approx \frac{e\kappa}{\varepsilon} \tag{1}$$

This last approximation errs on the side of being too large and improves rapidly for smaller concentrations and consequent larger values of $1/\kappa$. Substituting this value of ϕ_j in Eq. (3.6) and rearranging terms, we have the condition

$$\frac{1}{\kappa} \gg \frac{e^2}{\varepsilon kT} \tag{2}$$

which at 25°C in water ($\varepsilon = 78.54$) is only 7 Å. Since $1/\kappa \approx 30 \text{ Å}$ in a 0.01 molar solution, it is clear that the linear Poisson–Boltzmann equation obtained with Eq. (3.6) is a reasonable approximation for electrolytic

---

[1] R. A. Robinson and R. H. Stokes, *Electrolyte Solutions*, 2nd Ed., Butterworths, London, 1959, p. 237.

solutions at least as dilute as 0.01 molar.[2] Actually the requirement that $1/\kappa$ be considerably larger than σ occurs tacitly even earlier than Eq. (3.6). In order that we may assume the dielectric constant of the pure solvent to be that of the solution, it is necessary that ions be separated on the average from one another by at least a few solvent molecules, otherwise ε would be drastically reduced by a saturation effect.

[2] See Ref. 1.1.

15

SURFACE CHEMISTRY

1. Introduction

In the treatment of the properties of matter in bulk, the atoms or molecules at the boundary of a phase can be considered equivalent to those deep within the phase. It is quite apparent, however, that at the boundary between a liquid and a vapor phase, the molecules at (and near) the surface are subject to quite different forces from those in the interior. Liquid vapor phase boundaries are not arbitrarily abrupt, but rather are transitional layers. Other surface phenomena such as gases adsorbed on solids and colloidal systems are also characterized by an asymmetry of intermolecular forces.

2. Surface and Interfacial Tension, the Gibbs Adsorption Isotherm

To increase the surface area of a liquid, molecules must be brought from the interior of the liquid to its surface. Since the intermolecular forces acting on an interior molecule are greater than those at the surface, work must be done to move these molecules to the surface. The work done on the surface is $\gamma \, d\sigma$ where γ is the surface tension and σ is the area of the surface. There is thus a change in the Gibbs free energy of the system, which by Eq. (3.5.22) is

$$\left(\frac{\partial G}{\partial \sigma}\right)_{T,p,n_i} = \gamma \tag{1}$$

Further consideration of the thermodynamics of the surface or interface is facilitated by the concept of the dividing surface which is due to Gibbs. Consider a system consisting of two phases, α and β, with a planar interface. In passing from phase α to phase β, the properties do not change abruptly from those of α to those of β, but rather there is a continuous transition from one to the other through the small but finite thickness of the surface or interfacial region. Any parallel plane in this region is called a dividing surface and constitutes a two-dimensional surface phase so that the surface volume is zero.

By definition, the concentration of the ith component in the surface phase is the number of moles per unit area in excess of that which would

416

result if phases α and β had remained homogeneous to the surface. This concentration is denoted by Γ_i. Because of the continuous nature of the transition from phase α to phase β, it is possible to place the dividing surface so that the surface concentration of one component is exactly equal to that which would result if the two bulk phases were homogeneous to the surface. Let this be component 1, and then we have

$$\Gamma_1 = (n_1 - c_1^\alpha V_A - c_1^\beta V_\beta)/\sigma = 0 \tag{2}$$

Usually the other Γ_i will not vanish.

The thermodynamic functions are defined analogously in terms of the same dividing surface. Thus, the Gibbs free energy for the whole system is given by

$$G = G^\alpha + G^\beta + G^s \tag{3}$$

where α, β, and s denote the bulk phases and the surface phase respectively. From Eqs. (1) and (3.7.5), we obtain for the surface phase

$$dG^s = \gamma\, d\sigma - S^s\, dT + \sum_{i=2}^{n} \mu_i\, d(\Gamma_i \sigma) \tag{4}$$

since $dn_i^s = d(\Gamma_i \sigma)$ and $\mu_i = \mu_i^\alpha = \mu_i^\beta = \mu_i^s$. At constant temperature, integration of Eq. (4) by Euler's theorem gives

$$G^s = \gamma\sigma + \sum_{i=2}^{n} \mu_i \Gamma_i \sigma \tag{5}$$

and differentiation of Eq. (5) results in

$$dG^s = \gamma\, d\sigma + \sigma\, d\gamma + \sum_{i=2}^{n} [\mu_i\, d(\Gamma_i \sigma) + \Gamma_i \sigma\, d\mu_i] \tag{6}$$

Subtracting the constant temperature form of Eq. (4) from Eq. (6) and dividing by σ yields

$$d\gamma = -\sum_{i=2}^{n} \Gamma_i\, d\mu_i \tag{7}$$

which is Gibbs' adsorption isotherm.

In the case of a single component system, Eq. (5) becomes

$$G^s = \gamma\sigma \tag{8}$$

and the surface tension is equal to the Gibbs surface free energy per unit area.

The relationship between the Helmholtz free energy and surface tension analogous to Eq. (1) is given by

$$\left(\frac{\partial A}{\partial \sigma}\right)_{T,V,n_i} = \gamma \tag{9}$$

Since there is no volume change, we have

$$dA^s = dG^s \tag{10}$$

From Eqs. (4) and (10), we obtain for a single component system

$$\left(\frac{\partial A^s}{\partial \sigma}\right)_{T,V} = \gamma \tag{11}$$

and

$$\left(\frac{\partial A^s}{\partial T}\right)_{V,\sigma} = -S^s \tag{12}$$

Since the order of differentiation is immaterial, we have from Eqs. (11) and (12)

$$\left(\frac{\partial \gamma}{\partial T}\right)_{V,\sigma} = -\left(\frac{\partial S^s}{\partial \sigma}\right)_{V,T} = \frac{1}{T}\left[\frac{\partial A^s}{\partial \sigma} - \frac{\partial E^s}{\partial \sigma}\right]_{T,V} = \frac{1}{T}\left\{\gamma - \left(\frac{\partial E^s}{\partial \sigma}\right)_{T,V}\right\} \tag{13}$$

From Eqs. (8), (10), and (12), it follows that

$$A^s = \gamma\sigma = E^s - TS^s = E^s + T\left(\frac{\partial \gamma\sigma}{\partial T}\right)_{V,\sigma} \tag{14}$$

The surface energy per unit area is thus

$$E^s/\sigma = \gamma - T\left(\frac{\partial \gamma}{\partial T}\right)_{V,\sigma} \tag{15}$$

Using the mathematical methods of fluid mechanics, an alternative definition of surface tension is given (see Sect. 5). The internal forces acting between contiguous parts are represented as a stress acting across a boundary surface between the parts. The component of stress normal to the boundary surface is a tension, which is a negative pressure, and the component parallel to the surface is a shearing stress.

Consider a strip of unit width placed normal to the Gibbs dividing surface. The length of the strip, l, must be large in terms of intermolecular forces, i.e. it must extend into the bulk phases. If a similar strip were placed entirely in a bulk phase, the stress normal to the strip would be $-pl$. At any point on the strip in the interface, this stress $= -pl + \gamma$, where γ is the surface tension. The surface tension thus can be obtained by integrating the difference between the stress normal to the strip and the negative pressure over the length of the strip.

3. Statistical Mechanical Theory of Surface Tension by the Method of Significant Structures

The method of significant structures (see Chapter 12, Sects. 2 through 6), which proved to be a useful model for the calculation of the bulk properties of liquids, has been extended to give a successful theory of surface tension.[1]

[1] S. Chang, T. Ree, H. Eyring and I. Matzner in *Progress in International Research on Thermodynamic and Transport Properties* (J. F. Masi and D. H. Tsai, Eds.), Academic Press, New York, 1962, pp. 88–92.

The fundamental aspects of the model are retained; namely, that the significant structures are the solid-like degrees of freedom, positional degeneracy arising from the presence of the holes, and gas-like degrees of freedom. The principal modification required in the partition function for monatomic liquids, Eq. (12.3.1), arises from the differences in the forces acting on a surface molecule and on an interior molecule. The effect of the difference in the forces is on the value of E_s, the energy of sublimation, in Eq. (12.3.1)

$$f_N = \{(1-e^{-\theta/T})^{-3}e^{E_s/RT}(1+n_h e^{-aE_s/n_h RT})\}^{NV_s/V}\left\{\frac{(2\pi mkT)^{\frac{3}{2}}}{h^3}\frac{eV}{N}\right\}^{N(V-V_s)/V}$$

(12.3.1)

The correction for E_s is obtained by an iteration method which is based on the concept that molecular forces are of short range. This concept is supported by optical data which indicate that the thickness of the transition region is of the order of one molecular diameter.[2, 3, 4] The rare gases exhibit cubic closest packing in the solid state, and, as before, we assume a closest packing structure. It is easy to visualize that a given molecule has six nearest neighbors in the same molecular layer and three nearest neighbors in the layer below and three above to give a total of twelve nearest neighbors. Thus, to the nearest neighbor approximation, the correction which we need for E_s is given by

$$E_{si} = E_s\left(\frac{6}{12}\frac{\rho_i}{\rho_i} + \frac{3}{12}\frac{\rho_{i+1}}{\rho_i} + \frac{3}{12}\frac{\rho_{i-1}}{\rho_i}\right)$$

(1)

where E_{si} is the corrected value of E_s for the ith layer, and ρ_i, ρ_{i+1}, ρ_{i-1} are the densities of the ith layer, and the layers immediately below and above.

The thickness of a molecular layer can be deduced from the cubic closest packing structure, for the method of significant structures assumes that the volume increase on melting is due to introducing holes in the system so that there is no appreciable expansion of the lattice parameters. The face of the lattice which corresponds to the lowest surface free energy is the one exposed. Since cubic closest packing can be referred to a face-centered cubic unit cell with the (111) planes being the layers of closest packing, the (111) plane is in all probability the exposed face.[5, 6] The spacing of the (111) planes is given by

$$d = a/(3)^{\frac{1}{2}}$$

(2)

[2] Lord Rayleigh, *Phil. Mag.*, **33**, 1 (1892).
[3] C. V. Raman and L. A. Rambdas, *Phil. Mag.*, **3**, 220 (1927).
[4] N. K. Adam, *The Physics and Chemistry of Surfaces*, 2nd Ed., Oxford University Press, 1938.
[5] J. Corner, *Trans. Faraday Soc.*, **44**, 1036 (1948).
[6] A. Harasima, *Proc. Phys. Math. Soc. Japan*, **22**, 825 (1940).

where a is the lattice parameter of the face-centered cubic lattice, and is given by

$$a = (4V_s/N)^{\frac{1}{3}} \tag{3}$$

so that Eq. (2) becomes

$$d = (4V_s/N)^{\frac{1}{3}}/(3)^{\frac{1}{3}} = 0.9165(V_s/N)^{\frac{1}{3}} \tag{4}$$

The volume of a surface layer of unit area is thus

$$0.9165(V_s/N)^{\frac{1}{3}} \tag{5}$$

The surface tension is then given by

$$\gamma = \sum_i (G_{si} - G_l) \times 0.9165(V_s/N)^{\frac{1}{3}}/V_i \tag{6}$$

where G_{si} is the molar Gibbs free energy of the ith surface layer; G_l the molar Gibbs free energy of the bulk liquid; V_i the molar volume of the ith layer; and $0.9165 \ (V_s/N)^{\frac{1}{3}}/V_i$ the number of moles per unit area of the ith layer.

The molar free energy of the ith surface layer is calculated from the partition function Eq. (12.3.1) modified by substituting E_{si} of Eq. (1). The corresponding V_i is determined by plotting A_i versus $x \ (= V/V_s)$, and by drawing a tangent at a point near the minimum of the curve of A_i versus x parallel to the vapor pressure line, V_i being the volume at the tangential point, Figure 12.2.3.

To calculate the free energy of the ith layer of a surface, we need to know the densities of the $(i-1)$th, ith and $(i+1)$th layers. Unfortunately, we have no information about layer densities, and know only the densities of the bulk liquid and gas phases. Thus, an iteration method is applied, which will be explained below.

For the first step of the calculation the approximations used are that the density of the surface layer, ρ_1, and that of the layer immediately below, ρ_2, are equal to the bulk liquid density ρ_l, and that the density of the first gaseous layer, ρ_0, is equal to the gas density ρ_g. Introducing these approximations into Eq. (1) gives

$$E_{s1} = E_s \left(\frac{3}{4} + \frac{1}{4} \frac{\rho_g}{\rho_l} \right) \tag{7}$$

as the first estimate of E_s for the surface layer. This value is then used to calculate the Helmholtz free energy A for different values of x and leads to a new value ρ_1 for the surface layer. Then E'_{s1} is calculated by using ρ_1 in Eq. (1), and the procedure is repeated until ρ_1 converges to a constant value.

For the second layer, the same procedure is applied. The approximation for E_{s2}, which is used for the first calculation of the second layer, is

$$E_{s2} = E_s \left(\frac{3}{4} + \frac{1}{4} \frac{\rho_1}{\rho_l} \right) \tag{8}$$

where E_{s2} is the value of E_s for the second layer and ρ_1 is the density of the first layer, which was calculated previously. By a procedure similar to the first iteration, the value of ρ_2 is found, and E'_{s2} is calculated from Eq. (1). The converging value of ρ_2 is obtained again by iteration. This value of ρ_2 is then used to recalculate E_{s1} and the recalculated value of ρ_1 in turn is used to recalculate ρ_2. In the calculations of the surface tension of argon, however, the recalculation for the second layer does not give any appreciable difference. Also, the contribution of the third layer is negligible.

In the calculations thus far ρ_g, the gas phase density, has been used for the first gaseous layer, which means that interactions between the first gaseous layer and the surface layer have been neglected. To introduce the effect of these interactions into our calculations, we note that for the closest packing structure a molecule of the first gaseous layer can bond with three molecules of the surface layer, while a surface layer molecule has bonds with six molecules in that layer and three in the layer below, giving a total of nine. Thus, the difference in energy of a surface and first gaseous layer molecule is the difference between nine bonds and three bonds or $\frac{6}{12}E_s$. We can thus write for the density ratio

$$\frac{\rho_0}{\rho_1} = \exp\left[-\frac{E_s}{2RT}\left(\frac{T_c - T}{T_c} \right) \right] \tag{9}$$

which fulfils the requirement that ρ_0/ρ_1 increases to unity as T increases to T_c. Equation (9) and the previous results are then introduced into Eq. (1) and the iterative procedure is repeated to obtain the final value for E_{s1}. The values of the parameters used in the calculation of the surface tension of argon appear in Table 1, and the surface tensions, which were calculated using the calculated volumes from the liquid partition function at various temperatures, are compared with experimental observations in Table 2 and Figure 1. Δ in the last column is given by

$$\Delta = \frac{(\text{calculated value} - \text{observed value}) \times 100}{\text{observed value}} \tag{10}$$

TABLE 1. Parameters for argon

n	a	E_s (cal mole^{-1})	V_s (cm^3 mole^{-1})	θ ($^\circ$K)
10.8	0.00534	1888.6	24.98	60.0

TABLE 2. Surface tension of argon

$T(°K)$	V_l (cm³ mole⁻¹)	V_g (cm³ mole⁻¹)	γ calc. (dyne cm⁻¹)	Contribution of layers (%)			γ obs.[7] (dyne cm⁻¹)	Δ (%)
				1st	2nd	3rd		
83.85 (T_m)	28.90	10,208	13.78	87.16	12.84	0	13.5	2.07
85.5	29.08	8493	13.43	86.45	13.55	0	13.1	2.52
87.29 (T_b)	29.33	6944	13.02	85.87	14.13	0	12.6	3.33
90.0	29.80	5246	12.22	85.35	14.65	0	11.9	2.69

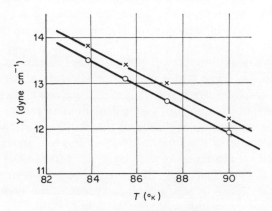

Figure 1. Surface tension of argon as a function of temperature. ×'s are calculated and O's are experimental values.

The Eötvös constant, k, which is equal to $\gamma V^{\frac{2}{3}}/(T_c - T)$, was calculated using the calculated values of γ and the observed molar volumes. It is compared with the observed value in Table 3.

TABLE 3. Eötvös constant, k, for argon ($T_c = 150.66°K$)

$T(°K)$	k (calc.)	k (obs.)
83.85	1.903	1.86
85.5	1.916	
87.29	1.926	
90.0	1.911	
	Avg. 1.91	

[7] E. C. C. Baly and F. G. Donnan, *J. Chem. Soc. (London)*, **81,** 907 (1902); G. Rudorf, *Ann. Physik* **29,** 751 (1909).

In Figure 2 are plotted the calculated densities of the liquid phase, ρ_l, the layer immediately below the surface, ρ_2, the surface layer, ρ_1, the first gaseous layer, ρ_0, and the gaseous phase at the four temperatures studied. It is seen that the range of densities decreases as T increases, which is expected since the density change curve approaches a horizontal line as T approaches T_c.

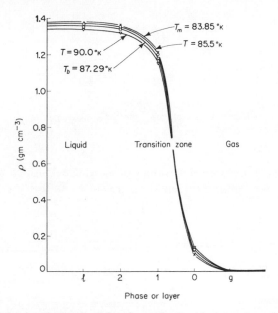

Figure 2. The density change in going from the liquid phase through the transition layers to the gas phase for argon at four temperatures. On this scale the gaseous densities are indistinguishable.

4. Surface Tension of Nitrogen and of Methane

The partition function for liquid nitrogen is given by[1]

$$f_N = \left\{ \frac{e^{E_s/RT}}{(1-e^{-\theta/T})^3} \frac{8\pi^2 I k T}{2h^2} \frac{1}{1-e^{-hv/kT}} \left[1 + n_h e^{-aE_s/n_h RT} \right] \right\}^{NV_s/V}$$

$$\times \left\{ \frac{(2\pi m k T)^{\frac{3}{2}}}{h^3} \frac{eV}{N} \frac{8\pi^2 I k T}{2h^2} \frac{1}{1-e^{-hv/kT}} \right\}^{N(V-V_s)/V} \tag{1}$$

where I is the moment of inertia and θ is the Einstein characteristic temperature[2] for the internal vibration of a nitrogen molecule. The expression $8\pi^2 IkT/2h^2$ is the partition function corresponding to a

[1] E. J. Fuller, Doctoral Dissertation, University of Utah, 1960.
[2] G. Herzberg, *Molecular Spectra and Molecular Structure I; Spectra of Diatomic Molecules*, Van Nostrand, New York, 1950.

classical rotator, where the energy levels are merged into a continuum. This is an approximation; the more exact summation form of the partition function for rotation could be used, but is more difficult to manipulate. In Eq. (1), the same rotational and internal vibrational terms appear in the solid-like and gas-like structure in the liquid, so the expression may be factored for simplicity. For liquid methane the partition function is given by

$$
f_N = \left\{ \frac{e^{E_s/RT}}{(1-e^{-\theta/T})^3} 8\pi^2 \frac{(8\pi^3 ABC)^{\frac{1}{2}}}{12h^3} (kT)^{\frac{3}{2}} \right.
$$
$$
\left. \times \prod_{i=1}^{9} \frac{1}{1-e^{-h\nu_i/kT}} [1 + n_h e^{-aE_s/n_h RT}] \right\}^{NV_s/V}
$$
$$
\times \left\{ \frac{(2\pi mkT)^{\frac{3}{2}}}{h^3} \frac{eV}{N} 8\pi^2 \frac{(8\pi^3 ABC)^{\frac{1}{2}}}{12h^3} (kT)^{\frac{3}{2}} \prod_{i=1}^{9} \frac{1}{1-e^{h\nu_i/kT}} \right\}^{N(V-V_s)/V}
$$

$$(2)$$

which can also be factored. The values of parameters[3] which were used for the nitrogen and methane calculations are shown in Table 1.

TABLE 1. Parameters for nitrogen and methane

	$T_m(°K)$	n	a	E_s (cal mole^{-1})	V_s (cm^3 mole^{-1})	$\theta(°K)$
N₂	63.14	12.9	0.00343	1529.9	29.31	55.94
CH₄	90.65	13.3	0.00296	2200	30.94	75.33

The surface tension calculations for nitrogen closely parallel those for the rare gases. The contribution of the third layer to the surface tension is also negligible up to the boiling point, but an appreciable contribution of the third layer is obtained at 90°K.

As the temperature is raised, the rate of conversion of the volume, V_i, to a self-consistent value becomes slower; and the approximation for the first calculation of the top layer, Eq. (3.6), is no longer justifiable. A graphical extrapolation method is instead applied for the nitrogen calculation at 90°K. This is as follows: (1) The values of Δx ($x_{\text{top layer}} - x_{\text{liquid}}$) and $x = V/V_s$ are calculated by making use of the data, $x_{\text{top layer}}$, which were

[3] E. J. Fuller, T. Ree and H. Eyring, *Proc. Natl. Acad. Sci. U.S.*, **45**, 1594 (1959).

obtained from the first iteration calculations of the top layer at lower temperatures than 90°K, and are plotted versus temperature. (2) This curve is extrapolated to 90°K as shown in Figure 1. The value of $x_{\text{top layer}}$ is thus obtained.

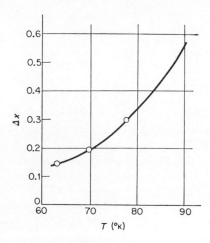

Figure 1. Extrapolation of the Δx *vs.* T curve for nitrogen.

For the second calculation, the method described in Sect. 3 is applied using the x_1 value obtained above. In the case of the top layer calculation at 90°K, more than thirty calculations were performed to get a consistent value of the volume, V_1. Some results of the calculations are shown in Table 2.

TABLE 2. Variation of x_1 in the calculations for nitrogen at 90°K

No.	x_1	No.	x_1	No.	x_1
1	1.548	5	1.580	9	1.605
2	1.721	6	1.683	10	1.663
3	1.565	7	1.599	11	1.609
4	1.703	8	1.667	12	1.660

As Table 2 shows, the change of x_1 with the number of calculations is oscillatory. This suggests the applicability of 'the deflection method' for avoiding the laborious calculations. The deflection from the consistent volume is calculated as follows:

No.	x_1		No.	x_2
12	1.660		13	1.609
14	1.663		15	1.605
16	1.667			
Average 1.663				1.607

The deflection is $(1.663 - 1.607)/2 = 0.028$. Hence, the consistent value of x_1 is $1.607 + 0.028 = 1.635$, which agrees with the result of the straight-forward calculation.

Next the effect on the densities of interactions between the first gaseous layer and the surface layer are computed by the method given in Sect. 3. The calculations for methane are similar.

The final results of the nitrogen and methane calculations are compared with experimental data[4] in Tables 3 and 4 and Figures 2 and 3. The tabulated values for $\gamma_{obs.}$ were obtained by interpolation and extrapolation of values given in the literature.

TABLE 3. Surface tension of nitrogen and methane

T (°K)	V_l (cm³ mole⁻¹)	V_g (cm³ mole⁻¹)	γcalc. (dyne cm⁻¹)	Contribution of layers (%)			$\gamma_{obs.}$[3.5, 4] (dyne cm⁻¹)	Δ(%)
				1st	2nd	3rd		
Nitrogen								
63.14(T_m)	32.59	41,620	12.00	90.92	9.08	0	12.05	− 0.41
70.0	33.71	15,534	10.58	88.66	11.34	0	10.50	+ 0.76
77.34(T_b)	35.05	6097	8.90	86.53	13.47	0	8.98	− 0.89
90.0	37.84	2169	6.33	78.52	17.06	4.42	6.2	+ 2.09
Methane								
90.65(T_m)	34.06	62,499	17.37	92.11	7.89	0	18.20	− 4.56
100	34.99	22,432	16.63	90.47	9.53	0	16.15	+ 3.22
111.67(T_b)	36.32	9667	13.36	87.95	12.05	0	13.70	− 2.46
120	36.82	3249	12.08	86.18	13.82	0	11.90	+ 1.51

4 F. D. Rossini, K. S. Pitzer, R. L. Arnett, R. M. Braun and G. C. Pimentel, *Selected Values of Physical and Thermodynamic Properties of Hydrocarbons and Related Compounds*, American Petroleum Institute Research Project 44, Carnegie Press, 1953. See also Ref. 3.5.

TABLE 4. Eötvös constant, k, for nitrogen and methane

N₂, $T_c = 126.1°$K		CH₄, $T_c = 190.7°$K	
$T(°$K)	k (calc.)	$T(°$K)	k (calc.)
63.14	1.92	90.65	1.87
70.0	1.96	100	1.89
77.34	1.94	111.67	1.91
90.0	1.93	120	1.97
Average 1.94		Average 1.91	
k (obs.) = 2.0		k (obs.) = 1.95	

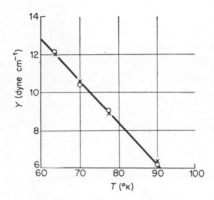

Figure 2. Surface tension of nitrogen as a function of temperature. ×'s are calculated and ○'s are observed values.

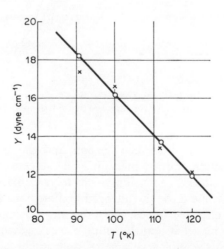

Figure 3. Surface tension of methane as a function of temperature. ×'s are calculated and ○'s are observed values.

The density transition curves for nitrogen at four temperatures and for methane at four temperatures are shown in Figures 4 and 5, respectively. The curves for nitrogen are the most interesting since a greater fraction of the range from T_m to T_c has been studied. Figure 4 illustrates the approach of the phase densities to a single value and the increase in the thickness of the transition zone as T increases to T_c.

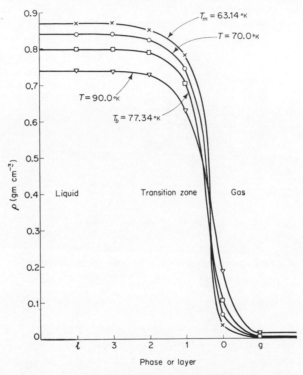

Figure 4. The density change in going from the liquid phase through the transition layers to the gas phase for nitrogen at four temperatures.

The calculated values of surface tension and the Eötvös constants presented in this section and the preceding one agree well with observed values. The calculated surface tension values for argon are slightly higher than the observed, while those for nitrogen and methane are close to, but oscillate about, the observed values. The latter may be simply an arithmetic artifact. By the significant structure theory, the calculated surface tension is quite sensitive to the molar volume of bulk liquid; e.g. one per cent increase in the liquid molar volume gives a surface tension increase of

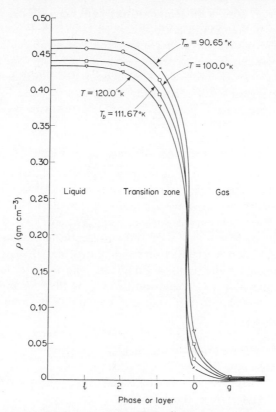

Figure 5. The density change in going from the liquid phase through the transition layers to the gas phase for methane at four temperatures.

two to five per cent. The parameters used here have a tendency to give a positive deviation in molar volume calculations.[3] This fact suggests that a more extended investigation of the liquid partition function is necessary. As the temperature is raised, the contribution of the inner surface layers to the surface tension increases. This result agrees with other statistical approaches on the transition zone between the gas and the liquid phases (see following sections). The temperature variation of the calculated surface tension shows good agreement with experimental observations.

The concepts on which this theory of surface tension is based are such that the theory should be capable of extension to describe interfacial adsorption. The surface tension–surface adsorption relation is a consequence of the difference in forces between solute and solvent molecules (or ions) and those between solvent molecules. As an example, consider an aqueous solution of a short fatty acid. The surface tension is less than that of water at the same temperature, and the surface concentration of the acid is greater than the bulk concentration. This results from the fact that the attractive forces between polar water molecules are greater than those between water molecules and the acid molecules with their non-polar hydrocarbon portions. A successful theory of this phenomenon must provide a method of calculating the effects of these forces, and the theory of surface tension presented above illustrates in general how this can be done.

5. Statistical Theory of Interfacial Phenomena of Kirkwood and Buff

Kirkwood and Buff[1] have developed a general statistical mechanical theory of surface tension for plane surfaces from Kirkwood's[2] statistical mechanical theory of homogeneous fluid phases. Buff[3] has extended the theory to include the curved surface case. The Kirkwood–Buff theory leads to rigorous formulations of the surface thermodynamic functions for a one-component system in terms of the potential of intermolecular force and molecular distribution functions. The resulting equations are not readily amenable to calculation, and a number of approximations must be introduced into the rigorous equations in order to compare theoretical and experimental values.

The mechanical definition of surface tension in terms of the stress per unit width in a plane normal to the surface is chosen as a more satisfactory basis for a molecular theory. This is illustrated in Figure 1, in which the x, y plane is the dividing surface; the stress acts in the x direction across a strip of unit dimension in the y direction and from $l/2$ to $-l/2$ in the z direction, where l is large compared with the range of molecular forces. If

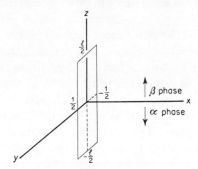

Figure 1. The dividing surface is the x, y plane; the strip in the y, z plane extends from $y = \frac{1}{2}$ to $-\frac{1}{2}$ and $z = l/2$ to $-l/2$.

1 J. G. Kirkwood and F. P. Buff, *J. Chem. Phys.*, **17**, 338 (1949).
2 J. G. Kirkwood, *J. Chem. Phys.*, **14**, 180 (1946).
3 F. P. Buff, *Phys. Rev.*, **82**, 773 (1951).

there were no surface tension, the stress would be $-pl$ so that the surface tension γ is

$$\gamma = \Sigma_x + \int_{-l/2}^{+l/2} p\,dz = \Sigma_x + pl \tag{1}$$

where Σ_x is the actual stress acting across the strip. Two molecular distribution functions are required, which are $\rho^{(1)}(\mathbf{r})$, the average number of molecules ($\rho^{(1)}\,dv$) in the volume element dv at a point $\mathbf{r}$ and $\rho^{(2)}(\mathbf{r}_1, \mathbf{r}_{12})$, the average number of molecular pairs ($\rho^{(2)}\,dv_1, dv_{12}$) of which one is in dv_1 at $\mathbf{r}_1$ and the other in dv_{12} at $\mathbf{r}_{12}$. The pair correlation function $g(\mathbf{r}_1, \mathbf{r}_{12})$ is defined by Eq. (12.10.10) which is rewritten below

$$\rho^{(2)}(\mathbf{r}_1, \mathbf{r}_{12}) = \rho^{(1)}(\mathbf{r}_1)\rho^{(1)}(\mathbf{r}_2)g(\mathbf{r}_1, \mathbf{r}_{12}) \tag{2}$$

In the interior of the phase $\rho^{(1)}$ is independent of $\mathbf{r}$ so that g becomes the radial distribution function depending only on the distance between pairs of molecules, $\mathbf{r}_{12}$. In a planar interfacial region as depicted in Figure 1, $\rho^{(1)}$ is a function of z so that $\rho^{(2)}$ and hence g depend on z and $\mathbf{r}_{12}$.

The Kirkwood[2] theory of fluid phases provides expressions for p which we need for Eq. (1). They are

$$p = kT\rho_\alpha^{(1)} - \frac{1}{6}\int r_{12}\frac{du}{dr_{12}}\rho_\alpha^{(2)}(r_{12})\,dv_{12} \tag{3}$$

and

$$p = kT\rho_\beta^{(1)} - \frac{1}{6}\int r_{12}\frac{du}{dr_{12}}\rho_\beta^{(2)}(r_{12})\,dv_{12} \tag{4}$$

in which $u(r_{12})$ is the potential between two molecules at the distance r_{12}. Viewing the interfacial region as a hypothetical heterogeneous system combining the properties of the α and β phases we define

$$\rho_{\alpha\beta}^{(1)} = [1 - A(z)]\rho_\alpha^{(1)} + A(z)\rho_\beta^{(1)} \tag{5}$$

$$\rho_{\alpha\beta}^{(2)} = [1 - A(z)]\rho_\alpha^{(2)} + A(z)\rho_\beta^{(2)} \tag{6}$$

with

$$A(z) = 0, \quad z < 0; \qquad A(z) = 1, \quad z \geqslant 0 \tag{7}$$

From Eqs. (3) through (7) we obtain

$$p = kT\rho_{\alpha\beta}^{(1)} - \frac{1}{6}\int r_{12}\frac{du}{dr_{12}}\rho_{\alpha\beta}^{(2)}\,dv_{12} \tag{8}$$

Next we consider Σ_x of Eq. (1) which can be expressed as

$$\Sigma_x = -kT\int_{-l/2}^{+l/2}\rho^{(1)}(z)\,dz + \Sigma_x' \tag{9}$$

in which the first term comes from the momentum transfer (e.g. for an ideal gas $\rho = N/V$ and $p = kT(N/V)$) and the second term arises from the intermolecular forces across the strip. Σ_x' is obtained by finding the x

component of the average force between molecules on either side of the strip and integrating over all molecular configurations. The x component, $d\Sigma'_x$, of the average force between molecules in dv_{12} at $(\mathbf{r}_1+\mathbf{r}_{12})$ to the right of the plane of the strip and those in dv_1 at $\mathbf{r}_1$ to the left is

$$d\Sigma'_x = \mathbf{e}_x \cdot \nabla u(r_{12})\rho^{(2)}(z_1,\mathbf{r}_{12})\,dv_{12}\,dv_1 \tag{10}$$

where $\mathbf{e}_x$ is a unit vector in the x direction. The integral over all configurations $\mathbf{r}_1$ to the left and all configurations $\mathbf{r}_1+\mathbf{r}_{12}$ to the right is

$$\Sigma'_x = \int_{-l/2}^{+l/2} \int_{-\frac{1}{2}}^{+\frac{1}{2}} \int_{-\infty}^{0} \int_{-x_1}^{+\infty} \int_{-\infty}^{+\infty} \int_{-\infty}^{+\infty} \frac{x_{12}}{r_{12}} \frac{du}{dr_{12}}$$
$$\times \rho^{(2)}(z_1,\mathbf{r}_{12})\,dy_{12}\,dz_{12}\,dx_{12}\,dx_1\,dy_1\,dz_1 \tag{11}$$

The volume to the left is determined by the area of the strip and values of x from $-\infty$ to 0, and the intermolecular coordinates can assume all values in the y, z directions and from $-x_1$ to $+\infty$, so that Eq. (11) becomes

$$\Sigma'_x = \frac{1}{2} \int_{-l/2}^{+l/2} \int \frac{x_{12}^2}{r_{12}} \frac{du}{dr_{12}} \rho^{(2)}(z_1,\mathbf{r}_{12})\,dv_{12}\,dz \tag{12}$$

Introducing this result into Eq. (9) gives

$$\Sigma_x = -\int_{-l/2}^{+l/2} \left[kT\rho^{(1)}(z) - \frac{1}{2} \int \frac{x_{12}^2}{r_{12}} \frac{du}{dr_{12}} \rho^{(2)}(z,\mathbf{r}_{12})\,dv_{12} \right] dz$$
$$= -\int_{-l/2}^{+l/2} p'(z)\,dz \tag{13}$$

which defines $p'(z)$. Substituting Eq. (13) into Eq. (1) and allowing l to increase without limit leads to

$$\gamma = \int_{-\infty}^{+\infty} [p-p'(z)]\,dz \tag{14}$$

We note that when $\rho^{(1)}$ and $\rho^{(2)}$ do not depend on z, $p'(z)$ becomes the pressure for the interior of a phase as given by Eqs. (3) and (4).

From Eqs. (8) and (13) we obtain, since $\bar{r}_{12} = \sqrt{3}\,\bar{x}_{12}$, where the bars indicate mean values, the expression

$$p-p'(z) = -kT\rho_s^{(1)}(z) + \frac{1}{2} \int \frac{x_{12}^2}{r_{12}} \frac{du}{dr_{12}} \rho_s^{(2)}(z,\mathbf{r}_{12})\,dv_{12} \tag{15}$$

in which

$$\rho_s^{(1)} = \rho^{(1)}(z)-\rho_{\alpha\beta}^{(1)} \tag{16}$$

and

$$\rho_s^{(2)}(z,\mathbf{r}_{12}) = \rho^{(2)}(z,\mathbf{r}_{12})-\rho_{\alpha\beta}^{(2)} \tag{17}$$

Thus $\rho_s^{(1)}$ and $\rho_s^{(2)}$ are the excess molecular and molecular pair densities relative to the dividing surface. Introducing these results into Eq. (14) gives

$$\gamma = -\Gamma_s^{(1)} kT + \frac{1}{2} \int \frac{x_{12}^2}{r_{12}} \frac{du}{dr_{12}} \Gamma_s^{(2)}(\mathbf{r}_{12}) \, dv_{12} \tag{18}$$

where $\Gamma_s^{(1)}$

$$\Gamma_s^{(1)} = \int_{-\infty}^{+\infty} \rho_s^{(1)}(z) \, dz \tag{19}$$

is the thermodynamic surface density, and $\Gamma_s^{(2)}$

$$\Gamma_s^{(2)} = \int_{-\infty}^{+\infty} \rho_s^{(2)}(z, \mathbf{r}_{12}) \, dz \tag{20}$$

is the surface density of molecular pairs. Equation (18) is a rigorous expression for the surface tension in terms of molecular distribution functions and the potential of intermolecular forces. Numerical calculation of γ for a particular molecular system requires introducing approximations, and the interested reader is referred to the original paper for details of the approximations. It is interesting to note that the authors' zero order approximation for γ is the same as that obtained by Fowler[4] by a different method.

Kirkwood and Buff calculated the surface tension γ and the surface energy E^s for argon at 90°K, and their results are given in Table 1. They used the equations of Born and Green[5] for the densities, $\rho^{(n)}$, a modified Lennard-Jones potential,[6] and data of Eisenstein and Gingrich[7] for the radial distribution functions.

TABLE 1. Surface tension and surface energy for argon at 90°K

	γ (dyne cm^{-1})	E^s (dyne cm^{-1})
Theory	14.9	27.2
Experiment	11.9	36

[4] R. H. Fowler, *Proc. Roy. Soc.* (*London*), **A159**, 229 (1937).
[5] M. Born and H. S. Green, *Proc. Roy. Soc.* (*London*), **A188**, 10 (1946); H. S. Green, *ibid.*, **189**, 103 (1947).
[6] G. S. Rushbrooke, *Proc. Roy. Soc.* (*Edinburgh*), **60**, 182 (1940); J. Corner, *Trans. Faraday Soc.*, **35**, 711 (1939).
[7] A. Eisenstein and N. S. Gingrich, *Phys. Rev.*, **62**, 261 (1942).

6. Calculation of Surface Energy by Jura

Jura[1] has calculated the total surface energy of liquid argon and mercury by a modification of a method formulated by Fowler and Guggenheim[2], who in turn had brought up to date a method proposed by Rayleigh.[3] The energy to remove a molecule from a liquid to zero pressure in the gas phase is

$$E_V = -\frac{2\pi N}{V} \int_0^\infty W_0(r)\phi(r)r^2 \, dr \qquad (1)$$

where V is the molal volume, $W_0(r)$ is the distribution function for the molecules in the liquid and $\phi(r)$ is the potential function between two molecules which are a distance r apart. Similarly, the energy of a molecule in the surface region is given by

$$E_i = -\frac{2\pi N}{V} \int_0^\infty W_i(r)\phi(r)r^2 \, dr \qquad (2)$$

so that, if the difference between surface and bulk molal volumes is neglected, the surface energy is given by

$$E^s = \frac{2\pi N}{V} \int_0^\infty \left[\sum_{i=1}^n \{W_0(r) - W_i(r)\} \right] \phi(r)r^2 \, dr \qquad (3)$$

Liquid distribution functions, $W_0(r)$, and potential functions, $\phi(r)$, were taken from the literature (as in Sect. 5). For the surface molecule distribution function, $W_i(r)$, it was assumed, on the basis of the short range of molecular forces, that $W_i(r)$ for the liquid side of the surface is the same as $W_0(r)$. The problem reduces to deciding where the surface region is, and then incorporating this information into the limits of integration of the energy integral. The assumption made is that that part of any molecule whose center is within a distance of $r_0/2$ of the surface plane (where r_0 is the closest distance between nearest neighbors) is included. Thus, for an interior molecule the integration is over a complete sphere; for a molecule whose center is on the surface plane, the integration is over the section of the sphere below the plane which is parallel to and at a distance $r_0/2$ above the surface plane. The results of the calculations appear in Table 1.

TABLE 1.   Surface energy of liquid argon and mercury

	$T\,(°K)$	$E_{calc.}$ (dyne cm^{-1})	$E_{obs.}$ (dyne cm^{-1})
Argon	87	32	35
Mercury	293	500	525

[1] G. Jura, *J. Phys. and Colloid Chem.*, **52**, 40 (1948).
[2] R. H. Fowler and E. A. Guggenheim, *op. cit.*, pp. 445–450.
[3] Lord Rayleigh, *Scientific Papers*, **3**, 397 (1890) (as quoted in (2)).

Another interesting result of Jura's calculations is that approximately 78% of the surface energy is in the first layer, and 99% is in the first four layers.

7. Theory of Interfacial Phenomena of Hill

Hill[1] has formulated an approximate statistical theory of the interfacial region, which, while lacking the rigor of that of Kirkwood and Buff, is more amenable to numerical calculation. The method used is to treat the transition density in the interfacial region as continuous, and to obtain the density transition curve from the expression for the constancy of the chemical potential in going from the first phase to the second. The model chosen is of the van der Waals type, and the potential energy per molecule and free volume per molecule are taken as functions of the density only. By this model the chemical potential for the liquid phase is given by the following equation and the subsequent definitions. They are

$$\mu = \mu_0(T) + kT \ln(kT/b) + kTv$$
$$v = \ln[\theta/(1-\theta)] + [\theta/(1-\theta)] - \alpha\theta$$
$$\theta = Nb/V = \rho b$$
$$\alpha = 2a/bkT \tag{1}$$
$$a = \varepsilon b$$
$$b = 2\pi r^{*3}/3$$

The molecules are considered as rigid spheres of diameter r^*. The potential energy of the interaction of a molecule with the rest of the fluid is $-\alpha\theta kT$; the other terms are entropy terms. The potential of intermolecular force is taken as

$$u(r) = -\varepsilon(r^*/r)^6, \qquad r \geqslant r^*$$
$$u(r) = +\infty, \qquad r < r^* \tag{2}$$

and the radial distribution function used is

$$g(r) = 1, \qquad r \geqslant r^*$$
$$g(r) = 0, \qquad r < r^* \tag{3}$$

For the transition region, Eqs. (1) must be modified in accord with the variation in mean local density. For a plane surface the potential energy variation is obtained as follows: the potential energy of interaction of a molecule at z with the rest of the fluid is $\phi(z)kT$ where z is normal to the dividing surface. Let z be the origin for a set of coordinates x', y', z' and

---

[1] T. L. Hill, *J. Chem. Phys.*, **20**, 141 (1952).

the spherical equivalent, r', φ', θ' such that z' is also normal to the dividing surface. Then we can write

$$\phi(z)kT = \int_{r^*}^{\infty} \int_{0}^{\pi} \int_{0}^{2\pi} u(r')\rho(z+z')r'^2 \sin\theta' \, d\varphi' \, d\theta' \, dr' \qquad (4)$$

Integration over φ' and a change of variable from θ' to z', followed by integration over r', leads to

$$\phi(s) = -\frac{3\alpha}{8}\left[\int_{-\infty}^{-1} \theta(s+t)t^{-4} \, dt + \int_{-1}^{+1} \theta(s+t) \, dt + \int_{+1}^{+\infty} \theta(s+t)t^{-4} \, dt\right]$$

$$(5)$$

where $s = z/r^*$ and $t = z'/r^*$.

Hill makes no density modifications, *per se*, of the other terms, but rather changes from van der Waals to Tonks' equation of state for a gas of rigid spheres.[2] Tonks' equation is

$$\frac{pb'}{kT} = \frac{\theta(1+2.9619\theta+5.483\theta^2)}{1-0.8517\theta^3-0.1483\theta^4} \qquad (6)$$

$$\theta = \rho b', \qquad b' = r^{*3}/\sqrt{2}$$

in contrast with the van der Waals equation

$$pb/kT = \theta/(1-\theta)$$

$$\theta = \rho b, \qquad b = 2\pi r^{*3}/3 \qquad (7)$$

with $\varepsilon = 0$ in both cases.

Thus, using Eq. (1) modified by Eqs. (5), (6), and (7) Hill has calculated density transition curves for the interfacial region which show that the transition is complete in about four molecular layers at $T/T_c = 0.5$. At higher temperatures the thickness increases.

Hill, too, has calculated the surface tension and total surface energy for liquid argon at 90°K, and his results are given in Table 1.

TABLE 1. Surface tension and surface energy for argon at 90°K

	γ (dyne cm^{-1})	E^s (dyne cm^{-1})
Theory	6.0	19.0
Experiment	11.9	36

8. Mobile Adsorbed Monolayers

A phase, one molecule in thickness, which is constrained to a surface but which can move freely on that surface is called a mobile adsorbed

2 L. Tonks, *Phys. Rev.*, **50**, 955 (1936).

monolayer. If interactions between the adsorbed molecules can be neglected, then the monolayer is simply a two-dimensional perfect gas, and its partition function follows immediately from Eq. (1.4.7). For a plane surface of area A we have for the partition function

$$f = \frac{2\pi m k T}{h^2} A(f_{\text{int}}) \tag{1}$$

When molecular interactions are considered, the monolayer can be treated as a two-dimensional real gas by methods presented in Chapter 11. We shall consider briefly the method of the virial (Sect. 11.4). For a surface the virial equation, Eq. (2.8.5), becomes

$$\overline{T} = -\tfrac{1}{2} \sum_i (X_i x_i + Y_i y_i) \tag{2}$$

Neglecting frictional resistance, the forces arise from interactions between molecules of the adsorbed layer and from the boundaries of the surface and molecules beyond the boundaries. Let F equal the stress per unit length of boundary. Then the analog of Eqs. (11.4.2, 3) is

$$\tfrac{1}{2} F \int (lx + my) \, ds = FA \tag{3}$$

where ds is a line element. Equation (3) is thus the contribution of the boundary interactions to the virial. If $u(r)$ is the interaction potential for molecules separated by a distance r, then Eq. (2) becomes

$$T = \tfrac{1}{2} \sum_i m_i v_i^2 = \tfrac{1}{2} F \int (lx + my) \, ds + \tfrac{1}{2} \sum r \frac{\partial u}{\partial r} \tag{4}$$

in which the rightmost summation is over all pairs of molecules. For two dimensions the mean kinetic energy for a perfect gas is

$$\sum_i m_i v_i^2 = 2NkT \tag{5}$$

and on substitution of Eqs. (3) and (5) in Eq. (4) we obtain

$$NkT = FA + \tfrac{1}{2} \sum r \frac{\partial u}{\partial r} \tag{6}$$

Noting again that there are $\tfrac{1}{2} N(N-1) \cong \tfrac{1}{2} N^2$ pairs of molecules, the average number of pairs of molecules separated by a distance between r and $r + dr$ is given by

$$\tfrac{1}{2} N^2 \frac{2\pi r}{A} \, dr \, e^{-u/kT} \tag{7}$$

if we consider short-range forces only. Using this result for the summation over pairs of Eq. (6) we have

$$\tfrac{1}{2}\sum r\frac{\partial u}{\partial r} = \tfrac{1}{2}\int_0^\infty \tfrac{1}{2}N^2\frac{2\pi r^2}{A}\frac{\partial u}{\partial r}e^{-u/kT}\,\mathrm{d}r \qquad (8)$$

and the equation of state for the mobile monolayer is

$$FA = NkT - \frac{N^2\pi}{2A}\int_0^\infty r^2\frac{\partial u}{\partial r}e^{-u/kT}\,\mathrm{d}r$$

$$= NkT - \frac{N^2\pi kT}{A}\int_0^\infty (e^{-u/kT}-1)r\,\mathrm{d}r \qquad (9)$$

Compare Eq. (9) with Eqs. (11.4.13, 15). Further development of the theory of mobile monolayers proceeds similarly to that of real gases.

9. Localized Monolayers

In this section we consider a layer in which each molecule is localized at some site on the adsorbing surface. Actual systems, of course, can be expected to exhibit varying degrees of mobility of which complete localization and complete mobility are the limiting cases. We proceed now to obtain an expression for the equilibrium between a gaseous phase and a localized adsorbed phase, i.e. the Langmuir adsorption isotherm which we have encountered previously in Sect. 1.13.

We consider a single component phase which is adsorbed on the surface of a solid and which is in equilibrium with a gaseous phase. Let ω equal the number of equivalent but distinguishable (by position) adsorption sites and let n equal the number of adsorbed molecules. Since only one molecule can be adsorbed at a given site, there are $\omega - n$ empty sites. The number of distinguishable ways the molecules can be adsorbed on n of the ω sites is thus

$$\frac{\omega!}{n!(\omega-n)!} \qquad (1)$$

The partition function of an adsorbed molecule is

$$a'(T)e^{-\varepsilon/kT} = a(T) \qquad (2)$$

where $a'(T)$ includes both vibrations about its equilibrium position on the site and the internal degrees of freedom, and ε is the energy of adsorption. The exponential factor refers the partition function for the adsorbed molecule to the energy zero of the gaseous state. The partition function for the monolayer is thus

$$f_n = \frac{\omega!}{n!(\omega-n)!}[a(T)]^n \qquad (3)$$

The Helmholtz free energy of the monolayer is, using Stirling's approximation,

$$A_m = -kT\ln f_n$$
$$= kT[-\omega\ln\omega + n\ln n + (\omega-n)\ln(\omega-n) - n\ln\{a(T)\}] \qquad (4)$$

and the chemical potential is

$$\mu_m = \left(\frac{\partial A_m}{\partial n}\right)_{T,V,\omega} = kT\left[\ln\left(\frac{n}{\omega - n}\right) - \ln\{a(T)\}\right] \tag{5}$$

At equilibrium μ_m of Eq. (5) must equal the chemical potential of the gas phase which is, for a perfect gas, from Eq. (4.16.5),

$$\mu_g = -kT\ln\left[\frac{(2\pi mkT)^{\frac{3}{2}}}{h^3}f_{int}\frac{kT}{p}\right] \tag{6}$$

The absolute activities of the two phases are

$$\lambda_m = \left(\frac{n}{\omega - n}\right)\bigg/a(T) = \lambda_g = \frac{h^3}{(2\pi mkT)^{\frac{3}{2}}f_{int}}\cdot\frac{p}{kT} \tag{7}$$

If we denote the fraction of the surface covered by $\theta = n/\omega$, we obtain from Eq. (7) the relation

$$\frac{\theta}{1-\theta} = \frac{h^3 a(T)}{(2\pi mkT)^{\frac{3}{2}}f_{int}}\cdot\frac{p}{kT} \equiv Kp \tag{8}$$

or

$$\theta = \frac{Kp}{1+Kp} \tag{9}$$

which is the Langmuir adsorption isotherm [see Eq. (1.13.7)].

The limited usefulness of the Langmuir formula to describe adsorption of gases on solids should be apparent from the model, i.e. a monolayer of a perfect gas on a perfectly uniform surface. Actually adsorbed phases present a diversity of interesting theoretical problems. Multilayer adsorption leading to condensation was treated in Sect. 1.14 and condensation in fissures and capillaries, an effect of a non-uniform surface, was considered in Sect. 1.16. The treatment of localized monolayers in this section can be refined by including the molecular interaction energy in the formulation of the partition function. This function must also include the enumeration of the number of distinguishable ways that n molecules, of which n' pairs are interacting closest neighbors, can be adsorbed on the ω sites. Several approaches to the problem are given by Fowler and Guggenheim.[1]

10. Hindered Rotation Model for H_2 and D_2 Adsorbed on Solid Surfaces

Sandler[1] and later Cunningham, Chapin, and Johnston[2] observed that ortho-hydrogen was more strongly adsorbed than para-hydrogen at low temperatures, and showed that nearly pure ortho-hydrogen could be prepared by successive adsorptions and desorptions. Sandler[1] proposed a

[1] R. H. Fowler and E. A. Guggenheim, *op. cit.*, pp. 429–443.

[1] Y. L. Sandler, *J. Phys. Chem.*, **58**, 58 (1954); *J. Chem. Phys.*, **29**, 97 (1958).

[2] C. M. Cunningham, D. S. Chapin and H. L. Johnston, *J. Am. Chem. Soc.*, **80**, 2382 (1958).

theory of the separation based on a hindered rotation model, and examined the limiting cases. This theory has been refined and extended by Evett[3] and by White and Lassettre.[4]

Moore and Ward[5] separated ortho- and para-hydrogen and ortho- and para-deuterium by gas chromatography. They used an alumina column at 77.4°K. Using the chromatographic retention times, Mortensen and Eyring[6] calculated the potential energy barrier for rotation and the condensation coefficients for H_2 and D_2 on alumina. From measurements of Moore and Ward's graph, the retention times t' for the ortho- and para-hydrogen and deuterium to pass through the column are

$$t'o\text{-}H_2 = 317 \text{ sec} \qquad\qquad t'o\text{-}D_2 = 418 \text{ sec}$$
$$t'p\text{-}H_2 = 259 \text{ sec} \qquad\qquad t'p\text{-}D_2 = 454 \text{ sec}$$

From the dimensions of the column and the flow rate of the helium carrier gas, the average length of time t_{He} for the helium to pass through the column is approximately three seconds. This is the same average time that the ortho- and para-hydrogen and deuterium spend in the vapor phase. The time, t, which the hydrogen and deuterium spend on the surface is, therefore

$$t\ o\text{-}H_2 = 314 \text{ sec} \qquad\qquad t\ o\text{-}D_2 = 415 \text{ sec}$$
$$t\ p\text{-}H_2 = 256 \text{ sec} \qquad\qquad t\ p\text{-}D_2 = 451 \text{ sec}$$

If we assume that the experiments were carried out on the linear portion of the isotherm, which is likely considering the small amounts of hydrogen or deuterium used, and if we assume that there is equilibrium between the vapor and the adsorbed molecules on the surface, then the ratio of the concentrations of ortho and para species on the surface to the concentration in the vapor phase is just proportional to t/t_{He}. Hence

$$\frac{[o\text{-}X_2(s)]}{[o\text{-}X_2(g)]} = \frac{at_{o\text{-}X_2}}{t_{He}}; \qquad \frac{[p\text{-}X_2(s)]}{[p\text{-}X_2(g)]} = \frac{at_{p\text{-}X_2}}{t_{He}} \qquad (1)$$

where a is the constant of proportionality and X represents either H or D. In addition we may write

$$\frac{[o\text{-}X_2(s)]}{[o\text{-}X_2(g)]} = K'_o(X_2)\frac{f^r_{o,s}(X_2)}{f^r_{o,g}(X_2)}$$
$$\frac{[p\text{-}X_2(s)]}{[p\text{-}X_2(g)]} = K'_p(X_2)\frac{f^r_{p,s}(X_2)}{f^r_{p,g}(X_2)} \qquad (2)$$

where $f^r_{o,s}(X_2)$, $f^r_{o,g}(X_2)$ and $f^r_{p,s}(X_2)$, $f^r_{p,g}(X_2)$ are the rotational partition functions for the surface and vapor, and $K'_o(X_2)$ and $K'_p(X_2)$ that part

3 A. A. Evett, *J. Chem. Phys.*, **31**, 565 (1959).
4 D. White and E. N. Lassettre, *J. Chem. Phys.*, **32**, 72 (1960).
5 W. R. Moore and H. R. Ward, *J. Am. Chem. Soc.*, **80**, 2909 (1958).
6 E. M. Mortensen and H. Eyring, *J. Phys. Chem.*, **64**, 433 (1960).

of the equilibrium constant containing the translational and vibrational degrees of freedom for the ortho and para species, respectively. In Eq. (2) we are not completely justified in separating the rotational motion from that of translation because we know that the molar volume[7] for liquid para-hydrogen is greater than that for the ortho species indicating that the rotational motion of ortho-hydrogen in the liquid is more restricted, which results in greater orientation and, hence, a tighter packing due to van der Waals forces. We might expect a similar situation to exist for the adsorbed hydrogen or deuterium and the alumina surface. Now if the rotational and translational degrees of freedom were separable, then we would expect that $K'_o(X_2)$ would equal $K'_p(X_2)$. Instead a better approximation would be to put

$$\frac{K'_o(H_2)}{K'_p(H_2)} \cdot \frac{K'_o(D_2)}{K'_p(D_2)} = 1 \tag{3}$$

In Eq. (3) the configuration integral for $K'_o(H_2)$, which includes both the contributions of the potential energy associated with translation and that due to the coupling of the rotational and translational motions, should equal the configuration integral of $K'_p(D_2)$. Likewise the configuration integrals of $K'_p(H_2)$ and $K'_o(D_2)$ should be equal. Upon combining Eqs. (1) and (2) using Eq. (3) we obtain

$$\frac{f^r_{o,s}(H_2)f^r_{p,g}(H_2)f^r_{p,g}(D_2)f^r_{o,s}(D_2)}{f^r_{o,g}(H_2)f^r_{p,s}(H_2)f^r_{p,s}(D_2)f^r_{p,g}(D_2)} = \frac{t_{o\text{-}H_2}t_{o\text{-}D_2}}{t_{p\text{-}H_2}t_{p\text{-}D_2}} \tag{4}$$

On the alumina surface we shall assume that there is some preferential direction of orientation and that the potential energy V may be approximated by an equation of the form

$$V = \tfrac{1}{2}V_0(1 - \cos 2\theta) \tag{5}$$

Wilson[8] solved the wave equation for the linear rotator using Eq. (5) for the potential energy. Stern[9] calculated the energy levels of the hindered rotation for a few of the lowest levels in terms of the two parameters μ and λ defined by[10]

$$\lambda^2 = \frac{8\pi^2 I V_0}{h^2}; \qquad \mu = \frac{8\pi^2 I}{h^2}W - \lambda^2 \tag{6}$$

where I is the moment of inertia and W is the energy of the state. For the left-hand side of Eq. (4) to agree with the ratio of experimental t's on the right-hand side it was necessary to take

$$V_0 = 460 \text{ cal mole}^{-1} \tag{7}$$

---

[7] R. B. Scott and F. G. Brickwedde, *J. Chem. Phys.*, **5**, 736 (1937).
[8] A. H. Wilson, *Proc. Roy. Soc. (London)*, **A118**, 628 (1928).
[9] T. E. Stern, *ibid.*, **A130**, 551 (1931).
[10] We are using a definition of V_0 which is twice as large as Stern's.

The rotational energy levels $W_{J, M}$ were then determined from Stern's paper,[9] where the subscript J is the total angular momentum quantum number of the state when the hindering potential vanishes and M is the quantum number which specifies the component of angular momentum along the z-axis. A few of the lowest rotational energy levels for both hydrogen and deuterium are given in Table 1. Note that $W_{J, M} = W_{J, -M}$.

TABLE 1. Rotational energy levels for H_2 and D_2.

Hydrogen	Deuterium
$W_{0, 0} = 260$ cal/mole	$W_{0, 0} = 260$ cal/mole
$W_{1, 0} = 480$	$W_{1, 0} = 340$
$W_{1, 1} = 670$	$W_{1, 1} = 520$
$W_{2, 0} = 1230$	$W_{2, 0} = 760$
$W_{2, 1} = 1260$	$W_{2, 1} = 750$
$W_{2, 2} = 1350$	$W_{2, 2} = 910$

The results given by Eq. (7) and Table 1 are illustrated in Figure 1.

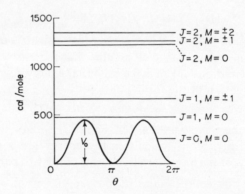

Figure 1. Rotational energies and potential barrier to rotation for hydrogen.

Now, if we assume that there is no activation energy needed for condensation, the condensation coefficient α is the ratio of the internal partition function for the surface molecules to the internal partition function for the molecules in the vapor phase.[11] Since the vibrational partition function for the molecules on the surface and in the vapor is

11 O. Knacke and I. N. Stanski, *Progress in Metal Physics*, Vol. 6, Pergamon Press Ltd., London, 1956, pp. 181–235; E. M. Mortensen and H. Eyring, *J. Phys. Chem.*, **64**, 846 (1960). See also Chapter 16.

expected to be the same, the ratio of the internal partition functions just becomes the ratio of rotational partition functions.

Since the energies of the rotational partition functions for the surface are referred to a state having no rotation rather than to the zero-point energy, the above rotational partition functions must be suitably corrected. The zero-point energy for the para state of hydrogen is just $W_{0,0}$ and for the ortho state $W_{1,0} - E_1$, where E_1 is the rotational energy for a molecule in the vapor phase with $J = 1$. The condensation coefficients for hydrogen are then given by

$$\alpha_{p\text{-}H_2} = \frac{e^{-(W_{0,0} - W_{0,0})/RT} + e^{-(W_{2,0} - W_{0,0})/RT} + 2e^{-(W_{2,1} - W_{0,0})/RT} + 2e^{-(W_{2,2} - W_{0,0})/RT} + \cdots}{f^r_{p,g}(H_2)} \tag{8}$$

$$\alpha_{o\text{-}H_2} = \frac{e^{-[W_{1,0} - (W_{1,0} - E_1)]/RT} + 2e^{-[W_{1,1} - (W_{1,0} - E_1)]/RT} + \cdots}{f^r_{o,g}(H_2)} \tag{9}$$

so that

$$\begin{aligned} \alpha_{p\text{-}H_2} &= 1.0 \\ \alpha_{o\text{-}H_2} &= 0.53 \end{aligned} \tag{10}$$

Similarly we find

$$\begin{aligned} \alpha_{p\text{-}D_2} &= 0.55 \\ \alpha_{o\text{-}D_2} &= 0.97 \end{aligned} \tag{11}$$

We note that the condensation coefficients of both para-hydrogen and ortho-deuterium are at or near their maximum value. This is not surprising since neither species is rotating (except a few in excited states) in the vapor phase, and so all of these molecules which evaporate from the surface have essentially the gas phase distribution of rotational states giving rise to the maximum rate of evaporation. The molecules of ortho-hydrogen and para-deuterium do not have the same distribution of rotational states on the surface as in the vapor phase, and so upon evaporation these molecules do not go over into the same distribution as found in the vapor phase. As a result these molecules do not evaporate at the maximum rate. The reason that the condensation coefficient of ortho-deuterium is not unity is because there is an appreciable number of molecules in excited rotational states and these behave in a similar manner to the molecules in the rotational states of ortho-hydrogen and para-deuterium. In para-hydrogen the number of molecules in excited rotational states is negligible.

11. Multilayer Adsorption

The well-known Brunauer, Emmett and Teller theory of multilayer adsorption was derived by a kinetic approach.[1] More recently the theory has been derived on a statistical mechanical basis and the derivation given

[1] S. Brunauer, P. H. Emmett and E. Teller, *J. Am. Chem. Soc.*, **60**, 309 (1938).

here is essentially that of Hill.[2] As in Sect. 9, we consider the problem only in its simplest form, a single component adsorbed on a uniform surface.

Let ω equal the number of equivalent but distinguishable adsorption sites, n_1 equal the number of molecules adsorbed on these sites, and n_2 equal the number of molecules adsorbed on the n_1 molecules of the first adsorbed layer. From Sect. 9 we have that the number of distinguishable ways that n_1 molecules can be adsorbed, one per site, on the ω sites is given by

$$\frac{\omega!}{n_1!(\omega-n_1)!} \tag{1}$$

and that the partition function for the n_1 molecules of the first layer is

$$f_1 = \frac{\omega!}{n_1!(\omega-n_1)!}[a_1'(T)e^{-\varepsilon_1/kT}]^{n_1} = \frac{\omega!}{n_1!(\omega-n_1)!}[a_1(T)]^{n_1} \tag{2}$$

where ε_1 is the energy of adsorption.

The number of ways in which the n_2 molecules of successive layers can be adsorbed on the first layer of n_1 molecules is

$$\frac{(n_1+n_2-1)!}{n_2!(n_1-1)!} \tag{3}$$

since there is no restriction on the number of molecules adsorbed per molecule of the first layer. (Compare Eq. (3) with Eq. (1.1.1), the expression for the number of ways of distributing n quanta among s oscillators.) Neglecting lateral interactions, we write for the partition function of a molecule in a higher layer

$$a_2'(T)e^{-\varepsilon_2/kT} = a_2(T) \tag{4}$$

in which ε_2 is taken as the energy of the liquid state referred to the same gaseous state energy zero as ε_1 of Eq. (2). Thus, the partition function for adsorbed molecules in layers other than the first is

$$f_2 = \frac{(n_1+n_2-1)!}{n_2!(n_1-1)!}[a_2(T)]^{n_2} \tag{5}$$

Equation (5) in combination with Eq. (2) gives the complete partition function for the adsorbed molecules, which is

$$F = \sum_{n_1=1}^{k} f_1 f_2 = \sum_{n_1=1}^{k} \frac{\omega!}{n_1!(\omega-n_1)!}\frac{(n_1+n_2)!}{n_2!n_1!}[a_1(T)]^{n_1}[a_2(T)]^{n_2} \tag{6}$$

$$k = n_1 + n_2, \qquad n_1 + n_2 < \omega$$

$$k = \omega, \qquad n_1 + n_2 > \omega$$

In Eq. (6) unity has been considered negligible with respect to n_1+n_2 and n_2.

2 T. L. Hill, *J. Chem. Phys.*, **14**, 263 (1946).

Next the approximation is made that the logarithm of F of Eq. (6) is equal to the logarithm of the largest term of the sum.[3] This term and the corresponding value of n_1 are obtained from the relation

$$\frac{\partial(\ln f_1 f_2)}{\partial n_1} = 0 \tag{7}$$

Writing $n_2 = N - n_1$ and using Stirling's approximation we have

$$\ln f_1 f_2 = \omega \ln \omega - \omega + N \ln N - N - 2(\ln n_1 - n_1)$$
$$- \{(N - n_1) \ln (N - n_1) - (N - n_1)\} - \{(\omega - n_1) \ln (\omega - n_1) - (\omega - n_1)\}$$
$$+ n_1 \ln a_1(T) + (N - n_1) \ln a_2(T) \tag{8}$$

Differentiating Eq. (8) with respect to n_1 we obtain

$$\frac{\partial(\ln f_1 f_2)}{\partial n_1} = -2 \ln n_1 + \ln (N - n_1) + \ln (\omega - n_1) + \ln \frac{a_1(T)}{a_2(T)} \tag{9}$$

so that by Eq. (7) we have

$$(N - n_1)(\omega - n_1) = n_1^2 \{a_2(T)/a_1(T)\} \tag{10}$$

The chemical potential of the adsorbed molecules is given by

$$\mu_2 = \left(\frac{\partial A}{\partial N}\right)_{T,V,\omega} = -kT \left(\frac{\partial \ln f_1 f_2}{\partial N}\right)_{T,V,\omega} = -kT \left\{\ln \frac{N}{N - n_1} + \ln a_2(T)\right\} \tag{11}$$

in which n_1 is given by Eq. (10). The absolute activity of the adsorbed phase equals that of the gas phase and we have, using Eq. (9.7), the relation

$$\lambda_a = \left(\frac{N - n_1}{N}\right) \Big/ a_2(T) = \lambda_g = \frac{h^3}{(2\pi m k T)^{\frac{3}{2}} f_{\text{int}}} \cdot \frac{p}{kT} \tag{12}$$

If $n_1 \ll N$, we have the liquid phase, and Eq. (12) becomes

$$\frac{1}{a_2(T)} = \frac{h^3}{(2\pi m k T)^{\frac{3}{2}} f_{\text{int}}} \cdot \frac{p_0}{kT} \tag{13}$$

Combining Eqs. (12) and (13) we thus obtain

$$x = p/p_0 = (N - n_1)/N \tag{14}$$

The BET equation now follows from Eqs. (10) and (14) which, when they are combined, give

$$\frac{N}{\omega} = \frac{x\{a_1(T)/a_2(T)\}}{(1 - x)[1 - x + \{a_1(T)/a_2(T)\}x]} \tag{15}$$

[3] R. H. Fowler and E. A. Guggenheim, *op. cit.*, pp. 438–441.

If we write $N/\omega = V/V_m$; $c = a_1(T)/a_2(T)$ and introduce these changes into Eq. (15), we obtain, after rearranging, the more familiar form of the BET equation, which is

$$\frac{x}{v(1-x)} = \frac{1}{v_m c} + \frac{(c-1)x}{v_m c} \tag{16}$$

This theoretical approach to multilayer adsorption has been extended by Hill[2, 4] to describe other cases.

Finally we note that in this section and in Sects. 8 and 9 we have not differentiated between physical and chemical adsorption. The reason is that for the ideal case of a uniform surface and no lateral interactions between adsorbed molecules, the theoretical treatment is the same. Only the potential energy of a molecule on the surface differs. For further discussion the reader is referred to the review of theories of heterogeneous catalysis by Parlin et al.[5] It should also be noted that the method of significant structures, which we used for surface tension in Sect. 3, could also be applied to multilayer surface adsorption. The significant structure method does not neglect lateral interactions and hence should be a more powerful approach.

4 T. L. Hill, *J. Chem. Phys.*, **14,** 268 (1945).
5 See Ref. 1.16.2.

16

RELAXATION TIMES

1. Chaos

The antithesis of complete equilibrium is complete chaos. In complete equilibrium there is no net flow between any pair of states. In complete chaos there is a universal imbalance with a tendency to flow between every pair of states. Because relaxation in certain parts of a chaotic system outruns relaxation in other parts such a system first develops pools, embracing a collection of states which are at equilibrium, while currents continue to flow between these equilibrated pools. In many cases the equilibrated pools represent compounds separated by potential barriers across which the activated complexes flow in a never ending drift toward complete equilibrium. Fluctuations of a system away from equilibrium are either small or rare. Activated complexes are violent and infrequent fluctuations from the mean state for a system. At equilibrium the activated complexes crossing a barrier in one direction, on the average, balance those crossing in the opposite direction.

2. Times of Relaxation

Equilibrium statistical mechanics presupposes an equilibrium distribution over the available states. But what the occupied states for a system are depends on its rates of relaxation and the time allowed for the system to reach equilibrium. Thus the orbits of the planets in our solar system still cluster about the ecliptic after originating in this non-equilibrium situation some five billion years ago. That the orbital planes are not randomized with respect to each other reflects the infrequency of perturbing collisions which could relax this highly ordered state. In this case the relaxation time which would allow one to assume the random distribution, which is to be expected of systems at equilibrium, is far longer than the present age of the earth. Typical of many metastable systems where a physically applicable description must take account of relaxation times are radioactive decay, para to ortho equilibration of hydrogen, other nuclear magnetic relaxations and all kinds of chemical reactions such as the catalyzed or uncatalyzed reaction of hydrogen with oxygen to form water.

Sometimes a single step limits the rate of relaxation but often a complicated chain of reactions is involved. The hydrogen–bromine reaction is the classical example of a chain reaction and will now be considered briefly.

3. Chain Reactions

In 1906 Bodenstein and Lind[1] found that hydrogen reacting with bromine obeys the equation

$$\frac{d(HBr)}{dt} = \frac{k'(H_2)(Br_2)^{\frac{1}{2}}}{1 + k''[(HBr)/(Br_2)]} \tag{1}$$

where $k' \propto e^{-40,200/RT}$ and $k'' = \frac{1}{10}$.

Christiansen,[2] Herzfeld,[3] and Polanyi[4] thirteen years later proposed independently the following reaction scheme which leads to the observed equations

$$Br_2 + M \overset{1}{\underset{2}{\rightleftharpoons}} 2\,Br + M \qquad -46.1\ kcal$$

$$Br + H_2 \overset{3}{\underset{4}{\rightleftharpoons}} HBr + H \qquad -16.6\ kcal$$

$$H + Br_2 \overset{5}{\rightarrow} HBr + Br \qquad +41.4\ kcal$$

The listed heats of reaction are for the standard temperatures and pressures 25°C and 1 atmosphere. M may be any gaseous molecule.

The equations for the rate of formation of intermediate compounds are

$$\frac{d(Br)}{dt} = 2k_1(Br_2)(M) + k_4(H)(HBr) + k_5(H)(Br_2)$$

$$\qquad\qquad\qquad - 2k_2(Br)^2(M) - k_3(Br)(H_2) \tag{2}$$

$$\frac{d(H)}{dt} = k_3(Br)(H_2) - k_4(H)(HBr) - k_5(H)(Br_2) \tag{3}$$

and the rate of forming the final product (HBr) is

$$\frac{d(HBr)}{dt} = k_3(Br)(H_2) + k_5(H)(Br_2) - k_4(HBr)(H) \tag{4}$$

As Bodenstein and Lind's work shows Eq. (1) holds below 1000°K to as near the beginning of the reaction as can be measured even though it is at the beginning that the concentration of the intermediates must build up. Matsen and Franklin[5] estimate the induction period in which the steady state builds up at 10^{-9} seconds. Neglecting this build up of intermediate

[1] M. Bodenstein and S. C. Lind, *Z. Physik. Chem.*, **57**, 168 (1907).
[2] J. A. Christiansen, *Kgl. Danske Videnskab. Selskab. Mat.-Fys. Medd.*, **1**, 14 (1919).
[3] K. F. Herzfeld, *Ann. Physik*, **59**, 635 (1919).
[4] M. Polanyi, *Z. Electrochem.*, **26**, 50 (1920).
[5] F. A. Matsen and J. L. Franklin, *J. Am. Chem. Soc.*, **72**, 3337 (1950).

compounds one makes the usual steady state approximation

$$\frac{d(Br)}{dt} = \frac{d(H)}{dt} = 0$$

Setting $K = k_1/k_2$ and solving the steady state equations yields

$$(Br)_{ss} = \left[\frac{k_1(Br_2)}{k_2}\right]^{\frac{1}{2}} = K^{\frac{1}{2}}(Br_2)^{\frac{1}{2}} \tag{5}$$

$$(H)_{ss} = \frac{k_3(Br)(H_2)}{k_4(HBr) + k_5(Br_2)} \tag{6}$$

On substituting Eqs. (5) and (6) into (4) we have

$$\frac{d(HBr)}{dt} = \frac{2k_3 k_5 K^{\frac{1}{2}}(H_2)(Br_2)^{\frac{3}{2}}}{k_5(Br_2) + k_4(HBr)} \tag{7}$$

or alternatively

$$\frac{d(HBr)}{dt} = \frac{2k_3 K^{\frac{1}{2}}(H_2)(Br_2)^{\frac{1}{2}}}{1 + k_4(HBr)/k_5(Br_2)} \tag{8}$$

It is possible to show that other conceivable reactions such as $H_2 \rightarrow 2\,H$ are too slow to affect the results.[6] If such reactions were significant they would require changes in Eq. (8) which would in general spoil the accord with experiment. Skrabal[7] has treated a variety of examples of simultaneous chemical reactions. Hinshelwood[8] has been especially successful in inhibiting chain reactions with NO and Rice[9] has obtained similar results with propylene. Semenov,[10] also, has been conspicuously successful in interpreting chain reactions.

Certain salient points in this summary discussion of a chain reaction should be noted. (1) Even though reactants disappear and products appear in chain reactions certain fleeting intermediates such as Br and H atoms, present at low concentrations, vary in amount but slightly and are satisfactorily treated as not changing their concentration with time. This assumption greatly simplifies chain reaction calculations. (2) Out of the various possible reaction paths from reactant to product frequently a single path is so much faster than competing paths that the latter may be ignored. (3) In order to calculate the rate of chain reactions and compare the rates by alternate pathways the specific reaction rate constants for the various elementary steps must be determined.

[6] E.g. A. A. Frost and R. G. Pearson, *Kinetics and Mechanism*, 2nd Ed., Wiley, New York, 1961; Sidney W. Benson, *The Foundations of Chemical Kinetics*, McGraw-Hill, New York, 1960.

[7] A. Skrabal, *Monatsh. Chem.*, **24**, 203 (1943).

[8] L. A. K. Staveley and C. N. Hinshelwood, *Nature*, **137**, 29 (1936).

[9] F. O. Rice and O. L. Polly, *J. Chem. Phys.*, **6**, 273 (1938).

[10] N. Semenov, *Some Problems of Chemical Kinetics*, Vol. 1, Pergamon Press, New York, 1958.

4. Elementary Reactions

It is well known that a general solution of even the classical three body problem, in closed form, is unattainable. A general solution of a many body collision in quantum mechanics is correspondingly more intractable. In contrast with the difficulty of solving the general many body problem is the ease of solution for configurations where the potential is adequately described by a quadratic. The theory of small vibrations provides a complete mechanical solution yielding the vibration frequencies and moments of inertia which are necessary to calculate all the statistical mechanical properties. Since both at saddle points and at minima the potentials are expressible as quadratics the statistical mechanical properties at equilibrium of both the activated complexes, at the saddle points, and the stable compounds, at minima, are calculable. Further, at equilibrium an activated complex lying as it does at the saddle point, or transition point, has the same activity as does the same set of atoms present as reactants. The activity, λ, is the number of representatives of a system in a volume divided by the partition function for the volume. If the volume taken is one cm^3 the activity becomes the concentration divided by the specific partition function.

As noted earlier when $C^\ddagger$ is used to represent the concentration of activated complexes in a distance $\delta = h/(2\pi mkT)^{\frac{1}{2}}$ along the reaction coordinate then the velocity of reaction is (Sect. 1.12)

$$v = \kappa \frac{kT}{h} C^\ddagger \tag{1}$$

This choice of the length δ makes the partition function along the reaction coordinate of the activated complex equal to unity.

When Eq. (1) is used to represent the rate of reaction at equilibrium, κ is the average quantum mechanical transmission coefficient for wave packets crossing the barrier. If there is appreciable leakage through the barrier this requires adding additional terms to Eq. (1) or correcting for leakage by a κ in excess of unity, but in the absence of leakage κ will ordinarily be a proper fraction near unity. It is customary and convenient to use Eq. (1) to represent the velocity of reaction under non-equilibrium conditions, i.e. when there is partial or total absence of products. In such systems κ must take account of slight departures of $C^\ddagger$ from its equilibrium value as well as of the quantum mechanical transmission coefficient. Kramers,[1] using classical diffusion theory, and Zwolinski and Eyring,[2] using discrete energy levels, found rates of reaction over barriers about 0.9

---

[1] H. A. Kramers, *Physica*, **7**, 284 (1940).
[2] B. J. Zwolinski and H. Eyring, *J. Am. Chem. Soc.*, **68**, 2702 (1947).

as large as those calculated using equilibrium reaction rate theory. Later results on non-equilibrium kinetics have been summarized in an article by Montroll and Shuler[3] and also in a paper by F. Ree, Teresa Ree, T. Ree and H. Eyring.[4] Barrier leakage has also been investigated recently by H. S. Johnston[5] and by Mortensen and Pitzer.[6] Eyring, Walter and Kimball[7] present certain quantum mechanical aspects of reaction rates that are not repeated here.

Returning to Eq. (1) the concentration, $C^{\ddagger}$, of the activated complex is to be related to the reactants by some equilibrium equation such as

$$A + B \rightarrow C^{\ddagger} + D \rightarrow E + F \tag{2}$$

Thus

$$K^{\ddagger} = \frac{(C^{\ddagger})\gamma_C(D)\gamma_D}{(A)\gamma_A(B)\gamma_B} \tag{3}$$

Substituting Eq. (3) in Eq. (1) gives

$$v = \kappa \frac{kT}{h} K^{\ddagger} \frac{(A)(B)\gamma_A\gamma_B}{(D)\gamma_C\gamma_D} \tag{4}$$

Any other equilibrium than that given by Eq. (2) between reactants and activated complex will lead to an equation analogous to Eq. (3). The equilibrium constant $K^{\ddagger}$ can be written in terms of partition functions, like any other equilibrium constant. It is only necessary to remember that the partition function for the degree of freedom along the reaction coordinate is equal to unity. The activity coefficients, γ, are all unity if the partition functions for the actual concentrations are used. If the partition functions used are for the standard states of the various species then the activity coefficients, γ_i, are used to correct the actual concentrations to effective thermodynamic concentrations and must be so chosen that each γ_i takes the value unity for the species in its standard state.

5. Steady State Reaction Networks

Many processes in the physical world proceed by random walk. A particle continues in one direction until it encounters an obstacle. After a shorter or longer delay it moves off in a new direction until a second obstacle is encountered. Here the particle again changes direction.

[3] E. W. Montroll and K. E. Shuler, *Advan. Chem. Phys.*, **1**, 361 (1958), Interscience, New York.

[4] F. Ree, Teresa Ree, T. Ree and H. Eyring, *Advan. Chem. Phys.*, **4**, 1 (1962), Interscience, New York.

[5] H. S. Johnston, *Advan. Chem. Phys.*, **3**, 131 (1961).

[6] E. M. Mortensen and K. S. Pitzer in *The Transition State*, Special Publication No. 16, The Chemical Society, London, 1962, p. 57.

[7] *Q.C.*, Chapter 16.

The diffusion of particles in a condensed phase under a gradient in concentration, temperature, or electrical potential provides an interesting example of a random walk problem. We use the simplified one-dimensional diagram of Figure 1 for illustration.

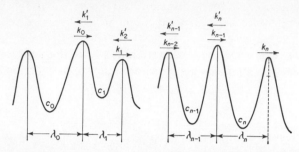

Figure 1. Migration from an equilibrium state with one ring of neighbors in a liquid or solid to an adjacent position with a new ring of neighbors involves passing over a potential energy barrier as indicated. A molecule with z neighboring positions may move into any one of the neighboring positions.

Each molecule is surrounded by z neighboring positions to which the molecule can jump. Half of these, $z/2$, will advance the particle in the positive x direction, and the remaining $z/2$ jumps correspond to motion in the $-x$ direction. If a molecule jumps the distance λ' into the ith position, it will advance the distance $\lambda' \cos \theta_i$ along the x axis. Here $\cos \theta_i$ is the angle between the path to the ith position and the x axis. The x component of the forward velocity, u_i, of a particle in the ith position is thus $u_i = \sum_i \lambda_i' k_i \cos \theta_i$, where the summation is over all $z/2$ forward positions into which a molecule can jump. Thus one can write

$$u_i = \sum_i \lambda_i' k_i \cos \theta_i = k_i \lambda_i' \frac{z}{2} \langle \cos \theta_i \rangle \equiv k_i \lambda_i \tag{1}$$

To obtain the last equality we have set $\lambda_i'(z/2)\langle \cos \theta_i \rangle = \lambda_i$ which is of the order of a lattice distance. The net[1] current, J, across a barrier is the product of velocity and concentration in the forward direction minus the corresponding product for the backward direction. For the steady state, which we now consider, J is a constant. Thus

$$
\begin{aligned}
J &= c_0 \lambda_0 k_0 - c_1 \lambda_1 k_1' \\
J &= c_1 \lambda_1 k_1 - c_2 \lambda_2 k_2' \\
J &= c_2 \lambda_2 k_2 - c_3 \lambda_3 k_3' \\
&\quad \cdots \\
J &= c_{n-1} \lambda_{n-1} k_{n-1} - c_n \lambda_n k_n'
\end{aligned}
\tag{2}
$$

[1] B. J. Zwolinski, H. Eyring and C. E. Reese, *J. Phys. and Colloid Chem.*, **53**, 1427 (1949).

If the top equation is multiplied by 1 and successive ones by k_1'/k_1, $k_1'k_2'/k_1k_2$, etc. and the final one by $(k_1' \ldots k_{n-1}')/(k_1 \ldots k_{n-1})$ and all equations are added, the result is

$$J = \frac{k_0\left(c_0\lambda_0 - \dfrac{c_n\lambda_n k_1' \ldots k_{n-1}'k_n'}{k_0 k_1 \ldots k_{n-1}}\right)}{1 + \dfrac{k_1'}{k_1} + \dfrac{k_1'k_2'}{k_1k_2} + \ldots \dfrac{k_1'k_2' \ldots k_{n-1}'}{k_1k_2 \ldots k_{n-1}}} \tag{3}$$

If all barriers and all λ's are equal Eq. (3) becomes

$$J = \frac{\lambda_0 k_0(c_0 - c_n)}{n} \tag{4}$$

Here n is the number of barriers lying between the zeroth and nth positions. We define the diffusion coefficient as $D = k_0\lambda_0\tau/n$, where τ is the thickness of the layer between the zeroth and nth positions. The permeability, P, is then

$$P = \frac{k_0\lambda_0}{n} = \frac{D}{\tau} \tag{5}$$

This is the usual definition of the permeability.

Writing for each k_i the expression

$$k_i = \kappa_i \frac{kT}{h} e^{-\Delta G_i \ddagger/RT} \tag{6}$$

and substituting in Eq. (3) yields, in the case where the κ's are equal, the expression

$$J = \kappa \frac{kT}{h} e^{-\Delta G_0\ddagger/RT} \frac{(c_0\lambda_0 - c_n\lambda_n e^{\Delta G/RT})}{1 + e^{\delta G_1\ddagger/RT} + e^{\delta G_2\ddagger/RT} + \ldots e^{\delta G_{n-1}\ddagger/RT}} \tag{7}$$

Here ΔG is the excess free energy of the final or nth state over the initial or zeroth state, and $\delta G^\ddagger$ is the excess free energy of activation of the ith over the zeroth barrier.

Consider next the case where there is an applied potential, E, across equal maxima each having the same free energy of activation, ΔG_0, providing the potential is zero, i.e. when $E = 0$, and with all barriers the same distance λ apart. In the case of a uniform gradient, i.e. when the space between the initial and final state remains electroneutral, the free energy of activation becomes

$$\Delta G_i^\ddagger = \Delta G_0^\ddagger + \frac{(2i+1)zE}{2n} \tag{8}$$

and

$$\Delta G = zE$$

Here z is the valence and the voltage E should be expressed in calories. Substituting these results in Eq. (7) using the notation

$$x = e^{-zE/nRT} \tag{9}$$

and k_0^0 for the specific rate over the first barrier in the absence of a field gives:

$$
\begin{aligned}
J &= \lambda k_0^0 x^{-\frac{1}{2}} \frac{(c_0 - c_n x^n)}{1 + x + x^2 + \ldots + x^{n-1}} = \frac{\lambda_0 k_0 x^{-\frac{1}{2}}(1-x)(c_0 - c_n x^n)}{1 - x^n} \\
&= \lambda_0 k_0^0 \frac{(x^{-\frac{1}{2}} - x^{\frac{1}{2}})}{1 - x^n}(c_0 - x^n c_n)\frac{x^{-n/2}}{x^{-n/2}} \\
&= \lambda_0 k_0^0 \frac{x^{-\frac{1}{2}} - x^{\frac{1}{2}}}{x^{-n/2} - x^{n/2}}(x^{-n/2}c_0 - x^{n/2}c_n)
\end{aligned}
\tag{10}
$$

Expanding the exponentials, we find that

$$\frac{g}{n} \equiv \frac{x^{-\frac{1}{2}} - x^{\frac{1}{2}}}{x^{-n/2} - x^{n/2}} \approx \frac{1}{n} \tag{11}$$

provided that the total electrical work zE is somewhat smaller than RT. In this case

$$\lambda_0 k_0^0 g/n \approx \lambda_0 k_0^0/n \equiv P \tag{12}$$

and

$$J = P(c_0 e^{-z\mathscr{F}E/2RT} - c_n e^{z\mathscr{F}E/2RT}) \tag{13}$$

Thus material transport, J, is proportional to a permeability P. If the exponentials in Eq. (13) are expanded, which is justified if $z\mathscr{F}E/2$ is somewhat less than RT, the result is:

$$J = P\left\{(c_0 - c_n) - \tfrac{1}{2}(c_0 + c_n)\frac{z\mathscr{F}E}{RT}\right\} \tag{14}$$

These equations have provided the basis for interesting discussions of nerve impulses.[2, 3, 4, 5]

6. Absolute Rate Theory Reduces to Irreversible Thermodynamics and Yields the Onsager Reciprocity Relations near the Equilibrium Limit

It is convenient to illustrate the general result stated in the above heading by considering the change in the current density J_1 of some ion such as Na^+ due to the concentration gradient of some substance X flowing with

2 H. Eyring, R. Lumry and W. J. Woodbury, *Record of Chemical Progress*, **10**, 100 (1949).

3 A. L. Hodgkin and A. F. Huxley, *J. Physiol.*, **117**, 500 (1952).

4 H. T. Clarke, Ed., *Ion Transport Across Membranes*, Academic Press, New York, 1954. See p. 103 by R. B. Parlin and H. Eyring.

5 David Nachmansohn, Ed., *Molecular Biology. Elementary Processes of Nerve Conductions and Muscle Contraction*, Academic Press, New York, 1960.

a current density J_2 which coordinates with the sodium ion to make a complex which has a different permeability for the existing set of barriers. It will be advantageous to rewrite Eq. (5.15) using activities instead of concentrations in the limit of low driving forces, i.e. near equilibrium. Under these circumstances, J becomes

$$J = \frac{P}{\gamma_0}\left\{(a_0-a_n)-\tfrac{1}{2}(a_0+a_n)\frac{z\mathscr{F}E}{RT}\right\}$$

$$\equiv P^0\bar{a}\left(-\frac{\delta a}{a}-\frac{z\mathscr{F}E}{RT}\right) \equiv P^0\bar{a}\left(-\frac{\delta\mu}{RT}-\frac{z\mathscr{F}E}{RT}\right) \tag{1}$$

Here we have written

$$P^0 = \frac{P}{\gamma_0} \tag{2}$$

$$\bar{a} = \tfrac{1}{2}(a_0+a_n) \tag{3}$$

The P that should be used in Eq. (2) is $k^0\lambda/n$ at the standard state where the activity coefficients γ and γ_0 are unity, and

$$-\delta a = a_0-a_n \tag{4}$$

Since

$$\mu = RT\ln a+\mu_0 \tag{5}$$

it follows that

$$\frac{\delta\mu}{RT} = \frac{\delta a}{a} \tag{6}$$

Using Eq. (1) for Na^+ ions flowing by themselves added to the flow of the complex gives for the current J_1 for sodium ions the value:

$$J_1 = P_1^0\bar{a}_1\left(-\frac{\delta\mu_1}{RT}-\frac{z_1\mathscr{F}E}{RT}\right) + P_r^0\bar{a}_n\left(-\frac{\delta\mu_r}{RT}-\frac{z_r\mathscr{F}E}{RT}\right) \tag{7}$$

Similarly the current density J_2 of compound X has the value:

$$J_2 = P_2^0\bar{a}_2\frac{(-\delta\mu_2)}{RT} + rP_r^0\bar{a}_r\left(\frac{(-\delta\mu_r)}{RT}-\frac{z_r\mathscr{F}E}{RT}\right) \tag{8}$$

The subscripts 1, 2, and r represent the species Na^+, X, and Na^+X_r, respectively.

$$Na^+ +rX \rightleftharpoons Na^+X_r \tag{9}$$

The equation for the chemical potential at each point is $\mu_1+r\mu_2 = \mu_r$, so that from one side of our set of barriers to the other

$$\delta\mu_1+r\,\delta\mu_2 = \delta\mu_r \tag{10}$$

Introducing Eq. (10) into Eq. (7) and Eq. (8) yields:

$$J_1 = (P_1^0 \bar{a}_1 + P_r^0 \bar{a}_r)\frac{(-\delta\mu_1)}{RT} + rP_r^0 \bar{a}_r \frac{(-\delta\mu_2)}{RT}$$

$$+ (P_1^0 \bar{a}_1 z_1 + P_r^0 \bar{a}_r z_r)\left(-\frac{\mathscr{F}E}{RT}\right) \quad (11)$$

$$J_2 = rP_r^0 \bar{a}_r \frac{(-\delta\mu_1)}{RT} + (P_2^0 \bar{a}_2 + r^2 P_r^0 \bar{a}_r)\frac{(-\delta\mu_2)}{RT}$$

$$+ (rP_r^0 \bar{a}_r z_r)\left(-\frac{\mathscr{F}E}{RT}\right) \quad (12)$$

and finally for the flow of charge, J_3, the current is obtained by multiplying each flux in J_1 by the appropriate value of the valence z. This gives

$$J_3 = \mathscr{F}(z_1 P_1^0 \bar{a}_1 + z_r P_r \bar{a}_r)\frac{(-\delta\mu_1)}{RT} + \mathscr{F} z_r r P_r^0 \bar{a}_r \frac{(-\delta\mu_2)}{RT}$$

$$+ \mathscr{F}(z_1^2 P_1^0 \bar{a}_1 + P_r^0 \bar{a}_r z_r^2)\left(-\frac{\mathscr{F}E}{RT}\right) \quad (13)$$

It is immediately obvious that Onsager's reciprocal relations are obeyed.[1] If we write

$$-\delta\mu_1 = -\frac{d\mu_1}{dx}\tau = X_1 \tau, \qquad -\delta\mu_2 = -\frac{d\mu_2}{dx}\tau = X_2 \tau$$

$$-E = -\frac{\partial E}{\partial x}\tau = X_3 \tau$$

where τ is the thickness of the diffusion layer, the three currents are:

$$J_1 = \frac{\tau}{RT}(P_1^0 \bar{a}_1 + P_r^0 \bar{a}_r)X_1 + \frac{\tau r}{RT}P_r^0 \bar{a}_r X_2 + \frac{\tau}{RT}(P_1^0 \bar{a}_1 z_1 + P_r^0 \bar{a}_r z_r)X_3 \quad (14)$$

$$J_2 = \frac{\tau r}{RT}P_r^0 \bar{a}_r X_1 + \frac{\tau}{RT}(P_2^0 \bar{a}_2 + r^2 P_r^0 \bar{a}_r)X_2 + \frac{\tau}{RT}(rP_r^0 \bar{a}_r z_r)X_3 \quad (15)$$

$$J_3 = \frac{\mathscr{F}\tau}{RT}(z_1 P_1^0 \bar{a}_1 + z_r P_r \bar{a}_r)X_1 + \frac{\mathscr{F}\tau}{RT}(z_r r P_r^0 \bar{a}_r)X_2$$

$$+ \frac{\mathscr{F}^2\tau}{RT}(z_1^2 P_1^0 \bar{a}_1 + P_r^0 \bar{a}_r z_r^2)X_3 \quad (16)$$

Thus

$$L_{12} = L_{21} = \tau r P_r^0 \bar{a}_r / RT$$

$$L_{13} = L_{31} = \mathscr{F}\tau(P_1^0 \bar{a}_1 z_1 + P_r^0 \bar{a}_r z_r)/RT \quad (17)$$

and

$$L_{23} = L_{32} = \mathscr{F}\tau r z_r P_r^0 \bar{a}_r / RT$$

[1] L. Onsager, *Phys. Rev.*, **37**, 405 (1931); **38**, 2265 (1938).

Since the reciprocal relationships hold independent of the value of r, whether integral or fractional, and also hold for the simultaneous formation of any number of complexes with different values of r, it is a good limiting law. The coupling between respiration and phosphorylation is another interesting area where these considerations apply. Experiment bears out the reciprocal relations.[2, 3, 4, 5]

However, when the driving forces are large enough that the exponentials in Eq. (5.14) should be retained, i.e. the expansions that lead to Eq. (5.15) and Eq. (1) are not permissible: irreversible thermodynamics and the Onsager relations must be given up in favor of the more general reaction rate approach. Far away from equilibrium the J's can still be written using Eq. (5.14).

The results just developed are useful in understanding many types of coupled reactions. Living cells provide an example. Most cells are surrounded by membranes about 100 Å thick with the outside of the cell 0.1 volt more positive than the inside. By some process not completely understood sodium ions are pumped out of the cell thus generating on the outside a positive potential. The most probable mechanism is that metabolism inside the cell produces a product, X, which, when coordinated with sodium ions, makes the resulting ion able to diffuse through the membrane to the outside of the cell much more easily, whereas the uncoordinated Na^+ and molecule X pass through the membrane only with difficulty. Potassium ions, on the other hand, pass through the membrane readily and consequently obey the Nernst potential, being about 45 times more concentrated inside the cell than out. Sodium ion, as a result of the active pumping by X, is about seven times more concentrated outside than inside. Outside the cell X is modified chemically so that it coordinates with K^+ for the return journey to the inside of the cell. Production of X inside the cell and its destruction outside produces a gradient of Na^+X decreasing from inside to outside so that this complex ion in turn obeys the Nernst equation although the Na^+ ion itself does not. The detailed behavior of nerve cells has been considered, from this kinetic point of view, elsewhere.

7. Thermal Diffusion and the Soret Effect

These effects can be based on Eq. (5.3) providing the local temperature is introduced into the absolute rate expression for each value of k_i and k_i'.

[2] S. R. DeGroot, *Thermodynamics of Irreversible Processes*, Interscience, New York, 1951.

[3] K. G. Denbigh, *The Thermodynamics of the Steady State*, Methuen, London, 1951.

[4] I. Prigogine, *Thermodynamics of Irreversible Processes*, Charles C. Thomas Publisher, Springfield, Illinois, 1955.

[5] R. F. Wendt, *J. Phys. Chem.*, **66**, 1279 (1962).

Assuming that each minimum i is characterized by a temperature T_i with the maxima on either side with temperatures $T_{i+\frac{1}{2}}$ and $T_{i-\frac{1}{2}}$, then

$$k_i = \frac{\kappa k T_{i+\frac{1}{2}}}{h} \frac{F^{\ddagger}(T_{i+\frac{1}{2}})}{F(T_i)} e^{-E_{0,\,i+\frac{1}{2}}/kT_{i+\frac{1}{2}}} \tag{1}$$

and

$$k_i' = \frac{\kappa T_{i-\frac{1}{2}}}{h} \frac{F^{\ddagger}(T_{i-\frac{1}{2}})}{F(T_i)} e^{-E_{0,\,i-\frac{1}{2}}/kT_{i-\frac{1}{2}}} \tag{2}$$

and

$$\frac{k_i'}{k_i} = \frac{T_{i-\frac{1}{2}}}{T_{i+\frac{1}{2}}} \frac{F^{\ddagger}(T_{i-\frac{1}{2}})}{F^{\ddagger}(T_{i+\frac{1}{2}})} e^{-\{(E_{0,\,i-\frac{1}{2}}/kT_{i-\frac{1}{2}}) - (E_{0,\,i+\frac{1}{2}}/kT_{i+\frac{1}{2}})\}} \tag{3}$$

Case I. Suppose the barriers are all of equal height and that $T_{i-\frac{1}{2}} = T_i = T_{i+\frac{1}{2}}$. In this case Eq. (5.3) becomes

$$J = \frac{k_0 \lambda_0}{n} \left(c_0 - c_n \frac{\lambda_n T_n F_n F_0^{\ddagger}}{\lambda_0 T_0 F_0 F_n^{\ddagger}} e^{-\{E_0(T_0 - T_n)/kT_n T_0\}} \right) \tag{4}$$

In a liquid each constituent obeys an equation of the form of (5.3) with each species moving in a lattice of the other materials. Since the center of gravity of the system as a whole is stationary the compensating bulk flow with respect to the walls is a correction that must be made to each lattice. The other complication is that the k's for each species are a function of composition. However, enough has been said to indicate the framework in which thermal diffusion considered as a rate process must be discussed.

Case II. If $T_{i-\frac{1}{2}} \neq T_i \neq T_{i+\frac{1}{2}}$ then Eq. (3) is no longer unity and there is an added complication ordinarily ignored in the usual irreversible thermodynamic discussion. The question as to how different an activated complex is when passing from a hot to a cold minimum from those complexes passing in the reverse direction is a nice point which needs further experimental and theoretical study. One can readily write down the J for the case where the activated complex has a temperature determined by position but independent of direction. It would be valuable to have experiments which would distinguish between such a J and the J for case I.

8. Significant Structures Theory of Viscosity and Diffusion

Significant structures theory leads to a useful expression for the Helmholtz free energy, A, as a function of V and T as shown by the good agreement between experimental and calculated thermodynamic properties in Chapter 12. According to this model, a fraction V_s/V of the molecules manifests solid-like behavior and the remaining fraction $(V - V_s)/V$ is gas-like.

The agreement with experiment of this liquid theory model, which pictures molecules in the gas phase as in approximate one-to-one correspondence with liquid vacancies that execute gas-like motions, indicates that this model is in fact correct or that at least it differs very little from the true model as measured by the free energy.

Because of the successful treatment of thermodynamic properties, it is interesting to see what results the significant structures theory yields for transport properties. Viscous flow occurs along shear planes separating layers of molecules. We designate the mean distance between such shear planes as λ_1. Consider now the mechanism of shear relaxation along a particular shear plane. An applied stress results in a displacement in a direction to relieve the elastically stored stress. Wherever vacancies exist neighboring molecules jump into them. This is true whether there is stress or not. A molecule in jumping from one position to another along the shear plane retains elastic contact with all of its neighbors, not on the shear plane, with the result that the shift to a new minimum either releases or increases the stress depending upon the direction of motion. Batschinski's[1] relation, which states that the fluidity is closely proportional to the excess volume over that of the solid, is a natural consequence of our model since excess volume measures the probability of a vacancy occurring. The molecules on a shear plane are like the feet of a living creature as they individually jump into an available vacancy, carrying with them their superstructure. Thus the frequency of moving any foot forward is proportional to the chance of the position being vacant, which in turn is proportional to the excess volume.

By definition the viscosity, η, satisfies the relation

$$\eta = \frac{f}{\dot{s}} \tag{1}$$

where f is the shear stress and $\dot{s}$ is the rate of shear. The area on the shear plane of a system can be divided up into fractions, χ_i, of the total area having relaxing units, molecules or groups of molecules, of kind i, for which the shear stress is f_i with the whole shear plane sharing a common rate of shear, $\dot{s}$. The viscosity for such a system is then

$$\eta = \frac{f}{\dot{s}} = \sum_i \frac{\chi_i f_i}{\dot{s}} = \sum_i \chi_i \eta_i \tag{2}$$

For a simple liquid

$$\eta = \frac{V_s}{V}\eta_s + \frac{V - V_s}{V}\eta_g \tag{3}$$

[1] A. J. Batschinski, *Z. Physik. Chem.*, **84,** 643 (1913).

Here V_s/V, $(V-V_s)/V$, η_s, and η_g are the surface fractions of solid-like and gas-like structures and the viscosities of solid- and gas-like structures respectively. In more complicated systems there are additional varieties of flowing structures. For the rate of shear of solid-like degrees of freedom of the liquid one has:

$$\dot{s} = \sum_{i=1}^{z} \frac{\lambda}{\lambda_1} \cos\theta_i \, k' \, e^{f\lambda_2\lambda_3 \cos\theta_i \lambda/2kT} \tag{4}$$

See Figure 1.

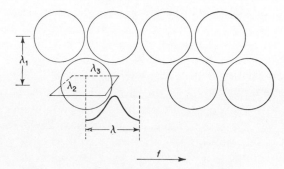

Figure 1. Shear plane in the fluid with area $\lambda_2\lambda_3$ of a molecule in the shear plane and a distance λ_1 between shear planes.

Here the summation is over all z neighboring positions, any one of which when vacant permits a molecule to jump into it. $\lambda_2\lambda_3$ is the area in the shear plane which when multiplied by the force per unit area gives the force biasing a molecule's motion in the direction of the stress. θ_i is the angle which the displacement vector of the molecule jumping into the neighboring ith lattice position makes with the directions of the stress. Thus $(f\lambda_2\lambda_3 \cos\theta_i\lambda)/2$ is the work done by the shear stress as the molecule moves the distance $\lambda/2$ to the top of a barrier which is half way to the next potential minimum. If we pair each forward motion with the oppositely directed one, Eq. (2) becomes

$$\dot{s} = \sum_{i=1}^{z/2} \frac{\lambda}{\lambda_1} k' \cos\theta_i (e^{f\lambda_2\lambda_3\lambda \cos\theta_i/2kT} - e^{-f\lambda_2\lambda_3\lambda \cos\theta_i/2kT}) \tag{5}$$

For Newtonian flow for which

$$\frac{f\lambda_2\lambda_3\lambda\cos\theta}{2kT} \ll 1 \tag{6}$$

the exponentials can be expanded and the rate of shear becomes:

$$\dot{s} = \frac{\lambda}{\lambda_1} k' \frac{f\lambda_2\lambda_3\lambda}{kT} \sum_{i=1}^{z/2} \cos^2\theta_i = \frac{\lambda^2\lambda_2\lambda_3 k' }{\lambda_1 kT} \frac{fz}{6} \tag{7}$$

The last equality in Eq. (7) follows since there are $z/2$ forward jumps for which the mean value of $\cos^2 \theta_i$ is

$$\frac{\displaystyle\int_{\theta=0}^{\pi/2} \cos^2 \theta_i \sin \theta \, d\theta}{\displaystyle\int_{\theta=0}^{\pi/2} \sin \theta \, d\theta} = \frac{1}{3}$$

When the driving potential causing shear is the chemical potential

$$\mu = kT \ln a + \mu_0 \tag{8}$$

the force driving a molecule is

$$F = -\frac{d\mu}{dx} = -kT \frac{d \ln a}{dx} = -kT \frac{d \ln a}{dc} \frac{dc}{dx} \tag{9}$$

In this case the relative velocity, u_{ij}, of the ith to the jth layer is $u_{ij} = \lambda_1 \dot{s}$. Using Eq. (5), we obtain

$$u_{ij} = \sum_{i=1}^{z/2} \lambda \cos \theta_i \, k'(e^{-(d \ln a/dc)(dc/dx)(\lambda/2)\cos \theta_i} - e^{(d \ln a/dc)(dc/dx)(\lambda/2)\cos \theta_i}) \tag{10}$$

When the exponents are small, Eq. (10) becomes

$$u_{ij} = -\sum_{i=1}^{z/2} \lambda \cos^2 \theta_i \, k' \frac{d \ln a}{dc} \frac{dc}{dx} \lambda = -\lambda^2 \frac{z}{6} k' \frac{d \ln a}{dc} \frac{dc}{dx} \tag{11}$$

Figure 2 shows that a molecule is surrounded by ξ neighbors, in this case six.

Figure 2. The central molecule diffusing up from the paper must slip past its six neighbors by six separate shearing motions.

In the slipping motion by which the central molecule passes its neighbors only one out of ξ of them are passed in any one shearing event. Since when it is all over there is no net displacement of the ring of neighbors, due to diffusion of the central diffusing molecules because of elastic adjustments, it follows that the average velocity, u, at which a molecule diffuses is

$$u = \frac{u_{iz}}{\xi} = -\frac{\lambda^2 z}{\xi 6} k' \frac{d \ln a}{dc} \frac{dc}{dx} \tag{12}$$

The result expressed by Eq. (12) is apparent in another way. To obtain u from u_{ij} one should note that in Eq. (11) the distance jumped, λ, should be divided by the frequency of jumping; k' must be multiplied by ξ to relate the motion of the diffusing molecule to the center of gravity of all its neighbors rather than to the position of a single neighbor; and since λ occurs squared while k' is to the first power we get Eq. (12) from Eq. (11).

The diffusing current is now

$$J = -D \frac{dc}{dx} = cu = -\frac{\lambda^2 z}{\xi 6} k' \frac{d \ln a}{d \ln c} \frac{dc}{dx} \tag{13}$$

Thus the diffusion coefficient for the solid-like structure in liquids is

$$D = \frac{\lambda^2 z}{\xi 6} k' \frac{d \ln a}{d \ln c} \tag{14}$$

Substituting Eq. (7) in Eq. (1) gives for the viscosity of the solid-like structure in liquids the result:

$$\eta = \frac{\lambda_1 kT}{\lambda^2 \lambda_2 \lambda_3} \frac{6}{k' z} \tag{15}$$

For $D\eta$ the result is then:[2, 3]

$$D\eta = \frac{\lambda_1 kT}{\lambda_2 \lambda_3 \xi} \frac{d \ln a}{d \ln c} \frac{(k'z)_m}{(k'z)_s} \tag{16}$$

Here the subscript m on $(k'z)_m$ indicates the values are for the mixture while subscript s labels these properties for the pure solute.

For self diffusion $(k'z)_m/(k'z)_s = 1$, also $d \ln a/d \ln c = 1$ and if it be assumed that $\lambda_1 = \lambda_2 = \lambda_3 \approx (V/N)^{\frac{1}{3}}$ then $\xi = kT/D\eta \, (N/V)^{\frac{1}{3}}$. We expect values for ξ near six. Li and Chang[4] have discussed the nature of ξ from a somewhat different point of view and also compiled the then available data on self diffusion. In the following list the value, or the values, found for ξ follow the substance: Water, 6.9, 5.4, 6.1, 6.1; benzene, 6.2; bromoethane, 5.6; methyl alcohol, 8.1; ethyl alcohol, 8.3; n-propyl alcohol, 6.5; isopropyl alcohol, 6.4; n-butyl alcohol, 6.1; t-butyl alcohol, 6.5; mercury, 5.2; lead, 3.8; sulfur, 5.5; carbon tetrachloride, 5.8.

Going back to Figure 2, another way of estimating ξ is to divide the

2 H. Eyring, *J. Chem. Phys.*, **4**, 283 (1936).
3 F. H. Ree, T. Ree and H. Eyring, *Ind. Eng. Chem.*, **50**, 1036 (1958).
4 J. C. M. Li and P. Chang, *J. Chem. Phys.*, **23**, 518 (1955).

circumference of the circle passing through the centers of first neighbors by this diameter of the molecule. This gives

$$\xi = \frac{2\pi(r_1 + r_2)}{2r_2} \qquad (17)$$

When the radius of the central molecule, r_1, is the same as r_2, the radius of the neighbors, Eq. (17) gives $\xi = 2\pi$, which fortunately agrees with the value calculated from hydrodynamics for zero sliding friction as will now be shown.

9. The Stokes–Einstein Equation for Diffusion

Using the hydrodynamical methods of Stokes,[1, 2, 3] it is found that the force, F, to drag a sphere of radius r through a continuous medium of viscosity η at a velocity u is

$$F = 6\pi r \eta u \frac{\beta r + 2\eta}{\beta r + 3\eta} \qquad (1)$$

Here β is the solid friction between the sphere and the viscous medium. When β is very large

$$F = 6\pi r \eta u \qquad (2)$$

With β small

$$F = 4\pi r \eta u \qquad (3)$$

The force driving the sphere is

$$F = -\frac{\partial u}{\partial x} = -kT \frac{d \ln a}{dx} \qquad (4)$$

Following Einstein[4] we equate these two values for F and solve the resulting equation for the velocity, u, of the particles, thus obtaining

$$u = -\frac{kT}{6\pi r \eta} \frac{\beta r + 3\eta}{\beta r + 2\eta} \frac{d \ln a}{dc} \frac{dc}{dx} \qquad (5)$$

Hence the current J is

$$J = -D \frac{dc}{dx} = uc = -\frac{kT}{6\pi r \eta} \frac{\beta r + 3\eta}{\beta r + 2\eta} \frac{d \ln a}{d \ln c} \frac{dc}{dx} \qquad (6)$$

Accordingly the diffusion coefficient for spheres is

$$D = \frac{kT}{6\pi r \eta} \frac{\beta r + 3\eta}{\beta r + 2\eta} \frac{d \ln a}{d \ln c} \qquad (7)$$

[1] G. Stokes, *Cambridge Phil. Soc. Trans.*, **9**, 51 (1856).
[2] Horace Lamb, *Hydrodynamics*, 6th Ed., p. 604, Dover Publications, New York.
[3] Lars Onsager, *Ann. N.Y. Acad. Sci.*, XLVI, 241 (1945).
[4] A. Einstein, *Ann. Physik*, (4) **17**, 549 (1905).

Thus when the coefficient of sliding friction is small, Eq. (7) becomes

$$D = \frac{kT}{4\pi r \eta} \frac{d \ln a}{d \ln c} \qquad (8)$$

Equation (8) is well founded for large molecules diffusing in a medium of much smaller ones, but is not well founded for self diffusion. Nevertheless, if $2r$ in Eq. (8) be identified with $\lambda_2 \lambda_3 / \lambda_1$ in Eq. (7.16), then 2π in Eq. (8) takes the place of ξ in Eq. (7.16). According to our models ξ should have the value 6. Hence 2π was to be expected as previously pointed out in connection with Eq. (7.17). Rearranging Eq. (7.16) gives

$$\frac{kT}{(V/N)^{\frac{1}{3}} D \eta} = \xi \frac{d \ln c \, (k_1' z)_s}{d \ln a \, (k' z)_m} = \xi' \qquad (9)$$

Values of ξ' are calculated from the left side of Eq. (9); a few representative values taken from a paper by Ree et al.[5] are now listed. The values quoted are for ξ' when iodine diffuses in the following solvents: $CHBr\!=\!\!CHBr$, 5.40; $CBr_2\!=\!\!CBr_2$, 3.00; $CHCl_3$, 6.42; CCl_4, 5.69, 5.80, 5.53; ethyl acetate, 7.53; isoamylacetate, 5.96; etc. Other values are for the diffusion of $CHBr_3$ in ether, 9.13; $CHBr_3$ in acetone, 9.38; $CHBr_3$ in methanol, 8.84; $CHBr_3$ in alcohol, 7.67; $CHBr_3$ in propyl alcohol, 5.57; etc. Examples where ξ' is quite large are diffusion of water in pyrogallol, 20; water in caffein, 22.6; etc. It would be interesting to establish which factors in ξ' are responsible for these large values. In any case the kinetic interpretation of ξ' using Eq. (9) is more suggestive than is Eq. (8), the Stokes–Einstein equation.

10. Viscosity in Dense Gases and Liquids[1]

Substituting the expression for the viscosity of the solid-like structure given in Eq. (7.15) and the usual expression for the viscosity of a gas

$$\eta_g = \frac{2}{3d^2} \left(\frac{mkT}{\pi^2} \right)^{\frac{1}{2}}$$

in Eq. (7.3) gives for the viscosity of the liquid

$$\eta = \frac{V_s}{V} \frac{\lambda_1 kT6}{\lambda^2 \lambda_2 \lambda_3 k' z} + \frac{V - V_s}{V} \frac{2}{3d^2} \left(\frac{mkT}{\pi^2} \right)^{\frac{1}{2}} \qquad (1)$$

Here d is the diameter of the molecule. Our liquid model leads us to write for the rate, k', at which a molecule jumps into a neighboring position the expression:

$$k' = \kappa \frac{kT}{h} n \frac{(V - V_s)}{V_s f} \exp \left(-\frac{a' E_s V_s}{(V - V_s) RT} \right) \exp \left(-P \frac{(V - V_s)}{RT} \right) \qquad (2)$$

[5] F. H. Ree, T. Ree and H. Eyring, Ind. Eng. Chem., 50, 1036 (1958).
[1] T. S. Ree, T. Ree and H. Eyring, Proc. Natl. Acad. Sci. U.S., 48, 4, 501 (1962).

Here the partition function f is for one solid-like normal mode and has the value

$$f = \frac{1-e^{-l\theta/T}}{1-e^{-\theta/T}} + e^{-l\theta/T} \frac{(2\pi mkT)^{\frac{1}{2}}}{h} \left[\left(\frac{V_s}{N}\right)^{\frac{1}{3}} - \left(\frac{b}{4N}\right)^{\frac{1}{3}} \right] \tag{3}$$

This expression for f assumes that when the vibrational energy of an argon molecule in the liquid reaches one-third the heat of vaporization, i.e. $l\theta = E_s/3$, the degree of freedom becomes gas-like with a free volume

$$V_f = \left[\left(\frac{V_s}{N}\right)^{\frac{1}{3}} - \left(\frac{b}{4N}\right)^{\frac{1}{3}} \right] \tag{4}$$

where b is van der Waals constant which, when divided by 4, measures the hard volume of the spherical molecule. This model of a degree of freedom gives an excellent account of the thermodynamic properties of argon. Also the relations $\lambda_1 = \lambda_2 = \lambda_3 = \lambda$ and $\lambda = 2^{\frac{1}{2}}(V_s/N)^{\frac{1}{3}}$ are introduced. The last exponential term on the right of Eq. (2) has been introduced in order to take care of the effect of pressure. Pressure favors jumping of the molecule since as pressure increases the kinetic energy of molecules becomes correspondingly larger lessening by this amount the activation energy. Whenever the pressures are sufficiently high to significantly compress the solid lattices, the volume, V_s', of the solid at the melting point is corrected to give the V_s of the solid-like structure at pressure p by the equation $V_s = V_s' (1-\beta_p)$. Here β is the coefficient of compressibility for the solid. Next we suppose that the activation energy for a molecule to jump into a neighboring position, $a'E_sV_s/(V-V_s)$ is the same as the thermodynamic energy of this position. Thus we put $a = a'$, and take for the number of neighboring positions $z = 12$ and for the transmission coefficient $\kappa = 0.375$. Using the resultant η of Eq. (1) we calculate the viscosity of argon under its vapor pressure at various temperatures. We use the calculated volume, V, and pressure, p, and obtain the calculated results shown in Table 1. The experimental values are given by Zhadanova.[2]

TABLE 1. Viscosities (millipoise) of argon under its vapor pressure

T (°K)	η calc.	η obs.	Δ (%)
94.25	2.91	2.82	+ 3.2
86.90	2.60	2.56	+ 1.6
90	2.32	2.32	+ 0.0
111	1.35	1.37	− 2.2
133.5	0.81	0.77	+ 2.6
143	0.65	0.63	+ 3.2
149	0.55	0.50	+ 2.0

[2] N. F. Zhadanova, *Soviet Physics, JETP*, **4**, 749 (1957).

Zhadanova[2] measured the viscosities of argon at constant volume in both the liquid and gaseous range. The experimental data shown in Fig. 1 are hers, where the fluidity, $\phi = \eta^{-1}$, is plotted against temperature.

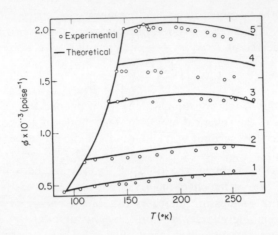

Figure 1. Fluidities (poise⁻¹) of argon at constant volume versus temperatures (°K). Curve 1 at $V = 29.660$ cm³; curve 2 at $V = 33.416$ cm³; curve 3 at $V = 40.59$ cm³; curve 4 at $V = 46.48$ cm³; curve 5 at $V = 52.78$ cm³. (Ree, Ree and Eyring, *Proc. Natl. Acad. Sci. U.S.*, **48**, 501 (1962).)

Curves 1 to 5 are the values calculated from Eq. (1). The nearly vertical curve on the left is a plot of the values in Table 1. This curve shows the fluidities of argon under its vapor pressure at various temperatures from near the boiling point to near the critical point. The agreement with experiment is quite good over the whole range.

Bulk viscosity shows up as a delay in the adjustment of the volume to a change in pressure. When an external pressure is applied, the number of holes decreases to the equilibrium number for this pressure. If holes disappeared by diffusion to the surface the rate would depend on the volume. This is not true.[3] Holes must disappear by neighboring molecules rearranging to change the hole into a rarefied volume in the lattice, a phonon, which then moves with the velocity of sound to the surface. The generation of holes in the liquid is by the reverse of this mechanism. The biased diffusion of molecules into the hole in bulk viscosity has the same activation energy as shear viscosity and diffusion but a different entropy. This theory has been developed for ordinary liquids and for high poly-

[3] W. Kauzmann, *Chem. Rev. (Japan)*, **43**, 219 (1948).

mers.[4, 5] Although the theory as developed assumed holes of less than molecular size, a development in terms of vacancies involves little more than reinterpretation of the parameters in the theory. A choice between a vacancy theory of liquids and a theory of holes of less than molecular size rests on the naturalness of the explanation of the parameters. The choice seems to lie with the vacancy model.

11. Non-Newtonian Viscosity

Returning to Eq. (7.5) the rate of shear is found to be

$$\dot{s} = \sum_{i=1}^{z/2} \frac{\lambda}{\lambda_1} k' \cos \theta_i (e^{f \lambda_2 \lambda_3 \lambda \cos \theta_i / 2kT} - e^{-f \lambda_2 \lambda_3 \lambda \cos \theta_i / 2kT}) \tag{1}$$

By summing and taking a mean value for $\cos \theta_i$ this becomes:

$$\dot{s} = \frac{z \lambda k'}{\lambda_1} \langle \cos \theta_i \rangle \left(\frac{e^{f \lambda_2 \lambda_3 \lambda \langle \cos \theta_i \rangle / 2kT} - e^{-f \lambda_2 \lambda_3 \lambda \langle \cos \theta_i \rangle / 2kT}}{2} \right) \tag{2}$$

Introducing the definitions

$$\beta^{-1} = \frac{z \lambda k' \langle \cos \theta_i \rangle}{\lambda_1} \tag{3}$$

and

$$\alpha = \frac{\lambda_2 \lambda_3 \lambda \langle \cos \theta_i \rangle}{2kT} \tag{4}$$

Eq. (2) becomes

$$\dot{s} = \beta^{-1} \sinh \alpha f \tag{5}$$

or

$$f = \frac{1}{\alpha} \sinh^{-1} (\beta \dot{s}) \tag{6}$$

Here β^{-1} is the mean rate of shear per second in the forward and backward directions of a flowing unit and may be called the intrinsic rate of shear. Thus β, aside from the shear factor, which is near unity, is a relaxation time. α^{-1} has the dimensions of stress and may be regarded as an intrinsic stress characterizing the flow unit. Substituting Eq. (6) into Eq. (8.2) gives:[1]

[4] N. Hirai and H. Eyring, *J. Appl. Phys.*, **29**, 5, 810 (1958).
[5] N. Hirai and H. Eyring, *J. Polymer Sci.*, XXXVII, 51 (1959).
[1] T. Ree and H. Eyring, *Rheology*, II, ed. F. R. Eirich, Academic Press, New York, 1958, p. 83.

$$\eta = \sum_i \frac{x_i f_i}{\dot{s}} = \sum_i \frac{x_i \beta_i}{\alpha_i} \frac{\sinh^{-1}(\beta_i \dot{s})}{(\beta_i \dot{s})}$$

$$= \sum_i x_i \eta_i \frac{\sinh^{-1}(\beta_i \dot{s})}{\beta_i \dot{s}} \tag{7}$$

The factor $(\sinh^{-1} \beta_i \dot{s})/\beta_i \dot{s}$ is unity for small values of the dimension-less argument $\beta_i \dot{s}$ and zero for large values. Thus the viscosities, η_i, of the various types of flow units weighted by the fractional area of the shear plane, x_i, which they cover add up to give the limiting viscosity at zero rate of shear. Each contribution to the viscosity falls off toward zero as a function of $\beta_i \dot{s}$ in the same characteristic way. Thus the viscosity is a simple concept only in the Newtonian range, i.e. for low values of $\beta_i \dot{s}$. In the non-Newtonian range the intrinsic rates of shear β_i^{-1}, the intrinsic stress α^{-1}, and the fractional area x_i covered by flow units of kind i are the properties which characterize a system rather than the viscosity. In Figures 1 and 2 some experimental data obtained by Philippoff[2] are compared with theory. The parameters used are given in Table 1.

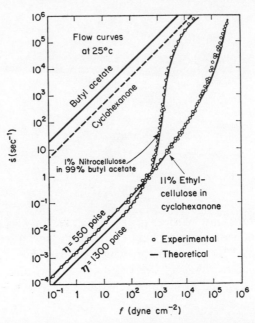

Figure 1. Flow curves for 1% nitrocellulose in 99% butyl acetate and 11% ethylcellulose in cyclohexanone. Flow curves for solvents are shown by the straight lines of 45° slope. (From Ree, Ree and Eyring, *Ind. Eng. Chem.*, **50**, 1036 (1958).)

[2] W. Philippoff, *Report of Symposium VII*, p. 21, Army Chemical Center, Maryland.

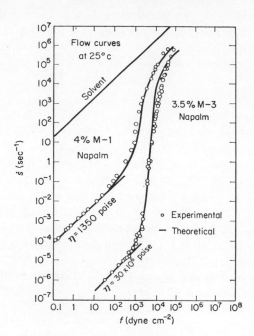

Figure 2. Flow curves for 4% M-1 and 3.5% M-3 napalm. The flow curve for the solvent is shown by the straight line of 45° slope. (From Ree, Ree and Eyring, *Ind. Eng. Chem.*, **50,** 1036 (1958).)

TABLE 1. Parametric values for non-Newtonian flow curves at 25°c

Flow system	$x_1\beta_1/\alpha_1$ (poise)	x_1/α_1 (dyne/ cm²)	β_1 (sec)	x_2/α_2 (dyne/ cm²)	β_2 (sec)
1% Nitrocellulose in 99% butyl acetate	3×10^{-2}	—	—	179.3	7.25
4% M-1 napalm[a]	0.1	—	—	235	5.75
3.5% M-3 napalm[a]	0.2	—	—	434	6.70×10^4
11% Ethylcellulose in cyclohexanone	—	4.0×10^4	1×10^{-3}	1000	0.50

[a] Mixture of aluminum soap in hydrocarbon solvents.

If there are structures which are changed by flow and which do not recover by the time the flowing unit flows again, they are said to be thixotropic if flow increases fluidity and dilatant if flow decreases fluidity. Typical examples have been discussed.[3] Plastic flow also exhibits characteristic relaxations.[4]

12. The Viscosity of High Polymers

A high polymer flows by forward and backward movement of its 'kinetic segments' which shift into suitable vacancies as the vacancies arise.[1] This motion is biased, by the shear stress, toward movement in the direction which relieves the stress, and a segment can only move when the sections to which it is attached are so situated as to permit the motion. In concentrated high polymer solutions[2] or in the pure high polymer itself, there will be $n_2 - 1$ tangling points where other molecules loop around the flowing molecule forcing it to circle (slalom) around these tangling points. Thus a high polymer may be characterized by its n_1 kinetic segments and its n_2 tangling segments. It is now of interest to see how the intrinsic stress, α^{-1}, and the intrinsic shear rate, β^{-1}, given by Eqs. (9.3) and (9.4) respectively, for the polymer differ from the value for the kinetic segment if it were unattached. It is also interesting to see how the limiting viscosity $\eta = \beta/\alpha$ at low shear rates differs for a polymer, as compared with an unattached kinetic segment. We shall indicate properties for the polymer and unattached kinetic segments by the subscripts p and s, respectively. Since $\lambda_2 \lambda_3$ of a kinetic segment is not changed by linking segments together we have

$$(\lambda_2 \lambda_3)_p = (\lambda_2 \lambda_3)_s \tag{1}$$

Because the distance between the centers of gravity of polymer molecules goes up with the cube root of the volume

$$(\lambda_1)_p = n_1^{\frac{1}{3}}(\lambda_1)_s \tag{2}$$

Since the center of gravity is displaced each time any segment jumps, the rate of displacement for the center of gravity of the polymer is n_1 times $(k')_s$

$$(k')_p = n_1(k')_s \tag{3}$$

Whereas the jump of a segment displaces the segment by a length $(\lambda)_s$, it

---

[3] S. J. Hahn, T. Ree and H. Eyring, *Ind. Eng. Chem.*, **51**, 856 (1959).

[4] F. H. Ree, T. Ree and H. Eyring, *Proc. Am. Soc. Civil Engrs*, Jan. 1960. #2333-EM 1.

[1] W. Kauzmann and H. Eyring, *J. Am. Chem. Soc.*, **62**, 3113 (1940).

[2] H. Eyring, T. Ree and N. Hirai, *Proc. Natl. Acad. Sci. U.S.*, **44**, 1213 (1958).

displaces the center of gravity of the polymer on the average by only the distance

$$\lambda_p = \frac{(\lambda)_s}{n_1 n_2} \tag{4}$$

The factor n_1^{-1} arises because a displacement of a single segment displaces the center of gravity of n_1 segments by only $1/n_1$ times the distance a single segment is displaced. The factor $1/n_2$ comes from the fact that only one tangling segment can move independently to advance the center of gravity in the shear direction, since the other tangling segments are then obliged to follow around the randomly located tangling points, so that their displacements cancel out, on the average, with respect to any effect they might have of advancing the center of gravity along the shear surface. There is no effect on the mean value of $\cos \theta_i$, where θ_i is the angle of displacement with respect to shear, i.e. $\langle \cos \theta_i \rangle$ is unchanged. Linking a lot of kinetic segments up into a polymer will change the number, z, of direction a segment can jump into a value, z', which will remain constant for the interior segments of a polymer with changing length. Substituting our results into α and β as given by Eqs. (10.3) and (10.4) gives:

$$(\beta^{-1})_p = z' \frac{(\lambda)_s}{n_1 n_2} \frac{n_1 (k')_s \langle \cos \theta_i \rangle}{n_1^{\frac{1}{3}} (\lambda_1)_s} = \frac{z'}{z} (\beta^{-1})_s \frac{1}{n_2 n_1^{\frac{1}{3}}} \tag{5}$$

$$(\alpha)_p = \frac{(\lambda_2 \lambda_3)_s (\lambda)_s \langle \cos \theta_i \rangle}{n_1 n_2 2kT} = \frac{(\alpha)_s}{n_1 n_2} \tag{6}$$

Thus

$$(\eta)_p = \frac{(\beta)_p}{(\alpha)_p} \frac{\sinh^{-1} (\beta)_p \dot{s}}{(\beta)_p \dot{s}} = \frac{z}{z'} \frac{(\beta)_s}{(\alpha)_s} n_2^2 n_1^{\frac{4}{3}} \frac{\sinh^{-1} (\beta)_p \dot{s}}{(\beta)_p \dot{s}} \tag{7}$$

In the Newtonian range of not too high rates of shear, this becomes:

$$(\eta)_p = \frac{z}{z'} \frac{(\beta)_s}{(\alpha)_s} \left(\frac{M}{m_2}\right)^2 \left(\frac{M}{m_1}\right)^{\frac{4}{3}} = \left(\frac{z}{z'} \frac{(\beta)_s}{(\alpha)_s m_2^2 m_1^{\frac{4}{3}}}\right) M^{\frac{10}{3}} \tag{8}$$

Here M, m_1, and m_2 are the molecular weights of the polymer, the kinetic segment, and the tangling segment respectively. Thus $n_1 = M/m_1$ and $n_2 = M/m_2$. Accordingly, we see that the viscosity of a high polymeric system is proportional to $M^{\frac{10}{3}}$ if the molecular weight, M, is larger than a critical value m_2, whereas the viscosity is proportional to $M^{\frac{4}{3}}$ for shorter unentangled molecules. By reviewing many experimental results, Fox, Gratch, and Loschaek[3] showed that in the high-molecular-weight region viscosity is proportional to $M^{3.4}$ while in the low-molecular region

[3] T. G. Fox, S. Gratch and S. Loschaek, *Rheology*, ed. F. R. Eirich, Academic Press, New York, **1**, 43, 1946.

viscosity is proportional to M^x, where x varies between 0.84 and 1.76. Bueche[4] explained the dependence of viscosity on molecular weight theoretically. According to his theory, the viscosities in the two regions are proportional to $M^{3.5}$ and M, respectively.

The curve of $\log_{10} \eta$ vs. $\log_{10} M$ for polydimethyl siloxane is shown in Figure 1.[2]

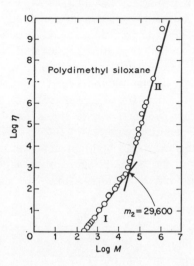

Figure 1. The curve of $\log \eta$ versus $\log M$ for polydimethyl siloxane. (From Eyring, Ree and Hirai, *Proc. Natl. Acad. Sci. U.S.*, **44**, 1213 (1958).)

In the figure, two straight lines cross at a point at which the molecular weight is m_2. The straight line II is for the equation:

$$\log \eta = \log \frac{\eta_1}{m_1^{\frac{4}{3}} m_2^2} + \tfrac{10}{3} \log M \tag{9}$$

and straight line I is for the equation:

$$\log \eta = \log \frac{\eta_1}{m_1^{\frac{4}{3}}} + \tfrac{4}{3} \log M \tag{10}$$

The test of the theory is made by comparing the slopes s_2 and s_1 of the two straight lines in the regions $M \geqslant m_2$ and $M \leqslant m_2$ with the theoretically expected slopes $\tfrac{10}{3}$ and $\tfrac{4}{3}$. In Table 1, s_1 and s_2 are listed for many cases. The investigators are listed in the paper by Eyring et al.[2]

4 F. Bueche, *J. Chem. Phys.*, **25** (1956); *J. Appl. Phys.*, **26**, 738 (1955).

TABLE 1. Effect of molecular weight on viscosity of high polymers

	s_1	s_2	$-A^b$	$-B^c$	log m_2 calc.	log m_2 obs.	Temperature (°C)
Polyisobutylene	1.75	3.40	13.7	6.30	3.70	4.29	217
Polystyrene	1.58	3.44	13.6	5.03	4.29	4.68	217
Polydimethyl siloxane	1.34	3.70	15.7	5.14	5.28	4.71	25
Polymethyl methacrylate[a]	1.4	3.4	14.2	5.50	4.35	4.20	60
Polydecamethylene adipate	1.34	3.40	12.1	4.47	3.82	3.68	109
Polydecamethylene sepacate	1.23	3.23	11.4	4.17	3.62	3.67	109
Polydiethylene adipate	1.26	2.92	10.0	4.11	2.95	3.56	109
Poly (ε-capcolactam)							
Linear chain	1.66	3.52	12.8	5.79	3.52	3.78	253
Dichain	1.70	3.50	12.5	5.80	3.35	3.72	253
Tetrachain	1.31	3.24	11.8	4.29	3.76	3.79	253
Octachain	1.31	3.24	12.7	4.75	3.93	4.09	253

[a] 25% solution in diethyl phthalate. [b] $A \equiv -\log(\eta_1/m_1^{\frac{1}{4}} m_2^2)$. [c] $B \equiv -\log(\eta_1/M_1^{\frac{1}{4}})$.

13. Potentials across Membranes and at Interfaces

Equation (5.13) gives the material current across a membrane or an interface for a particular ion. By multiplying by the valence z_i and changing to activities in moles per cm³ and E in volts we have for the current I_i the expression:

$$I_i - \mathscr{F}\frac{P_i^0}{\gamma_i} z_i(a_{0i} e^{-z_i \mathscr{F}E/2RT} - a_{ni} e^{z_i \mathscr{F}E/2RT})$$

$$\equiv P_i(a_{0i}z_i e^{-z_i \mathscr{F}E/2RT} - a_{ni}z_i e^{z_i \mathscr{F}E/2RT}) \tag{1}$$

Here $P_i = \mathscr{F}P_i^0/\gamma_i$ and $\mathscr{F}$ is the Faraday, i.e. 96,500 coulombs if I is measured in amperes per cm, whereas $\mathscr{F}$ is 23,060 calories in the exponents when R is taken as 2 calories. P_i^0 is the permeability at the standard state where the activity coefficient γ_i is taken as unity. Now the total current I is the sum of the currents for all ions, plus the current charging the condenser. Thus

$$I = \sum_i I_i + \frac{d(CE)}{dt}$$

$$= \sum_i P_i(a_{0i}z_i e^{-z_i 23,060E/2RT} - a_{ni}z_i e^{z_i 23,060E/2RT}) + \frac{d(CE)}{dt} \tag{2}$$

In the last term C is the capacitance per cm² of the interface. If the charging current $d(CE)/dt \approx 0$ and $I = 0$ because of an open circuit, we have the situation existing in the smelting of metals which proceeds by an electrolytic process.

In the smelting process molten iron at temperatures around 1500°c is overlain by a second phase, liquid slag, whose chief constituents are SiO_2, CaO, and Al_2O_3. Ions diffuse across the interface into the metal where they are neutralized by picking up electrons or releasing them as the case may be. At the interface an excess or deficiency of electrons on the metal attracts a cloud of charge of opposite sign in the slag. The resulting electrical potential across the barrier lying at the interface speeds up or slows down the diffusion of each ion across the interface in accordance with the charge it carries. It is unlikely that the potential acts exactly symmetrically across the interfacial potential barrier for each ion, but lacking information with which to make a better estimate we shall assume so.

The rate equations for diffusion of individual ionic species may thus be written:

$$-\dot{n}_{Fe,\,m} = \dot{n}_{Fe,\,s} = k_{Fe}a_{Fe,\,m}\exp\left\{-\tfrac{2}{2}E\mathscr{F}/RT\right\} - k_{Fe}a_{Fe,\,s}\exp\left\{\tfrac{2}{2}E\mathscr{F}/RT\right\} \quad (3)$$

$$\dot{n}_{Si,\,s} = k_{Si}a_{Si,\,m}\exp\left\{-\tfrac{4}{2}E\mathscr{F}/RT\right\} - k_{Si}a_{Si,\,s}\exp\left\{\tfrac{4}{2}E\mathscr{F}/RT\right\} \quad (4)$$

$$-\dot{n}_{O,\,s} = \dot{n}_{CO} = k_{O}a_{O,\,s}\exp\left\{-\tfrac{2}{2}E\mathscr{F}/RT\right\} \quad (5)$$

$$\dot{n}_{S,\,s} = k_{S}a_{S,\,m}\exp\left\{\tfrac{2}{2}E\mathscr{F}/RT\right\} - k_{S}a_{S,\,s}\exp\left\{-\tfrac{2}{2}E\mathscr{F}/RT\right\} \quad (6)$$

E is the charge on the slag minus the charge on the metal side of the interface. The suffix m denotes quantities which are related to the melt and suffix s is for the slag. For example $a_{Si,\,m}$ indicates the activity of silicon ion in the melt.

In some illuminating experiments King and Ramachandran[1] measured simultaneously the amount of iron, silicon, and sulfur transferred between phases and the amount of CO evolved at each instant. Their results can all be quantitatively explained in terms of an electrochemical theory of ion migration.

Since the voltage difference between metal and slag was not measured it must be evaluated from experiment. Equation (5) for the rate of evolution of CO considers only the migration of oxide ion from slag to metal, where it combines with carbon and is evolved as CO, and neglects any back reaction. Since the concentration of oxide ion in the slag is large and so does not vary with time the rate of evolution of CO is an exponential measure of the potential in accord with Eq. (5), and so $\dot{n}_{CO}/k_{O}a_{O,\,s}$ can be substituted in Eqs. (3), (4), and (6) to replace the potential-dependent terms. Further, in King and Ramachandran's experiments the silicon

[1] T. B. King and S. Ramachandran, *Phys. Chem. of Steelmaking*, p. 125, ed. T. B. Elliott, Tech. Press, Cambridge, Mass., and Wiley, New York, 1958.

concentration in the slag is constant and there is zero initial concentration of iron and sulfur in the slag. Consequently

$$\frac{da_{Fe,s}}{dt} = A\dot{n}_{CO} - Ba_{Fe,s}(\dot{n}_{CO})^{-1} \tag{7}$$

$$\frac{dAa_{Si,s}}{dt} = C(a_{0,Si} - \Delta a_{Si,s})(\dot{n}_{CO})^2 - D(\dot{n}_{CO})^{-2} \tag{8}$$

Here A, B, C, and D are constants and $a_{0,Si}$ is the initial concentration of silicon in the molten metal. Integrating these equations yields

$$a_{Fe,s} = \exp\left\{-\int_0^t B(\dot{n}_{CO})^{-1}\,dt\right\}\int_0^t A\dot{n}_{CO}\exp\left\{\int_0^t B(\dot{n}_{CO})^{-1}\,dt\right\}dt \tag{9}$$

$$a_{Si,s} = \exp\left\{-\int_0^t C(\dot{n}_{CO})^2\,dt\right\}\int_0^t Ca_{0,Si}(\dot{n}_{CO})^2$$

$$-D(\dot{n}_{CO})^{-2}\exp\left\{\int_0^t C(\dot{n}_{CO})^2\,dt\right\}dt \tag{10}$$

Thus a knowledge of the rate of evolution of CO at any time enables us to calculate the amount of all the other substances. Figure 1 shows the fit between theory and experiment.

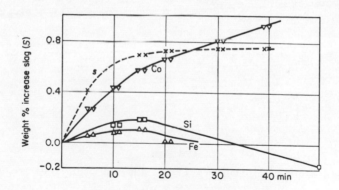

Figure 1. Weight percentage increase of sulfur, silicon, and iron in the slag, and of carbon monoxide evolved at 1505°c. Slag composition in per cent: CaO, 48; Al$_2$O$_3$, 21; and SiO$_2$, 31. Diffusion rates: $\dot{n}_{Si} = 9.5(\dot{n}_{CO})^2 - 2.6(\dot{n}_{CO})^{-2} \times 10^{-6}$; $\dot{n}_{Fe} = 0.28\dot{n}_{CO} - 0.003\dot{n}_{Fe}(n_{CO})^{-1}$. $(S_{init}) = 0.1\%$. (X. De Hemptinne, H. Eyring and T. Ree, *Physical Chemistry of Process Metallurgy*, St. Pierre, Ed., Part I, Vol. VII, Interscience, New York, 1961, p. 65.)

It is interesting that smelting, like the reverse process, corrosion, proceeds by an electrochemical mechanism.

14. Electrode Depolarization by Diffusion

An alternative way of writing Eq. (5.3) is

$$J = \frac{\lambda(a_0 - a_n)}{\dfrac{1}{k_0''} + \dfrac{1}{k_1''} + \ldots + \dfrac{1}{k_{n-1}''}} \tag{1}$$

Here k_i'' is the specific rate of going from the zeroth minimum over the ith barrier if the other barriers were absent. Inspection of Eq. (5.3) shows that if the rate of passage over a barrier is thought of as a conductance its reciprocal is a resistance and the series of resistances add in the denominator of Eq. (1) as would be expected. Mechanisms proceeding along parallel paths add their specific rates just as parallel conductances add in electric circuits.

If the envelope of the barriers of the specific rates in Eq. (1) is two straight lines crossing at a highest barrier, corresponding to the minimum rate k_m'', Eq. (1) becomes

$$J = \frac{k_m'' \lambda}{n}(a_0 - a_n) \tag{2}$$

Here n is the number of barriers lying within an energy kT down from the top, counting the highest barrier, providing the distance between successive barriers is small compared to kT. When the difference between free energies for successive barriers is fkT, f not necessarily small, and the last barrier on either side of the highest is lower by $(n-1)fkT$, then we have for the effective rate

$$k = (k_0''^{-1} + k''^{-1} + \ldots k_{m-1}''^{-1})^{-1} = \frac{k_m}{1 + 2(e^{-f} + \ldots e^{-(n-1)f})} \tag{3}$$

$$= \frac{k_m}{2\left(\dfrac{1 - e^{-nf}}{1 - e^{-f}}\right) - 1} = k_m \frac{1 - e^{-f}}{1 + e^{-f} - 2e^{-nf}}$$

When $f = 1$ and n is large enough so that $e^{-nf} \ll 1$ we have

$$k = 0{\cdot}46 k_m \tag{4}$$

Equation (3) applies also when the k''''s are the rate of jumping into successive quantum states in the passage over a single barrier. In this case it represents the small but interesting non-equilibrium correction to reaction rate theory.[1, 2] Let us return now to Eq. (2). The resistance offered by any other arrangement of barriers is readily calculated. If the species passing over the barriers are ions, charge may accumulate in such a way as to lower one or more high barriers with more or less effect on the others. The resistance for the ions is then that offered by these lowered barriers.[3]

[1] E. W. Montroll and K. E. Shuler, *Advan. Chem. Phys.*, **1**, 361 (1958).
[2] F. H. Ree, T. S. Ree, T. Ree and H. Eyring, *ibid.*, **4** (1962).
[3] T. N. Andersen and H. Eyring, *J. Phys. Chem.*, **67** 92 (1963).

In an interesting series of experiments, hydrogen was electrolyzed from oxidizing solutions onto a platinum electrode after which the circuit was opened and the decay of potential observed by comparison with a standard calomel electrode. In a first stage, the polarized electrode potential increases positively faster than it can be followed, reaching a potential characteristic of one atmosphere of hydrogen. In stage two, the potential rises linearly until hydrogen on the electrode is depleted to the point where it no longer controls the potential. In stage three, the potential rises more steeply as the oxidizing agent is reduced, finally leveling off at the characteristic potential of the oxidation–reduction couple.

The mechanistic interpretation is interesting. In stage one, excess hydrogen above one atmosphere pressure boils off the electrode until hydrogen drops to atmospheric pressure. In stage two, some oxidizing agents such as $K_2Cr_2O_7$, $KMnO_4$, $Ce(SO_4)$, $Fe_2(SO_4)_3$ or $Fe(NO_3)_3$, or $K_3Fe(CN)_6$ are reduced as fast as they reach the hydrogen on the electrode. Since there is constant stirring the oxidizer diffuses through a layer of thickness S at a constant rate.

Since the potential at the electrode is proportional to the amount of hydrogen adsorbed in a polarized layer on the electrode surface and since this disappears at a linear rate the potential rises linearly with time.

In stage three, the voltage ceases to be determined by adsorbed hydrogen and becomes increasingly governed by the oxidation–reduction couple until it finally reaches a value characteristic of the couple. The detailed evidence and calculations are presented elsewhere.[1] Again, a successful interpretation involves considering the elementary process for diffusion between and reaction in a succession of pools assumed to be at equilibrium.

15. Sticking Coefficients at Surfaces

When a molecule of vapor strikes its own liquid surface it becomes a surface molecule but the molecule immediately beneath is changed from a surface molecule into a bulk molecule. The overall reaction thus corresponds to one vapor molecule changing into a bulk molecule with no change in the number of surface molecules. The number of successful collisions per second with a square centimeter of surface is $\dot{n}$ and according to absolute rate theory it has the value:

$$\dot{n} = \frac{\kappa \dfrac{kT}{h} \dfrac{(2\pi m kT)}{h^2} f_r^{\ddagger} f_v^{\ddagger} e^{-E_0/kT}}{\dfrac{(2\pi m kT)^{\frac{3}{2}}}{h^3} f_{rg} f_v} C$$

$$= \kappa \frac{P}{(2\pi m kT)^{\frac{1}{2}} f_{rg}} f_r^{\ddagger} e^{-E_0/kT} \tag{1}$$

To obtain Eq. (1), the perfect gas law $CkT = P$ has been used, where C is the number of molecules per cm^3. The vibrational partition functions are not changed significantly by condensation and thus $f_v^\ddagger/f_v = 1$. The activation energy at absolute zero, E_0, for a molecule to stick upon collision with its own liquid surface is apparently negligible. Also the energy along the reaction coordinate is usually dissipated upon collision so that $\kappa \approx 1$. The rotational partition function $f_r^\ddagger$ of the activated complex closely approaches f_{rl} the rotational partition function of the bulk liquid. f_{rg} is the rotational partition function of the gas. Thus the number of molecules sticking on one cm^3 of surface per second is

$$\dot{n} = \frac{P}{(2\pi mkT)^{\frac{1}{2}}} \frac{f_{rl}}{f_{rg}} \tag{2}$$

The factor $P/(2\pi mkT)^{\frac{1}{2}}$ is the number of collisions per second per square centimeter. The fraction which sticks

$$s = f_{rl}/f_{rg} \tag{3}$$

is called the sticking coefficient.

Previously[1] s has been treated as a factor in the transmission coefficient. The present procedure is equivalent. The free-angle ratio, δ, has been defined as

$$\delta = f_{rl}/f_{rg} \tag{4}$$

The free-angle ratio was measured by the excess entropy of vaporization over that for normal liquids by Kincaid and Eyring[2] and is listed as δ_1 in column 4 of Table 1. The use of reduced temperatures to determine corresponding states of two liquids leads to δ_2 in column 5.

Hildebrand's comparison of entropies of vaporization of the liquid in question with a normal liquid at equal vapor concentrations yields δ_3 in column 6, and Pitzer's comparison of entropies of vaporization at the same ratio of liquid volume to vapor volume yields δ_4 for the free-angle ratio as listed in column 7. In column 8 the available experimental values are given. Columns 1, 2, and 3 specify the particular liquid considered, the critical temperature of the liquid and the temperatures, respectively. A value of a calculated free-angle ratio δ_i greater than unity reflects a difficulty with the estimation of δ_i.

In spite of the irregularities the sticking coefficient correlates very well with the free-angle ratio as was remarked by Wyllie.[3]

Boudart[4] carefully measured the sticking coefficient for glycerine and found that it correlated with the free-angle ratio, supporting Eq. (2).

[1] E. M. Mortensen and H. Eyring, *J. Phys. Chem.*, **64**, 846 (1960).
[2] J. F. Kincaid and H. Eyring, *J. Chem. Phys.*, **6**, 620 (1938).
[3] G. Wyllie, *Proc. Roy. Soc. (London)*, **A197**, 383 (1949).
[4] W. J. Heideger and M. Boudart, *Chem. Eng. Sci.*, **17**, 1 (1962).

TABLE 1. Comparison of free-angle ratios

Molecule	T_c (°K)	t (°C)	δ_1 (K & E)	δ_2 (Tr)	δ_3 (H)	δ_4 (P)	Obs.[a]
CCl_4	556.31	0	1.02	1.00	1.00	1.00	1(0)[b, c, d, e, f]
		50	1.31	1.00	1.00	1.00	
C_6H_6	561.7	0	0.86	0.70	0.74	1.42	0.85–0.95(6)
		50	1.14	0.77	0.79	0.82	
$CHCl_3$	536	0	0.26	0.25	0.20	0.22	0.16(2)[f]
		50	0.99	0.59	0.58	0.66	
CH_3I	528	0	0.37	0.31	0.21	0.32	
		40	1.25	0.84	0.57	0.77	
CH_3OH	513.4	0	0.034	0.078	0.14	0.20	0.045(0)[f]
		50	0.048	0.20	0.21	0.17	
C_2H_5OH	516.3	0	0.019	0.021	0.053	0.064	0.024(13)[g]
		50	0.028	0.024	0.047	0.061	0.036(0)[e]
H_2O	647.31	0	0.022	0.11	0.099	0.17	0.036(15)[h]
		100	0.17	0.11	0.067	0.17	0.02(100)[d]
CH_3COCH_3	508.2	0	0.16	0.10	0.13	0.15	
		50	0.54	0.30	0.35	0.42	
Cyclo-C_6H_{12}	553.9	10	0.69	0.74	0.82	0.78	
		80	1.55	0.97	1.09	1.02	
n-C_6H_{14}	507.9	0	0.57	0.57	0.84	0.70	
		50	0.99	0.65	1.01	0.86	
n-C_7H_{16}	540.17	0	0.23	0.32	0.65	0.54	
		50	0.36	0.45	0.83	0.65	
$C_6H_5CH_3$	594.0	0	0.60	0.59	0.74	0.71	
		50	0.91	0.67	0.85	0.80	
n-C_3H_7OH	536.9	0	0.008	0.007	0.028	0.024	0.037[f]
		100	0.050	0.030	0.051	0.059	

[a] A number in parentheses in the last column is the temperature (°C) at which the condensation coefficient was measured. [b] T. Alty and F. H. Nicoll, *Can. J. Research*, **4**, 547 (1931). [c] T. Alty, *Phil. Mag.*, **15**, 82 (1933). [d] W. Pruger, *Z. Physik*, **115**, 202 (1940). [e] L. von Bogdandy, H. C. Kleist and O. Knake, *Z. Electrochem.*, **59**, 460 (1955). [f] M. Baranaev, *J. Phys. Chem. (U.S.S.R.)*, **13**, 1035 (1939). [g] H. Bucka, *Z. Physik. Chem.*, **195**, 260 (1950). [h] T. Alty and C. A. Mackay, *Proc. Roy. Soc. (London)*, **A149**, 104 (1935).

When nitrogen gas strikes a tungsten wire a large proportion of the molecules are adsorbed at the first collision by weak physical forces. After physical adsorption there is competition between revaporization and at least two types of chemisorption. Interesting experiments of this type by Ehrlich[5] have been examined by absolute rate theory.[6] Cyclopentane when it collides with a platinum catalyst in the presence of deuterium has comparable probabilities of exchanging any number from one to five of the hydrogens on one side of the plane. The probability of exchanging the sixth hydrogen on the opposite face of the cyclohexane is small with the

[5] G. Ehrlich and F. G. Hudda, *J. Chem. Phys.*, **35**, 1421 (1961).
[6] F. J. Wanlass, Ph.D. Thesis, University of Utah, 1962.

probability rising to a considerably larger value that ten hydrogens will be exchanged. A wide variety of exchange reactions and racemizations give insight into the complexity of surface reactions as reported by Burwell.[7]

Evaporations and condensations are also interesting for the light they shed on unimolecular and association reactions, respectively. A careful study of a variety of free radical associations indicates that they follow closely equilibrium kinetics when a suitable, loose activated complex is considered.[8]

The thermal ionization of xenon studied by Johnston and Kornegay[9] is an interesting bimolecular reaction since the activation energy approximates the excitation energy rather than the ionization potential. This can be understood if the potential curve for collision of an excited xenon with a normal atom crosses the potential curve for the two unexcited atoms at about the excitation energy and if the probability of transfer between these two potential curves is small enough for a xenon once excited to be more likely to ionize than to revert to a normal atom by either collision or emission.

16. The Quasi-equilibrium Theory of Unimolecular Reactions

The theory of absolute reaction rates as it was originally formulated[1] applies to processes taking place at constant temperature and yields a reaction rate constant that is an average over a thermal distribution of energies of the reactant molecules. This theory presumes the reaction to be taking place on a given potential surface in configuration space so that the entire course of the reaction can be described by the motion of a mass point on this surface. Many situations arise, however, for which the distribution of energy in the reactant molecules is far from thermal equilibrium. For such unimolecular decompositions of isolated systems having a large but finite number of degrees of freedom a specific rate constant for decomposition has been derived[2,3] that can be averaged over a non-thermal distribution in the reactants.

The behavior of an isolated molecule of fixed total energy is describable in terms of a microcanonical ensemble, i.e. an assembly of systems at equilibrium with energies lying between E and $E+dE$. It is assumed that the systems of the assembly have nuclear configurations corresponding to the chemical structure of the molecule undergoing unimolecular de-

7 R. L. Burwell, Jr., *Chem. Rev.*, **57**, 895 (1957).
8 T. S. Ree, T. Ree and H. Eyring, *J. Chem. Phys.*, **36**, 1, 281 (1962).
9 H. S. Johnston and Wade Kornegay, *Trans. Faraday Soc.*, **57**, 1563 (1961).
1 H. Eyring, *J. Chem. Phys.*, **3**, 107 (1935).
2 H. M. Rosenstock, Ph.D. Thesis, University of Utah, 1952.
3 H. M. Rosenstock, M. B. Wallenstein, A. L. Wahrhaftig and H. Eyring, *Proc. Natl. Acad. Sci. U.S.*, **38**, 667 (1952).

composition and that these systems are uniformly distributed throughout the region of phase space corresponding to the above mentioned energy range. In order for the assumption of a uniform distribution of systems over the accessible states to be valid, transitions of the reactant systems between the accessible states must be rapid enough so that decomposition reactions do not appreciably disturb the distribution. The mechanism for this 'randomization of energy' in the particular case of a propane molecule-ion is the occurrence of many rapid radiationless electronic transitions at the intersections or 'crossings' of the potential surfaces of the accessible excited vibronic states of the ion. An extended discussion of this mechanism will be given later; for the present, it will be sufficient to note simply that the unimolecular decomposition is actually taking place on a 'parking terrace'[4] of many potential surfaces so that an average 'reaction coordinate' and 'activated complex' must be postulated to describe the reaction. It is also apparent that the validity of this treatment is restricted to a broad range of intermediate energies of the reactants. Near the threshold for decomposition, quantum restrictions on energy transfer between vibrational degrees of freedom interfere, while at extremely high energies there is insufficient time for energy transfer before decomposition occurs. Where energy randomization does take place, a quasi-equilibrium distribution of occupied energy states exists and the rate theory derived for such a case can be termed a quasi-equilibrium theory.

The fraction of the systems in states corresponding to reaction is given by the ratio of the number of such states to the total number of states. Since the number of accessible states lying in the energy range E to $E+dE$ is large, the distribution can be represented by a density function $\rho(E)\,dE$. The states corresponding to the activated complex are defined as those with total energy between E and $E+dE$ which also have potential energy or, if you prefer, activation energy ε_0 and kinetic energy ε_t localized in the reaction coordinate. Necessarily, the total energy E must be greater than or equal to the sum $\varepsilon_0 + \varepsilon_t$. It is possible to denote the distribution of activated complex states simply by the density function $\rho^{\ddagger}(E_t, \varepsilon_0, \varepsilon_t)\,dE$. It will be convenient to use an additional density function $\rho_t(\varepsilon_t)\,d\varepsilon_t$ for the states with kinetic energy in the reaction coordinate between ε_t and $\varepsilon_t+d\varepsilon_t$. The complete density function for the activated complex is therefore $\rho^{\ddagger}(E, \varepsilon_0, \varepsilon_t)\,\rho_t(\varepsilon_t)\,dE\,d\varepsilon_t$. Hence, the ratio

$$N(\varepsilon_t) = \frac{\rho^{\ddagger}(E, \varepsilon_0, \varepsilon_t)\rho_t(\varepsilon_t)\,dE\,d\varepsilon_t}{\rho(E)\,dE} \tag{1}$$

---

[4] The analogy is imperfect unless an earthquake causes a sag in each floor corresponding to the equilibrium internuclear distance for that excited state.

is the fraction of the total number of systems in the activated state at any given time. The rate constant, $k(\varepsilon_t)\,d\varepsilon_t$, for the decomposition of activated complexes with an amount of kinetic energy in the reaction coordinate between ε_t and $\varepsilon_t + d\varepsilon_t$ is just $N(\varepsilon_t)r(\varepsilon_t)$, where $r(\varepsilon_t)$ is the rate at which activated complexes traverse the pass on the potential surface that leads to decomposition. Thus we have

$$k(\varepsilon_t)\,d\varepsilon_t = N(\varepsilon_t)r(\varepsilon_t) = \frac{\rho^{\ddagger}(E, \varepsilon_0, \varepsilon_t)\rho_t(\varepsilon_t)r(\varepsilon_t)\,d\varepsilon_t}{\rho(E)} \tag{2}$$

In order to obtain a rate constant that will apply to all the activated complexes in the assembly of systems, Eq. (2) must be integrated over the kinetic or translational energy in the reaction coordinate ε_t, whence

$$k = \int_0^{E-\varepsilon_0} k(\varepsilon_t)\,d\varepsilon_t = \int_0^{E-\varepsilon_0} \frac{\rho^{\ddagger}(E, \varepsilon_0, \varepsilon_t)\rho_t(\varepsilon_t)r(\varepsilon_t)}{\rho(E)}\,d\varepsilon_t \tag{3}$$

From the quantum mechanical treatment of a particle in a box[5] we know that the energy of a one-dimensional translator is $\varepsilon_t = n_t^2 h^2/8\mu l^2$, where n_t is an integral translational quantum number, h is Planck's constant, μ is the reduced mass of the particle, and l is the length of the box in the direction of motion. Rearranging terms in this expression, we obtain $n_t = 2lh^{-1}(2\mu\varepsilon_t)^{\frac{1}{2}}$, where l represents the length of the reaction coordinate. The density function can therefore be written as

$$\rho_t(\varepsilon_t) \equiv \frac{dn_t}{d\varepsilon_t} = \frac{l}{h}\sqrt{\frac{2\mu}{\varepsilon_t}} \tag{4}$$

where μ is the 'reduced mass' for translation of the density of translational states. Since $\varepsilon_t = \frac{1}{2}\mu v^2$, the frequency of crossing the potential barrier is

$$\frac{v}{l} = \frac{\left(\dfrac{2\varepsilon_t}{\mu}\right)^{\frac{1}{2}}}{l} \tag{5}$$

and the rate may be written as

$$r(\varepsilon_t) = \frac{1}{2}\frac{\left(\dfrac{2\varepsilon_t}{\mu}\right)^{\frac{1}{2}}}{l} \tag{6}$$

The factor $\frac{1}{2}$ is required because only half of the equilibrium activated complexes pass through the saddle in the forward direction corresponding to reaction. Introducing $\rho_t(\varepsilon_t)$ and $r(\varepsilon_t)$ into Eq. (3), we obtain

$$\begin{aligned}
k(E) &= \int_0^{E-\varepsilon_0} \frac{\rho^{\ddagger}(E, \varepsilon_0, \varepsilon_t)}{\rho(E)}\cdot\frac{l}{h}\sqrt{\frac{2\mu}{\varepsilon_t}}\cdot\frac{1}{2l}\sqrt{\frac{2\varepsilon_t}{\mu}}\,d\varepsilon_t \\
&= \frac{1}{h}\int_0^{E-\varepsilon_0} \frac{\rho^{\ddagger}(E, \varepsilon_0, \varepsilon_t)}{\rho(E)}\,d\varepsilon_t
\end{aligned} \tag{7}$$

[5] Q.C., p. 71.

If only one decomposition path is possible, the density of states for the activated complex can be taken as a function of $(E - \varepsilon_0 - \varepsilon_t)$. Although we shall illustrate the application of Eq. (7) by discussing the special case of decomposition of the propane ion, it should be understood that this equation is applicable to the decomposition of any isolated molecule for which a quasi-equilibrium distribution of energy can be assumed.

Magee has shown that when Eq. (7) is averaged over a thermal distribution the familiar rate expression

$$k(T) = \frac{kT}{h} \frac{F^{\ddagger}(T)}{F(T)} e^{-\varepsilon_0/kT} \tag{8}$$

is obtained.[6] The derivation starts with the familiar result that the average value of a function y is

$$\bar{y} = \frac{\displaystyle\int_{x_0}^{x} y(x) f(x) \, dx}{\displaystyle\int_{x_0}^{x_1} f(x) \, dx} \tag{9}$$

from which we have for the average value of the specific rate constant for decomposition by a single path over a thermal distribution of energies in the reactant molecules

$$k(T) = \frac{\displaystyle\int_{0}^{\infty} \left[\frac{1}{h} \int_{0}^{E-\varepsilon_0} \frac{\rho^{\ddagger}(E - \varepsilon_0 - \varepsilon_t)}{\rho(E)} \, d\varepsilon_t \right] \rho(E) e^{-E/kT} \, dE}{\displaystyle\int_{0}^{\infty} \rho(E) e^{-E/kT} \, dE} \tag{10}$$

Now if the energy levels are closely spaced so that classical methods apply, the density function $\rho(E)$ for a system of N degrees of freedom is just the partial derivative

$$\left[\frac{\partial W(\varepsilon)}{\partial \varepsilon} \right]_{\varepsilon = E}$$

where

$$W(\varepsilon) = \int \cdots \int \frac{dp_1 \ldots dp_N \, dq_1 \ldots dq_N}{h^N}$$

and the integration is over all of phase space for which the energy is equal to or less than ε. As a consequence, the relation between the density of energy states for the reacting system and the partition function for the same system, $F(T)$, is

$$F(T) = \int_{0}^{\infty} \rho(E) e^{-E/kT} \, dE \tag{11}$$

---

6 J. L. Magee, *Proc. Natl. Acad. Sci. U.S.*, **38**, 764 (1952).

We can therefore rewrite Eq. (10) as

$$k(T) = \frac{1}{hF(T)} \int_0^\infty e^{-E/kT} \left[\int_0^{E-\varepsilon_0} \rho^{\ddagger}(E-\varepsilon_0-\varepsilon_t)\,d\varepsilon_t \right] dE \qquad (12)$$

where we have taken advantage of the fact that E is not a variable in Eq. (7) and consequently the density function in the denominator of that relation can be taken out from under the integral sign. It is convenient to make the following change of variables

$$E' = E - \varepsilon_0 - \varepsilon_t$$
$$\varepsilon_t' = \varepsilon_t \qquad (13)$$

Using any standard text[7] for a discussion of Jacobians, we see that

$$d\varepsilon_t\,dE = \left\| \begin{array}{cc} \dfrac{\partial E}{\partial E'} & \dfrac{\partial E}{\partial \varepsilon_t'} \\[2ex] \dfrac{\partial \varepsilon_t}{\partial E'} & \dfrac{\partial \varepsilon_t}{\partial \varepsilon_t'} \end{array} \right\| d\varepsilon_t'\,dE' \qquad (14)$$

Since the absolute value of the determinant is unity, we obtain the simple relation

$$d\varepsilon_t\,dE = d\varepsilon_t'\,dE' \qquad (15)$$

which with the change of variables permits the reduction of Eq. (12) to the form

$$k(T) = \frac{e^{-\varepsilon_0/kT}}{hF(T)} \int_0^\infty \int_0^\infty \rho^{\ddagger}(E') e^{-E'/kT} e^{-\varepsilon_t'/kT}\,d\varepsilon_t'\,dE' \qquad (16)$$

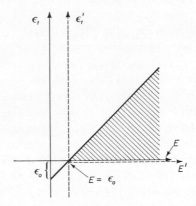

Figure 1. Change of variables required to integrate the expression for the rate constant, Eq. (12).

[7] H. Margenau and G. M. Murphy *The Mathematics of Physics and Chemistry*, 2nd Ed., van Nostrand, Princeton, 1956, pp. 17–20.

From Figure 1 we see that the range of the new variable E' extends from 0 to ∞. Integrating over ε_t', we find that

$$\int_0^\infty e^{-\varepsilon_t'/kT} \, \mathrm{d}\varepsilon_t' = \left. \frac{e^{-\varepsilon_t'/kT}}{-1/kT} \right|_0^\infty = kT \tag{17}$$

Therefore the rate constant averaged over a thermal distribution of energies is as given by Eq. (8) since the partition function for the activated state, $F^\ddagger(T)$, equals $\int_0^\infty \rho^\ddagger(E') \, e^{-E'/kT} \, \mathrm{d}E'$.

17. Equilibrium and Reaction Rate Theory

For a completely chaotic system in which there is a tendency to unbalanced flow between all pairs of states each state must be treated as a separate species in any satisfactory dynamical description of the system. The transition time for passing between a pair of states obeys the equation $1/\tau \approx \Delta\nu$ in accordance with the uncertainty principle. Here $\Delta\nu$ is the line width. Since the natural line width is broadened by collisions it follows that such encounters catalyze transitions by radiation as well as promoting radiationless transitions. It would be extremely difficult to prepare a completely chaotic system and impossible to maintain it for long. Certain relaxations are much faster than others and the states connected by the fast transitions equilibrate forming pools at equilibrium. Between these pools at equilibrium currents continue to flow. These pools at equilibrium are the chemist's compounds. They occupy the valleys and basins of the multi-dimensional potential energy surface in configuration space.

Moving vertically between potential surfaces, the Franck–Condon principle is obeyed and we have all the phenomena of photochemistry such as photosynthesis, flash photolysis and chemiluminescence.[1] Located at the saddle points between valleys we have activated complexes of transition state theory. Drifting down from the plateaus into the valleys we have the recombination reactions of atoms and free radicals with unimolecular and bimolecular decompositions reversing this path. Successful absolute reaction rate theories make as much use as possible of the fact that transition states, corresponding to crossing passes in a particular direction, recruit their populations almost exclusively from the valley being vacated, so that the equilibrium rate of passing through a transition state in a given direction is still a useful approximation under non-equilibrium conditions. Similar considerations apply to association and dissociation reactions as complexes pass through the gateways separating

[1] F. H. Johnson, H. Eyring and J. Polissar, *The Kinetic Basis of Molecular Biology*, Wiley, New York, 1954.

different chemical species.[2, 3] It is important to keep in mind the approximations made in the equilibrium approach to reaction kinetics and to calculate a transmission coefficient which makes the appropriate corrections. However, the attractiveness of using the equilibrium hypothesis, in addition to its simplicity, lies in the fact that, generally, where the right model is used, the factors correcting for non-equilibrium kinetics are near unity. Many different reactions have been treated from the point of view developed here[4, 5, 6, 7, 8] and much remains to be done.

[2] H. Eyring, H. Gershinowitz and C. E. Sun, *J. Chem. Phys.*, **3**, 786 (1935).

[3] E. Wigner, *J. Chem. Phys.*, **5**, 720 (1937).

[4] H. Eyring, J. Walter and G. E. Kimball, *Quantum Chemistry*, Chapter XVI, Wiley, New York, 1944.

[5] S. Glasstone, K. J. Laidler and H. Eyring, *The Theory of Rate Processes*, McGraw-Hill, New York, 1942.

[6] H. Eyring and E. M. Eyring, *Reaction Kinetics*, Reinhold, New York, 1963.

[7] A. A. Frost and R. G. Pearson, *Kinetics and Mechanisms*, 2nd Ed., Wiley, New York, 1961.

[8] K. J. Laidler, *Kinetics of Excited States*, The Clarendon Press, Oxford, 1955.

APPENDICES

Appendix 1

Some Physical Constants and Conversion Factors

The following table is based on the values of the physical constants reported by E. R. Cohen, J. W. M. DuMond, T. W. Layton and J. S. Rollett, *Rev. Mod. Phys.*, **27**, 363 (1955), except for the constants involving moles or atomic mass units which are based on the new atomic weight scale with the mass of $^{12}C = 12.00000$ u.

Velocity of light	$c = 2.997930 \times 10^{10}$ cm sec^{-1}
Planck's constant	$h = 6.62517 \times 10^{-27}$ erg sec
	$\hbar = h/2\pi = 1.05443 \times 10^{-27}$ erg sec
Avogadro's number	$N = 6.0229 \times 10^{23}$ molecules mole^{-1}
Electron charge	$e = 4.80286 \times 10^{-10}$ esu
	$= 1.60206 \times 10^{-19}$ coulomb
Electron rest mass	$m = 9.1083 \times 10^{-28}$ gm
	$= 0.54858 \times 10^{-3}$ u
	$= 0.510976$ Mev
Electron charge to mass ratio	$e/m = 5.27305 \times 10^{17}$ esu gm^{-1}
Proton rest mass	$M_p = 1.6724 \times 10^{-24}$ gm
	$= 1.0073$ u
	$= 938.211$ Mev
Boltzmann's constant	$k = 1.38044 \times 10^{-16}$ erg deg^{-1}
Gas constant	$R = Nk = 8.3143 \times 10^7$ erg deg^{-1} mole^{-1}
	$= 1.9872$ cal deg^{-1} mole^{-1}
	$= 0.082054$ liter atm deg^{-1} mole^{-1}
Absolute temperature of the ice point	$T_{0^{\circ}C} = 273.15^{\circ}$K
Bohr magneton	$\mu_B = e\hbar/2mc = 0.92731 \times 10^{-20}$ erg gauss^{-1}
Erg	$= 10^7$ joule
Calorie	$= 4.184 \times 10^7$ erg
Electron-volt	ev $= 1.60206 \times 10^{-12}$ erg
	$= 23.061$ kcal
Gram	gm $= 5.61000 \times 10^{26}$ Mev
Atomic mass unit	u $= 1.66034 \times 10^{-24}$ gm
	$= 931.45$ Mev

Appendix 2

Some Definite Integrals

$$\int_0^\infty x^n e^{-ax}\,dx = \frac{n!}{a^{n+1}} \tag{1}$$

$$\int_0^\infty x^n e^{-ax^2}\,dx = \begin{cases} \dfrac{(2m-1)!}{2^{2m}(m-1)!\,a^m}\sqrt{\dfrac{\pi}{a}}, & n = 2m \\[3mm] \dfrac{m!}{2a^{m+1}}, & n = 2m+1 \end{cases} \tag{2}$$

$$\int_0^\infty \sqrt{x}\,e^{-ax}\,dx = \frac{1}{2a}\sqrt{\frac{\pi}{a}} \tag{3}$$

To obtain (1) we change variables

$$\int_0^\infty x^n e^{-ax}\,dx = \frac{1}{a^{n+1}}\int_0^\infty u^n e^{-u}\,du$$

and then integrate by parts

$$I_n = \int_0^\infty u^n e^{-u}\,du = n\int_0^\infty u^{n-1} e^{-u}\,du$$

$$I_n = n \cdot I_{n-1}$$

It only remains to evaluate I_0

$$I_0 = \int_0^\infty e^{-u}\,du = 1$$

Hence $I_n = n!$ and therefore (1) follows.

To obtain (2) we make the change of variables

$$\int_0^\infty x^n e^{-ax^2}\,dx = \frac{1}{a^{(n+1)/2}}\int_0^\infty u^n e^{-u^2}\,du$$

and then integrate by parts

$$I_n = \int_0^\infty u^n e^{-u^2}\,du = \frac{n-1}{2}\int_0^\infty u^{n-2} e^{-u^2}\,du$$

$$I_n = \frac{n-1}{2} \cdot I_{n-2}$$

It only remains to evaluate I_1 and I_0. I_1 is easily obtained.

$$I_1 = \int_0^\infty u e^{-u^2}\,du = \tfrac{1}{2}\int_0^\infty e^{-y}\,dy = \tfrac{1}{2}$$

488

I_0 may be obtained by the following artifice

$$I_0^2 = \int_0^\infty e^{-x^2}\,dx \int_0^\infty e^{-y^2}\,dy$$

$$= \int_0^\infty \int_0^\infty e^{-(x^2+y^2)}\,dx\,dy$$

Changing to polar coordinates yields

$$I_0^2 = 2\pi \int_0^\infty e^{-r^2} r\,dr = \pi \int_0^\infty e^{-u}\,du$$

$$= \pi$$

$$I_0 = \sqrt{\pi}$$

Integrals (2) now follow directly.

To obtain (3) we change variables

$$\int_0^\infty \sqrt{x}\, e^{-ax}\,dx = 2 \int_0^\infty u^2\, e^{-au^2}\,du$$

and apply (2).

Appendix 3

Some Important Sums

$$\sum_{n=1}^{\infty} \frac{(-1)^{n-1}}{n^2} = \frac{\pi^2}{12} \tag{1}$$

$$\sum_{n=1}^{\infty} \frac{1}{n^2} = \frac{\pi^2}{6} \tag{2}$$

$$\sum_{n=1}^{\infty} \frac{1}{n^4} = \frac{\pi^4}{90} \tag{3}$$

To obtain (1) and (2) expand the function

$$f(x) = x^2, \qquad -\pi \leqslant x \leqslant \pi$$

in a Fourier series[1]

$$f(x) = \sum_{n=0}^{\infty} a_n \cos nx$$

$$a_0 = \frac{1}{\pi} \int_0^{\pi} x^2 \, dx = \frac{\pi^2}{3}$$

$$a_n = \frac{2}{\pi} \int_0^{\pi} x^2 \cos nx \, dx = (-1)^n \frac{4}{n^2}$$

Hence,

$$x^2 = \frac{\pi^2}{3} + 4 \sum_{n=1}^{\infty} \frac{(-1)^n}{n^2} \cos nx$$

Setting $x = 0$ gives (1) and setting $x = \pi$ gives (2).

To obtain (3) expand

$$f(x) = x^4, \qquad -\pi \leqslant x \leqslant \pi$$

in a Fourier series

$$a_0 = \frac{1}{\pi} \int_0^{\pi} x^4 \, dx = \frac{\pi^4}{5}$$

$$a_n = \frac{2}{\pi} \int_0^{\pi} x^4 \cos nx \, dx = -(-1)^n \frac{8\pi^2}{n^2} - (-1)^n \frac{48}{n^4}$$

Hence,

$$x^4 = \frac{\pi^4}{5} + 8\pi^2 \sum_{n=1}^{\infty} \frac{(-1)^n}{n^2} \cos nx - 48 \sum_{n=1}^{\infty} \frac{(-1)^n}{n^4} \cos nx$$

[1] C. R. Wylie, Jr., *Advanced Engineering Mathematics*, 2nd Ed., McGraw-Hill, New York, 1960, Chapter 7.

Setting $x = \pi$ gives

$$\pi^4 = \frac{\pi^4}{5} + 8\pi^2 \sum_{n=1}^{\infty} \frac{1}{n^2} - 48 \sum_{n=1}^{\infty} \frac{1}{n^4}$$

Substituting (2) and solving for $\sum_{n=1}^{\infty} \frac{1}{n^4}$ gives (3).

Appendix 4

Stirling's Approximation

$$\ln N! \simeq N \ln N - N \tag{1}$$

Since $\ln x$ is a monotonically increasing function of x

$$\sum_{k=1}^{N} \ln k < \int_{0}^{N} \ln x \, dx < \sum_{k=1}^{N} \ln (k+1)$$

Therefore

$$\int_{0}^{N-1} \ln x \, dx < \sum_{k=1}^{N} \ln k < \int_{0}^{N} \ln x \, dx$$

Integrating gives

$$(N-1)[\ln (N-1)-1] < \ln N! < N[\ln N - 1]$$

The difference between $(N-1)[\ln (N-1)-1]$ and $N[\ln N-1]$ is of the order of $\ln N$ and, therefore, for large N Eq. (1) follows.

AUTHOR INDEX

SUBJECT INDEX